STATIC POWER FREQUENCY CHANGERS

STATIC POWER FREQUENCY CHANGERS

THEORY, PERFORMANCE, AND APPLICATION

L. GYUGYI, Ph.D., F.I.E.E.

Westinghouse Research Laboratories
Pittsburgh, Pennsylvania

B. R. PELLY, F.I.E.E.

Formerly of Westinghouse Research Laboratories
Pittsburgh, Pennsylvania
(Currently of European Semiconductor Group
International Rectifier
Oxted, Surrey, England)

A WILEY-INTERSCIENCE PUBLICATION

JOHN WILEY & SONS NEW YORK/LONDON/SYDNEY/TORONTO

Library of Congress Cataloging in Publication Data

Gyugyi, L

Static power frequency changers.

"A Wiley-Interscience publication."
Bibliography: p.
Includes index.
1. Frequency changers. I. Pelly, B. R., joint author. II. Title.
TK2799.G94 621.313′6 76-6088
ISBN 0-471-67800-7

Printed in the United States of America

10 9 8 7 6 5 4 3 2 1

PREFACE

This book deals with a whole family of static a-c to a-c frequency changers in which power conversion is achieved by a single-stage electronic switching circuit without the use of electrical storage elements. Potential applications for such frequency changers include variable frequency speed control for a-c machines, constant frequency power supplies, controllable VAr generators for voltage support and power factor correction, and a-c system interties. The best known member of this family of direct a-c to a-c frequency changers is the phase-controlled, or naturally commutated, cycloconverter.

Some of the basic concepts of direct static a-c to a-c power conversion were established during the 1920s, and the principles of the cycloconverter were worked out in the early 1930s. The cycloconverter is a special member of the overall family of frequency changers to be considered; it does not require static switches with "intrinsic" turn-off capability. All other members of the family do require such switches or must be complemented by auxiliary *force commutating* circuitry. For this reason, the cycloconverter is the only member of the family that to date has found extensive use. Early cycloconverters developed in the 1930s used grid-controlled mercurcy arc rectifiers; the introduction of the silicon controlled rectifier, or thyristor, in the late 1950s spurred more widespread use.

In the mid-1960s, the authors, working at the Westinghouse Research Laboratories, were engaged in an investigation of the inherent operating limitations of the cycloconverter that appeared to disqualify it for certain types of application. This investigation led to a thorough theoretical analysis of its performance characteristics and to a search for new frequency conversion techniques that would overcome these inherent operating limitations. Various new types of frequency changers were found, offering better functional characteristics than the cycloconverter, at the expense of departing from simple natural commutation of the switches. A whole family of frequency changers was thus born, although in fact the existence of certain types had been known, though not exploited, since the 1920s.

The results of this parallel activity were published by the authors in two separate works: "Thyristor Phase-Controlled Converters and Cycloconverters" by Pelly (Wiley Interscience, 1971) and "Generalized Theory of Static Power Frequency Changers" by Gyugyi (Ph.D. Thesis, University of Salford, 1970). With this book, we now present a unified treatment of this whole family of static a-c to a-c frequency changers, of which the classical cycloconverter is a member, though not a preeminent one from the theoretical viewpoint.

The requirement for "forcibly" turning off the switches of the frequency changer is not one that at present can be easily satisfied economically; we believe however that further advances in device and circuit technology will inevitably pave the way for much more widespread use of the frequency changers we describe.

It is perhaps a dilemma for an author to decide whether the material to be included in a book should be restricted to that which is well established and supported by broad practical experience, or, alternatively, to present material that, although theoretically well founded, has not yet found its way from the research laboratories to the outside world. We have chosen the second approach for several reasons. First, as we have said, we believe that the circuit techniques described in this book undoubtedly will come into general use. Second, we believe that by conveying these new ideas now to engineers and students, this book may act as a "catalyst" in hastening more widespread application of this class of frequency changers. Third, we believe that the present state of the art in direct a-c to a-c frequency changers, represented mostly by the naturally commutated cycloconverter, cannot really be viewed in the proper perspective without an awareness of broader general principles, of which the cycloconverter represents but one realization. Fourth, we hope that the general analytical methods developed in this book will, in their own right, provide a useful tool for engineers and students dealing with different types of circuitry in the power electronics field.

Most of the material presented is new. It is, to a large extent, based upon our original work on a-c to a-c frequency changers, that, on and off, has stretched over a decade. Our main objective is to organize and unify the analytical treatment of the whole family of direct a-c to a-c frequency changers with which we deal to show the relationships between, and give physical explanations for, their operating characteristics. We also provide quantitative performance data for the most important practical frequency changers and illustrate their potential use in various applications. The underlying philosophy is to provide a coherent presentation that conveys an understanding of fundamental principles and concepts. Thus, we have endeavored throughout to relate the various types of frequency changers to each other and to provide physical explanations for the theoretical analytical results that we obtain.

The book is primarily intended for engineers and students working in the field of power electronics who want to gain an in-depth understanding of static frequency changers, the methods used to control them, and their potential applications. The material should also be useful as a reference and source of design data to engineers who design or employ frequency changers and to all who require an understanding of the basic principles and analytical techniques of this most interesting branch of static power conversion.

We have attempted to make as many of the chapters as possible self-contained. Chapter 1 gives a brief historical background and serves as an introduction to static a-c to a-c frequency changers; it presents the basic concepts and describes fundamental operating principles and circuits. Chapter 2 establishes the mathematical framework for analysis of static frequency changers. Chapters 3 and 4 deal with the synthesis of output voltage waveforms of different types of frequency changers, and Chapter 5 deals with the analysis of the corresponding input current waveforms. Chapter 6 provides extensive design data for various frequency changers, including the naturally commutated cycloconverter. Chapter 7 describes practical control techniques for static frequency changers. Chapter 8 deals largely with the basic principles of auxiliary forced commutation of static frequency changers and presents a number of basic commutating circuit approaches. Chapter 9 reviews potential applications and describes the operation of various practical frequency changers; numerous oscillograms, most of them taken from laboratory models, illustrate the performance of practical systems.

The effect of the a-c source impedance upon the operation of static frequency changers has, for brevity, been omitted. This impedance complicates the analysis considerably and makes the mathematical expressions complex and cumbersome. The reader who is particularly interested in this aspect may refer to both of the references quoted above. We feel this omission is justified here because a-c source impedance normally does not substantially alter the functional characteristics of frequency changers, and our main purpose is to convey an understanding of basic principles, operating characteristics, and application possibilities.

This book is published with the permission of the Westinghouse Electric Corporation; we wish to thank in particular Dr. F. T. Thompson, Manager, Electrical Sciences Division, Westinghouse Research Laboratories, for his help and support of this project and Mr. A. H. B. Walker, now retired from Westinghouse, who enthusiastically encouraged our initial work on frequency changers.

We wish to acknowledge the contributions of our colleagues, John Rosa, Manager, Power Electronics Research, who played a significant part in advancing the development of static frequency changers, Eric J. Stacey, Senior Engineer, who developed several of the practical circuits described in this book, and Peter Wood, Advisory Engineer, who performed an invaluable service in reading the manuscript and making suggestions to improve the text.

We also wish to thank Professor J. H. Calderwood and Dr. F. L. N-Nagy of the University of Salford for their earlier support of research into frequency changers.

Our thanks are due to Miss A. M. Tomasic, who typed the whole manuscript, and Mrs. E. Platte, who provided valuable administrative assistance.

Finally, and most of all, we wish to thank our wives for their understanding, patience, and help, which made this book possible.

L. GYUGYI
B. R. PELLY

Pittsburgh, Pennsylvania
January 1976

CONTENTS

NOMENCLATURE

The following is a list of principal symbols used throughout this book.

$E(\rho)$, $E_\pi(\rho)$	diagonal existence matrices, specifying construction of the *consecutive* composite output voltage waveform, defined in equations (3.28) and (3.29)
f_E	frequency of extrabasal component in the input current
f_I	frequency of the a-c source (*input frequency*)
f_O	wanted output frequency of the frequency changer
f_U	frequency of unwanted component in the output voltage
$i_{I1(2,3,\ldots)}$	instantaneous value of current in frequency changer input line 1(2,3, . . .)
$[i_I]$	column matrix formed from the set of input line currents
i_{IF}	fundamental component of input line current
i_{IR}	real component of fundamental input line current
i_{IQ}	quadrature component of fundamental input line current
I_I	amplitude of the fundamental component of input line current
I_{IQ}	amplitude of quadrature component of input line current
I_{IR}	amplitude of real component of input line current
$i_{O1(2,3,\ldots)}$	instantaneous value of the output current in frequency changer output line 1 (2,3, . . .)
$[i_O]$	column matrix formed from the set of output currents
I_O	amplitude of the wanted component in the frequency changer output current
$[H]$	existence matrix specifying the operation of power switches in the frequency changer
h_{pq}	an element of matrix $[H]$ defining the operation of the power switch connecting output terminal p to input terminal q
J	Bessel function
$M(t)$	modulating function used to generate the output voltage waveform
P	pulse number
P_O	average power at the output of a frequency changer
r	output voltage ratio, that is, the amplitude of the wanted sinusoidal component in the output voltage divided by the maximum possible amplitude of the wanted component obtained with *sinusoidal mean* output voltage
t	time
$v_{I1(2,3,\ldots)}$	instantaneous value of the phase to neutral voltage at input terminal 1 (2,3, . . .) of a frequency changer
$[v_I]$	column matrix formed from the set of input phase voltages
V_I	amplitude of phase to neutral voltage at a frequency changer's input

$v_{O1(2,3,\ldots)}$ instantaneous value of the phase to neutral output voltage at output terminal 1 (2,3, . . .) of a frequency changer

$[v_O]$ column matrix formed from the set of output phase voltages

$v_{Ow1(2,3,\ldots)}$ instantaneous value of the wanted sinusoidal component in the voltage at output terminal 1 (2,3, . . .)

V_O amplitude of the wanted component in the output voltage

β angle, measured at the wanted angular output frequency, determining the amplitude of the wanted component when the output voltage is controlled by pulse-width modulation

γ_I amplitude ratio of the extrabasal component to the fundamental input current

γ_O amplitude ratio of the unwanted component to the wanted output voltage

δ_I displacement factor at the input of a frequency changer ($\delta_I = \cos \phi_I$)

κ normalized amplitude of desired output voltage, or reference wave ($\kappa = r$ for $\kappa \leq 1.0$)

λ_I power factor at the input of a frequency changer ($\lambda_I = \mu_I \delta_I$)

μ_I distortion factor of frequency changer input current

μ_O total r.m.s. distortion of the output voltage waveform

ν_I frequency ratio of the extrabasal component to the fundamental input current

ν_O frequency ratio of the unwanted component to the wanted output voltage

ξ angle, measured at the wanted angular output frequency, determining the amplitude of the wanted component, when the output voltage is controlled by phase shift

ρ angle, measured at the wanted angular output frequency, determining the instants of change over between *positive-type* and *negative-type* waves in the construction of *consecutive* composite output voltage waveforms

σ control angle defined by $\sigma = \phi_O - \rho - \pi$

ϕ_I displacement angle of fundamental component of a frequency changer's input current

ϕ_O output load displacement angle of a frequency changer

ω_I $\omega_I = 2\pi f_I$

ω_O $\omega_O = 2\pi f_O$

TERMS AND EXPRESSIONS

The following is a list of definitions for the descriptive terms and expressions recurring frequently in this book.

Complementary waveforms are generally two related waveforms that are produced by the same form of modulating function. They are usually composed of the same components, with each pair of corresponding components either inphase or in antiphase with one another.

Composite waveforms are waveforms that are constructed from two complementary waveforms or sections thereof.

A **concurrent composite waveform** is an output voltage waveform that is produced as the sum or arithmetic mean of two complementary *positive-type* and *negative-type* waves.

A **consecutive composite waveform** is an output voltage waveform that is produced by "piecing" together consecutive half-cycle sections of complementary *positive-type* and *negative-type* waves.

The term **control** is often used in the narrow sense to describe the method of output voltage waveform construction. The control determines the timing of the conduction intervals of the static switches in the frequency changer circuit.

The **desired output voltage wave** is the output voltage wave that the control attempts to generate, and in general this could have any shape. The desired output voltage wave is generally the "mean" of the output voltage waveform actually generated.

An **existence function** is a function that has unit value for values of the independent variable in specified ranges and zero value for all other values of the independent variable. Existence functions are used in this book to describe mathematically the state of the switches of the frequency changer circuit. Unit value represents a closed switch, and zero value represents an open switch.

An **existence matrix** is a matrix whose elements are existence functions.

The **extrabasal components** of the input current are the sinusoidal constituents that appear in addition to the fundamental component; the frequencies of these components are generally not integrally related to the fundamental component.

Forced commutation is the process whereby the current in a controlled-rectifier-type circuit element is interrupted by auxiliary forcing. This is achieved by an external commutating circuit that forces the current in the switching element to zero and impresses a reverse voltage across it until it regains its voltage-blocking capability.

The term **frequency changer**, as used in this book, refers to a static system, using solid-state switching devices, that directly converts a-c power of a given frequency to a-c power of some chosen frequency, without an intermediate d-c link, by making connection for controlled time intervals between given input and output terminals.

Full output voltage is the maximum attainable output voltage with a given method of output voltage waveform construction.

The **fundamental component** of the input current wave is the component having the frequency of the a-c source.

Harmonic components of the output voltage waveform are unwanted components whose frequencies are integral multiples of the wanted output frequency. Harmonic components are generally present in the output only if the desired output voltage wave is not a sinusoid.

The **input current** is the current drawn by the frequency changer from each phase of the a-c source; with a sinusoidal output current the waveform of the input current is generally nonsinusoidal.

The **input current wave indices** are measures of the performance of the frequency changer at the input terminals. These include the input displacement factor (δ_I), the current distortion factor (μ_I), the input power factor (λ_I), and the normalized frequencies and amplitudes of the extrabasal current components (ν_I and γ_I).

The **input displacement factor** is the ratio of the real input power to the *fundamental* volt-ampere product (i.e., the product of the source phase voltage and the corresponding fundamental component of the input current wave). The input displacement factor thus shows the relationship between the real and reactive input power.

The **input power factor** is the ratio of the real input power to the *r.m.s.* volt-ampere product (i.e., the product of the source voltage, assumed sinusoidal, and the r.m.s. input current). The input power factor thus shows the relationship between the real power and the reactive plus extrabasal input power.

The **mean a-c output voltage** refers to the average value of the segments of the input voltage waves that form the output voltage waveform.

A **modulating function** is a time-dependent function that describes the angular variation of the existence functions with respect to their quiescent angular position. The modulating function defines the operation of the power switches in the frequency changer circuit and thereby the method of output voltage waveform construction.

Natural commutation is the process whereby the current is transferred without external forcing between controlled-rectifier-type circuit elements. This is achieved by proper selection of the switching instants relative to the instantaneous polarities of the input voltage waves.

An **odd function** is a function that satisfies the condition $f(-x) = -f(x)$. The graph of an odd function is symmetric with respect to the origin. When a periodic function is an odd function it contains only *sine* components.

An **odd harmonic function** is a periodic function that satisfies the condition $f(x + T/2) = -f(x)$, where T is the period. An odd harmonic function contains only *odd* harmonic (generally sine and cosine) components.

The **output current** is the current supplied to the load by the frequency changer. It is generally assumed to be sinusoidal.

The **output voltage control** refers to the technique that is used to vary the amplitude of the wanted component.

The **output voltage ratio** is the amplitude of the wanted sinusoidal component in the output voltage divided by the maximum possible amplitude of the wanted component obtained with sinusoidal mean output voltage.

The **output voltage wave indices** are measures of the quality of the output voltage wave. These include the normalized frequencies and amplitudes of the unwanted components (ν_O and γ_O) and the total rms distortion of the output voltage waveform (μ_O).

Positive-type and **negative-type** output voltage waveforms are produced in such a way that the "incoming" input voltage wave is, in the first case, always more positive and, in the second case, always more negative, than the "outgoing" input voltage wave.

The **pulse number** of a frequency changer circuit defines the number of segments in the output voltage waveform (and therefore the number of switchings) during one cycle of the a-c input voltage at zero output frequency. A frequency changer with pulse number P is called a *P-pulse* frequency changer. The output waveshapes of frequency changers with the same pulse number and with identical control are the same, notwithstanding the actual circuit configuration.

A **subfrequency component** is an unwanted output voltage or extrabasal input current component whose frequency is lower than the wanted output frequency or fundamental input frequency, respectively.

A **superfrequency component** is an unwanted output voltage or extrabasal input current component whose frequency is higher than the wanted output frequency or fundamental input frequency, respectively.

The **unwanted components** of the output voltage waveform are the sinusoidal constituents that appear in addition to the wanted component.

The **wanted component** of the output voltage waveform is the *sinusoidal* voltage component that has the wanted output frequency.

The **wanted output frequency** is the frequency of the wanted component of the output voltage waveform.

STATIC POWER FREQUENCY CHANGERS

CHAPTER ONE
FUNDAMENTAL IDEAS

1.1 DEFINITION OF BASIC CLASS OF FREQUENCY CHANGERS TO BE TREATED

The term *power frequency changer* in the general sense could apply to any electrical system that converts a-c power of one frequency to a-c power of another frequency. In general, such systems can employ rotating electrical machinery, nonlinear magnetic devices, or static circuits containing controllable electric power switches of one sort or another.

This latter category of static power frequency changers can be further subdivided into two main classes. In the first, the power is converted in two stages with an intermediate d-c link. In the second, the power is converted directly in one stage.

This latter type of *direct* a-c to a-c frequency changer consists basically of an array of static switches, connected directly between the input and output terminals. The basic operating principle is to piece together an output voltage waveform with the wanted *fundamental* component from selected segments of the input voltage waves.

The best-known example of this type of power frequency changer probably is the classical *cycloconverter*, devised in the early 1930s. We suspect, indeed, that it may be the only example of which many of our readers, picking up this book for the first time, will be aware. However, the cycloconverter is but one of a whole family of frequency changers, most of which have been devised much more recently, that fall within this general class.

It is our intent in this book to address ourselves to this whole family of direct a-c to a-c power frequency changers.

1.2 HISTORICAL BACKGROUND

The first static frequency changer characterized by variable frequency ratio and bi-directional power flow was conceived by Hazeltine(5)* in 1923. He established the fundamental principle, common to all static frequency changers, of constructing an alternating voltage wave of chosen frequency from successive voltage waves of a given-frequency multiphase a-c supply. To this end, he proposed the use of various arrangements of electric valves to switch the load sequentially to successive voltage waves of the a-c source, thereby generating the output waveform. Hazeltine's system was remarkable in several respects: it allowed a free power flow to and from the load, and the output to input frequency ratio could be chosen and varied arbitrarily; in addition, the control technique was very simple. However, the practical utilization of this system was seriously hindered by the lack of electric valves with suitable characteristics and ratings.

* Parenthetical references placed superior to the line of text refer to bibliography.

A different and practically important frequency changer was developed by Schenkel[6] and Von Issendorff[7] in the early 1930s, using the principles of phase-controlled mercury arc converters. This frequency changer also allowed bidirectional power flow; however, in contrast to Hazeltine's system, the attainable useful output frequency, while variable, was less than the supply frequency. Nevertheless, the system had two important features that ensured its usefulness in practical applications: first, it employed mercury arc valves, which were available with adequate ratings; second, the amplitude of the generated output wave could be varied simply by controlling the ignition angle of the valves. This frequency changer was originally developed to convert the standard three-phase, 50-Hz, a-c power to single-phase a-c power at 15, $16\frac{2}{3}$ or 25 Hz, which was used for traction in Europe.

A thorough review on the subject of mercury arc frequency converters was given by Rissik[1,2] who introduced the term *cycloconversion* to designate the process by which an alternating voltage wave of *lower* frequency is constructed from successive voltage waves of a *higher* frequency multiphase supply; he also designated the static frequency converters using the above principle as *cycloconverters.* Thereafter this type of system, employing controlled rectifiers, has usually been referred to as the *phase-controlled* or *naturally commutated* cycloconverter in the literature.

The discovery and fast industrial development of the transistor and the subsequent introduction of the silicon controlled rectifier or thyristor,* together with the rapid technological advances in the fields of circuitry and control, have resulted in a renewed interest in static frequency changers, dating from the late 1950s. The small size, rugged construction, low voltage drop, and fast switching characteristics of silicon semiconductor devices made the static frequency changer attractive for use in aircraft *variable-speed-constant-frequency* (VSCF) power-generating systems and industrial variable-frequency a-c motor supplies. In 1959, Jesse and Spaven[9] proposed a static frequency changer based on principles similar to those established by Hazeltine, using power transistors to generate a constant frequency output from a variable frequency source. Others[8,10,11,13] promoted the seemingly more practical naturally commutated cycloconverter employing thyristors for the same application, and ever since there has been intense activity[15,21,22,24,40,54,63] to perfect this system for all-electric aircraft power generation. This trend was encouraged by the availability of thyristors with sufficiently high ratings to make the naturally commutated cycloconverter applicable to practical systems.

Other types of static frequency changers, on the other hand, require switches with *intrinsic* gate turn-off ability (transistors or gate-controlled switches) or *artificial* forced commutation. The lack of sufficiently large devices and the awkwardness of forced commutation have generally been impediments to static frequency changer development.

The advent of semiconductor devices for power conversion and control also marked the beginning of new development efforts to utilize naturally commutated cycloconverters in variable-speed drives employing a-c machines. The basic characteristics of the cycloconverter, such as continuously controllable output frequency and voltage, as well as an inherent capability for regenerative braking, indicated that it could provide an "ideal" variable frequency supply for a-c motor drives. An a-c machine driven by such a supply could have speed range, torque, and efficiency similar to

* The term *thyristor* is in fact a generic one that applies generally to all four-layer devices. We use it in this book, however, to refer specifically to the silicon controlled rectifier.

those of a d-c machine operated with armature voltage control. The combination of cycloconverter and squirrel-cage induction motor seemed particularly attractive from the practical point of view, and therefore considerable effort[14,17–20,23,25,27–32,34,36] has been devoted to the development of such systems in the last decade. The cycloconverter variable frequency power supply appears to be especially advantageous for driving very large a-c motors in those applications[41,43,44,47,61,62] in which low running speeds are required.

Besides the practical accomplishments, considerable conceptual and theoretical work was also carried out in the 1960s. New static frequency changers with previously unattainable characteristics were conceived[48,56,57,59] and new applications proposed.[66,67] In 1970–1971, the authors published two theoretical works,[3,48] in which exact analytical expressions for the output voltage and input current waves were derived, and comprehensive quantitative data on the external performance of different frequency changers, including the first in-depth characterization of the naturally commutated cycloconverter, were given. In 1972, McMurray published a monograph[4] summarizing the design and application aspects of the naturally commutated cycloconverter.

In considering the historical background, one must recognize that frequency changer developments have always been largely dependent on the technological advances in high-power electronic switches. The discovery of grid-controlled mercury arc rectifiers and subsequent introduction of semiconductor thyristors led to the invention and later perfection of the naturally commutated cycloconverter. There is little doubt that future advances in high-power electronic switching devices will provide further impetus for and have a profound effect on the development and practical application of static frequency changers.

1.3 BASIC OPERATIONAL FEATURES

The term *frequency changer* actually does not wholly describe the functional characteristics of the types of circuits to be described. In addition to the capability of providing continuous control of the output frequency relative to the input frequency, these types of electrical *power conditioner* also have the capability of providing continuous control of the amplitude of the output voltage; in general, too, they have the property that the phase or *displacement* angle of the load presented to the input source is different from the phase angle of the load at the output terminals. Depending on the particular type of frequency changer, the angular displacement of the input current with respect to the input voltage may either be a dependent function of the operating parameters at the output or it may be adjustable independently of these parameters, at least within certain limits. All members of this family of frequency changers have the inherent property that power can flow in *either direction* through them.

A general representation of a hypothetical ideal frequency changer, which by definition is assumed to have complete functional flexibility and sinusoidal terminal voltages and currents, would thus be that of a *general transformer*, with the capability both of independently transforming the frequency and amplitude of the alternating input voltage and of transforming the phase angle of the output load to some different input phase angle. This ideal frequency changer is theoretically lossless; hence it is a necessary condition that the real power at the input terminals must be equal to the real power at the output terminals. Moreover, as stated above, power can flow in either direction through it.

A simplified functional representation of such a general hypothetical frequency changer is shown in Figure 1.1. A sinusoidal a-c voltage source (which would, in general, have multiple phases), having a given amplitude V_I and angular frequency $\omega_I(=2\pi f_I)$, is connected to the input terminal of the frequency changer. This applied sinusoidal voltage is converted into an output voltage wave with amplitude V_O and angular frequency, $\omega_O(=2\pi f_O)$, which is applied to the load. At the output terminal, therefore, the frequency changer, taken in conjunction with the input source, may be viewed as a simple "black box" voltage generator establishing output voltage v_O across the load. In response to this voltage, an a-c output current i_O flows through the load. The amplitude I_O and phase angle ϕ_O of current i_O are determined by the impedance characteristic of the load.

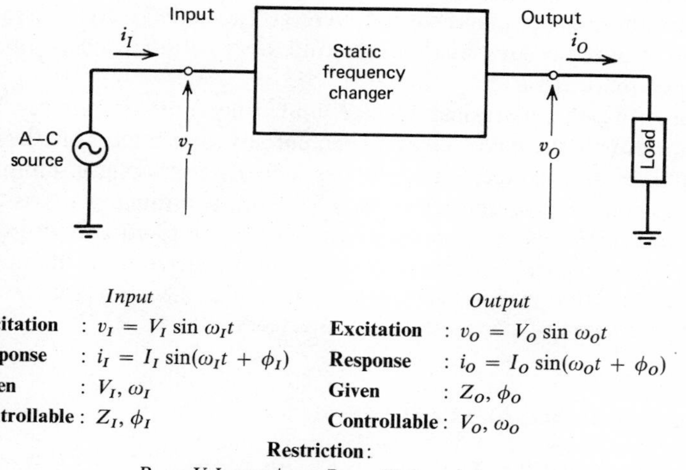

Input		*Output*	
Excitation	: $v_I = V_I \sin \omega_I t$	**Excitation**	: $v_O = V_O \sin \omega_O t$
Response	: $i_I = I_I \sin(\omega_I t + \phi_I)$	**Response**	: $i_O = I_O \sin(\omega_O t + \phi_O)$
Given	: V_I, ω_I	**Given**	: Z_O, ϕ_O
Controllable	: Z_I, ϕ_I	**Controllable**	: V_O, ω_O

Restriction:

$$P_I = V_I I_I \cos \phi_I \equiv P_O = V_O I_O \cos \phi_O$$

Figure 1.1 Simplified functional representation of a general hypothetical static frequency changer.

Looking at the frequency conversion process in the reverse direction, that is, from the input terminal, the frequency changer converts the output current wave of frequency f_O, to an input current wave of frequency f_I.

Basic considerations tell us that this has to be so, regardless of the internal operating mechanism of the frequency changer, because current at frequency f_I, and at this frequency only, can account for a net component of power drawn from the input source, which of course is necessary to balance the net component of power absorbed by the load at the output. The requirement for equality of input and output power does not, however, uniquely determine the amplitude I_I and phase angle ϕ_I of the input current wave. Indeed, these quantities are functions of the output to input current (or, if preferred, impedance) transformation characteristics of the frequency changer. At the input terminal, therefore, this *hypothetical* frequency changer with its output load can be viewed as a "black box" impedance, terminating the a-c source with a real power component equal to that of the output load, and a displacement angle that can be independently adjusted.

In summary, a *hypothetical* frequency changer with completely flexible operating characteristics is capable of making the following basic transformations, with the restriction that the input power must be equal to the output power:

INPUT		OUTPUT
ω_I	$\rightarrow$	ω_O
V_I	$\rightarrow$	V_O
ϕ_I	$\leftarrow$	ϕ_O

In practice, no one member of the family of frequency changers to be described has the unlimited functional flexibility of this hypothetical model; the operating characteristics of each are restricted in some way or other. It is generally true for all types that the output frequency, f_O, and the amplitude of the output voltage, V_O, can be continuously adjusted independently of one another. For all types but one, however, the upper limit of the range of variation of the output frequency lies at a point lower than the input frequency. For one type (the classical *cycloconverter* to which we have already referred) the input displacement angle, ϕ_I, is a function of the output load angle, ϕ_O, and the relative level of output voltage; for others, it is a function just of the output load angle; for another, it is invariably zero, regardless of the output load angle; for another, it can be adjusted within certain limits, independent of the output parameters.

A summary of the most important members of the family of frequency changers treated in this book and their basic operating characteristics is given in Table 1.1. This table is offered here without explanation. The reasons for the different functional characteristics of the various members of the family become evident as the reader progresses further through the book.

1.4 A CONCEPTUAL VIEW OF SELECTED APPLICATIONS

To exemplify the practical usefulness of and the design flexibility offered by the different functional characteristics of the various types of frequency changers, we now discuss in a rudimentary way three different frequency changer applications with widely differing requirements.

The first application is a variable-speed a-c motor drive. Here, the input is a multiphase a-c input voltage source with essentially fixed frequency and amplitude; the frequency changer generates a multiphase output voltage with continuously variable frequency and amplitude that is applied to the a-c machine for the purpose of controlling its speed. In the second application, the frequency changer provides a closely regulated fixed-frequency output from an input source of varying frequency. The third application is a controllable reactive power supply for an a-c system. Here the frequency changer is used essentially as a continuously variable reactance; it provides controllable reactive power for the a-c system to which it is connected, to compensate the reactive power consumption of the loads connected to the system.

1.4.1 Variable Speed Control of A-C Machines Using a UFC

D-c motors are commonly used in variable speed drives because their speed can be varied simply by controlling the armature voltage or the field current. The d-c machine does, however, have the practical disadvantages, because of its commutator, that it requires periodic maintenance, it cannot be operated in certain environmental conditions, and it cannot be designed for very high voltages or currents.

A-c induction motors work without commutators, and thus they are simpler and mechanically more robust than their d-c counterparts and require practically no maintenance. Induction motors are usually regarded as essentially constant-speed

TABLE 1.1. Basic Types of Frequency Changers Dealt with in This Book and Their Basic Operating Characteristics

Name of Frequency Changer	Abbreviation	Output Frequency	Output Voltage	Input Displacement Angle
Unrestricted frequency changer	UFC	$0 \leq f_O \leq \infty$	$0 \leq V_O \leq V_{O_{max}}$	$\Phi_I = -\Phi_O$
Slow switching frequency changer	SSFC	$0 \leq f_O < f_I$	$0 \leq V_O \leq V_{O_{max}}$	$\Phi_I = \Phi_O$
Unity displacement factor frequency changer	UDFFC	$0 \leq f_O < f_I$	$0 \leq V_O \leq V_{O_{max}}$	$\Phi_I = 0$
Controllable displacement factor frequency changer	CDFFC	$0 \leq f_O < f_I$	$0 \leq V_O \leq V_{O_{max}}$	$-\Phi_{I_{max}} \leq \Phi_I \leq \Phi_{I_{max}}$ $\Phi_{I_{max}} = f(V_O, \Phi_O)$
Naturally commutated cycloconverter	NCC	$0 \leq f_O^a \leq f_I$	$0 \leq V_O \leq V_{O_{max}}$	$\Phi_I = -\lvert f(V_O, \Phi_O)\rvert$

[a] Except for $\Phi_O = 90°$ and $V_O \rightarrow V_{O_{max}}$, when $0 \leq f_O \leq \infty$.

machines because they normally operate from a supply of fixed frequency. The speed of an induction motor is, however, proportional to the frequency of the applied stator voltage, and the obtainable torque is dependent on the stator flux. Thus, by controlling the frequency and amplitude of the applied stator voltage, in a proper relationship to maintain constant-rated flux in the machine, it is possible to operate the motor efficiently from standstill up to the maximum rated speed and to obtain full torque over, this whole range, while the maximum current consumed never exceeds the normal rated value. The external characteristics of this type of drive are virtually identical to those of a separately excited d-c motor with continuous armature voltage control.

Different applications require different operating characteristics of the frequency changer. Some special types of drive require only a limited range of frequency, from 0 to, for example, 10–20 Hz; in this event, the naturally commutated cycloconverter is often an ideal candidate for supplying the required variable frequency power from a fixed-frequency (usually 60 or 50 Hz) industrial power source. Many industrial applications, however, require a much wider frequency range than this—typically from 0 to 180 Hz. It is this latter type of application that we now consider.

From Table 1.1, it is evident that the only type of frequency changer that could produce the desired range of output frequency (from a normal 60 or 50 Hz industrial supply) is the UFC. It will be noted too that this frequency changer has the property that it inverts the load phase angle. Since in this case the load is to be an induction motor, the phase angle of which is invariably lagging, this means that the phase angle of the drive, as viewed from the input source, will invariably be leading. This is perhaps an unexpected but nonetheless welcome side benefit. A further functional feature (as previously stated, applicable to all the frequency changers considered in this book) is that power flow in either direction is possible. Thus this type of drive can automatically provide full regenerative braking of the motor over the whole speed range.

A simplified functional diagram of a variable-speed induction motor drive embodying a UFC is shown in Figure 1.2. The amplitude and frequency of the output

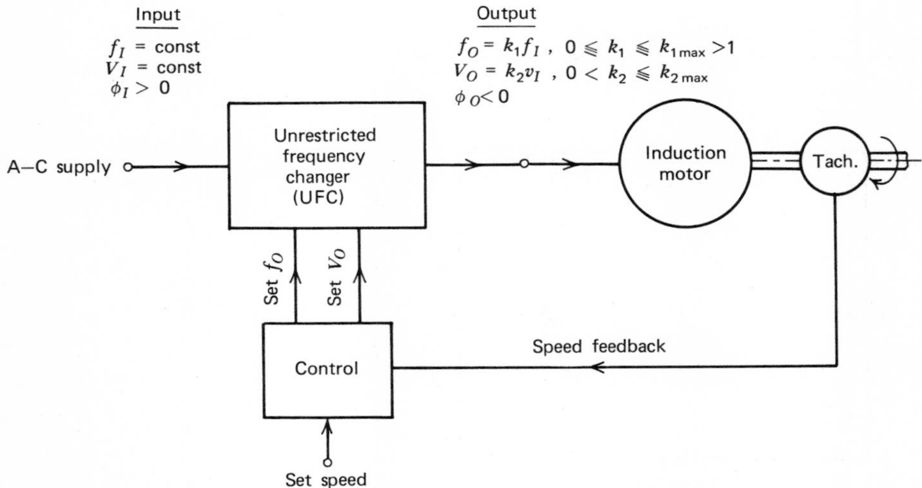

Figure 1.2 Schematic representation of a variable-speed induction motor drive using an unrestricted frequency changer.

voltage are controlled concurrently to maintain a constant flux in the machine. The shaft speed may be regulated by conventional tacho-generator feedback, as indicated.

The frequency changer, viewed as a generalized "transformer," together with the output load and the input source, can be represented (on a per-phase basis) by two simple two-terminal networks, as shown in Figure 1.3. At the output terminals, the frequency changer (UFC) and the a-c supply are, in effect, equivalent to an ideal a-c voltage source with variable amplitude and frequency, terminated by the impedance of the induction motor. (For simplicity, the motor impedance is assumed to consist of only the magnetizing reactance, $X_\varphi = \omega_O L_\varphi$, the reflected motor leakage reactance, $\omega_O L_r$, and the effective reflected rotor resistance, R_r/s, in which s is the slip.) Because of the constant V_O/f_O ratio, the magnetizing current is constant and independent of the output frequency, and only the reflected rotor current changes as a function of

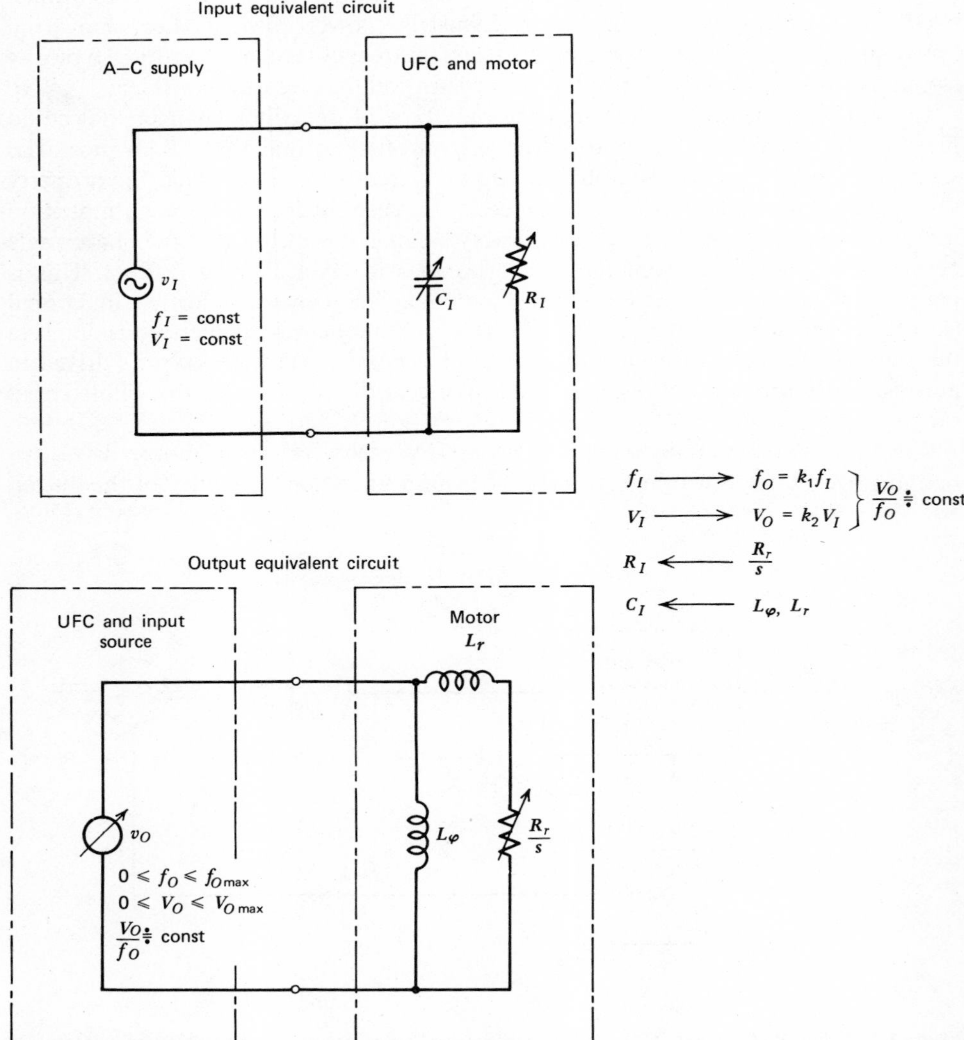

Figure 1.3 Simplified representation of the UFC–a-c motor drive of Figure 1.2 by input/output equivalent circuits.

the torque. Due to the unique phase-angle transformation, the UFC and the motor can be represented at the input terminals as an impedance consisting of a parallel connected variable resistor, representing the power consumed by the motor, and a capacitor.

The equivalent impedance of the UFC and the motor at the input terminals can readily be calculated. The real output power must be equal to the real input power:

$$\frac{V_O^2}{(R_r/s)^2 + (\omega_O L_r)^2} \cdot \frac{R_r}{s} = \frac{V_I^2}{R_I} \tag{1.1}$$

Thus:

$$R_I = \left(\frac{V_I}{V_O}\right)^2 \left\{\frac{R_r}{s} + \frac{(\omega_O L_r)^2}{R_r/s}\right\} \tag{1.2}$$

Using the basic definition for the slip, namely,

$$s = \frac{\omega_O - \omega_r}{\omega_O} = \frac{\omega_s}{\omega_O} \tag{1.3}$$

in which ω_r is the rotor frequency and ω_s is the absolute slip frequency, and taking into account the stipulated relationship

$$\frac{V_O}{\omega_O} = \frac{K_2}{K_1} \cdot \frac{V_I}{\omega_I} = \text{constant} \tag{1.4}$$

the equivalent input resistance R_I can be written in the following form

$$R_I = \underbrace{\frac{K_1}{K_2}\,\omega_I V_I R_r}_{\text{constant}} \frac{1}{V_O} \cdot \frac{1}{\omega_s}\left\{1 + \frac{\omega_s^2 L_r^2}{R_r^2}\right\} \tag{1.5}$$

Thus R_I varies in inverse proportion with the amplitude of the output voltage and is a somewhat more complex function of the absolute slip frequency, ω_s.

The value of the equivalent input capacitor C_I can be calculated by recognizing that the basic relationship $\phi_I = -\phi_O$ implies the equality of the reactive output and input powers, that is,

$$\frac{V_O^2}{X_m} = \frac{V_I^2}{X_{C_I}} \tag{1.6}$$

in which X_m is the equivalent parallel reactance of the motor due to its magnetizing reactance and the rotor circuit reactance. Therefore

$$X_{C_I} = \left(\frac{V_I}{V_O}\right)^2 X_m \tag{1.7}$$

From the above basic relationship, and using the relationship of equation (1.4), it can easily be shown that

$$C_I = \underbrace{\frac{K_2}{K_1} \cdot \frac{1}{\omega_I^2 V_I}}_{\text{constant}} \cdot V_O \left\{\frac{1}{L_\varphi} + \frac{\omega_s^2 L_r}{R_r^2 + \omega_s^2 L_r^2}\right\} \tag{1.8}$$

Equation (1.8) reflects the fact that for any given slip frequency the motor absorbs an increasing (lagging) reactive power as the output voltage (and hence speed) is raised, and thus the equivalent input capacitance, C_I, correspondingly increases.

1.4.2 Constant-Frequency Power Supplies

In several applications the mechanical power available for electric power generation is delivered at a shaft speed that is not compatible with the desired frequency. An example is electric power generation in an aircraft. Here the mechanical power is supplied by the aircraft engine, whose speed generally varies over a range of about two to one. The desired electrical power, on the other hand, must have an accurately regulated frequency and voltage. Clearly, if an alternator is coupled directly to the engine, the frequency of the generated electrical power will vary in direct proportion to the engine speed, and this "wild" electrical power would not be compatible with the aircraft requirements.

The conventional solution to this problem has been to insert a hydraulic constant-speed coupling device (usually with a step-down gear) between the engine and the alternator. This provides an appropriate constant-speed drive for the alternator, which thus produces an essentially constant frequency output. The constant-speed drive, however, has the disadvantages of requiring regular and costly maintenance, as well as periodic replacement.

Another example of this general type of application is a mobile ground power-generating system. A conventional scheme uses a regulated-speed diesel engine driving an alternator, which in turn supplies the required electrical power. From the standpoint of size and weight, however, it would be more advantageous to employ a high-speed turbine as the prime mover. A potential problem with this is that the shaft speed, although relatively constant, is usually too high to produce the required output frequency, and the gearbox required for mechanical speed reduction would be too heavy and unreliable to be practical.

A static frequency changer is ideally suited to solve the problems of constant-frequency power generation encountered in airborne or mobile ground power-generating systems, employing variable or fixed high-speed alternators. The basic approach is simple: a high-speed alternator is coupled directly to the prime mover (which may be the aircraft engine or the turbine), and this produces electrical power at a high, and generally variable, frequency. This "wild" electrical power is then converted to a precisely regulated fixed frequency output, through a frequency changer. This type of system is generally referred to as a *variable-speed-constant-frequency* (VSCF) scheme.

For this type of system, such factors as weight, size, and reliability are of prime importance. An attractive feature of the VSCF approach is that it allows for the optimization of the alternator (and, when possible, the prime mover) for minimum weight and size. Also, the use of a static frequency changer offers the potential for higher reliability and a better quality, more closely regulated electrical power output than can be obtained with a conventional system.

In considering which of the functional characteristics of the static frequency changers listed in Table 1.1 are potentially most important in a VSCF application, we can reason in the following way:

Restrictions on the attainable maximum output frequency will probably be unimportant, since the alternator frequency will generally be much higher than the required output frequency. This is because the shaft speed of the prime mover will generally be relatively high.

By contrast, the displacement factor reflected by the frequency changer on the alternator can be of considerable importance because, for given output requirements, it will determine the VA rating, and thus the weight and size, of the alternator. The importance of being able to keep the input displacement factor within controlled limits becomes readily apparent when it is appreciated that the load power factor, which may be lagging or leading, typically varies over a wide range.

From the above discussion, it appears that the unrestricted frequency changer, generally a promising candidate for variable-speed-drive applications, may not offer any particular functional advantages. This preliminary conclusion is reviewed later in this book when other factors, such as the distortion of the output voltage and input current waves, are also considered. The UFC would again become the only candidate from the family of frequency changers considered, if the frequency of the available input power is not higher than that of the required output power.

The unity displacement factor frequency changer provides a unity displacement factor load for the alternator, regardless of the phase angle of the actual output load. It can thus be expected to require something close to the minimum possible VA rating of the input alternator. It can also be visualized that the controllable displacement factor frequency changer, controlled to provide leading displacement factor for the alternator under all output load conditions, could be advantageous in supplying reactive excitation for the generator. Each of these candidate systems is now discussed in more detail.

1.4.2.1 *VSCF System Using a UDFFC.* A VSCF system employing a unity displacement factor frequency changer (UDFFC) is illustrated in simplified schematic form in Figure 1.4. Here, a *synchronous* generator, externally excited to give constant

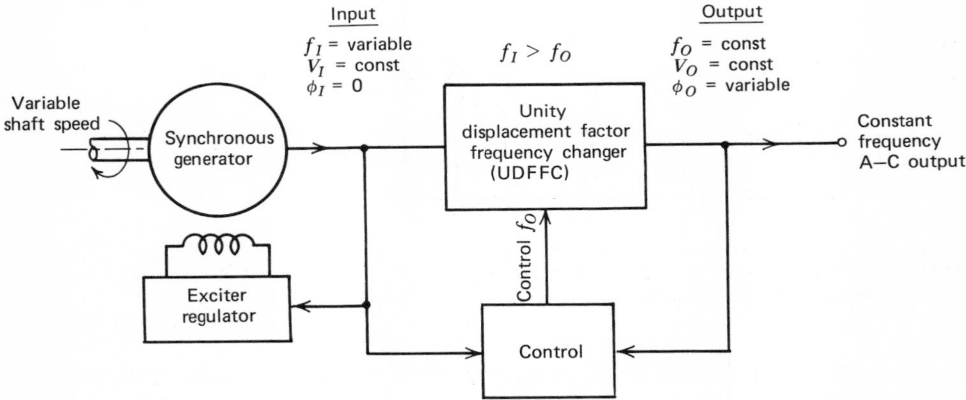

Figure 1.4 Schematic representation of a variable-speed constant frequency (VSCF) system embodying a synchronous generator and a unity displacement factor frequency changer.

terminal voltage, supplies power to the frequency changer at a frequency proportional to the variable shaft speed. This variable frequency power is converted to accurately regulated constant frequency power output by the UDFFC. The speed range of the generator is such that its frequency is always higher than the required output frequency.

Since the UDFFC exhibits a unity input displacement factor, regardless of the load power factor, the generator has to supply *only* the real output power. Viewing the frequency changer as a generalized transformer, the equivalent input and output circuit representation of the system again can be readily derived in the form of two two-terminal networks, as shown in Figure 1.5.

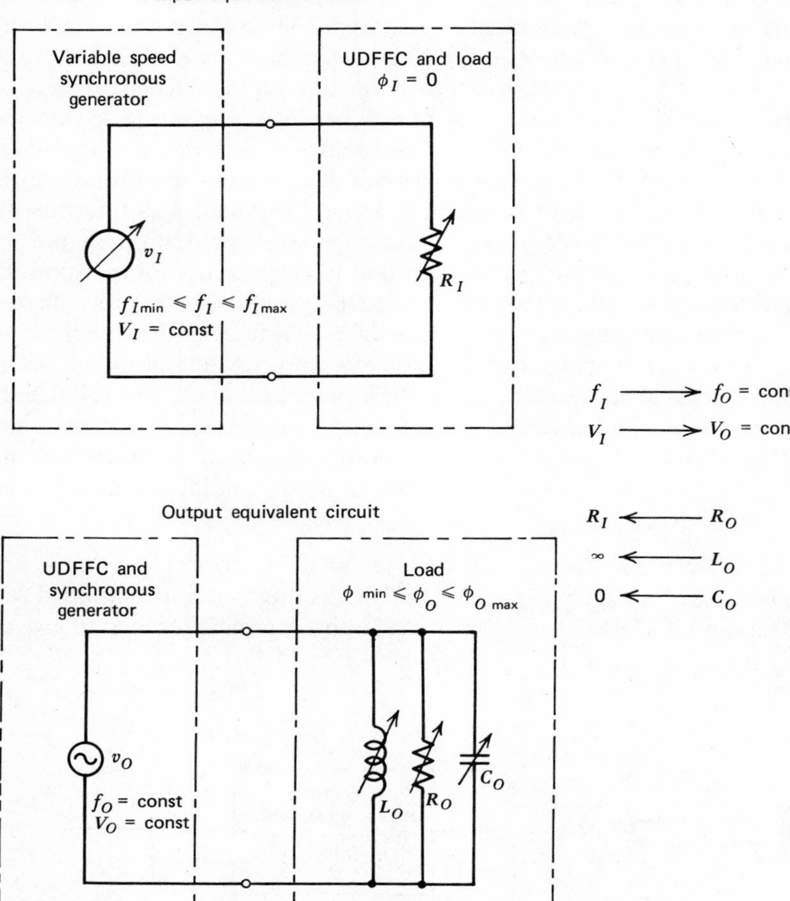

Figure 1.5 Simplified representation of the UDFFC–synchronous generator VSCF system of Figure 1.4 by input/output equivalent circuits.

Again, using the condition of equal real output and input power, R_I is easily calculated:

$$R_I = \left(\frac{V_I}{V_O}\right)^2 R_O \tag{1.9}$$

Since the reactive input power is stipulated as being zero, it follows that C_O is transformed to $C_I \equiv 0$, and L_O to $L_I \equiv \infty$.

1.4.2.2 *VSCF System Using a CDFFC.* In some VSCF systems, the operating conditions and reliability requirements are such that the use of a wound rotor synchronous generator is not attractive. This is the case in which the operating speed is high, perhaps above 50,000 r.p.m. (as when a turbine provides the mechanical power); it is difficult to construct a wound rotor with sufficient mechanical ruggedness to operate reliably at such speeds. Therefore this type of application usually requires the use of a generator rotor without windings.

The squirrel-cage induction machine, due to its simplicity and ruggedness, is mechanically well suited for high-speed applications. Hitherto, however, such a machine has largely been used as a motor, because in the generating mode it can feed only a leading load, the power factor of which varies with the real power loading. Any lagging reactive power demand of the load, plus the reactive power necessary to excite the machine must be supplied externally. This reactive power could be provided by externally switched capacitors or by a rotating synchronous condenser. This is inelegant and in any case would be largely impractical for the type of VSCF system under consideration.

By contrast, the combination of a squirrel-cage induction machine and a controllable displacement factor frequency changer provides a potentially ideal solution for systems requiring high generator speed, high reliability, and low weight. The CDFFC can provide a controllable leading input displacement factor, at any load power factor, while it converts the generator input frequency f_I to the required output frequency f_O ($f_I > f_O$). In a VSCF system using a squirrel-cage induction generator, the CDFFC thus can fulfill two simultaneous functions, as illustrated in Figure 1.6.

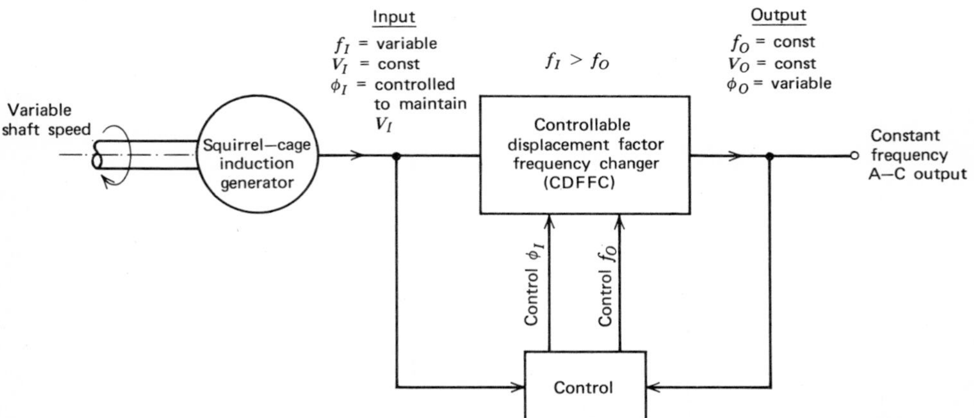

Figure 1.6 Schematic representation of a variable-speed constant-frequency (VSCF) system embodying a squirrel-cage induction generator and a controllable displacement factor frequency changer.

First, it can convert the variable generator frequency to precisely regulated output frequency; second, it can provide controllable excitation for the induction machine, thus sustaining its voltage under all output load conditions.

The two-terminal input/output equivalent circuits are shown in Figure 1.7. The transformation of the output load is complex and cannot be derived by simple considerations. Of course, the real output and input powers must be equal. This gives the already known expression for R_I;

$$R_I = \left(\frac{V_I}{V_O}\right)^2 \cdot R_O \tag{1.10}$$

Suffice it here to say for C_I that independent of the relative values of R_O, L_O, and C_O (excluding the case not encountered in a practical system, in which they represent such a high output impedance that the output current is not compatible with the required excitation current of the generator), the actual output admittance

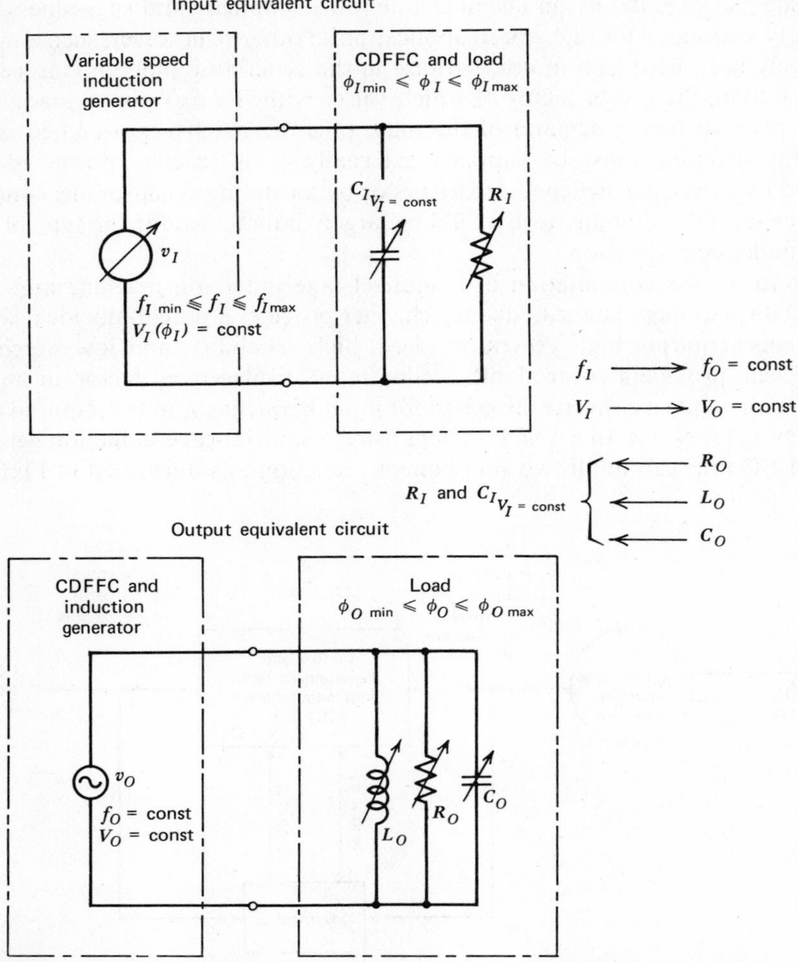

Figure 1.7 Simplified representation of the CDFFC–induction generator VSCF system of Figure 1.6 by input/output equivalent circuits.

$Y_O = (1/R_O) + (1/j\omega_O L) + j\omega_O C_O$ can be transformed to input admittance $Y_I = (1/R_I) + j\omega_I C_I$, with the value of C_I such that the excitation requirement of the induction machine, for constant terminal voltage, can always be satisfied.

1.4.3 Controllable VAr Supply Using an NCC

Today there is a growing demand for controllable reactive energy sources for industrial and power systems use. Typical applications include correction of the power factor of electrical machines and static conversion equipments in industrial plants, reduction of voltage flicker and voltage regulation of arc furnaces, and voltage stablization for transmission and distribution lines.

In the past, this type of function has typically been provided by rotating synchronous machines or mechanically switched static capacitors. Today, attention is being focused more and more on static solutions.

One possible conceptual approach, based upon the use of an NCC as a controllable reactive power source, is now considered. Other types of frequency changers can also be applied to provide a similar function, as can other static circuit approaches, which are not the subject of this book. The following description therefore is offered merely to exemplify the diverse functional possibilities offered by the frequency changers dealt with in this book.

The concept is explained by reference to the input/output equivalent circuits of the NCC shown in Figure 1.8.

At *a*, an NCC supplies an adjustable capacitive load at its output, at an output voltage close to the maximum level, $V_{O\max}$. The output frequency f_O is equal to the input frequency f_I, which for this particular load condition is feasible (as noted at the foot of Table 1.1). The impedance reflected to the equivalent input circuit is a variable inductor. For $V_O \doteqdot V_{O\max}$, as is the case here, the following relationship is valid:

$$\omega_I L \doteqdot \left(\frac{V_I}{V_O}\right)^2 \cdot \frac{1}{\omega_O C_O} \tag{1.11}$$

The variable capacitive load at the output could be replaced by a voltage source v of fixed amplitude and frequency $f_O(=f_I)$, which is in phase with v_O, and a small series connected inductor, as shown at *b*. The amplitude of the leading current delivered at the output of the NCC could then be adjusted, by appropriate fine control of the amplitude of v_O, below the amplitude of v, to produce the requisite small driving voltage across the inductor L.

Looking back from the voltage source v, the output circuit of the NCC appears as a variable inductor, as illustrated at *c*. If, therefore, the voltage source v is now designated as being one and the same as the input voltage source v_I, so that the output terminals can be connected back to the input terminals, the equivalent circuit shown at *d* is obtained. The input source voltage v_I now views two parallel connected equivalent inductors, one due to the equivalent input impedance, the other due to the equivalent impedance looking back into the output terminals of the NCC.

This is a rather remarkable situation, since the only reactive element physically in-circuit is the small series inductor L, which theoretically could be made vanishingly small. Thus the NCC—which basically consists of no more than an array of static switches—can be made to behave as a variable reactor, even though theoretically it may contain no energy storage elements. This is quite in accord with basic theoretical considerations; a balanced three-phase reactive load (as tacitly assumed here) does not of itself require the presence of components capable of storing energy. The net instantaneous power drawn from all three phases of a source feeding a balanced reactive load is at all times zero, which means that power instantaneously drawn from a given phase (or phases) is simultaneously returned to the other(s). Thus the NCC in this type of connection can be viewed simply as a vehicle for transferring energy to and fro between the phases of the source.

The equivalent variable inductive load offered to the source by the input and output circuits of the NCC can of course be represented as a single equivalent inductive element, as shown in Figure 1.9*a*. In practice, most applications would require a variable capacitive reactance rather than a variable inductive reactance (although in some cases, either might be required under different operating conditions). A variable capacitance can be provided by connecting a fixed capacitor across the NCC, as

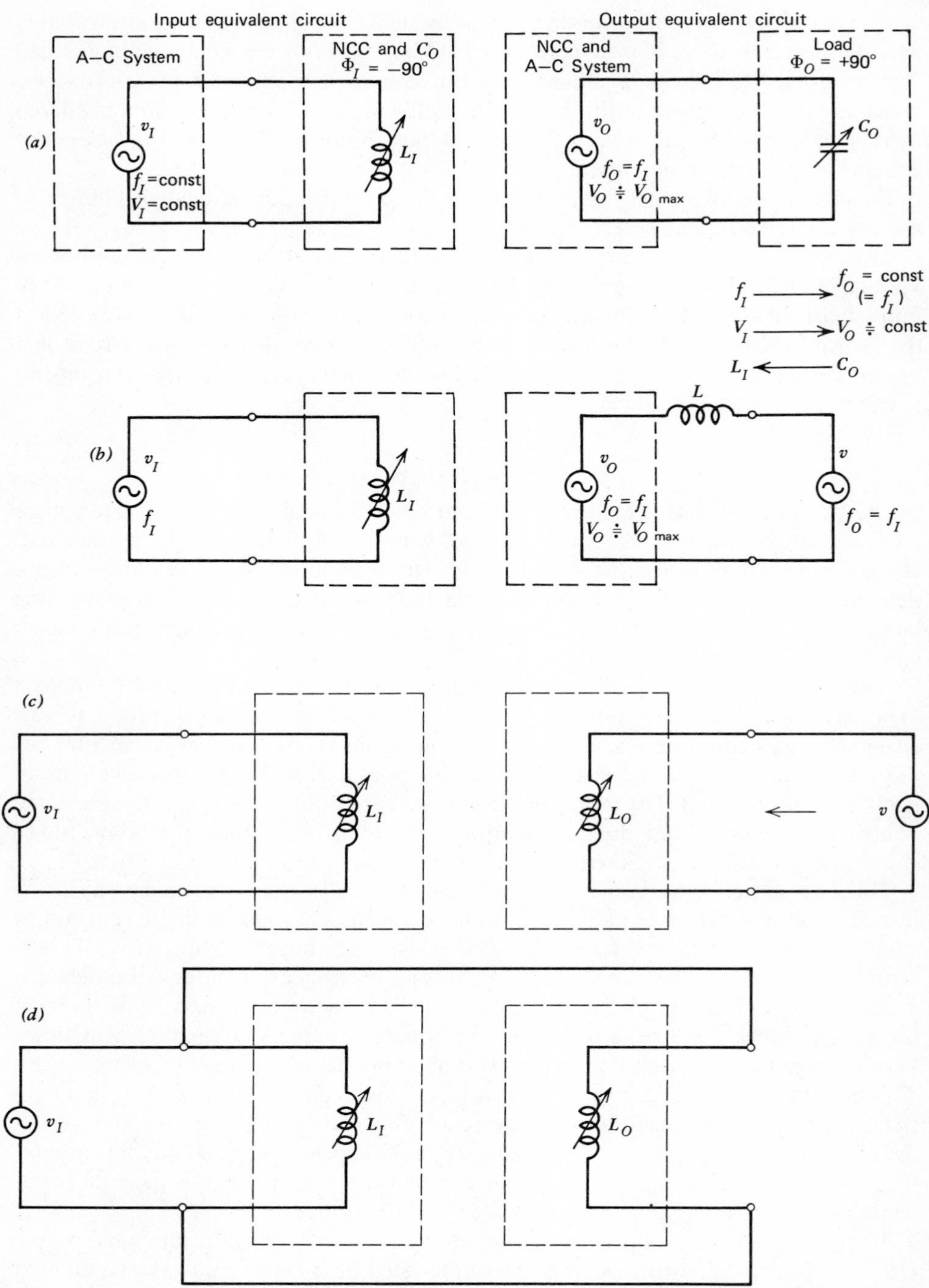

Figure 1.8 Formation of continuously variable equivalent inductor using a naturally commutated cycloconverter. *a* Basic equivalent input and output circuits, with variable capacitive load at output. *b* Substitution of variable capacitor with fixed voltage source v and small series inductance L. Leading current flowing out of NCC is adjusted by fine control of V_O. *c* Equivalent output circuit of NCC, as viewed by voltage source v. *d* Substitution of voltage source v with input voltage source v_I by connecting output terminals back to input. (NCC in this configuration appears to source as lumped variable inductor.)

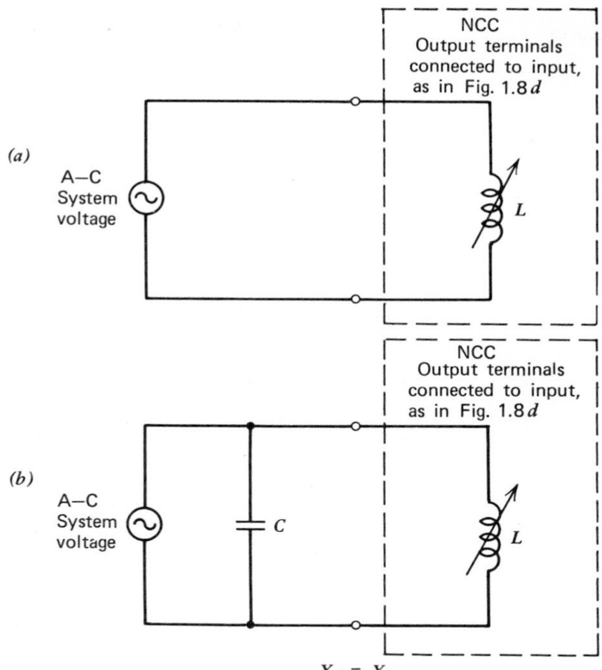

Figure 1.9 Formation of continuously variable capacitive reactance using a fixed capacitor and a naturally commuted cycloconverter with its output terminals connected back to its input terminals. *a* Continuously variable equivalent inductive reactance provided by NCC. *b* Continuously variable capacitive reactance formed by fixed capacitor and NCC.

shown in Figure 1.9*b*. By dimensioning this capacitor so that it draws a leading current equal to the maximum lagging current drawn by the NCC, the total lagging VArs supplied to the connected system by the combination can be continuously controlled from zero up to the full rating of the capacitor.

A simplified schematic representation of a power factor correction scheme based on this principle is shown in Figure 1.10.

1.5 OPERATING PRINCIPLES

The frequency changers considered in this book directly convert generally multiphase power of given characteristics to single- or multiphase power of different characteristics.

Operationally, the frequency changer is a *wave synthesizer*. Output voltage wave(s) of the desired amplitude and frequency are produced by sequentially switching chosen segments of the voltage waves of the a-c input source to the output terminal(s). The resulting waveforms of current flowing at the input terminals are built up of segments of the current wave(s) flowing at the output terminals.

The construction of the output voltage wave(s) is accomplished by arrays of *bidirectional* static switches—comprising the frequency changer *circuit*—that provide a matrix of alternative connections between the input and output terminals.

Each *bidirectional* switch—so named because it allows current flow in either direction while in the "on" state and blocks voltage of either polarity while in the "off"

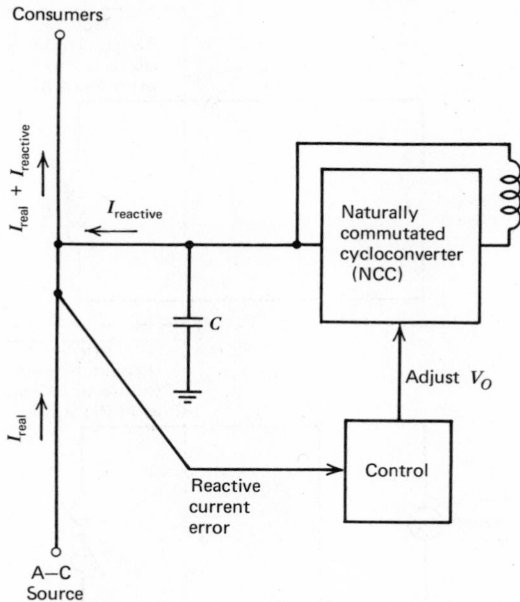

Figure 1.10 Schematic representation of static controllable power factor correction scheme using a fixed capacitor and a naturally commutated cycloconverter with its output terminals connected back to its input terminals.

state—in general is capable of being turned on and off at any desired instant, regardless of the instantaneous direction of the current or the instantaneous polarity of the circuit voltage.* Although no single solid-state component with such characteristics exists today, static bidirectional switches that provide the desired features can be implemented by means of various different circuit techniques using state-of-the-art solid-state devices, as discussed in Section 1.5.3. For the present, in order to understand the basic operating principles of the static frequency changer circuit as a whole, it is sufficient simply to assume the use of hypothetical "ideal" bidirectional switches, which can be turned on and off instantaneously and at will, regardless of the external circuit conditions. These hypothetical switches are assumed to have no voltage drop while in the "on" state and no leakage current while in the "off" state.

In order to eliminate distracting second-order effects from the elementary discussion that follows, it will be assumed that the impedance of the a-c source that feeds the frequency changer is negligible.

1.5.1 Output Waveform Synthesis

The various possible approaches to output voltage waveform synthesis are discussed with reference to one of the most commonly used circuits, the three-phase *bridge* circuit, illustrated in Figure 1.11. Although this is not the most basic circuit, it has

* The only exception is for the NCC, which is a particular and special member of the family of frequency changers treated in this book. The bidirectional switches of the NCC—formed by antiparallel pairs of thyristors—are commutated (i.e., turned off) naturally by choosing the switching instants in the proper relationship to the instantaneous polarity of the source voltage, as discussed in Section 1.5.3.

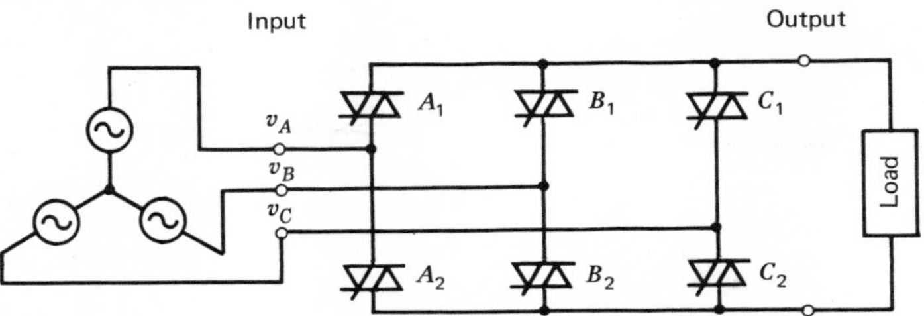

Figure 1.11 Schematic of a three-phase to single-phase frequency changer *bridge* circuit.

been chosen for purposes of illustration in order to demonstrate distinctly enough the characteristics of different possible waveshapes; the waveforms obtained from simpler circuits are usually too "rough" to show clearly their actual character.

As the reader will probably recognize, the circuit shown is the same as a conventional three-phase full wave rectifier circuit, with the exception that it contains bidirectional switches rather than unidirectional rectifier devices.

A single three-phase bridge circuit employing bidirectional switches is capable of converting the voltage waves of the three-phase input source (assumed balanced and sinusoidal) to a single composite output voltage waveform. It is therefore categorized as a three-phase to single-phase frequency changer circuit.

The basic operating principle of the bridge circuit is simple: diagonally opposite pairs of switches (e.g., A_1B_2, A_1C_2, B_1C_2, B_1A_2) are made to conduct in sequence; thus each of the input (phase-to-phase) voltages are in turn connected to the output terminals for a period of time (which may be variable), and thus a voltage waveshape composed of selected segments of the input voltage waves is constructed at the output terminals. The actual shape of the output voltage wave is determined by the conduction intervals of the switches.

Suppose that the objective is to produce an output voltage waveform that approximates a sine wave of some frequency, f_O, less than the input frequency f_I. The simplest (and crudest) approximation would be a pseudo-square wave, obtained by always switching the instantaneously most positive phase-to-phase input voltage to the output terminals during the positive half-cycle, and always switching the most negative phase-to-phase input voltage to the output terminals during the negative half-cycle, as illustrated in Figure 1.12*a*.

A better approximation of the desired sine wave could be obtained by repeatedly switching the output between the most positive and most negative input voltages, for controlled time intervals, such that the average of the successive negative and positive voltage "areas" is equal to the average of the desired sinusoidal output, over the same subcycle interval of time, as illustrated in Figure 1.12*b*. This technique is called *pulse-width modulation* (PWM).

The common characteristic of the two output waveforms derived is that they are constructed only from the most positive and most negative segments of the input voltage waves. Obviously, waveforms that are similar except for the small a-c "ripple" could readily be generated by switching a *d-c source* in alternate directions to the load. In point of fact, such techniques of waveform construction are commonly used in *static inverters*, which convert d-c to a-c. The types of waveforms shown in Figure 1.12*a* and *b* can therefore be referred to as *inverter-type waveforms*. These waveform types may occasionally be used in direct a-c to a-c power conversion; however, there

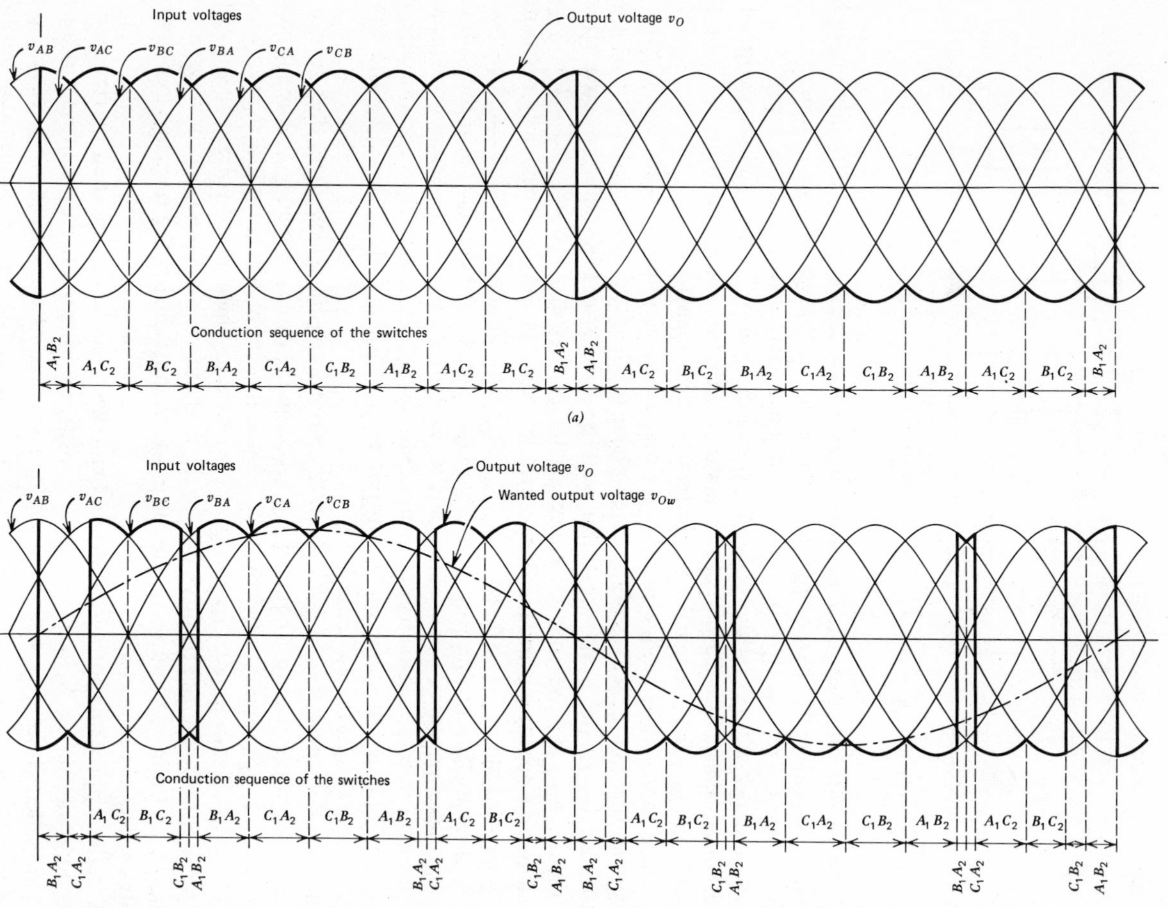

Figure 1.12 Inverter-type output voltage waveforms.

are a number of reasons why they are not often employed, and they will not be considered any further here* because they basically belong to d-c to a-c *inverter* technology, rather than to the special class of a-c to a-c converters we have chosen to call *frequency changers*, which are the topic of this book.

We now turn our attention to the construction of what we call *frequency changer-type* output waveforms, which are fundamentally different from the above *inverter-type* waves. Unlike the d-c to a-c inverter, in which the input voltage level is normally fixed and steady, the a-c to a-c frequency changer is supplied with a selection of time-varying alternating input voltage waves. Thus at any given time a choice is possible between several instantaneous voltage levels that could be switched to the output terminals. The basic technique behind the construction of the output voltage wave of a frequency changer is the selection of an input voltage whose value instantaneously approximates the desired instantaneous value of the output voltage. As the instantaneous deviation between the selected input voltage and the desired output voltage increases due to the time-varying nature of each of these waves, a particular input voltage wave is rejected, and a new one, whose instantaneous value better approximates the desired output voltage, is connected to the output terminals in its place. This process is repeated ad infinitum. Thus, frequency changer-type output waves are constructed from those segments of the input voltage waves that give a good local approximation to the desired output wave within each successive time frame.

Consider Figure 1.13*a*, in which the input voltage waves and a segment of the desired output voltage wave (i.e., the desired wave that is to be approximated by the actual output waveform) are shown. Inspection of this figure shows that the input voltage waves in succession, one after the other, intersect the desired output voltage wave. It is thus quite natural to choose, for best approximation, segments of the successive input voltage waves *around* the intersection points to construct the output waveform. It can be further reasoned that, for minimum r.m.s. distortion, the instantaneous deviation of the constructed output waveform from the desired wave should be as small as possible, and the average of each segment of the output waveform should be at least approximately equal to the average of the desired wave over the same period.

Further inspection of Figure 1.13*a* shows that with the above principles it is possible to construct two kinds of waveforms: one in which the incoming voltage wave to be switched to the output terminals is always more *positive* than the outgoing wave, as shown at *b*, and one in which the incoming voltage wave is always more *negative* than the outgoing wave, as shown at *c*. In all further discussion, these two basic waveform types are referred to as *positive-type* and *negative-type* voltage waves, respectively.

It is also possible to combine selected intervals of the above two waveforms; thus the output waveform contains both positive-type and negative-type segments, as shown at *d*.

A further possibility is to produce the arithmetic mean of the two waveforms *b* and *c*, to obtain still another approximation of the desired output, as shown at *e*. In this case, however, two frequency changer circuits are needed, the separate output

* A simple *inverter-type* square waveform is treated briefly in Chapter 3 during the analysis of nonsinusoidal "mean" output voltages.

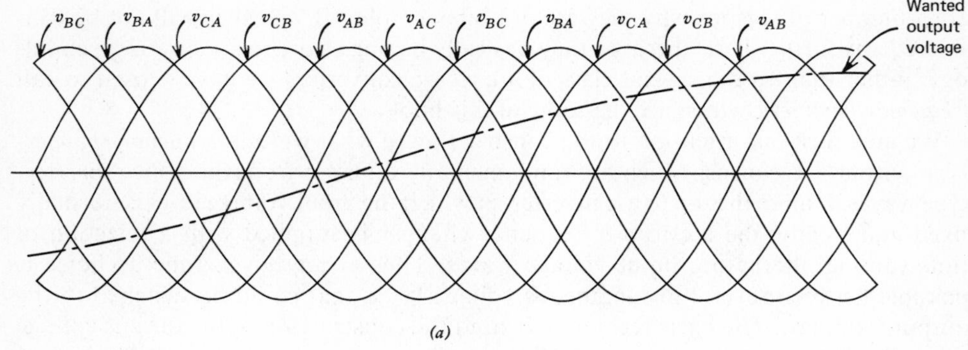
v_{BC}
v_{BA}
v_{CA}
v_{CB}
v_{AB}
v_{AC}
v_{BC}
v_{BA}
v_{CA}
v_{CB}
v_{AB}
Wanted output voltage

(a)

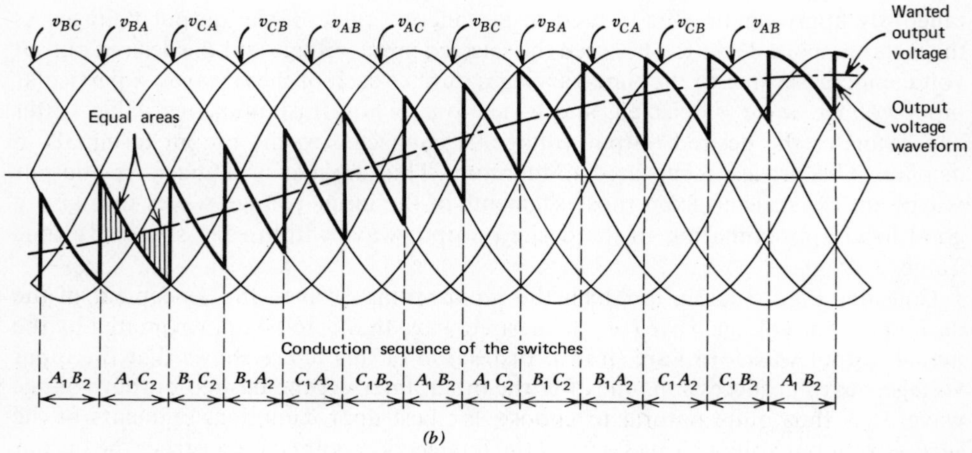
v_{BC}
v_{BA}
v_{CA}
v_{CB}
v_{AB}
v_{AC}
v_{BC}
v_{BA}
v_{CA}
v_{CB}
v_{AB}
Wanted output voltage
Output voltage waveform
Equal areas
Conduction sequence of the switches
$A_1 B_2$
$A_1 C_2$
$B_1 C_2$
$B_1 A_2$
$C_1 A_2$
$C_1 B_2$
$A_1 B_2$
$A_1 C_2$
$B_1 C_2$
$B_1 A_2$
$C_1 A_2$
$C_1 B_2$
$A_1 B_2$

(b)

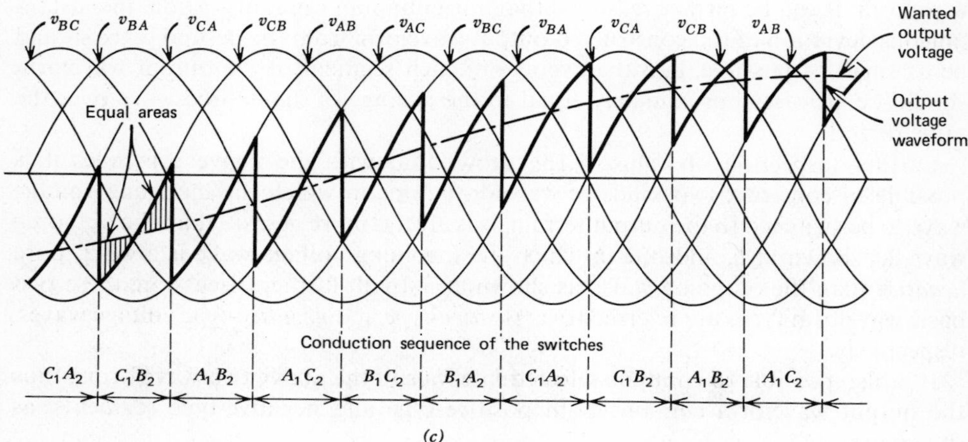
v_{BC}
v_{BA}
v_{CA}
v_{CB}
v_{AB}
v_{AC}
v_{BC}
v_{BA}
v_{CA}
v_{CB}
v_{AB}
Wanted output voltage
Output voltage waveform
Equal areas
Conduction sequence of the switches
$C_1 A_2$
$C_1 B_2$
$A_1 B_2$
$A_1 C_2$
$B_1 C_2$
$B_1 A_2$
$C_1 A_2$
$C_1 B_2$
$A_1 B_2$
$A_1 C_2$

(c)

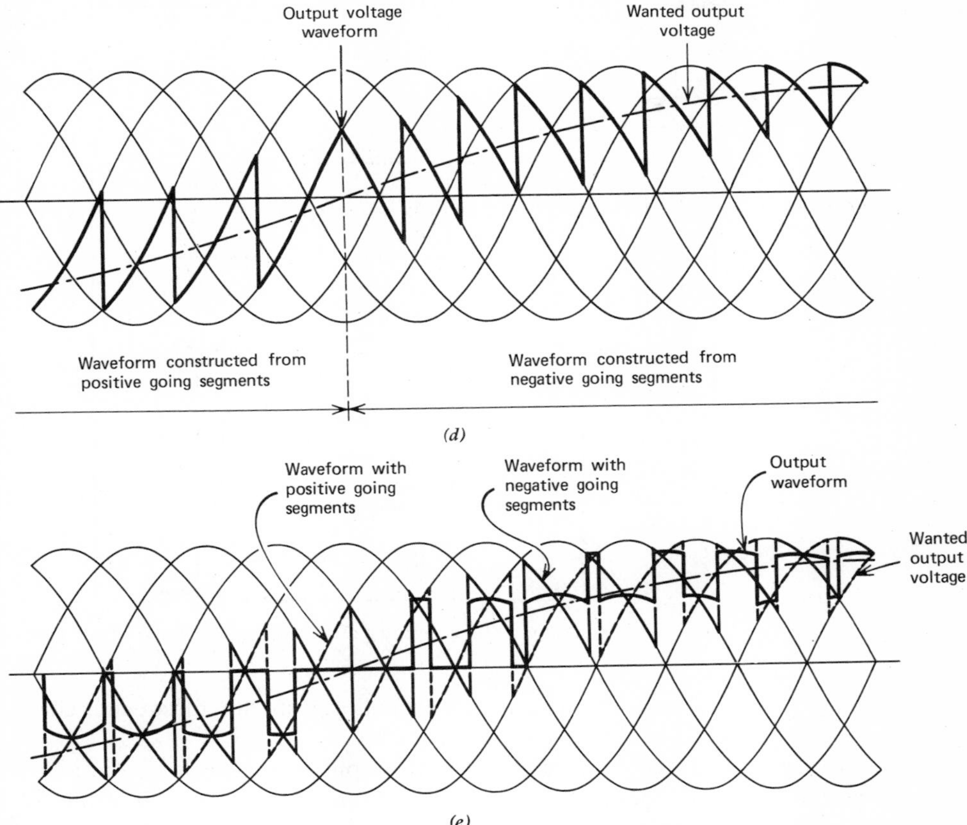

Figure 1.13 Waveforms illustrating various approaches to output waveform construction. *a* Input voltage and wanted output voltage waves. *b* Positive-type output voltage waveform. *c* Negative-type output voltage waveform. *d* Consecutive composite output voltage waveform. *e* Concurrent composite output voltage waveform.

waveforms of which can either be added directly in series or in parallel through an interphase reactor, as shown schematically in Figure 1.14.

The output waveforms constructed from successive segments of positive-type and negative-type voltage waves are referred to as *consecutive composite* waves, and those constructed from both waveform types in their entirety are referred to as *concurrent composite* waves.

It can probably be visualized readily that for each of the waveform types shown in Figure 1.13, the output frequency and the amplitude of the desired component of the output voltage can be adjusted independently by appropriate control of the conduction periods of the switches relative to the input voltage waves. It is not immediately evident, however, where the limits of such a control process may lie. Intuitively we may expect some difficulties as the wanted output frequency is pushed closer to the input frequency.

Actually, by constructing the complete output voltage cycle from judiciously chosen segments of the two basic waveform types shown in Figure 1.13*a* and *b*, it is possible to derive a frequency changer (the UFC) that has no theoretical restriction on the range of output frequency attainable; this is stated in Table 1.1 and is explained in

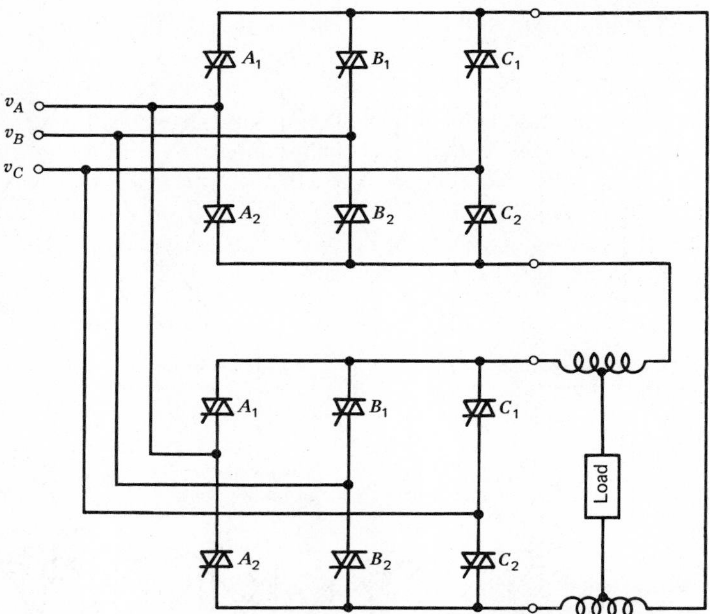

Figure 1.14 Frequency changer circuit suitable for generating the output waveform shown in Figure 1.13*e*.

Chapter 3. The maximum output frequency attainable from other frequency changers, however, is generally less than the input frequency.

The method of construction of the overall output waveform from the two basic constituent waveform types can also influence the operating requirements of the switches; thus, by suitable choice of the waveform segments, natural commutation of the current from one switch to the other can always be achieved, thereby eliminating the need for switches with "intrinsic" turn-off capability. This is explained in Section 1.5.3.

Finally, the particular choice of the constituent positive-type and negative-type segments within the overall output voltage wave has a direct impact on the displacement angle of the input current of the frequency changer. It is this latter phenomenon to which we now turn our attention.

1.5.2 Dependence of the Input Displacement Angle on the Construction Method of the Output Voltage Waveform

As we have seen, the frequency changer constructs an output voltage waveform by means of sequentially connecting segments of the alternating input voltage waves to the output terminals, via an array of switches. The "average" value of the resulting output voltage waveform corresponds to the desired output voltage component; superimposed onto this component is a complex *ripple* or *distortion* voltage wave. The waveform of current that flows at the output depends upon the impedance of the load, both to the wanted component of voltage and to the superimposed *distortion* or *unwanted* components. In most applications the impedance of the load to the unwanted components is relatively high (either because of its natural impedance characteristic or because filter components are purposefully added), and thus the waveshape of the output current is generally a relatively smooth sinusoid at the wanted output frequency, the amplitude and phase of which are determined by the impedance and phase angle of the load at the wanted output frequency. In the following discussion and generally in the theoretical treatment throughout this book, it is assumed that the waveform of the output current is in fact a pure sinusoid.

The current flowing in a given input line is either equal to the output current—whenever this current flows through a switch connected to that line—or it is zero—whenever the switch (or switches) connected to that line are off. The waveform of current in a given input line due to the current in a given output phase therefore consists of a series of discontinuous pulses, as shown in general illustrative form in Figure 1.15. The amplitudes of the current pulses vary over the course of the output

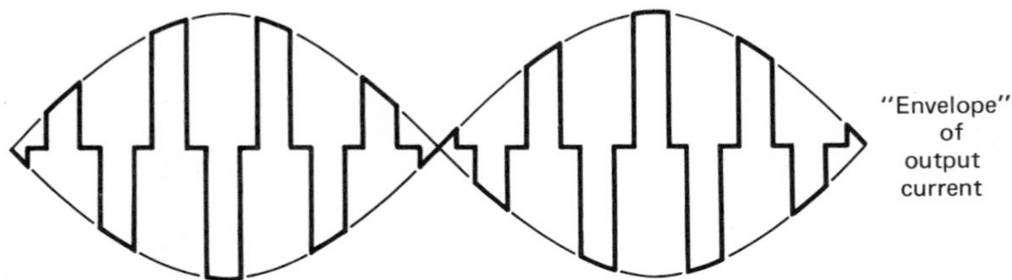

Figure 1.15 General form of the current wave in an input line due to current flowing at a given output phase of the frequency changer.

cycle in correspondence with the sinusoidally varying amplitude of the output current wave; the *timing* of these current pulses relative to the associated input voltage wave is determined by the timing of the closures of the switch (or switches) connected to that line, which is itself dependent upon the particular technique employed for constructing the output voltage waveform.

This complex input current waveform can be represented as a *fundamental* component—that is, a component at the input frequency—and a series of superimposed *distortion* or *extrabasal* terms. What is of interest in the present discussion is the phase of the fundamental component relative to the associated input voltage wave and how this phase relationship depends upon the particular technique of constructing the output voltage wave.

Let us assume for the moment that the frequency changer is controlled to produce a steady average level of output voltage, and that the resulting current that flows at the output is pure d-c. This simplification may not appear relevant to the case in hand; it will be seen, however, that certain basic conclusions can be made from a consideration of this simple case, from which the influence of the voltage waveform construction technique on the input displacement angle of the frequency changer can be deduced immediately.

Assume, then, that the circuit of Figure 1.11 is controlled to produce some intermediate steady positive average voltage level. Using first the approach of producing the output from the previously defined positive-type wave, the desired average voltage is represented by the waveform shown in Figure 1.16*a*1. Assuming, as stipulated, a smooth positive d-c output current, and using the conduction sequence of the switches shown, the input current waveforms can be readily constructed, as illustrated for input phase A at *a*2. Comparison of this waveform with the corresponding line to neutral input voltage, v_{AN}, shows that the two waves are phase displaced; the current *lags* the voltage by angle ϕ_I.

The desired average output can also be produced by the previously defined negative-type voltage wave, as illustrated at *b*1. The corresponding current waveform for input

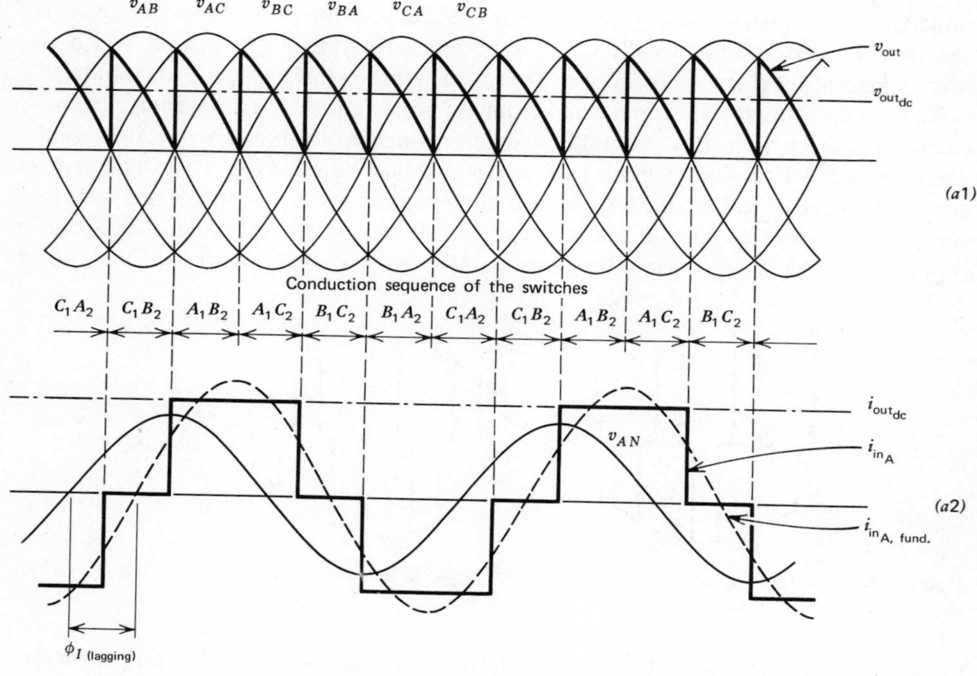

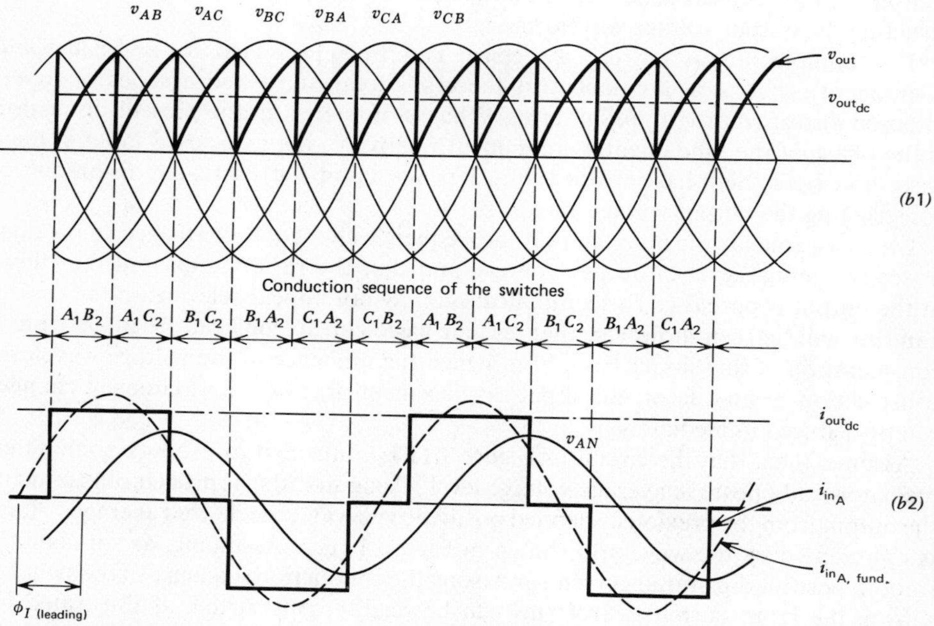

Figure 1.16 Waveforms illustrating the complementary phase relationships of the input current with respect to the input voltage, for the complementary positive-type and negative-type output voltage waveforms. *a*1 Positive-type output voltage waveform. *a*2 Corresponding input current waves. *b*1 Negative-type output voltage waveform. *b*2 Corresponding input current waves.

phase A, together with the line to neutral voltage v_{AN}, are shown at $b2$. It may readily be observed that the current wave now *leads* the voltage wave by the angle ϕ_I.

It can thus be concluded that the two quite similar output waveforms result in two similar but phase-displaced input current waveforms. This is really not surprising, since the segments of the input voltage waves used to construct the output waveform in the first case followed, and in the second case preceded, the relevant positive crests of the input waves. Thus the positions of the conduction intervals compelled the input source to supply lagging current in the first case, and leading current in the second case, for identical output current.

In these two examples, a positive output voltage and a positive output current are assumed. In practice, of course, the frequency changer produces an alternating output voltage. Just as the positive portions of the output voltage wave can be constructed either from a positive-type or a negative-type waveform, so the negative portions of the output voltage wave can also be constructed from either of these waveform types.

The polarity of the output current of the frequency changer of course also alternates during each output cycle. In general, the output current wave can bear any phase relationship with respect to the output voltage wave, between 0 and $\pm 180°$, depending upon the reactive component of the load and the direction of the average power flow through the frequency changer. Thus in general either polarity of current may be obtained with either polarity of voltage, which means with either voltage waveform type.

It can be deduced readily that for each of the four possible combinations of voltage waveform type and polarity of output current the input current either lags or leads the input voltage, according to Table 1.2.

With this information in hand, it is now a simple matter to deduce how the input displacement angle of the frequency changer is influenced by the particular method of construction of the output voltage.

Consider, first, an output voltage constructed in its entirety from a positive-type waveform, as illustrated in Figure 1.17*a*l. The output current, shown at $a2$, is arbitrarily assumed to be 45° lagging the voltage. From Table 1.2 it is evident that during the positive half-cycle of output current the input phase angle will be instantaneously lagging, and during the negative half-cycle of output current, it will be instantaneously leading, as indicated.

We must now ask what we mean by *instantaneously lagging* and *instantaneously leading*. If we suppose, as is the teaching of basic Fourier waveform analysis, that the complex input current waveform must contain a single fundamental component

TABLE 1.2. Input Displacement Angle for Different Combinations of Voltage Waveform Type and Output Current Polarity

Voltage Waveform	Polarity of Output Current	Input Displacement Angle
Positive type	Positive	Lagging
	Negative	Leading
Negative type	Positive	Leading
	Negative	Lagging

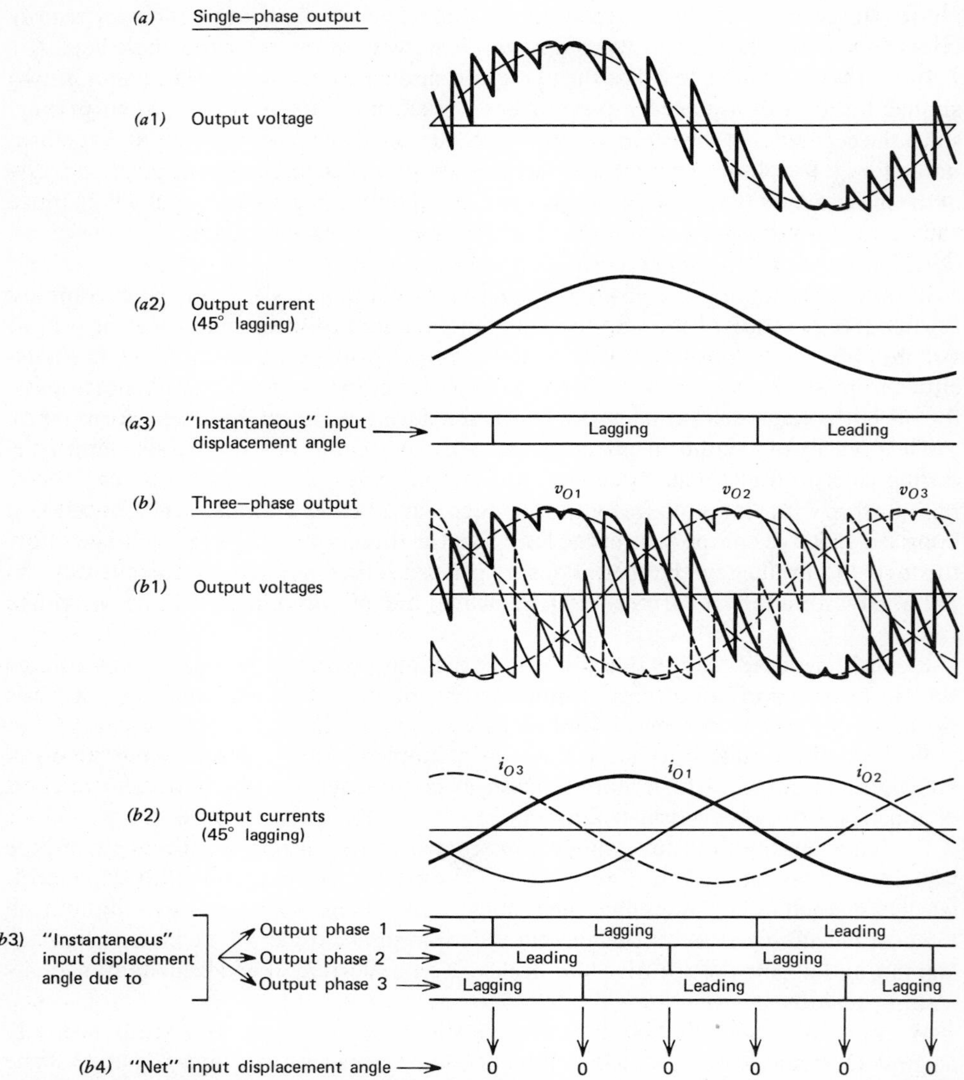

Figure 1.17 Qualitative derivation of the input displacement angle of a frequency changer producing a continuous positive-type output voltage wave.

whose phase is stationary (because, by its very definition, the fundamental component is a pure "stationary" sine wave), with superimposed distortion terms, then, from basic considerations of symmetry, we must conclude that this fundamental component neither lags nor leads, but is in-phase with the associated input voltage. In other words, we are postulating that a waveform whose "apparent" phase periodically oscillates between lagging and leading actually consists of a stationary in-phase fundamental component, with some sort of superimposed extrabasal terms that "beat" in such a way with the fundamental to give the appearance of an oscillating phase angle.

This may seem to be a somewhat academic thesis that has no real bearing on the practicality of the matter. After all, if the input frequency is low enough—to take a suitably extreme example, it could be one cycle per day—the fact is that for half a day the input current will lag the input voltage, and for the other half day, it will lead it. The proposition that we can represent this current as a fixed in-phase component with superimposed ultra-low-frequency beat components—even though theoretically plausible—may not appear to have any real practical meaning.

Consider now, however, a frequency changer supplying a balanced three-phase output comprising three separate circuits that generate three mutually displaced positive-type voltage waves, as shown in Figure 1.17*b*1. Again, the output current of each phase is arbitrarily assumed to lag its respective voltage by 45°, as shown at *b*2. The significance of this theoretical representation of the input current wave now becomes evident.

According to our postulated theory, the current in a given input line due to the current in each output phase can be represented by an in-phase fundamental component, with superimposed "beating" extrabasal terms. Obviously, the fundamental components due to all three output phases must add directly in a given input line, to yield a net fundamental in-phase component of three times the magnitude of the individual components associated with each output phase. But what of the "beat" components? Since the output currents of the three output phases are mutually displaced by 120°, it would be reasonable to expect that these components of current in any given input line will largely cancel one another, leaving a net input current waveform that is comprised principally of the "stationary" fundamental component and that no longer has the "oscillating" appearance associated with a single-phase output.

That this supposition is correct is supported by the fact that the oscillations of the "instantaneous" input displacement angles of the individual currents due to the three output phases are indeed mutually displaced with respect to one another, as indicated at *b*3 in Figure 1.17. It is evident that at the particular instants indicated—in which the currents of two output phases are instantaneously equal but opposite, whereas the third current is instantaneously zero—the net input displacement angle is 0°. This is so because the two output currents in question instantaneously impose equal but opposite leading and lagging displacement angles on the input system. It would certainly be reasonable to conclude—as is indeed the case—that the net "instantaneous" input displacement angle is always 0°—and not just at those points on the output current waveform at which it is indicated to be so at *b*4 in Figure 1.17.

To conclude the discussion for the positive-type voltage waveform, we see, as can be readily deduced from Table 1.2, that the input displacement angle obtained with this voltage wave is always 0° (or 180°, depending upon the direction of power flow), regardless of the phase angle of the output load. Further discussion of this rather remarkable fact is deferred to Chapter 5.

Consider now a frequency changer, as shown in Figure 1.14, that contains two constituent circuits, one continually producing a positive-type output voltage waveform, the other continually producing a negative-type waveform, as illustrated in Figure 1.18*a* and *b*. The output voltages of these two circuits are added to give the composite output voltage waveform shown at *c*. The net current in a given input line feeding such an arrangement is the sum of the input currents due to the (equal) currents flowing at the output terminals of the constituent positive-type and negative-type circuits. An output current waveform with an arbitrarily assumed 45° leading angle is shown at *d*. It is evident that the "instantaneous" input displacement angles of the individual components of input current feeding each of the constituent circuits are always opposite to one another. The net "instantaneous" input displacement angle is therefore 0° at all points in the output cycle.

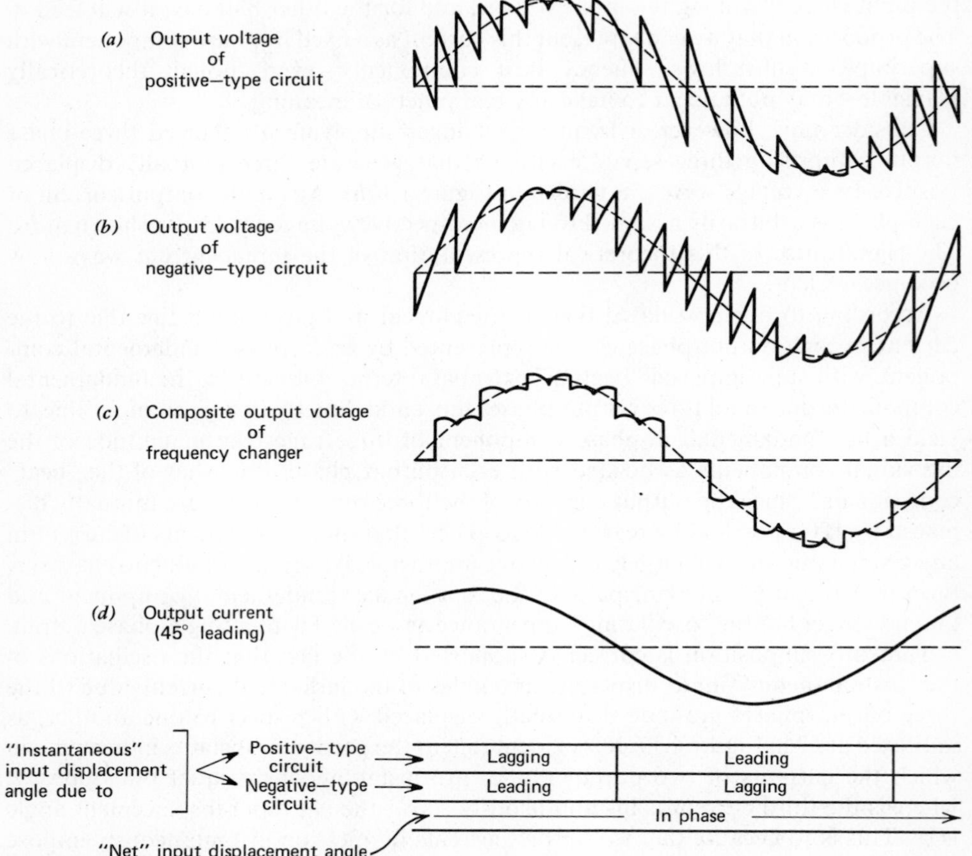

Figure 1.18 Qualitative derivation of the input displacement angle of the unity displacement factor frequency changer.

Again, we will point out that it is readily deducible that the input displacement angle of this arrangement in fact is invariably 0° (or 180°), regardless of the phase angle of the current at the output terminals. It is for this reason that we call this particular type of frequency changer the *unity displacement factor frequency charger* (UDFFC).

Another form of construction of the output voltage waveform is shown in Figure 1.19. Here, the positive slopes of the voltage waveform are constructed from the positive-type voltage wave, and the negative slopes are constructed from the negative-type voltage wave.

At *a*, the phase angle of the output current is 0°, and it is evident that the net input displacement angle is also 0°. At *b*, the output current *leads* the voltage by 90°; the input displacement angle, however, is *lagging*. Further, since the average output power must be zero, the average input power must also be zero, and we can deduce that the input displacement angle must therefore be lagging by 90°. At *c*, the output current *lags* the voltage by 90°; the input displacement angle, however, is *leading*, and again we can reason that it must be leading by 90°.

Here, then, we have a frequency changer that has the property of *inverting* the sign of the output phase angle at the input. In fact, as we show in Chapter 5, the input

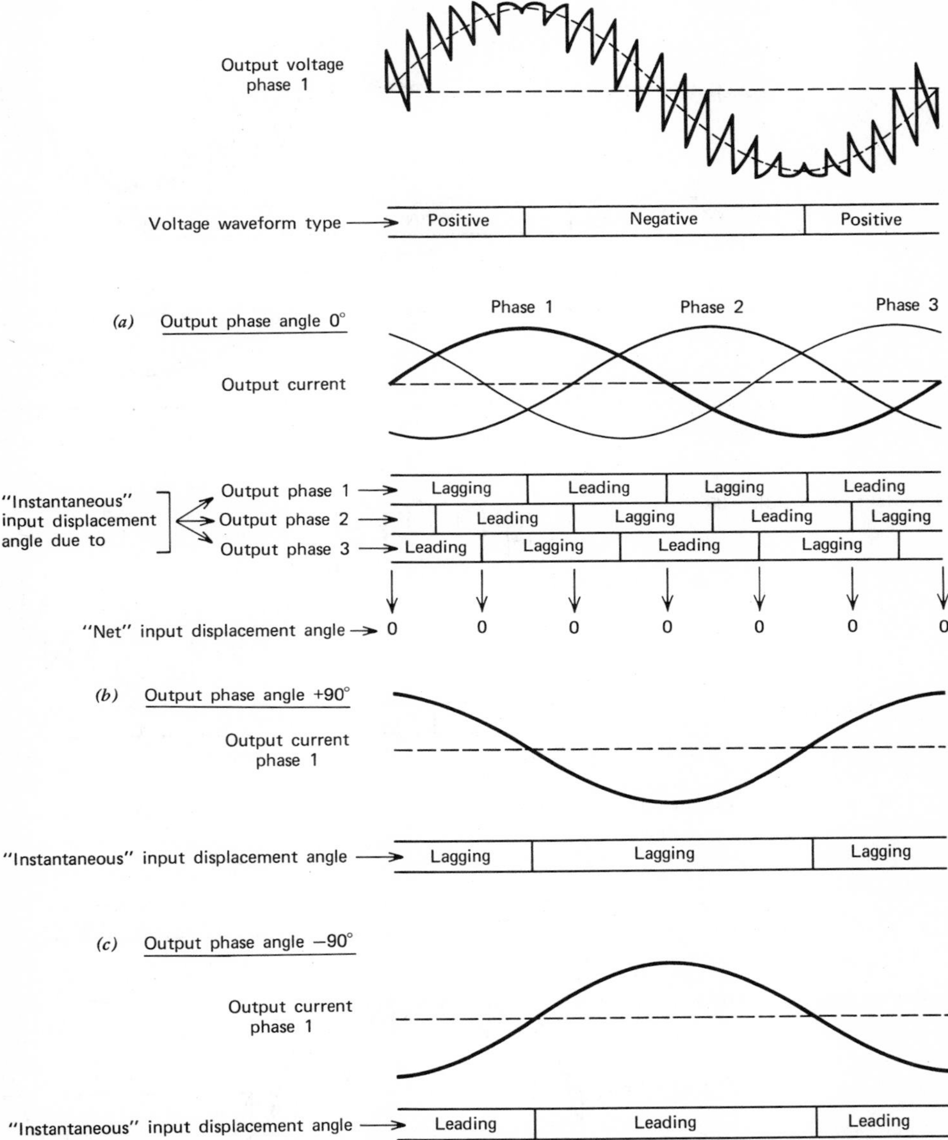

Figure 1.19 Qualitative derivation of the input displacement angle of the unrestricted frequency changer with varying output load angle.

displacement factor of this type of frequency changer (the UFC) is always equal, but in the opposite sense, to that of the load at the output.

Another rather special form of construction of the output voltage waveform is illustrated in Figure 1.20. Here the waveform construction process is arranged so that the positive-type *voltage* wave is produced whenever the output *current* is instantaneously positive, and the negative-type voltage wave is produced whenever the output *current* is instantaneously negative. This type of waveform construction in fact belongs to the classical *cycloconverter*. In this book we refer to it as the *naturally commutated cycloconverter* for reasons that become evident in Section 1.5.3.

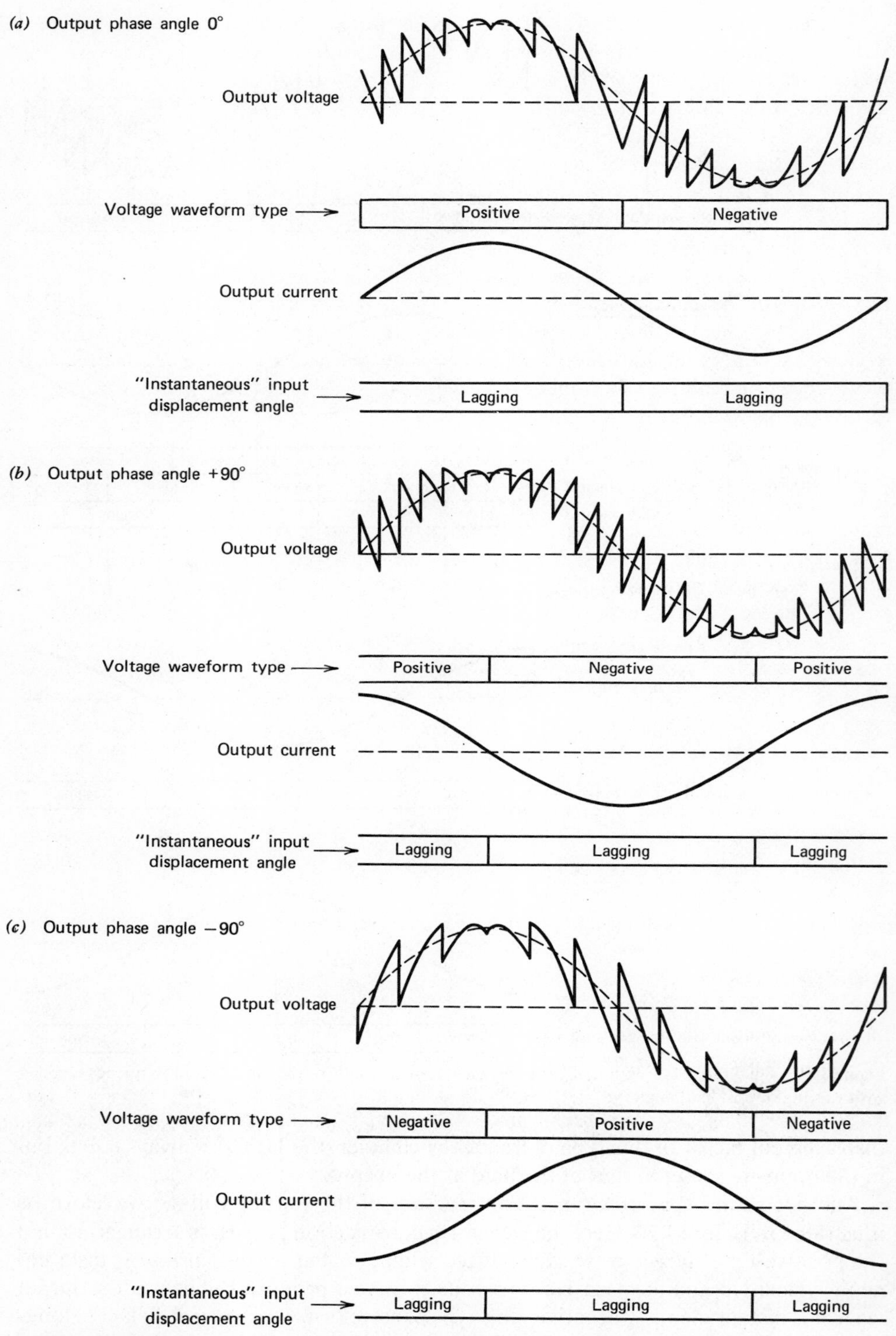

Figure 1.20 Qualitative derivation of the input displacement angle of the naturally commutated cycloconverter, with varying output load angle.

Whereas, with the waveform construction techniques illustrated in Figures 1.17–1.19, the voltage waveform is independent of the output current, here we have a voltage waveform construction technique that is dependent upon and doggedly responsive to the *polarity* of the output current wave. It is evident that the input displacement angle is *invariably lagging*, regardless of whether the output phase angle is leading, lagging, or in-phase.

This is an interesting observation when compared with the conclusions already reached for other forms of construction of the output voltage wave. For the voltage waveforms illustrated in Figures 1.17 and 1.18, we saw that the input displacement angle is invariably 0°, and hence the reactive power at the input is invariably zero, regardless of the reactive component of power at the output. The waveforms of Figure 1.20 indicate that precisely the opposite situation is also possible—that is, a reactive component of power can be obtained at the input regardless of the presence or absence of a reactive component of power at the output. For the particular waveform construction technique illustrated, in which the positive-type voltage wave coincides with positive current, and vice versa, the input displacement angle is always lagging.

It is now but a small step to predict the possibility for actively *controlling* the displacement angle of the current at the input, by suitably *controlling* the periods of positive-type and negative-type voltage waves in relation to the output current wave.

Such a control process is illustrated by the waveforms of Figure 1.21. The phase angle of the load at the output is assumed to be invariably 0°. At *a*, as in Figure 1.20*a*, the positive-type output voltage wave is produced whenever the output current is positive, and vice versa. As we have already seen, the input displacement angle is lagging. At *b*, as in Figure 1.19*a*, the positive-type voltage wave straddles successive negative and positive quarter-cycles of the output current, and vice versa. The input displacement angle is now 0°. Comparing this situation with that illustrated in Figure 1.21*a*, we can imagine that the *segmentation* of the voltage wave has been shifted 90° to the left with respect to the *fixed* current wave. At *c*, the segmentation of the voltage wave has been shifted to the left by a *further* 90°. Now the positive-type voltage wave is produced whenever the output current is negative, and vice versa. The input displacement angle is now leading.

It is evident, then, that by continuously shifting the positive-type and negative-type voltage segments with respect to the output current wave it is possible to obtain continuous *control* of the displacement factor of the current at the input, from lagging, through unity, to leading. The displacement factor of the output current, on the other hand, has remained at unity.

Again, we do not carry the discussion any further at this point. We expect, however, that the alert reader will be able to foresee—quite correctly—the possibility for controlling the input displacement angle with an output current of any displacement angle.

This type of frequency changer, for obvious reasons, we call the *controllable displacement factor frequency changer* (CDFFC).

1.5.3 Conceptual Realization of Bidirectional Switches: Forced and Natural Commutation

In the foregoing discussion, the use of a static bidirectional switch within the frequency changer circuit that has the capability of instantaneously changing its state from

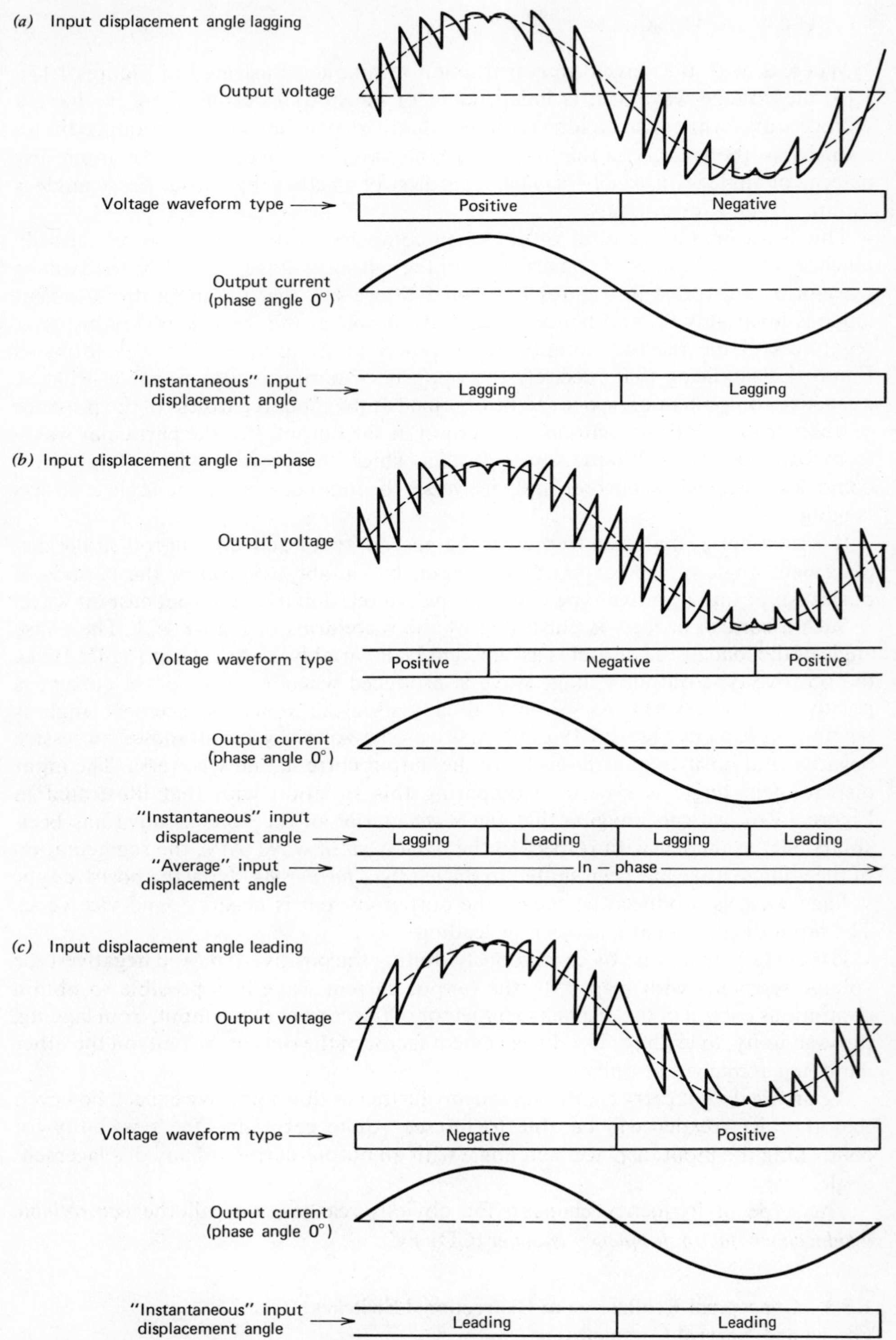

Figure 1.21 Qualitative illustration of the controllability of the input displacement angle of the controllable displacement factor frequency changer.

conducting to nonconducting, and vice versa, independent of the external circuit conditions, on the command of an appropriate control signal, is assumed. The reader who is familiar with the state of the art of solid-state devices, however, will know that (at the time of writing) no such device exists as a *single entity.*

Why, then, have we taken the liberty of assuming such a switching device? The answer is that it is possible, in several different ways, to synthesize such a bidirectional switch from combinations of commonly used solid-state devices.

In considering how we might construct a bidirectional switch, we must bear in mind that most available solid-state devices (and certainly those that we would consider for use in a static frequency changer) are *unidirectional* in nature; that is, they are capable of conducting load current only in one direction.

In order to form a composite bidirectional switch with the capability of conducting current in both directions, it is necessary, therefore, either to connect two such devices in "inverse parallel" with one another or to surround a single unidirectional switching device with rectifiers in such a way that the external bidirectional current flow is routed unidirectionally through the switching device itself.

Another important point to be recognized is that, whereas some solid-state switching devices—specifically, in the context of the present discussion, transistors and the gate-controlled switches—have the capability of being turned off, regardless of the external circuit conditions, by application (or nonapplication) of an electrical signal to the control electrode, this is not so for the thyristor. This latter device may generally be considered to be a strong potential candidate for power frequency changers because of its vastly greater power-handling capability, compared with the transistor or gate-controlled switch. As we will see, thyristors can in fact be applied in power frequency changers, but only through the use of special circuit techniques.

For the moment, we turn our attention to the relatively simple question of how transistors and gate-controlled switches can be applied. Possible methods of constructing the required bidirectional switch with these devices are illustrated in Figure 1.22*a* and *b*, respectively. Each of these arrangements permits external current to flow and voltage to be blocked in either direction; the overall switch combination can be turned on and off by appropriate signalling of the control electrode(s) of the active switching device(s), regardless of the external circuit conditions. The arrangements shown therefore completely satisfy the basic operational requirements of the bidirectional switch; in general, however, they are practically useful only for applications in which the total power to be delivered by the frequency changer is relatively low—for example, a few tens of kilowatts at most. (These remarks, of course, reflect the present state of the art of these devices; it is quite conceivable that in the future gate-controlled switches with ratings comparable to those of present-day high-power thyristors may become available.)

When considering the use of thyristors—potentially much more attractive candidates at present for higher-power applications—obviously the same *basic* "back-to-back" or "rectifier bridge" arrangements shown for the gate-controlled switch can be employed to achieve the basic *bidirectional* capability. Whereas, however, such a basic arrangement can always be turned on at any instant by appropriate pulsing of the thyristor gate, turn-off can be accomplished only by bringing the main anode current of the thyristor to zero through the action of the external circuit. With a back-to-back arrangement of thyristors (but not with the "rectifier bridge" arrangement), it is possible to achieve "natural commutation" of the current from the "outgoing" thyristor to the "incoming" thyristor in the frequency changer circuit by

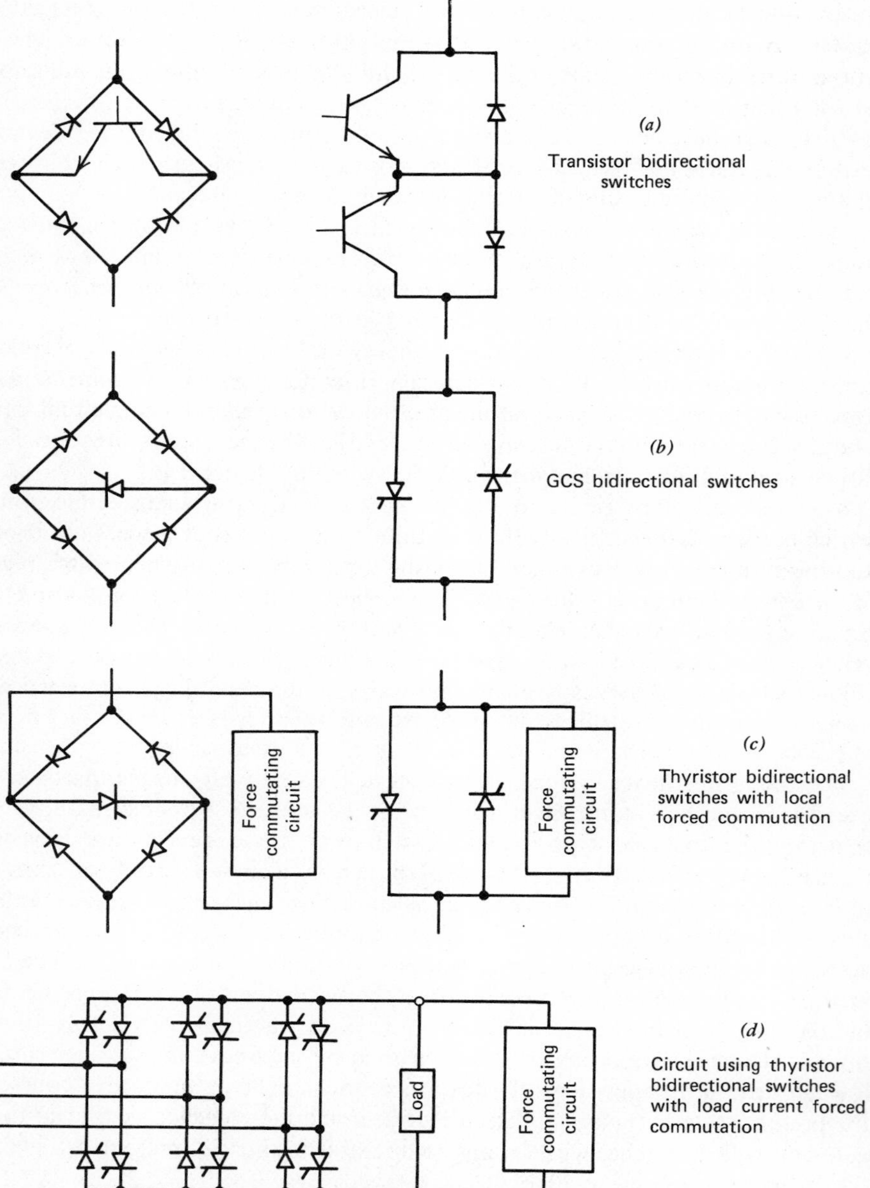

Figure 1.22 Various bidirectional switch arrangements with transistors, gate-controlled switches, and thyristors.

appropriate choice of the switching instants in relation to the external circuit conditions. This special operating mode, which is applicable only to one specific type of frequency changer, the NCC, is discussed further below.

If the thyristor is to be generally applied as the main switching element in each of the types of frequency changers considered in this book, it must be complemented by an additional circuit that turns it off "forcibly" at any desired instant, regardless of the external circuit conditions. This auxiliary circuit we call a *force commutating* circuit; it is generally comprised of passive storage elements—capacitors and inductors—and an auxiliary static switch or switches. Forced commutation may be applied to an individual bidirectional switch arrangement or to a complete portion of the overall power circuit, as shown schematically in Figures 1.22*c* and *d*, respectively. In either case, the forced commutation is achieved by diverting temporarily the load current from the conducting thyristor to the commutating circuit and then, after the thyristor has regained its blocking state, bringing the next device in sequence in the main power circuit into conduction to "retake" the load current from the commutating circuit. Thus, during the period *between* commutations, the auxiliary force commutating circuit remains, as it were, unobtrusively in the background and plays no active role. Its sole function is one of making it practically possible to switch from one input wave to the next at the desired instant; beyond that it theoretically has no effect upon the shape of the wave thereby created. These ideas are discussed in greater detail in Chapter 8. It is sufficient here to remember that for the forced commutation of thyristors, an external auxiliary circuit has to be employed that is capable of applying a momentary reverse voltage across the conducting device while temporarily providing an alternative path for the load current.

We now consider briefly the special mechanism of natural commutation. As stated, natural commutation of the output current from one thyristor to the next can be accomplished in a frequency changer circuit that uses back-to-back pairs of thyristors to form the bidirectional switches. Basically, it is achieved by choosing the switching instants, in relation to the instantaneous polarity of the input voltages, so that firing of the incoming thyristors always results in the relevant line-to-line input voltage being applied in the reverse direction across the outgoing thyristor, thus automatically turning it off. The need for auxiliary force commutating circuitry is therefore eliminated.

A typical three-phase to one-phase frequency changer circuit comprised of back-to-back thyristor pairs is shown in Figure 1.23. This overall circuit can be partitioned into separate positive and negative constituent converter circuits, as shown in Figure 1.24. Since current can flow only in the "forward" direction through the thyristors, it is evident that whenever the output current is positive, this must be carried by the positive converter, and whenever it is negative, it must be carried by the negative converter. This means that during the positive half-cycle of output current, only the thyristors of the positive converter need to be fired, whereas the firing signals of the negative converter can be removed, and this converter can be allowed to remain temporarily idle. Conversely, during the negative half-cycle of output current, the positive converter can be allowed to remain idle.

The problem now becomes one of establishing the necessary conditions for natural commutation within each of the constituent converters, since, at any given time, the presence of the other converter can be ignored.

The answer to this question actually lies tacitly within our basic definition of the positive-type and negative-type voltage waves. Remember that we defined the

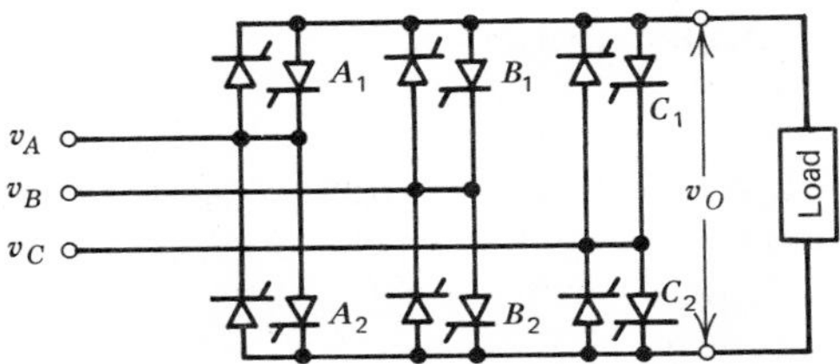

Figure 1.23 Bridge circuit composed of inverse parallel connected thyristors.

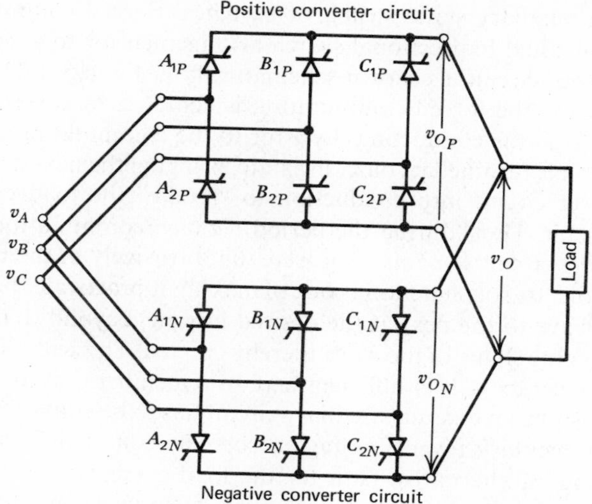

Figure 1.24 Partitioning of the circuit of Figure 1.23 into constituent positive and negative converter circuits.

positive-type voltage wave as being one in which the incoming input voltage wave to be switched to the output terminals is always *more positive* than the outgoing wave, and the negative-type voltage wave as being one in which the incoming input voltage wave is always *more negative* than the outgoing wave. A moment's reflection tells us that in order invariably to achieve natural commutation of the constituent positive converter of the NCC, it must, by definition, always be made to produce a positive-type voltage wave; the opposite is obviously true for the constituent negative converter.

These deductions lead us to the final conclusion that for natural commutation of the frequency changer the *positive-type* voltage wave must always be produced whenever the output current is instantaneously positive, and the negative-type output voltage wave must always be produced whenever the output current is instantaneously negative. This, of course, is precisely the state of affairs illustrated by the waveforms in Figure 1.20.

As might be expected, the practical circuit advantage of using natural commutation has its compensating disadvantages. One we deduced in Section 1.5.2, namely, that that the input displacement angle is invariably *lagging*. The other, spelled out in Table 1.1, is that the maximum output frequency obtainable is less than the input frequency; this disadvantage, however, is not peculiar to natural commutation—it is also shared by the other members of the family of frequency changers considered in this book, with the exception of the UFC.

1.6 FREQUENCY CHANGER CIRCUITS

As already stated, frequency changer circuits are essentially arrays of bidirectional static switches—or *switching matrices*—capable of sequentially connecting the voltages of a generally multiphase input source to a generally multiphase load. Many circuit configurations are possible; the most common of these are presented in this section.

It has already been indicated that frequency changer circuits are closely related to conventional rectifier or a-c to d-c *converter* circuits. In fact, for any given a-c to d-c converter circuit, there is a corresponding a-c to a-c frequency changer circuit that furnishes a single-phase output. A three- or multiphase output generally is obtained simply by repeating the basic circuit configuration for the requisite number of output phases. The only difference between the basic frequency changer circuit and the corresponding converter circuit resides in the types of devices employed; thus, whereas the converter circuit generally employs unidirectional devices, the frequency changer always employs bidirectional switches.

The reader who is familiar with basic a-c to d-c converter circuits may be aware of the fact that there are two basic types of circuit: the *midpoint* circuit, in which the output current is returned to the neutral or *midpoint* of the a-c source, and the *bridge* circuit, which in essence consists of two midpoint circuits with their output connected in series with one another, in which the output current flows between pairs of input lines, and no current flows in the neutral connection of the source.

The concept of circuit *pulse number* may also be familiar. The pulse number of an a-c to d-c converter circuit is related to the number of input phases that feed it and may be defined as the number of distinct segments of the output voltage wave that are produced during the course of one cycle of the input source voltage. The higher the circuit pulse number, the higher is the frequency of the unwanted ripple voltage produced at the output, and concomitantly, the lower is its amplitude; thus, the more perfect is the a-c to d-c conversion process.

The total number of basic *device positions* within any basic d-c to a-c converter circuit is always equal to the pulse number of the circuit. For midpoint circuits, the total number of mutually displaced input phases is also always equal to the pulse number. For bridge circuits, the total number of mutually displaced input phases is always equal to *half* the circuit pulse number, because the constituent "upper" and "lower" halves of the bridge operate with portions of the input voltage waves that are 180° displaced with respect to one another and therefore produce ripple voltage waveforms that are mutually displaced by 180°.

All these basic considerations are equally applicable to frequency changer circuits. Thus, we can define the pulse number of the frequency changer as being the number of discrete segments of the output voltage wave that are produced during the course of one input cycle, *when the output frequency is zero*. Or, if we prefer not to relate the pulse number to the specific condition of a d-c output, we can equally well define it simply as the total number of basic *switch positions* within the overall circuit (because each basic switch position has a uniquely defined conduction period). We should stipulate, however, that the pulse number of the frequency changer is defined in terms of the pulse number of each separate output phase, and it is unaffected by the number of output phases.*

With the above general thoughts in mind, we now proceed to consider possible basic frequency changer circuit configurations. These basic circuits are equally applicable to each type of frequency changer considered in this book, since fundamentally the frequency changer *type* is not determined by the arrangement of its power *circuit*, but rather by the manner in which it is controlled. We should point

* We should also stipulate that the pulse number of the UDFFC, which comprises two similar circuits fed from common input phases whose output voltages are summed together, is that of each of the constituent circuits.

out, though, that the power circuit of the UDFFC is in the nature of an exception to this rule, inasmuch as it requires *complete duplication* of the power circuitry—of whatever specific type is to be employed—together with appropriate interphase reactors or input transformer windings, in order to produce its final composite output voltage wave.

It is assumed that the input source has $3n$ ($n = 1, 2, 3, 4$) appropriately displaced phase voltages. In practice, where more than three input phases are required, these would normally be provided by an input transformer or transformers fed from a three-phase source, with the appropriate winding connections, to provide the necessary phase-displaced voltages to the frequency changer. Occasionally, however, the source itself could have six or more phases—for example, a local generator used in a VSCF system.

The simplest frequency changer circuit that we consider is a three-pulse circuit with single-phase output, shown in Figure 1.25*a*. Three of these circuits can be combined to provide three output phases, as shown at *b*. In this case, the neutral connection can be omitted if the output load is balanced; in fact, there is an advantage in so doing, from the viewpoint of the cancellation of certain unwanted components of voltage developed at each output phase. (The pulse number, of course, remains three, as previously stated.)

The bidirectional switch symbols generally represent any one of the previously described bidirectional switch arrangements shown in Figure 1.22. To simplify the diagrams of the more complex circuits, it is convenient to introduce switch matrix symbols to represent frequency changer circuits. Thus, the three-pulse circuit with three-phase output shown at *b* can be represented by the matrix shown at *c*. Each double-arrowed line joining each input terminal with each output terminal simply represents a bidirectional switch. Thus the three heavy lines in Figure 1.25*c* represent the particular circuit that produces the output phase voltage v_{O1}.

The complementary positive-type and negative-type voltage waveforms that can be produced by this circuit are illustrated at *d* for the special case of zero mean output voltage.

This simple three-pulse frequency changer circuit in fact is the basic building block of most practical circuits of higher pulse number. These more complex circuits are almost invariably arranged in such a way that each three-pulse group within the system operates in the same way as if it were by itself, and the final output voltage waveform is directly proportional to the sum of the individual output voltage waveforms of each constituent three-pulse group.

The *ripple* voltages of each three-pulse group are staggered in phase with respect to one another; thus, the ripple content of the final "summed" output voltage wave is appropriately reduced, in accord with the overall circuit pulse number.

Where the outputs of individual three-pulse groups are to be combined in parallel, it is necessary, in order to allow each group to remain in continuous operation and continuously carry its share of the total output current, to combine the individual group output voltages through windings of a so-called interphase reactor. In theory, the output terminals of the individual three-pulse groups could be connected directly in parallel, but in this case, although the overall pulse number of the output voltage wave thereby obtained would be the same as with the interphase reactor connection, it is no longer possible to maintain independent operation of the constituent three-pulse groups. This is because for any given output phase it is now permissible for

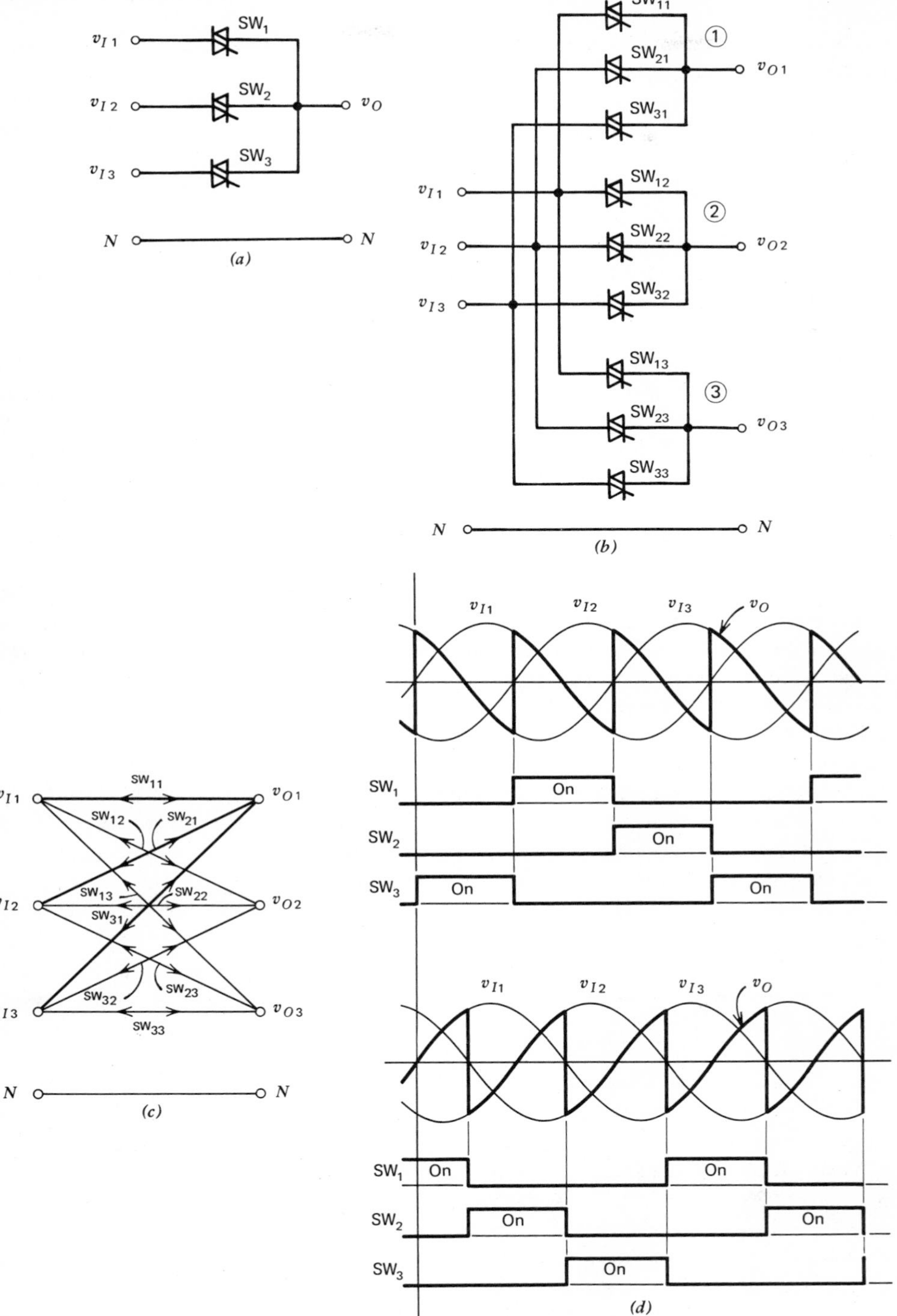

Figure 1.25 Three-pulse frequency changer circuits and basic waveforms. *a* Three-pulse frequency changer circuit with single-phase output. *b* Three-pulse frequency changer circuit with three-phase output. *c* Switch matrix symbol for three-pulse frequency changer circuit shown in *b*. *d* Basic positive-type and negative-type output waveforms for zero mean output voltage.

only one switch from all the three-pulse groups, rather than one switch from *each* three pulse group, to be in conduction at any one time (otherwise the input supply lines would be short-circuited). This means that for a given output current the peak current carried by each switch is n times higher (in which n is the number of three-pulse groups connected in parallel), whereas the conduction period of each switch is $1/n$ times shorter. This is generally undesirable, and thus this type of circuit connection is infrequently used in practice.

Six-pulse midpoint and bridge frequency changer circuits with single-phase output are shown in Figure 1.26*a*1, *b*1, and *c*1. The corresponding circuits with three-phase output are shown at *a*2, *b*2, and *c*2. The symbol M represents the generation of the arithmetic mean of the entering signals. Thus, in general, if signals $v_1, v_2, \ldots, v_M$ enter into this symbol, the output signal is equal to $1/m(v_1 + v_2 + \cdots + v_M)$. In practice, of course, this operation is performed by the interphase reactor. The circuits with single-phase output are represented with conventional symbols (for easy identification) and those with three-phase output with switch matrix symbols (for simplicity). This double representation is maintained in each of the circuit diagrams that follow.

The generation of positive-type output voltage waveforms with six-pulse circuits is illustrated at *a*3, *b*3, and *c*3 in Figure 1.26 for zero mean output voltage.

Following the pattern of the six-pulse circuits shown in Figure 1.26, nine- and twelve-pulse circuits comprising combinations of basic three-pulse groups can be readily constructed, as illustrated in Figures 1.27–1.29. Remembering that each of these circuits can be viewed as a particular combination of basic three-pulse groups, which operate independently of each other from appropriately displaced three-phase sources, the reader can easily establish the phase requirements for the input voltages and derive the basic conduction patterns of the switches.

As an example, the input voltages and a portion of a positive-type output voltage wave for the twelve-pulse circuit of Figure 1.29*b*1, are shown in Figure 1.30. The considerably reduced ripple content of this final output wave, as compared with the constituent six-pulse waves shown at *a* and *b*, is readily apparent.

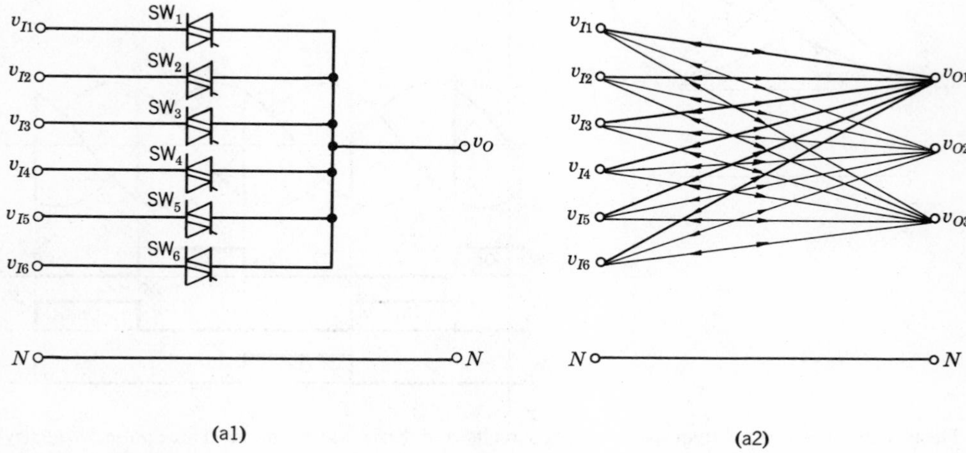

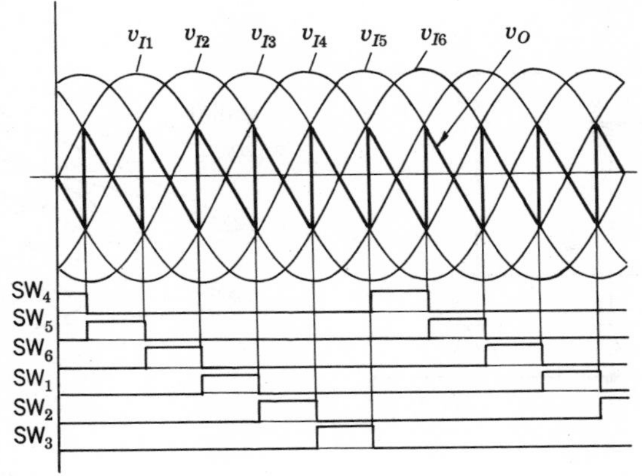

v_{I1}
v_{I2}
v_{I3}
v_{I4}
v_{I5}
v_{I6}
v_O
SW_4
SW_5
SW_6
SW_1
SW_2
SW_3

(a3)

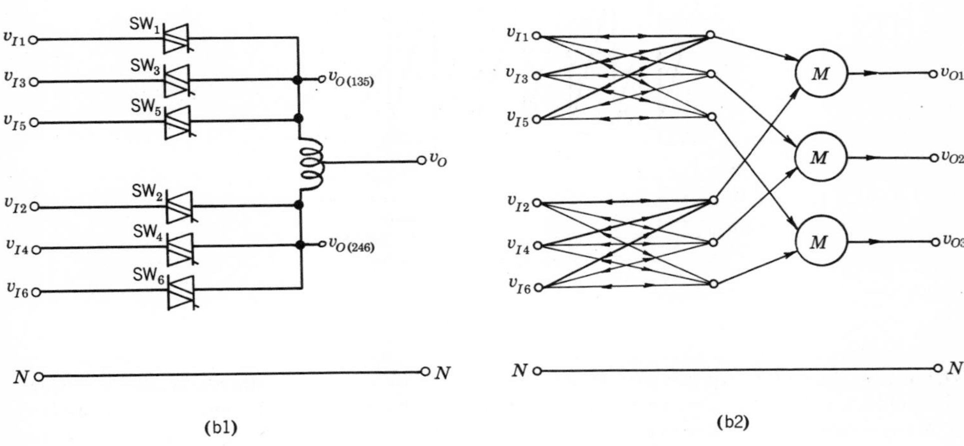

v_{I1}
v_{I3}
v_{I5}
v_{I2}
v_{I4}
v_{I6}
SW_1
SW_3
SW_5
SW_2
SW_4
SW_6
$v_{O(135)}$
v_O
$v_{O(246)}$
N
N
M
M
M
v_{O1}
v_{O2}
v_{O3}

(b1)

(b2)

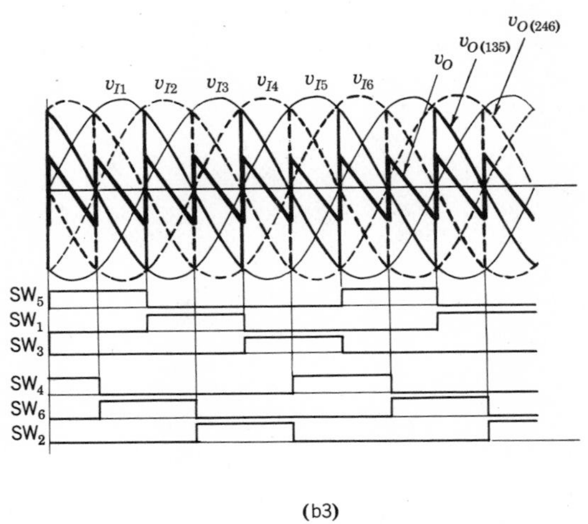

$v_{O(246)}$
$v_{O(135)}$
v_O
v_{I1}
v_{I2}
v_{I3}
v_{I4}
v_{I5}
v_{I6}
SW_5
SW_1
SW_3
SW_4
SW_6
SW_2

(b3)

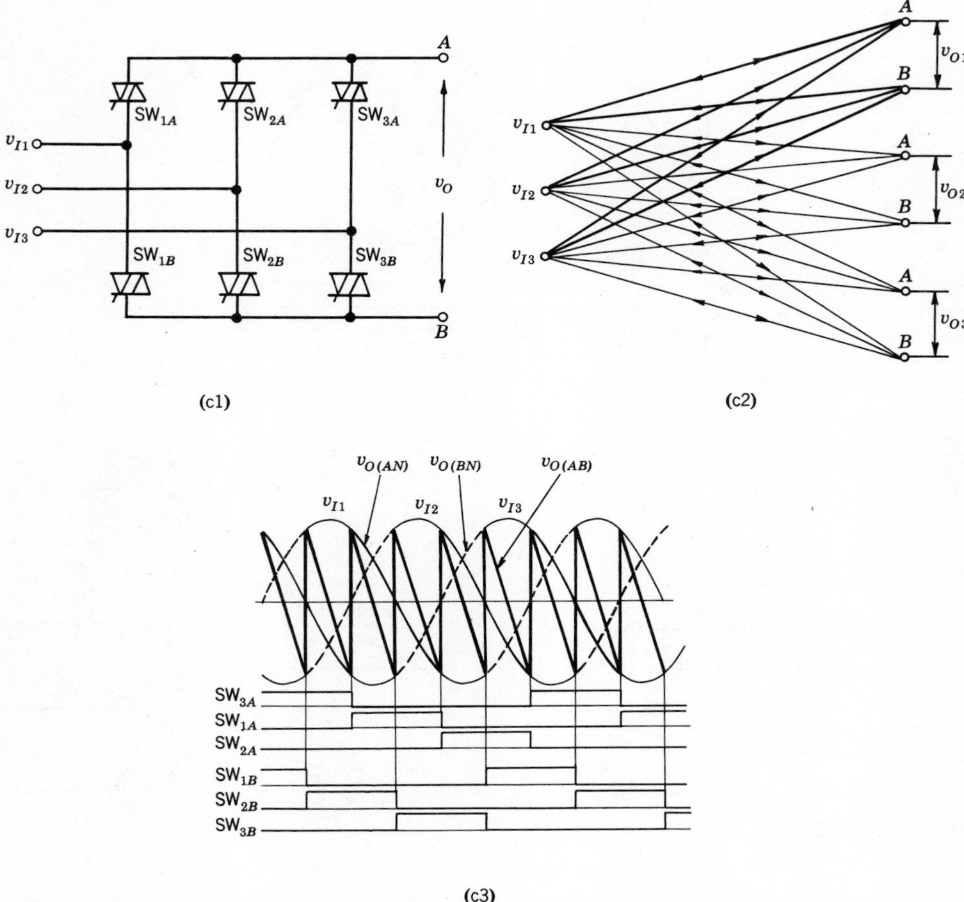

Figure 1.26 Six-pulse frequency changer circuits and basic waveforms. *a*1 Midpoint circuit with single-phase output. *a*2 Midpoint circuit with three-phase output. *a*3 Basic positive-type output voltage waveform. *b*1 Midpoint circuit with interphase reactor, with single-phase output. *b*2 Midpoint circuit with interphase reactor, with three-phase output. *b*3 Basic positive-type waveforms showing construction of final output voltage waveform. *c*1 Bridge circuit with single-phase output. *c*2 Bridge circuit with three-phase output. *c*3 Basic positive-type waveforms showing construction of final output voltage waveform.

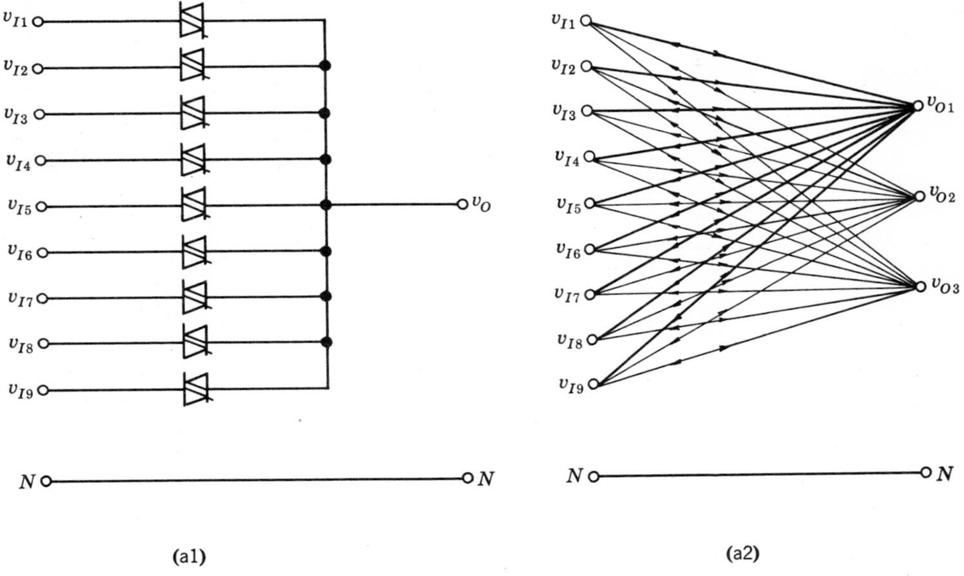

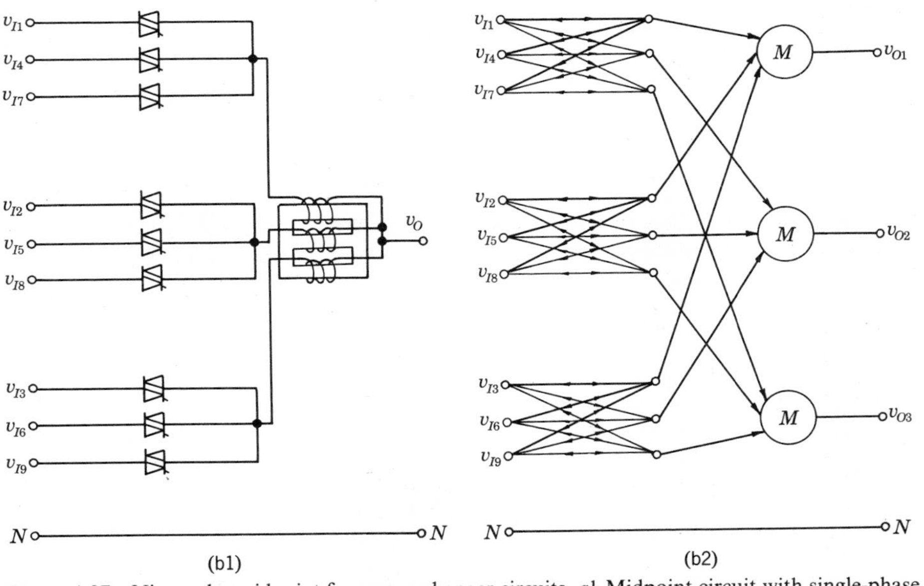

Figure 1.27 Nine-pulse midpoint frequency changer circuits. *a*1 Midpoint circuit with single-phase output. *a*2 Midpoint circuit with three-phase output. *b*1 Midpoint circuit with interphase reactor, with single-phase output. *b*2 Midpoint circuit with interphase reactor, with three-phase output.

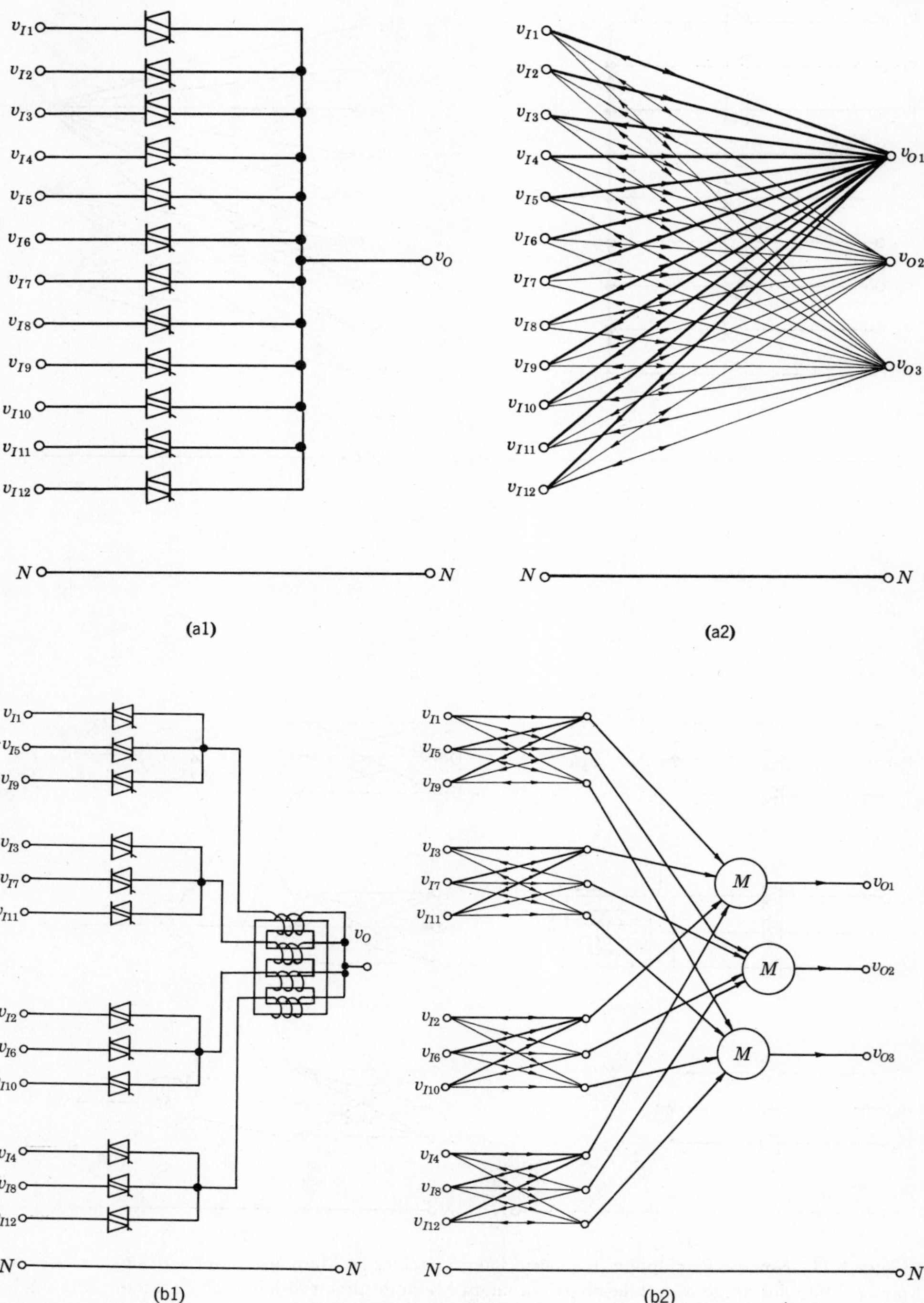

Figure 1.28 Twelve-pulse midpoint frequency changer circuits. *a*1 Midpoint circuit with single-phase output. *a*2 Midpoint circuit with three-phase output. *b*1 Midpoint circuit with interphase reactor, with single phase-output. *b*2 Midpoint circuit with interphase reactor, with three-phase output.

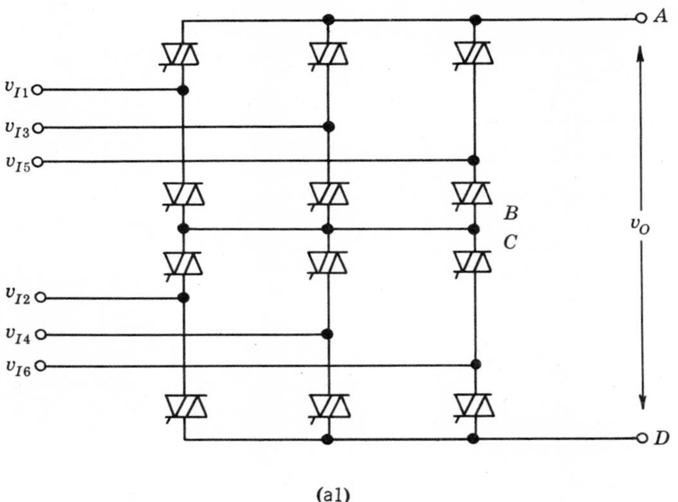

v_{I1}
v_{I3}
v_{I5}
v_{I2}
v_{I4}
v_{I6}
A
B
C
D
v_O

(a1)

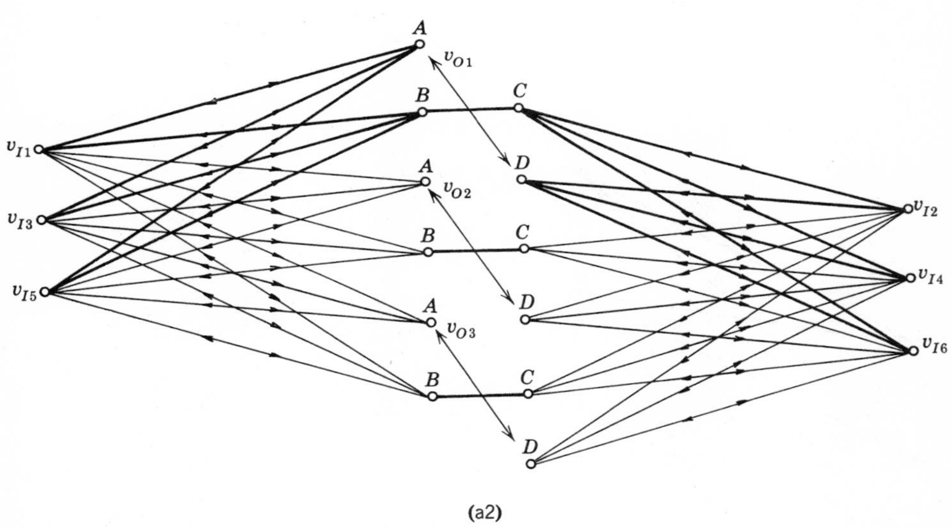

v_{I1}
v_{I3}
v_{I5}
v_{I2}
v_{I4}
v_{I6}
A
B
C
D
v_{O1}
v_{O2}
v_{O3}

(a2)

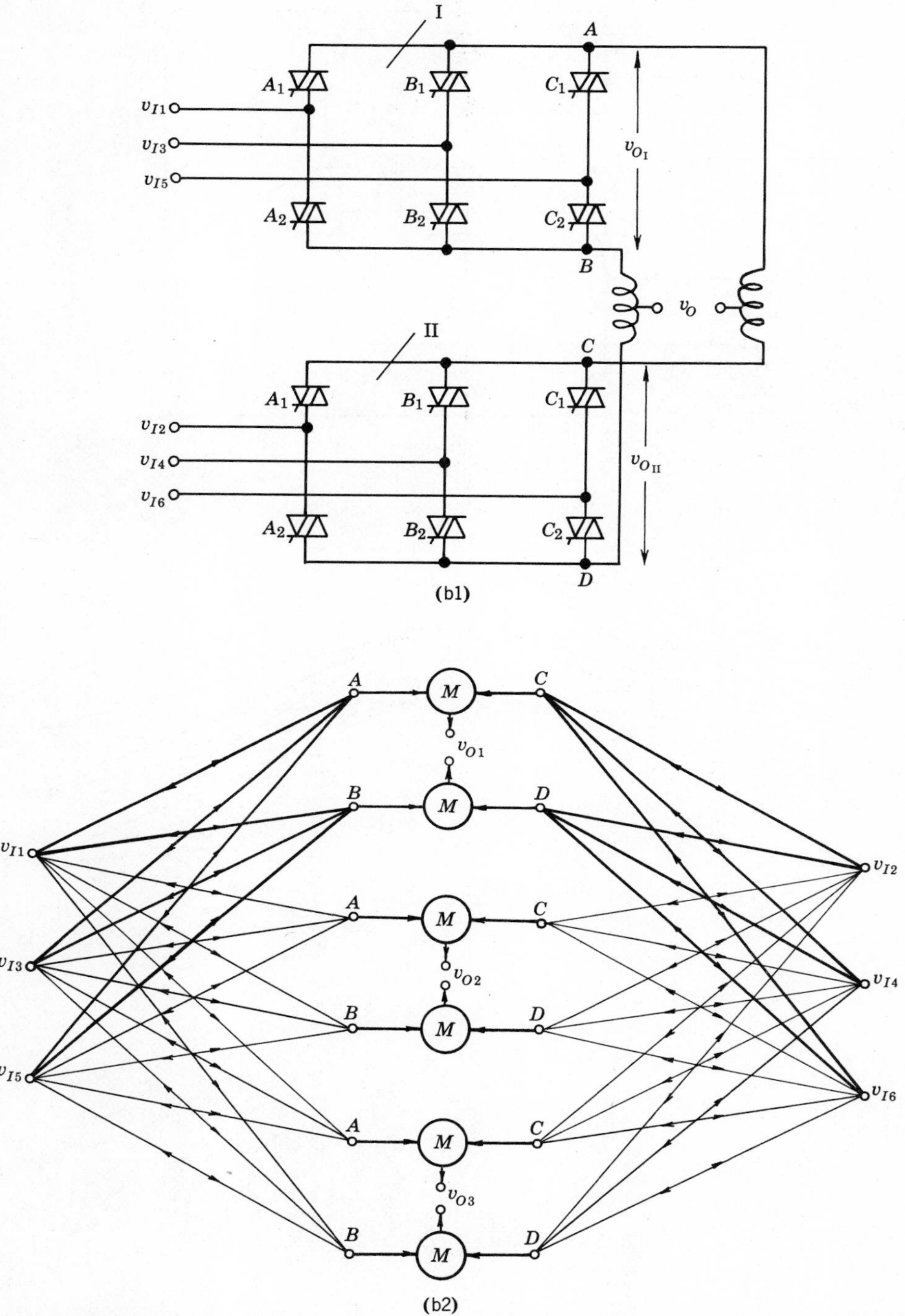

Figure 1.29 Series and parallel connected twelve-pulse bridge frequency changer circuits. *a*1 Series connected with single-phase output. *a*2 Series connected circuits with three-phase output. *b*1 Parallel connected circuits with single-phase output. *b*2 Parallel connected circuits with three-phase output.

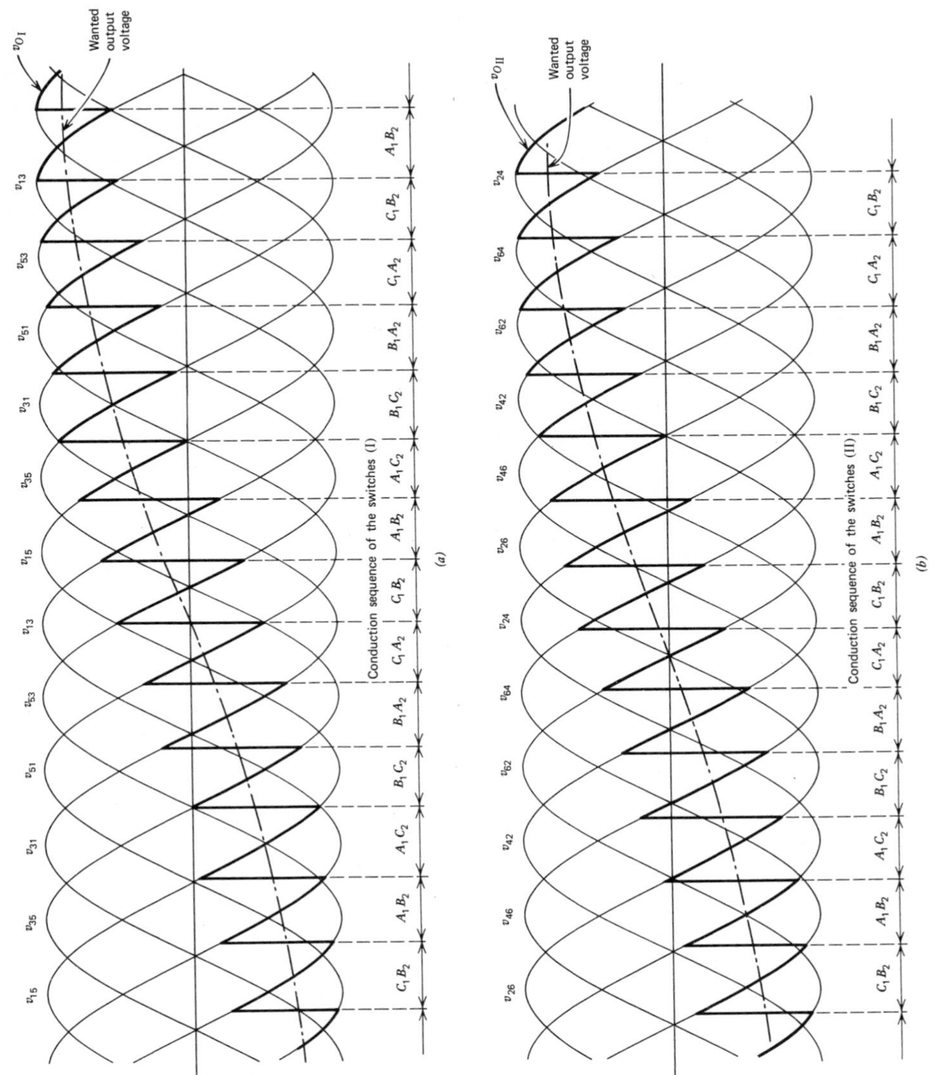

v_{15} v_{35} v_{31} v_{51} v_{53} v_{13} v_{15} v_{35} v_{31} v_{51} v_{53} v_{13}
v_{O_I}
Wanted output voltage
C_1B_2 A_1B_2 A_1C_2 B_1C_2 B_1A_2 C_1A_2 C_1B_2 A_1B_2 A_1C_2 B_1C_2 B_1A_2 C_1A_2 C_1B_2 A_1B_2
Conduction sequence of the switches (I)

(a)

v_{26} v_{46} v_{42} v_{62} v_{64} v_{24} v_{26} v_{46} v_{42} v_{62} v_{64} v_{24}
$v_{O_{II}}$
Wanted output voltage
C_1B_2 A_1B_2 A_1C_2 B_1C_2 B_1A_2 C_1A_2 C_1B_2 A_1B_2 A_1C_2 B_1C_2 B_1A_2 C_1A_2 C_1B_2
Conduction sequence of the switches (II)

(b)

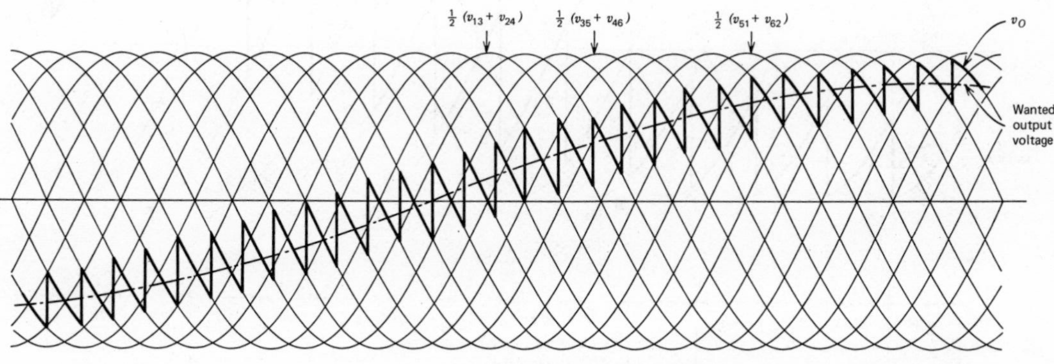

Figure 1.30 Waveforms illustrating the operation of the twelve-pulse circuit shown in Figure 1.29*b*1. *a* Six-pulse voltage waveform produced by bridge I. *b* Six-pulse voltage waveform produced by bridge II. *c* Final twelve-pulse output voltage waveform.

CHAPTER TWO
MATHEMATICAL REPRESENTATION OF STATIC FREQUENCY CHANGERS

A static frequency changer is comprised of two main constituents: the power circuit and the control. The *power circuit*, characterized by pulse number P, essentially consists of a number of arrays (equal to the number of output phases) of P bidirectional switches formed to make connections, for controlled time intervals, between the input and output terminals—that is, between the input source and the load. The *control* determines the onsets and durations of the conduction intervals of the power switches and thereby specifies the process of output voltage waveform construction. Thus, the output voltage waveform(s) of static frequency changers are constructed with the wanted frequency and amplitude by sequentially connecting, via the power switches, the input voltages to the output terminal(s) for appropriate time intervals determined by the control. The output voltage waveforms are therefore composed of segments of the input voltage waves. The lengths of the segments are determined by the durations of the corresponding switch closures in the power circuit.

2.1 MATHEMATICAL DESCRIPTION OF THE OUTPUT VOLTAGE WAVEFORM

Consider the general case of an n input, m output-phase static frequency changer employing m n-pulse ($P = n$) circuits, as shown in Figure 2.1. The frequency changer is operated from an n-phase a-c supply of frequency f_I and controlled to generate m output phase voltages with a wanted frequency of f_O.

Since the output voltage waveforms are composed of segments of successive input voltage waves, the output voltage waveform at, for example, output terminal p, v_{Op}, can be described mathematically as follows:

$$\begin{aligned}
v_{Op}(t) &= v_{I1}\{u(t_O) - u(t_1)\} + v_{I2}\{u(t_1) - u(t_2)\} + \cdots + v_{Iq}\{u(t_{q-1}) - u(t_q)\} \\
&\quad + \cdots + v_{In}\{u(t_{n-1}) - u(t_n)\} + v_{I1}\{u(t_n) - u(t_{n+1})\} + v_{I2}\{u(t_{n+1}) \\
&\quad - u(t_{n+2})\} + \cdots + v_{Iq}\{u(t_{q-1+n}) - u(t_{q+n}) + \cdots + v_{In}\{u(t_{2n-1}) \\
&\quad - u(t_{2n})\} + \cdots \\
&= v_{I1}(\{u(t_O) - u(t_1)\} + \{u(t_n) - u(t_{n+1})\} + \{u(t_{2n}) - u(t_{2n+1})\} + \cdots) \\
&\quad + v_{I2}(\{u(t_1) - u(t_2)\} + \{u(t_{n+1}) - u(t_{n+2})\} + \{u(t_{2n+1}) - u(t_{2n+2})\} + \cdots) \\
&\quad \vdots \\
&\quad + v_{Iq}(\{u(t_{q-1}) - u(t_q)\} + \{u(t_{q-1+n}) - u(t_{q+n})\} + \{u(t_{q-1+2n}) \\
&\quad\quad - u(t_{q+2n})\} + \cdots) \\
&\quad \vdots \\
&\quad + v_{In}(\{u(t_{n-1}) - u(t_n)\} + \{u(t_{2n-1}) - u(t_{2n})\} + \{u(t_{3n-1}) \\
&\quad\quad - u(t_{3n})\} + \cdots)
\end{aligned} \tag{2.1}$$

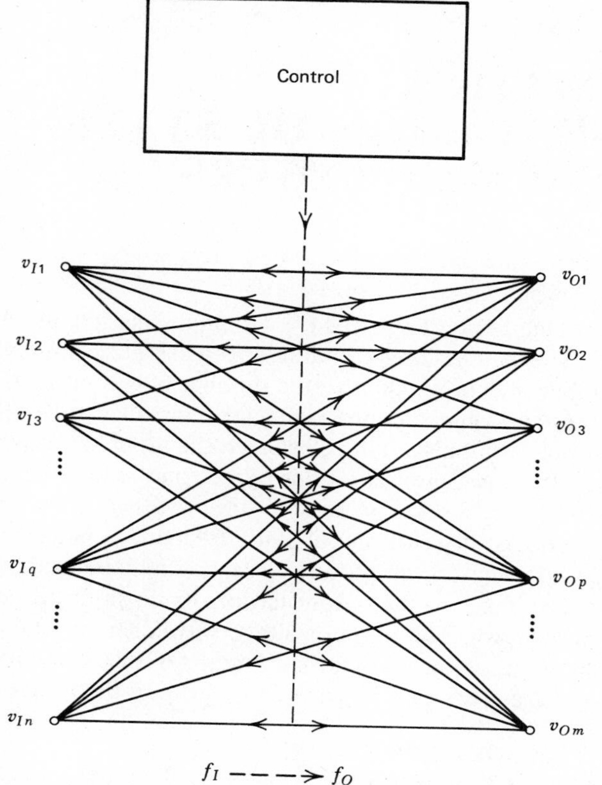

Figure 2.1 Symbolic representation of a general n to m phase frequency changer.

where $v_{I1}, v_{I2}, \ldots v_{In}$ are time functions of the input voltage waves, and $u(t_q)$ is a unit step function entering at $t = t_q$.

Equation (2.1) may be written in the following concise form:

$$v_{Op}(t) = v_{I1} \sum_{k=0}^{\infty} \{u(t_{kn}) - u(t_{kn+1})\} + v_{I2} \sum_{k=0}^{\infty} \{u(t_{kn+1}) - u(t_{kn+2})\} + \cdots$$
$$+ v_{Iq} \sum_{k=0}^{\infty} \{u(t_{kn+q-1}) - u(t_{kn+q})\} + \cdots + v_{In} \sum_{k=0}^{\infty} \{u(t_{kn+n-1}) - u(t_{kn+n})\} \tag{2.2}$$

The coefficients of the input voltages represent a train of rectangular pulses with unity amplitude. They are termed *existence functions* and are defined in the following way:

$$h_{p1}(t) = \sum_{k=0}^{\infty} \{u(t_{kn}) - u(t_{kn+1})\}; \qquad h_{p2}(t) = \sum_{k=0}^{\infty} \{u(t_{kn+1}) - u(t_{kn+2})\}; \qquad \cdots$$
$$h_{pq}(t) = \sum_{k=0}^{\infty} \{u(t_{kn+q-1}) - u(t_{kn+q})\}; \cdots \qquad h_{pn}(t) = \sum_{k=0}^{\infty} \{u(t_{kn+n-1}) - u(t_{kn+n})\}; \tag{2.3}$$

Thus

$$v_{Op}(t) = h_{p1}(t)v_{I1}(t) + h_{p2}(t)v_{I2}(t) + \cdots + h_{pq}(t)v_{Iq}(t) + \cdots + h_{pn}(t)v_{In}(t) \tag{2.4}$$

The existence function $h_{pq}(t)$ ($p = 1, 2, \ldots m$; $q = 1, 2, \ldots n$) describes mathematically the operation of the power switch connecting the input phase voltage, v_{Iq}, to the output terminal p. That is to say, whenever $h_{pq} = 1$, input voltage v_{Iq} is connected to output terminal p, and whenever $h_{pq} = 0$, v_{Iq} is removed from this terminal.

Output voltages v_{O1} through v_{Om} can similarly be expressed in terms of the input voltages and appropriate existence functions. Thus a frequency changer having n input and m output phases can be characterized by a set of m equations, as follows:

$$\left.\begin{aligned}
v_{O1}(t) &= h_{11}(t)v_{I1}(t) + h_{12}(t)v_{I2}(t) + \cdots + h_{1q}(t)v_{Iq}(t) + \cdots + h_{1n}(t)v_{In}(t)\\
v_{O2}(t) &= h_{21}(t)v_{I1}(t) + h_{22}(t)v_{I2}(t) + \cdots + h_{2q}(t)v_{Iq}(t) + \cdots + h_{2n}(t)v_{In}(t)\\
&\vdots\\
v_{Op}(t) &= h_{p1}(t)v_{I1}(t) + h_{p2}(t)v_{I2}(t) + \cdots + h_{pq}(t)v_{Iq}(t) + \cdots + h_{pn}(t)v_{In}(t)\\
&\vdots\\
v_{Om}(t) &= h_{m1}(t)v_{I1}(t) + h_{m2}(t)v_{I2}(t) + \cdots + h_{mq}(t)v_{Iq}(t) + \cdots + h_{mn}(t)v_{In}(t)
\end{aligned}\right\} \tag{2.5}$$

The above set of equations can be written more concisely in the following matrix form:

$$\begin{bmatrix} v_{O1}(t)\\ v_{O2}(t)\\ \vdots\\ v_{Op}(t)\\ \vdots\\ v_{Om}(t)\end{bmatrix} = \begin{bmatrix} h_{11}(t) & h_{12}(t) & \cdots & h_{1q}(t) & \cdots & h_{1n}(t)\\ h_{21}(t) & h_{22}(t) & \cdots & h_{2q}(t) & \cdots & h_{2n}(t)\\ \vdots & & & & & \\ h_{p1}(t) & h_{p2}(t) & \cdots & h_{pq}(t) & \cdots & h_{pn}(t)\\ \vdots & & & & & \\ h_{m1}(t) & h_{m2}(t) & \cdots & h_{mq}(t) & \cdots & h_{mn}(t)\end{bmatrix} \begin{bmatrix} v_{I1}(t)\\ v_{I2}(t)\\ \vdots\\ v_{Iq}(t)\\ \vdots\\ v_{In}(t)\end{bmatrix} \tag{2.6}$$

or

$$[v_O(t)] = [H(t)][v_I(t)] \tag{2.7}$$

Matrix $[H]$ ($\dim[H] = m \times n$, that is, $[H]$ has m rows and n columns), whose elements are existence functions, is termed an *existence matrix*. It defines the relationship between the input and the generated output voltage waves and therefore specifies the operation of the power switches in the frequency changer.

In practice, the input voltages are usually sinusoidal time functions forming a multiphase balanced set, namely,

$$[v_I(t)] = \begin{bmatrix} v_{I1}(t)\\ v_{I2}(t)\\ \vdots\\ v_{In}(t)\end{bmatrix} = V_I \begin{bmatrix} \sin \omega_I t\\ \sin\left(\omega_I t - \dfrac{2\pi}{n}\right)\\ \vdots\\ \sin\left(\omega_I t - (n-1)\dfrac{2\pi}{n}\right)\end{bmatrix} \tag{2.8}$$

in which V_I is the common amplitude of $v_{I1}(t)$ through $v_{In}(t)$. It follows from equation (2.6) that, with a given input source (i.e., given V_I, ω_I, and n), the waveshape of the output voltages are completely determined by matrix $[H]$. In principle, the *mean* of the output voltage waveform, that is, the average value of the successive input voltage segments of which the output voltage wave is composed, could follow any prescribed function. In practical applications, however, frequency changers are usually required to generate sinusoidal "mean" output waveforms with prescribed frequency and amplitude; in some cases, however, a waveshape that approximates a sinusoid reasonably well, for example, a trapezoid, may also be generated. (Of course, even in the latter case, only the fundamental component of the "mean" wave is normally useful in the output.) In general, matrix $[H]$ is therefore required to transform the given set of n input voltages characterized by frequency f_I ($f_I = \omega_I/2\pi$) and amplitude V_I into a set of m balanced output voltage waves having (sinusoidal) wanted* components with frequency ($f_O = \omega_O/2\pi$) and amplitude V_O. Consequently, each element of matrix $[H(t)]$ will generally be a function of f_I, f_O, V_O/V_I and time t, namely,

$$h_{pq} = h_{pq}\left(f_I, f_O, \frac{V_O}{V_I}, t\right) \tag{2.9}$$

Since, by definition, the existence functions at any given time can have either unit or zero amplitude, equation (2.9) implies that appropriate and regular variation (modulation) of their temporal parameters (pulse position, width, and repetition rate) must provide the means of satisfying equation (2.6) for given f_I, V_I and specified f_O, V_O. It therefore follows that, in general, the existence functions that describe the operation of the power switches of a practical frequency changer represent rectangular pulse trains with *modulated* temporal parameters.

As previously explained, the output voltage waveform is composed of segments of successive input voltage waves. The length of each successive segment is mathematically defined by the corresponding existence function in such a way as to produce a prescribed (sinusoidal) "mean" output waveform with the wanted frequency and amplitude. Thus the output voltage waveform will, as a consequence of the static frequency changing process, inevitably contain (except for $n = \infty$) components with frequencies differing from f_O (unwanted components). Furthermore, since each existence function (and hence also the duration of each constituent segment of the output voltage waveform) is a function both of the input frequency f_I and of the wanted output frequency f_O, it can be expected intuitively that the frequency of each unwanted component will generally be some function of f_I as well as f_O. Therefore, each output voltage wave may be described as an ensemble of sinusoidal components having frequencies that are functions of f_I and f_O (as seen below, they are generally linear combinations of f_I and f_O in the form $Pkf_I \pm nf_O$, in which P is the pulse number and k is a positive integer) and, consequently, are generally *not* integrally related, that is,

$$v_{Op} = [h_{p1}h_{p2}\cdots h_{pn}]\begin{bmatrix} v_{I1} \\ v_{I2} \\ \vdots \\ v_{In} \end{bmatrix} = V_O \sin\left(\omega_O t - (p-1)\frac{2\pi}{m}\right) + \sum_{\ell=1}^{\infty} V_{U\ell} \sin(\omega_{U\ell} t - \phi_{U\ell}) \tag{2.10}$$

* Quantities referred to as "wanted" are those which characterize the sinusoidal output voltage component that is desired as the load's supply.

where $V_{U\ell}$ is the amplitude,

$\omega_{U\ell} = 2\pi f_{U\ell}$ is the angular frequency, and

$\phi_{U\ell}$ is the phase of the ℓth unwanted component. Thus

$\sum_{\ell=1}^{\infty} V_{U\ell} \sin(\omega_{U\ell} t - \phi_{U\ell})$ represents the ensemble of the unwanted output voltage components.

The performance of the frequency changer, as related to the output voltage waveform, may be characterized by the following quantities, termed *output voltage wave indices*: the normalized frequencies of the unwanted components, namely,

$$\nu_{O\ell} = \left|\frac{f_{U\ell}}{f_O}\right| \qquad \ell = 1, 2, \ldots \tag{2.11}$$

the normalized amplitudes of the unwanted components, namely,

$$\gamma_{O\ell} = \left|\frac{V_{U\ell}}{V_O}\right| \qquad \ell = 1, 2, \ldots \tag{2.12}$$

the total r.m.s. distortion, namely,

$$\mu_O = \frac{\sqrt{\sum_{\ell=1}^{\infty} V_{U\ell}^2}}{V_O} \tag{2.13}$$

It is generally an objective in power frequency conversion to minimize $\gamma_{O\ell}$, μ_O and to maximize $\nu_{O\ell}$. It is clear that, for a given value of P (in the present case $P = n$), f_I, f_O, and V_O/V_I, the output voltage wave indices depend only upon the character of the existence function, $h_{pq}(f_I, f_O, V_O/V_I)$, that is, upon the modulation used to generate the output voltage waveform. Fortunately, the wanted output component, characterized by V_O and f_O, does not uniquely specify the existence functions. Indeed, various characters of h_{pq}, representing different modulation techniques, may produce waveforms with identical wanted components but widely differing spectral characteristics. (Recall the qualitative review of output voltage waveform syntheses given in Chapter 1.) It is therefore important to find the optimal characters of the existence functions for specific application requirements.

To illustrate the general principles and mathematical techniques so far described, consider the simple frequency changer shown in Figure 2.2*a* that converts two antiphase sinusoidal input voltages of frequency f_I to two antiphase output voltage waves of wanted frequency f_O. The output voltages of this system may be given with the use of the basic equation $[v_O] = [H][v_I]$, that is,

$$\begin{bmatrix} v_{O1}(t) \\ v_{O2}(t) \end{bmatrix} = \begin{bmatrix} h_{11}(t) & h_{12}(t) \\ h_{21}(t) & h_{22}(t) \end{bmatrix} \begin{bmatrix} v_{I1}(t) \\ v_{I2}(t) \end{bmatrix} \tag{2.14}$$

It is convenient, for easy computation, to define the input voltage (column) matrix in exponential form, namely,

$$[v_I] = \frac{V_I}{2j} \begin{bmatrix} \exp j\omega_I t - \exp(-j\omega_I t) \\ -\exp j\omega_I t + \exp(-j\omega_I t) \end{bmatrix} \tag{2.15}$$

where $j = \sqrt{-1}$.

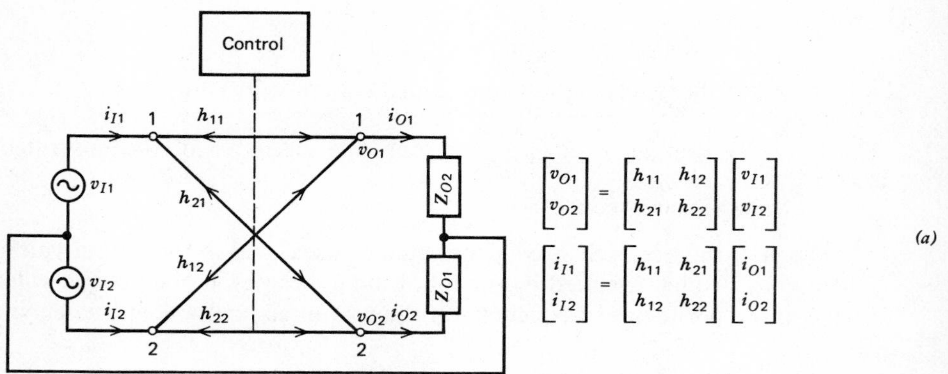

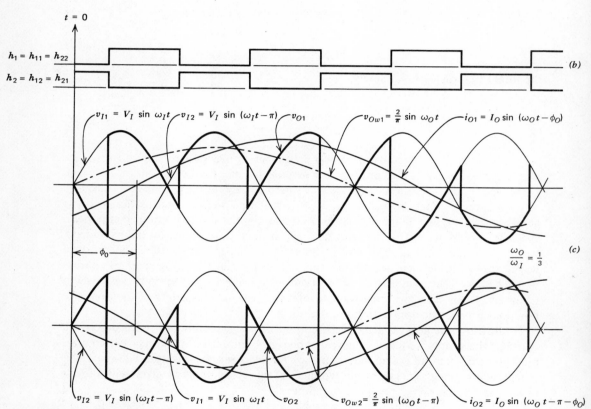

Figure 2.2 A two-phase to two-phase frequency changer and associated waveforms illustrating two operating modes analyzed in Chapter 2.

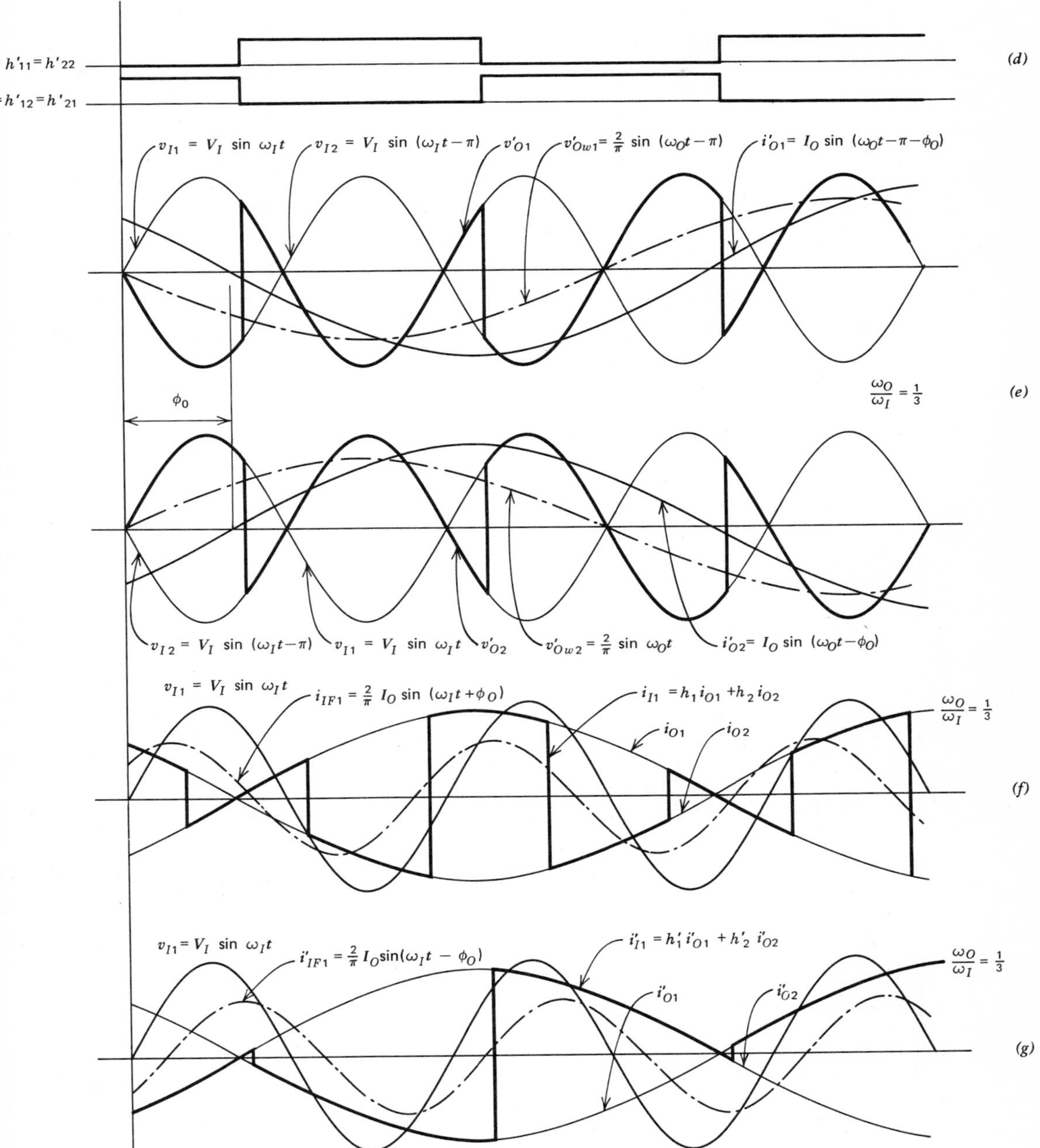

Figure 2.2 (*Continued*)

Let the existence functions, h_{11} and h_{12}, be chosen arbitrarily to be periodic square waves with a repetition rate of f_S as shown in Figure 2.2*b*. To evaluate equation (2.14), h_{11} and h_{12} are represented by two appropriate Fourier series, given in exponential form:

$$\left.\begin{aligned} h_{11} &= \frac{1}{2} + \frac{1}{\pi}\sum_{k=-\infty}^{\infty} \frac{\exp jk(\omega_s t - \pi/2)}{kj} \\ h_{12} &= \frac{1}{2} + \frac{1}{\pi}\sum_{k=-\infty}^{\infty} \frac{\exp jk(\omega_s t + \pi/2)}{kj} \end{aligned}\right\} \tag{2.16}$$

where $k = 2\ell - 1$, $\ell = 1, 2, \ldots$ and $\omega_S = 2\pi f_S$.

Since the objective is to generate the two output voltages in phase opposition to one another, it is plausible that the diagonal elements of matrix $[H]$ can be represented by the same existence functions, namely,

$$\left.\begin{aligned} h_{11} &= h_{22} = h_1 \\ h_{12} &= h_{21} = h_2 \end{aligned}\right\} \tag{2.17}$$

Therefore

$$\begin{bmatrix} v_{O1} \\ v_{O2} \end{bmatrix} = \begin{bmatrix} h_1 & h_2 \\ h_2 & h_1 \end{bmatrix} \begin{bmatrix} v_{I1} \\ v_{I2} \end{bmatrix} \tag{2.18}$$

Substituting equations (2.15) and (2.16) into (2.18) with the use of (2.17), $[v_O]$ becomes

$$\begin{aligned}
[v_O] = {} & \frac{V_I}{2j}\underbrace{\left\{\begin{bmatrix} \frac{1}{2} & \frac{1}{2} \\ \frac{1}{2} & \frac{1}{2} \end{bmatrix}\begin{bmatrix} 1 \\ -1 \end{bmatrix} e^{j\omega_I t} + \begin{bmatrix} \frac{1}{2} & \frac{1}{2} \\ \frac{1}{2} & \frac{1}{2} \end{bmatrix}\begin{bmatrix} -1 \\ 1 \end{bmatrix} e^{-j\omega_I t}\right\}}_{=0} - \frac{V_I}{2\pi}\sum_{k=1}^{\infty}\frac{1}{k} \\
& \times \left\{\begin{bmatrix} e^{-jk\frac{\pi}{2}} & e^{jk\frac{\pi}{2}} \\ e^{jk\frac{\pi}{2}} & e^{-jk\frac{\pi}{2}} \end{bmatrix}\begin{bmatrix} 1 \\ -1 \end{bmatrix} e^{j(k\omega_S + \omega_I)t} + \begin{bmatrix} e^{jk\frac{\pi}{2}} & e^{-jk\frac{\pi}{2}} \\ e^{-jk\frac{\pi}{2}} & e^{jk\frac{\pi}{2}} \end{bmatrix}\begin{bmatrix} 1 \\ -1 \end{bmatrix} e^{-j(k\omega_S + \omega_I)t}\right. \\
& \left. - \begin{bmatrix} e^{-jk\frac{\pi}{2}} & e^{jk\frac{\pi}{2}} \\ e^{jk\frac{\pi}{2}} & e^{-jk\frac{\pi}{2}} \end{bmatrix}\begin{bmatrix} 1 \\ -1 \end{bmatrix} e^{j(k\omega_S - \omega_I)t} - \begin{bmatrix} e^{jk\frac{\pi}{2}} & e^{-jk\frac{\pi}{2}} \\ e^{-jk\frac{\pi}{2}} & e^{jk\frac{\pi}{2}} \end{bmatrix}\begin{bmatrix} 1 \\ -1 \end{bmatrix} e^{-j(k\omega_S - \omega_I)t}\right\}
\end{aligned} \tag{2.19}$$

Equation (2.19) can easily be evaluated by inspection. Replacing k with $2\ell - 1$, the result may be written in the following form:

$$\begin{aligned}
[v_O] &= \begin{bmatrix} v_{O1} \\ v_{O2} \end{bmatrix} \\
&= \frac{2V_I}{\pi}\begin{bmatrix} \displaystyle\sum_{\ell=1}^{\infty}\left\{\frac{-(-1)^\ell}{2\ell - 1}\left(\sin\{(2\ell - 1)\omega_S - \omega_I\}t - \sin\{(2\ell - 1)\omega_S + \omega_I\}t\right)\right\} \\ \displaystyle\sum_{\ell=1}^{\infty}\left\{\frac{(-1)^\ell}{2\ell - 1}\left(\sin\{(2\ell - 1)\omega_S - \omega_I\}t - \sin\{(2\ell - 1)\omega_S + \omega_I\}t\right)\right\} \end{bmatrix}
\end{aligned} \tag{2.20}$$

Inspection of equation (2.20) indicates that, at $\ell = 1$, two antiphase components with the wanted output frequency, f_O, can be obtained by making the repetition rate of the existence functions equal to the sum of the input and the output frequency, namely, $f_S = f_I + f_O$. Substituting therefore $\omega_S = \omega_I + \omega_O$, equation (2.20) becomes

$$[v_O] = \frac{2V_I}{\pi}\begin{bmatrix} \sin \omega_O t \\ -\sin \omega_O t \end{bmatrix}$$

$$+ \frac{2V_I}{\pi}\sum_{\ell=1}^{\infty}(-1)^{\ell}\begin{bmatrix} \dfrac{\sin\{2\ell\omega_I + (2\ell+1)\omega_O\}t}{2\ell+1} + \dfrac{\sin\{2\ell\omega_I + (2\ell-1)\omega_O\}t}{2\ell-1} \\ -\dfrac{\sin\{2\ell\omega_I + (2\ell+1)\omega_O\}t}{2\ell+1} - \dfrac{\sin\{2\ell\omega_I + (2\ell-1)\omega_O\}t}{2\ell-1} \end{bmatrix}$$

(2.21)

The first term of equation (2.21) represents the two wanted components: $v_{Ow1} = (2V_I/\pi)\sin\omega_O t$ and $v_{Ow2} = -(2V_I/\pi)\sin\omega_O t$. Thus the original objective of producing two wanted output voltage components in antiphase, each with angular frequency ω_O, has been accomplished. The two output waveforms, v_{O1} and v_{O2}, are shown for $\omega_O/\omega_I = 1/3$ in Figure 2.2*c*.

The output voltage wave indices of this simple frequency changer can be readily determined.

The normalized frequencies of the unwanted components are given by

$$\nu_{O\ell} = (2\ell \pm 1) + 2\ell\frac{f_I}{f_O} \qquad \ell = 1, 2, \ldots \tag{2.22}$$

The normalized amplitudes of the unwanted components are given by

$$\gamma_{O\ell} = \frac{1}{2\ell \pm 1} \qquad \ell = 1, 2, \ldots \tag{2.23}$$

The total r.m.s. distortion is given by

$$\mu_O = \sqrt{\sum_{\ell=1}^{\infty}\frac{1}{(2\ell \pm 1)^2}} \tag{2.24}$$

Observe that any normalized unwanted frequency defined by index ℓ is a linear function of the input to output frequency ratio, f_I/f_O. Consequently, the normalized unwanted frequencies given by equation (2.22) are not like harmonics in that they cannot generally be characterized by integer "order" numbers (except, of course, when f_I/f_O is itself an integer). As was previously stated, this type of spectral characteristic, in which the frequencies of the unwanted components are not, except at discrete f_O/f_I ratios, integrally related to each other and to the wanted output frequency, is typical of all "frequency changer type" output voltage waveforms. Equation (2.22) also reveals another important characteristic, namely that every unwanted frequency is higher than f_O (i.e., $\nu_{O\ell} > 1$ for all ℓ) at all finite f_O/f_I ratios.

The choice of the existence functions [equation (2.16)] was arbitrary. Although the primary objective of generating two antiphase sinusoidal components with the wanted frequency f_O was accomplished, the question still remains whether the output voltage wave indices [equations (2.22)–(2.24)] obtained are optima. In other words, the question really is whether the output voltage waveshape could be improved by choosing different existence functions. We do not attempt to answer this question in a definite way in this chapter. However, in order to illustrate this problem, assume that the repetition frequency of the existence functions [equations (2.16)] is changed from the original $f_S = f_I + f_O$ to $f'_S = f_I - f_O$ as illustrated by Figure 2.2*d*. This new value of f_S, $f'_S = f_I - f_O$, is chosen because equation (2.20) will again provide, at $\ell = 1$, the two wanted components in antiphase, as required. Note, however, the limitation imposed by this choice on f_O. That is, f_O cannot be greater than f_I since $f_O = f_I - f_S$, which allows the variations of f_O between 0 ($f_S = f_I$) and f_I ($f_S = 0$).

The two new output voltage waves obtained with $f'_S = f_I - f_O$ can readily be expressed from equation (2.20) by substituting $\omega_I - \omega_O$ for ω_S, namely,

$$[v'_O] = \frac{2V_I}{\pi}\begin{bmatrix} -\sin \omega_O t \\ \sin \omega_O t \end{bmatrix} + \frac{2V_I}{\pi}\sum_{\ell=1}^{\infty}(-1)^{\ell}\begin{bmatrix} \dfrac{\sin\{2\ell\omega_I - (2\ell+1)\omega_O\}t}{2\ell+1} + \dfrac{\sin\{2\ell\omega_I - (2\ell-1)\omega_O\}t}{2\ell-1} \\ -\dfrac{\sin\{2\ell\omega_I - (2\ell+1)\omega_O\}t}{2\ell+1} - \dfrac{\sin\{2\ell\omega_I - (2\ell-1)\omega_O\}t}{2\ell-1} \end{bmatrix} \tag{2.25}$$

The waveforms expressed by equation (2.25) are shown for $\omega_O/\omega_I = 1/3$ in Figure 2.2*e*. The wanted components again have the same amplitude ($2V_I/\pi$) and frequency (f_O) as before, and they are in phase opposition to one another. Note, however, that the phases of v'_{Ow1} and v'_{Ow2} in equation (2.25) are opposite to those of the corresponding wanted components v_{Ow1} and v_{Ow2} in equation (2.21). The normalized amplitudes of the corresponding unwanted components $\gamma_{O\ell}$ are the same for both equation (2.25) and (2.21), and therefore the two waveforms must also have identical r.m.s. distortion. However, the frequency spectrum of the waveform defined by equation (2.25) differs significantly from that of the previous waveshape given by equation (2.21). Whereas in equation (2.21) the unwanted frequencies are the sums of multiples of f_I and f_O, that is, $f_{U\ell} = 2\ell f_I + (2\ell \pm) f_O$, in equation (2.25) they are the differences of those terms, that is, $f'_{U\ell} = 2\ell f_I - (2\ell \pm 1) f_O$. In this latter case, the frequency of the $2f_I - 3f_O$ component becomes less than the wanted frequency at all output to input frequency ratios greater than 1/2 (except at the theoretical limiting point of $f_O/f_I = 1.0$, where $|2f_I - 3f_O|$ becomes equal to f_O). In general, for the component having frequency $2\ell f_I - (2\ell + 1) f_O$:

$$v'_{O\ell} = \left| 2\ell \frac{f_I}{f_O} - (2\ell + 1) \right| \tag{2.26}$$

and $v'_{O\ell}$ becomes smaller than unity for $f_O/f_I > \ell/(\ell + 1)$ (again, except at the theoretical limiting point of $f_O/f_I = 1$, where $v'_{O\ell} = 1$). Moreover, $v'_{O\ell}$ is zero—indicating the presence of a d-c component—at all output to input frequency ratios given by $f_O/f_I = 2\ell/(2\ell + 1)$.

It can thus be concluded that, in the present example, by the simple act of changing the repetition frequency of the existence functions from $f'_S = f_I - f_O$ to $f_S = f_I + f_O$, the frequency spectrum of the generated output waveforms can be considerably improved without affecting the other output voltage wave indices. As will be seen in the next chapter, there are other, more complex characters of the existence functions that would also produce output waveforms with the same wanted component, but with widely differing output voltage wave indices.

2.2 MATHEMATICAL DESCRIPTION OF THE INPUT CURRENT WAVEFORM

In the previous section, the mathematical description and characterization of the output voltage waveform are considered. In this section, we investigate the general characteristics of the input current wave. The principal quantities of interest are the input displacement factor and the spectrum of the input current waveform.

Some general observations about the nature of the input current waveforms of static frequency changers can be deduced from the already established basic operating principle. The output voltage waveforms are produced by means of sequentially connecting the input voltages to the output terminals (and thus to the loads) via arrays of bidirectional switches. Each output voltage waveshape is therefore composed of segments of the input voltage waves. For the time duration of such a segment of, for example, output waveform p, one switch in the array of output phase p is closed, and the corresponding load is connected to one phase, for example q, of the input source (see Figure 2.1). Thus, during this time, the total output current at terminal p is supplied from input phase q. For the duration of the next segment, the consecutive switch in the array is closed, and output terminal p is connected to the input phase $q + 1$. The total current of output phase p is therefore transferred from input phase q to input phase $q + 1$. Similarly, during the following segments, the output terminal p is successively connected to input phases $q + 2$, $q + 3$, etc., and, after n steps (n being the number of input phases), the output phase p is reconnected to the input phase q, and the operating cycle of the switches is repeated. As a consequence of this operating mode, the current drawn from each phase of the input source by *one* phase of the load is composed of generally nonuniform segments of the output current wave separated by intervals of zero current. Of course, every output phase draws current in a similar fashion from every phase of the input source. Consequently, the total current in each input line is the sum of the currents supplied to all of the individual outputs by the input phase in question. The total input current wave is therefore generally composed of segments, or sums of generally nonsynchronized segments, of the output current waves.

In the analysis of the input current waves it is assumed that the output currents of the frequency changer are sinusoids with the wanted frequency f_O, displaced from the wanted component of voltage by the phase angle of the load at the wanted frequency. Since the actual waveform of the output current generally has some distortion determined by the impedance of the load to the unwanted components in the output voltage waveshape, this assumption is not strictly valid. Nevertheless, it is a sufficiently good approximation for describing most of the practical operating conditions and for making possible a relatively simple characterization of the frequency changer with regard to its effect on the input source.

With the above assumption, the set of output currents may be described by the following time functions:

$$[i_O(t)] = \begin{bmatrix} i_{O1}(t) \\ i_{O2}(t) \\ \vdots \\ i_{Op}(t) \\ \vdots \\ i_{Om}(t) \end{bmatrix} = \begin{bmatrix} I_{O1}\sin(\omega_O t + \phi_{O1}) \\ I_{O2}\sin\left(\omega_O t - \dfrac{2\pi}{m} + \phi_{O2}\right) \\ \vdots \\ I_{Op}\sin\left(\omega_O t - (p-1)\dfrac{2\pi}{m} + \phi_{Op}\right) \\ \vdots \\ I_{Om}\sin\left(\omega_O t - (m-1)\dfrac{2\pi}{m} + \phi_{Om}\right) \end{bmatrix} \tag{2.27}$$

where I_{Op} ($p = 1, 2, \ldots m$) is the amplitude, and ϕ_{Op} is the phase of the pth output current wave.

The input current waves of the frequency changer can be expressed from the output currents by the *transpose* of existence matrix $[H]$, namely,

$$[i_I(t)] = \begin{bmatrix} i_{I1}(t) \\ i_{I2}(t) \\ \vdots \\ i_{Iq}(t) \\ \vdots \\ i_{In}(t) \end{bmatrix} = [H(t)]^T[i_O(t)] = \begin{bmatrix} h_{11}(t) & h_{21}(t) & \cdots & h_{m1}(t) \\ h_{12}(t) & h_{22}(t) & \cdots & h_{m2}(t) \\ \vdots & & & \\ h_{1q}(t) & h_{2q}(t) & \cdots & h_{mq}(t) \\ \vdots & & & \\ h_{1n}(t) & h_{2n}(t) & \cdots & h_{mn}(t) \end{bmatrix} \begin{bmatrix} i_{O1}(t) \\ i_{O2}(t) \\ \vdots \\ i_{Op}(t) \\ \vdots \\ i_{Om}(t) \end{bmatrix} \tag{2.28}$$

The input current waves expressed by equation (2.28) are, as are the corresponding output voltage waveforms given by equation (2.6), complex waveforms having components with generally nonintegrally related frequencies. Therefore, each input current wave may also be represented as an ensemble of sinusoidal components, namely,

$$i_{Iq}(t) = [h_{1q} \quad h_{2q} \quad \cdots \quad h_{mq}] \begin{bmatrix} i_{O1}(t) \\ i_{O2}(t) \\ \vdots \\ i_{Om}(t) \end{bmatrix} = I_I \sin\left(\omega_I t - (q-1)\frac{2\pi}{n} + \phi_I\right) + \sum_{\ell=1}^{\infty} I_{E\ell} \sin(\omega_{E\ell} t + \phi_{E\ell}) \tag{2.29}$$

where I_I, $\omega_I = 2\pi f_I$, and ϕ_I are the amplitude, frequency and phase, respectively, of of the fundamental* current component, and

I_E , $\omega_{E\ell} = 2\pi f_{E\ell}$, and $\phi_{E\ell}$ are the amplitude, frequency and phase, respectively, of the ℓth *extrabasal*† component.

Thus $\sum_{\ell=1}^{\infty} I_{E\ell} \sin(\omega_{E\ell} t + \phi_{E\ell})$ represents the ensemble of extrabasal input current components.

The nature of the load presented by the frequency changer to the input source may be characterized by the following quantities of the input current waveform, referred to as *input current wave indices*:

The ratio of fundamental to total r.m.s. input current, termed the *current distortion factor*, is

$$\mu_I = \frac{I_I}{\sqrt{I_I^2 + \sum_{\ell=1}^{\infty} I_{E\ell}^2}} \tag{2.30}$$

the input *displacement factor* is

$$\delta_I = \cos \phi_I \tag{2.31}$$

the input *power factor* is

$$\lambda_I = \mu_I \, \delta_I \tag{2.32}$$

* The input current component with supply frequency f_I will be called *fundamental*, with the understanding that frequencies of the remaining components are not necessarily integral multiples of this frequency.

† A component of the input current having any frequency different from f_I, or integral multiples of f_I, will be called an *extrabasal* component.

the normalized frequencies of the extrabasal components are

$$\nu_{I\ell} = \left|\frac{f_{E\ell}}{f_I}\right| \qquad \ell = 1, 2, \ldots \tag{2.33}$$

and the normalized amplitudes of the extrabasal components are

$$\gamma_{I\ell} = \left|\frac{I_{E\ell}}{I_I}\right| \qquad \ell = 1, 2, \ldots \tag{2.34}$$

The input current wave indices expressed by equations (2.30)–(2.34) are, of course, generally functions of the existence matrix $[H]$.

To illustrate the basic concepts described above, consider again the simple frequency changer of Figure 2.2, the two output voltage waves of which are given for two operating modes by equations (2.21) and (2.25), respectively. With balanced output loads the two output currents (output current matrix) may be given [per equation (2.27)] in the following form:

$$[i_O(t)] = \frac{I_O}{2j}\begin{bmatrix} \exp j(\omega_O t + \phi_O) - \exp\{-j(\omega_O t + \phi_O)\} \\ -\exp j(\omega_O t + \phi_O) + \exp\{-j(\omega_O t + \phi_O)\} \end{bmatrix} \tag{2.35}$$

The input current waves can be expressed [per equation (2.28)] from the output currents, by the transpose of matrix $[H]$, namely,

$$[i_I(t)] = [H(t)]^T[i_O(t)] = \begin{bmatrix} h_1(t) & h_2(t) \\ h_2(t) & h_1(t) \end{bmatrix}\begin{bmatrix} i_{O1}(t) \\ i_{O2}(t) \end{bmatrix} \tag{2.36}$$

The substitution of equations (2.16) and (2.35) into (2.36) with the use of (2.17) gives

$$[i_I(t)] = \frac{I_O}{2j}\underbrace{\left\{\begin{bmatrix} \frac{1}{2} & \frac{1}{2} \\ \frac{1}{2} & \frac{1}{2} \end{bmatrix}\begin{bmatrix} e^{j\phi_O} \\ -e^{j\phi_O} \end{bmatrix} e^{j\omega_O t} + \begin{bmatrix} \frac{1}{2} & \frac{1}{2} \\ \frac{1}{2} & \frac{1}{2} \end{bmatrix}\begin{bmatrix} -e^{-j\phi_O} \\ e^{-j\phi_O} \end{bmatrix} e^{-j\omega_O t}\right\}}_{=0} - \frac{I_O}{2\pi}\sum_{k=1}^{\infty}\frac{1}{k}$$

$$\times\left\{\begin{bmatrix} e^{-jk\frac{\pi}{2}} & e^{jk\frac{\pi}{2}} \\ e^{jk\frac{\pi}{2}} & e^{-jk\frac{\pi}{2}} \end{bmatrix}\begin{bmatrix} e^{j\phi_O} \\ -e^{j\phi_O} \end{bmatrix} e^{j(k\omega_S+\omega_O)t} + \begin{bmatrix} e^{jk\frac{\pi}{2}} & e^{-jk\frac{\pi}{2}} \\ e^{-jk\frac{\pi}{2}} & e^{jk\frac{\pi}{2}} \end{bmatrix}\begin{bmatrix} e^{-j\phi_O} \\ -e^{-j\phi_O} \end{bmatrix} e^{-j(k\omega_S+\omega_O)t}\right.$$

$$\left. - \begin{bmatrix} e^{-jk\frac{\pi}{2}} & e^{jk\frac{\pi}{2}} \\ e^{jk\frac{\pi}{2}} & e^{-jk\frac{\pi}{2}} \end{bmatrix}\begin{bmatrix} e^{-j\phi_O} \\ -e^{-j\phi_O} \end{bmatrix} e^{j(k\omega_S-\omega_O)t} - \begin{bmatrix} e^{jk\frac{\pi}{2}} & e^{-jk\frac{\pi}{2}} \\ e^{-jk\frac{\pi}{2}} & e^{jk\frac{\pi}{2}} \end{bmatrix}\begin{bmatrix} e^{j\phi_O} \\ -e^{j\phi_O} \end{bmatrix} e^{-j(k\omega_S-\omega_O)t}\right\} \tag{2.37}$$

$k = 2\ell - 1,\ \ell = 1, 2, \ldots$

Evaluation of equation (2.37) yields

$$[i_I(t)] = \frac{2I_O}{\pi}\begin{bmatrix} \displaystyle\sum_{\ell=1}^{\infty}\left\{\frac{-(-1)^\ell}{2\ell-1}\left(\sin\{[(2\ell-1)\omega_S-\omega_O]t-\phi_O\}-\sin\{[(2\ell-1)\omega_S+\omega_O]t+\phi_O\}\right)\right\} \\ \displaystyle\sum_{\ell=1}^{\infty}\left\{\frac{(-1)^\ell}{2\ell-1}\left(\sin\{[(2\ell-1)\omega_S-\omega_O]t-\phi_O\}-\sin\{[(2\ell-1)\omega_S+\omega_O]t+\phi_O\}\right)\right\} \end{bmatrix} \tag{2.38}$$

Substituting first $\omega_S = \omega_I + \omega_O$ (i.e., the originally chosen repetition frequency of the existence functions), the input current matrix can be written as

$$[i_I(t)] = \frac{2I_O}{\pi}\begin{bmatrix} \sin(\omega_I t - \phi_O) \\ -\sin(\omega_I t - \phi_O) \end{bmatrix} + \frac{2I_O}{\pi}\sum_{\ell=1}^{\infty}(-1)^{\ell}$$
$$\times\begin{bmatrix} \dfrac{\sin\{[(2\ell+1)\omega_I + 2\ell\omega_O]t - \phi_O\}}{2\ell+1} + \dfrac{\sin\{[(2\ell-1)\omega_I + 2\ell\omega_O]t + \phi_O\}}{2\ell-1} \\ -\dfrac{\sin\{[(2\ell+1)\omega_I + 2\ell\omega_O]t - \phi_O\}}{2\ell+1} - \dfrac{\sin\{[(2\ell-1)\omega_I + 2\ell\omega_O]t + \phi_O\}}{2\ell-1} \end{bmatrix} \tag{2.39}$$

The input current waveform, i_{I1}, is illustrated for $\omega_O/\omega_I = 1/3$ in Figure 2.2*f*.

The input current waves corresponding to the existence function having a repetition frequency $f'_S = f_I - f_O$ can be expressed in a similar manner. Note, however, that in this case the wanted output voltages appear with opposite signs, that is, the sign of v_{Ow1} is negative and that of v_{Ow2} is positive [see equation (2.25)], which necessitates a corresponding change of sign in the two output currents when substituted in equation (2.36). The input current waves can, of course, also be obtained from equation (2.38) by substituting $\omega_S = \omega_I - \omega_O$ and interchanging the upper and lower expressions. Thus

$$[i'_I(t)] = \frac{2I_O}{\pi}\begin{bmatrix} \sin(\omega_I t + \phi_O) \\ -\sin(\omega_I t + \phi_O) \end{bmatrix} + \frac{2I_O}{\pi}\sum_{\ell=1}^{\infty}(-1)^{\ell}$$
$$\times\begin{bmatrix} \dfrac{\sin\{[(2\ell+1)\omega_I - 2\ell\omega_O]t + \phi_O\}}{2\ell+1} + \dfrac{\sin\{[(2\ell-1)\omega_I - 2\ell\omega_O]t - \phi_O\}}{2\ell-1} \\ -\dfrac{\sin\{[(2\ell+1)\omega_I - 2\ell\omega_O]t + \phi_O\}}{2\ell+1} - \dfrac{\sin\{[(2\ell-1)\omega_I - 2\ell\omega_O]t - \phi_O\}}{2\ell-1} \end{bmatrix} \tag{2.40}$$

The input current wave, i'_{I1}, is illustrated for $\omega_O/\omega_I = 1/3$ in Figure 2.2*g*.

The input current wave indices characterizing the current waveforms given by equations (2.39) for $f_S = f_I + f_O$, and (2.40) for $f'_S = f_I - f_O$ can be written readily as follows:

The input current distortion factor is

$$\mu_I = \mu'_I = \frac{1}{\sqrt{1 + \sum_{\ell=1}^{\infty}\dfrac{1}{(2\ell \pm 1)^2}}} \tag{2.41}$$

The input displacement factor is

$$\delta_I = \cos\phi_I = \cos(-\phi_O) \tag{2.42}$$

$$\delta'_I = \cos\phi'_I = \cos\phi_O \tag{2.43}$$

The input power factor is

$$\lambda_I = \frac{\cos(-\phi_O)}{\sqrt{1 + \sum_{\ell=1}^{\infty}\dfrac{1}{(2\ell \pm 1)^2}}} \tag{2.44}$$

$$\lambda'_I = \frac{\cos \phi_O}{\sqrt{1 + \sum_{\ell=1}^{\infty} \frac{1}{(2\ell \pm 1)^2}}} \tag{2.45}$$

The normalized frequencies of the extrabasal components are

$$\nu_{I\ell} = (2\ell \pm 1) + 2\ell \frac{f_O}{f_I} \tag{2.46}$$

$$\nu'_{I\ell} = \left|(2\ell \pm 1) - 2\ell \frac{f_O}{f_I}\right| \tag{2.47}$$

The normalized amplitudes of the extrabasal components are

$$\gamma_I = \gamma'_{I\ell} = \frac{1}{2\ell \pm 1} \tag{2.48}$$

From equations (2.41)–(2.48) it can be concluded that the quality of the input current waveform as expressed by the input current wave indices, similarly to that of the output voltage waveform, is greatly dependent upon the character of the existence functions. It may have been expected, on the basis of the results obtained for the output voltage waveforms, that the frequency spectra of the two input current waves [equations (2.39) and (2.40)] corresponding to existence functions of different repetition rates would be dissimilar. It may be somewhat surprising, however, that the input phase angle ϕ_I (i.e., the angle between the fundamental input current component and the corresponding input voltage), and consequently the input displacement factor, are different for the two types of existence function. Equation (2.42) shows that, for $f_S = f_I + f_O$, the input phase angle ϕ_I is the *negative* of the load phase angle ϕ_O. Thus, the frequency changer whose operation is defined by existence functions of repetition frequency $f_S = f_I + f_O$ transfers the negative of the load phase angle to the input source. An inductive load at the output is, therefore, "seen" by the source as a capacitive load, and vice versa. On the other hand, equation (2.43) shows that the frequency changer whose operation is defined by existence functions of repetition frequency $f'_S = f_I - f_O$ transfers the load phase angle directly to the input source. Therefore, the input source "sees" the actual load phase angle.

These conclusions based on analytical results are of course in agreement with the qualititative deductions made in Chapter 1 and summarized in Table 1.1. The reader may already have recognized that the characteristics obtained with the existence function having a repetition frequency $f_S = f_I + f_O$ are similar to those stipulated for the *unrestricted frequency changer*, and the characteristics corresponding to $f_S = f_I - f_O$ are similar to those stipulated for the *slow switching frequency changer*.

It should perhaps be pointed out here that the input phase angle for the particular existence functions considered is completely, though indirectly, determined by the phase angle of the load at the output. As explained in the previous chapter, the frequency changer at the output terminals is equivalent to a voltage source of frequency f_O. For a given load impedance, the frequency f_O will thus determine the output phase angle ϕ_O. If therefore f_O is varied ϕ_O may also vary. The input phase angle ϕ_I, measured at the angular input frequency ω_I, will, in absolute value, always be equal to ϕ_O—which is, of course, measured at the angular output frequency ω_O. Thus, if variation of the output frequency causes the output load phase angle to vary, this will be reflected as a corresponding variation of the input phase angle. On the other hand, since the input frequency has no effect on the output phase angle, varying f_I with constant f_O will not cause any change in ϕ_I.

2.3 SUMMARY

In this chapter the mathematical representation and characterization of static frequency changers are examined. It is shown that the operation of a general n input, m output phase frequency changer can be described by an $m \times n$ matrix, $[H]$, whose elements are time-dependent existence functions. Each element describes the operation of one switch in the power circuit. Thus element $h_{pq}(t)$ defines whether the corresponding switch, connecting output terminal p to input terminal q, is open ($h_{pq} = 0$) or closed ($h_{pq} = 1$) at a given time t. Since an existence function by definition has unit value for values of variable t within specified ranges and zero value for all other values of t, it can generally be expressed as sums of appropriate (positive and negative) unit step functions. Thus the generated terminal quantities of the frequency changer (i.e., output voltage and input current waves) can be defined precisely as sums of products of the applied forcing functions (input voltage and output current) and the relevant existence functions (which in practice are always periodic). In order to determine the steady-state spectral characteristics of the generated waveforms (i.e., amplitudes, frequencies, and phases of the constituent components), it is convenient to express the existence functions in the form of trigonometric series. Then the output voltage as well as the input current waveforms can be described mathematically as ensembles of sinusoidal components, having frequencies that generally are sums and differences of multiples of the input (source) frequency and the wanted output frequency.

The spectral characteristics of the output voltage and input current waves indicate the performance of the frequency changer. The practically important measures of the output performance (output voltage wave indices) are the normalized amplitudes (γ_O) and frequencies (ν_O) of the unwanted components and the total r.m.s. distortion (μ_O) of the output voltage waveform. The practically important measures of the input performance (input current wave indices) are the input current distortion factor (μ_I), the input displacement (δ_I) and power (λ_I) factors, and the normalized amplitudes (γ_I) and frequencies (ν_I) of the extrabasal components. The output voltage and input current wave indices are generally dependent upon the character of the existence functions. With the proper choice of the existence functions, selected performance indices can be optimized to meet particular application requirements.

CHAPTER THREE

SYNTHESIS OF OUTPUT VOLTAGE WAVEFORMS

It is indicated in the previous chapter that the output voltage waveform of a frequency changer with a given pulse number is determined by the character of the existence functions, which describe mathematically the operation of the switches in the power circuit. In the present chapter, a systematic investigation is carried out to establish pertinent relationships between existence functions of different characters and the corresponding output voltage waveforms. To this end, various existence functions of appropriate character are introduced, and analytical expressions for the corresponding output voltage waveforms are derived. From these expressions the output voltage wave indices appropriate to different waveform construction (control) methods are determined with the intent of classifying their merits for practical applications.

The major aim of the investigation is the discovery of ways of operating the switches of the power circuit so as to generate output waveforms that approximate a prescribed, usually sinusoidal, wave as closely as possible, within the natural limitations imposed by the basic mechanism of constructing the output waveform from segments of the input voltage waves. The investigation is restricted to *frequency changer type* output waveforms (see definition in Chapter 1) which are characterized by minimum instantaneous deviation from the prescribed desired output waves and, consequently, by minimum total r.m.s. distortion. Thus, *inverter type* output waveforms are not considered.

In the initial investigation, methods of controlling the amplitude of the desired output voltage wave are not considered; it is assumed that the frequency changer is operated so as to produce the maximum wanted component of output voltage obtainable from the given input source—referred to as *full* output voltage. This assumption makes it possible to derive the basic, and usually unique, characteristics of differently controlled frequency changers. It becomes apparent later that the method of voltage control is generally not unique. Various techniques are applicable to individual systems that may or may not cause a departure from the basic characteristics obtained at full output voltage.

The problem of output voltage control is investigated separately in the next chapter with the objective of finding, for each different output waveform—that is, for each different type of frequency changer—control methods that allow the basic characteristics obtained at full output voltage to be retained.

3.1 DERIVATION OF GENERAL EXPRESSIONS FOR THE OUTPUT VOLTAGE WAVE

3.1.1 General Expressions for Positive-Type and Negative-Type Voltage Waveforms

As shown in Chapter 1, frequency changer circuits with pulse number of $3n$ ($n = 1, 2, 3, \ldots$) can be constructed from appropriate numbers of basic three-pulse units. It is logical, therefore, to start the investigation with the relatively simple three-pulse circuit and later to generalize the results obtained for more complex circuits. Moreover, initially only a single-phase output is considered. It has been shown that three-phase output is generated by three independent circuits. It can thus be expected that the analytical expressions for all three waveforms will have the same basic characteristics.

The general relationship between the input and output voltages is given by equation (2.7):

$$[v_O] = [H][v_I]$$

which, for a single-phase output, may be written in the following form

$$v_O = [H_{1r}][v_I] = [h_{11} \quad h_{12} \quad h_{13}] \begin{bmatrix} v_{I1} \\ v_{I2} \\ v_{I3} \end{bmatrix} \tag{3.1}$$

where $[v_I]$ represents, as stipulated at the outset, a balanced set of three sinusoidal voltages, namely

$$[v_I] = \begin{bmatrix} v_{I1} \\ v_{I2} \\ v_{I3} \end{bmatrix} = \frac{V_I}{2j} \begin{bmatrix} e^{j\omega_I t} - e^{-j\omega_I t} \\ e^{-j\frac{2\pi}{3}}(e^{j\omega_I t} - e^{-j\omega_I t}) \\ e^{-j\frac{4\pi}{3}}(e^{j\omega_I t} - e^{-j\omega_I t}) \end{bmatrix} \tag{3.2}$$

and h_{11}, h_{12}, h_{13} are (so far unspecified) existence functions describing the state (which may be open or closed) of the corresponding power switches in the frequency changer circuit.

As a starting point for finding suitable analytical expressions for the existence functions, assume that the frequency changer characterized by equation (3.1) is called upon to generate a desired output voltage wave with zero frequency (i.e., a d-c voltage). It is known from the theory of phase-controlled a-c to d-c converters that minimum ripple in the output voltage (which gives optimal values for the output voltage wave indices) is obtained if the output voltage waveshape is constructed from *identical* segments of the input voltage waves. This requirement is satisfied if the elements of $[H_{1r}]$ are defined as *periodic* existence functions with period T_I ($T_I = 1/f_I$), namely,

$$\left.\begin{aligned} h_{11} &= \sum_{k=0}^{\infty} \left\{ u\left(t_0 + (1 + 3k)\frac{T_I}{3}\right) - u\left(t_0 + (2 + 3k)\frac{T_I}{3}\right) \right\} \\ h_{12} &= \sum_{k=0}^{\infty} \left\{ u\left(t_0 + (2 + 3k)\frac{T_I}{3}\right) - u\left(t_0 + (3 + 3k)\frac{T_I}{3}\right) \right\} \\ h_{13} &= \sum_{k=0}^{\infty} \left\{ u\left(t_0 + 3k\frac{T_I}{3}\right) - u\left(t_0 + (1 + 3k)\frac{T_I}{3}\right) \right\} \end{aligned}\right\} \tag{3.3}$$

where t_0 is a fixed time defining the level of the mean d-c output voltage. Existence functions h_{11}, h_{12}, and h_{13} are shown for zero mean output voltage, obtained by setting $t_0 = 0$, and $t_0 = T_I/2$, in Figure 3.1*a* and *b*, respectively. It can be observed that the same mean output voltage, but a different output waveshape, is obtained when time t_0 is changed to $T_I/2 - t_0$ in the arguments of the existence functions given by equation (3.3). The waveform obtained with t_0 (for example, $t_0 = 0$ in Figure 3.1*a*) is, of course, the positive-type voltage wave defined in Section 1.5.1, whereas the waveform obtained with $T_I/2 - t_0$ (for example, $T_I/2 - t_0 = T_I/2$ in Figure 3.1*b*) is the complementary negative-type voltage wave. The type of bi-directional converter circuit considered here can, of course, produce *either* of these two waveforms; as has already been indicated, this fact can be utilized to construct

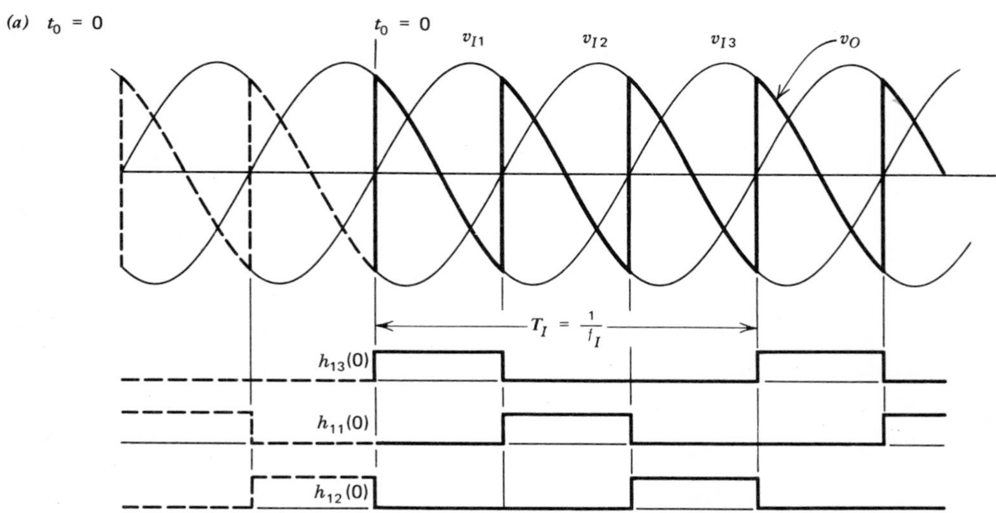

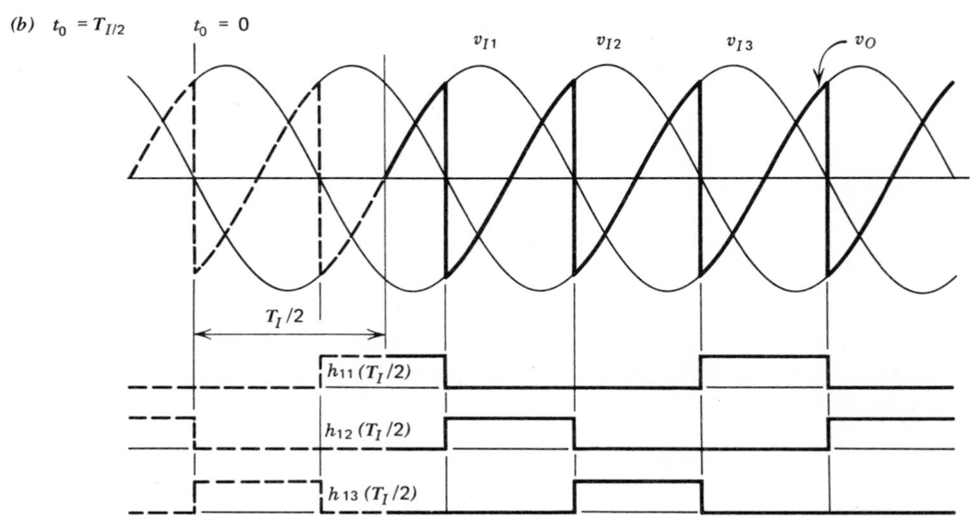

Figure 3.1 Basic existence functions for zero mean output voltage and the corresponding output waveforms.

"composite" waveforms of various types that provide different performance characteristics. For this reason we continue to investigate both sets of existence functions—that is, the one with variable t_0, and the other with variable $T_I/2 - t_0$. These two sets of existence functions and the corresponding output waveforms are termed *complementary*, and to distinguish them subscript π will be assigned to those quantities which correspond to variable $T_I/2 - t_0$.

Since in the present investigation only the steady state operation of the system is of interest, the existence functions expressed by equation (3.3) can be substituted by their corresponding Fourier series. Thus:

$$\left.\begin{aligned} h_{11} &= \frac{1}{3} - \sum_{n=-\infty}^{\infty} \frac{\sin n \frac{2\pi}{3}}{n\pi} \exp jn(\omega_I t + \zeta) \\ h_{12} &= \frac{1}{3} - \sum_{n=-\infty}^{\infty} \frac{\sin n \frac{2\pi}{3}}{n\pi} \exp jn\left(\omega_I t - \frac{2\pi}{3} + \zeta\right) \\ h_{13} &= \frac{1}{3} - \sum_{n=-\infty}^{\infty} \frac{\sin n \frac{2\pi}{3}}{n\pi} \exp jn\left(\omega_I t - \frac{4\pi}{3} + \zeta\right) \end{aligned}\right\} \quad (3.4)$$

where $\zeta = \omega_I t_0$. It is pointed out that, in the interval $-\pi/2 \le \zeta \le \pi/2$, angle ζ is closely related to the firing angle of the corresponding naturally commutated a-c to d-c converter. That is, $\alpha = \pi/2 - \zeta$. The difference is due to the change of reference point; thus, when $\alpha = 0$, the mean output voltage is maximum (thus for natural commutation, α is restricted to the operating interval $0 \le \alpha \le \pi$), whereas, for convenience, ζ is defined so that when it is equal to 0, the mean output voltage is zero.

Substituting $T_I/2 - t_0$ in place of t_0 in equations (3.3), the existence functions thereby obtained can be expressed by the following Fourier series:

$$\left.\begin{aligned} h_{\pi 11} &= \frac{1}{3} + \sum_{n=-\infty}^{\infty} \frac{\sin n \frac{\pi}{3}}{n\pi} \exp jn(\omega_I t - \zeta) \\ h_{\pi 12} &= \frac{1}{3} + \sum_{n=-\infty}^{\infty} \frac{\sin n \frac{\pi}{3}}{n\pi} \exp jn\left(\omega_I t - \frac{2\pi}{3} - \zeta\right) \\ h_{\pi 13} &= \frac{1}{3} + \sum_{n=-\infty}^{\infty} \frac{\sin n \frac{\pi}{3}}{n\pi} \exp jn\left(\omega_I t - \frac{4\pi}{3} - \zeta\right) \end{aligned}\right\} \quad (3.5)$$

The basic existence functions that define a constant (i.e., d-c) mean output voltage represent rectangular pulses with repetition period $T_I = 1/f_I$, pulse duration $1/3f_I$, and unit amplitude. As explained in Chapter 2, a *mean** a-c output voltage wave

* The *mean* a-c output voltage wave refers to the average value of the segments of the input voltage waves from which the actual output waveform is constructed. The *mean* a-c output voltage wave is also called the *desired* output voltage wave because this is what the control attempts to produce.

with prescribed *wanted* frequency can be generated by appropriately modulating the temporal parameters (e.g., the repetition frequency, pulse duration, etc.) of the existence functions.

As a recapitulation, recall that the existence functions describe the operation of the switches in the power converter. Thus the modulation of the temporal parameters of the existence functions simply means that the commencement and/or duration of the conduction intervals of the corresponding converter switches are appropriately varied (*modulated*) in order to generate a mean a-c output voltage wave. It can be visualized, for example, that by periodically varying angle ζ between $-\pi/2$ and $\pi/2$, the mean output voltage will also periodically vary between maximum positive and negative values, thus providing a mean a-c output.

Thus, in general, *frequency changer type* output voltage waveforms can be generated by judiciously modulating the *repetition rate* of the existence functions about their quiescent frequency f_I. This is represented mathematically by replacing angle ζ in equations (3.4) and (3.5) with a time-dependent function, $M(t)$, hereafter called the *modulating function*, namely,

$$\left.\begin{aligned}
h_{11} &= \frac{1}{3} - \sum_{n=-\infty}^{\infty} \frac{\sin n\dfrac{2\pi}{3}}{n\pi} \exp jn\{\omega_I t + M(t)\} \\
h_{12} &= \frac{1}{3} - \sum_{n=-\infty}^{\infty} \frac{\sin n\dfrac{2\pi}{3}}{n\pi} \exp jn\left\{\omega_I t - \frac{2\pi}{3} + M(t)\right\} \\
h_{13} &= \frac{1}{3} - \sum_{n=-\infty}^{\infty} \frac{\sin n\dfrac{2\pi}{3}}{n\pi} \exp jn\left\{\omega_I t - \frac{4\pi}{3} + M(t)\right\}
\end{aligned}\right\} \quad (3.6)$$

and

$$\left.\begin{aligned}
h_{\pi 11} &= \frac{1}{3} + \sum_{n=-\infty}^{\infty} \frac{\sin n\dfrac{\pi}{3}}{n\pi} \exp jn\{\omega_I t - M(t)\} \\
h_{\pi 12} &= \frac{1}{3} + \sum_{n=-\infty}^{\infty} \frac{\sin n\dfrac{\pi}{3}}{n\pi} \exp jn\left\{\omega_I t - \frac{2\pi}{3} - M(t)\right\} \\
h_{\pi 13} &= \frac{1}{3} + \sum_{n=-\infty}^{\infty} \frac{\sin n\dfrac{\pi}{3}}{n\pi} \exp jn\left\{\omega_I t - \frac{4\pi}{3} - M(t)\right\}
\end{aligned}\right\} \quad (3.7)$$

Equations (3.6) and (3.7) are the complementary general expressions for the existence functions that describe the operation of the power switches of the three-pulse frequency changer.

By substituting now either equations (3.6) and (3.2) or (3.7) and (3.2) into equation (3.1), an expression for the output voltage waveform in terms of $\omega_I t$ and $M(t)$ may be obtained. Using first equations (3.6) and (3.2), and introducing for convenience the customary notations, $a = \exp(j2\pi/3) = \exp(-j4\pi/3)$, $a^2 = \exp(j4\pi/3) = \exp(-j2\pi/3)$, $a^n = \exp(jn2\pi/3) = \exp(-jn4\pi/3)$ and $a^{2n} = \exp(jn4\pi/3) = \exp(-jn2\pi/3)$, v_O can be written in the following form:

$$v_O = \frac{V_I}{2j}\frac{1}{3}\left\{[1 \quad 1 \quad 1]\begin{bmatrix}1\\a^2\\a\end{bmatrix}e^{j\omega_I t} - [1 \quad 1 \quad 1]\begin{bmatrix}1\\a\\a^2\end{bmatrix}e^{-j\omega_I t}\right\} - \frac{V_I}{2j}\sum_{n=1}^{\infty}\frac{\sin n\dfrac{2\pi}{3}}{n\pi}$$

$$\times\left\{[1 \quad a^{2n} \quad a^n]\begin{bmatrix}1\\a^2\\a\end{bmatrix}e^{j\{(n+1)\omega_I t + nM(t)\}} - [1 \quad a^n \quad a^{2n}]\begin{bmatrix}1\\a\\a^2\end{bmatrix}e^{-j\{(n+1)\omega_I t + nM(t)\}}\right.$$

$$\left. - [1 \quad a^{2n} \quad a^n]\begin{bmatrix}1\\a\\a^2\end{bmatrix}e^{j\{(n-1)\omega_I t + nM(t)\}} + [1 \quad a^n \quad a^{2n}]\begin{bmatrix}1\\a^2\\a\end{bmatrix}e^{-j\{(n-1)\omega_I t + nM(t)\}}\right\} \tag{3.8}$$

Equation (3.8) can be evaluated easily by inspection. The first two terms independent of index n is zero because $1 + a^2 + a = 0$. The coefficients of terms of index n resulting from the indicated matrix multiplications are either 0 or 3. Thus, if $n = 3k - 1$, $k = 1, 2, \ldots$ then the coefficient of $\exp \pm j\{(n + 1)\omega_I t + nM(\omega t)\}$ is $\pm[3\sqrt{3}/j4\pi(3k - 1)]$ because $1 + a^{2(n+1)} + a^{n+1} = 1 + a^{6k} + a^{3k} = 3$ and $\sin(3k - 1)(2\pi/3) = -\sin(2\pi/3) = -\sqrt{3}/2$, and for any other value of n it is zero; if $n = 3k + 1$, $k = 0, 1, 2, \ldots$ then the coefficient of $\exp \pm j\{(n - 1)\omega_I t + nM(\omega t)\}$ is $\pm[3\sqrt{3}/j4\pi(3k + 1)]$ because $1 + a^{2n+1} + a^{n+2} = 1 + a^{3(2k+1)} + a^{3(k+1)} = 3$ and $\sin(3k + 1)(2\pi/3) = \sin(2\pi/3) = \sqrt{3}/2$, and for any other value of n it is zero. The output voltage, v_O, therefore may be written directly in the following form:

$$v_O = \frac{3\sqrt{3}}{2\pi}V_I\left\{\sin M(t) + \sum_{k=1}^{\infty}\left(\frac{\sin\{3k\omega_I t + (3k + 1)M(t)\}}{3k + 1} + \frac{\sin\{3k\omega_I t + (3k - 1)M(t)\}}{3k - 1}\right)\right\} \tag{3.9}$$

This equation can be written in a shorter form by using double sign notation, that is:

$$v_O = \frac{3\sqrt{3}}{2\pi}V_I\left(\sin M(t) + \sum_{k=1}^{\infty}\frac{\sin\{3k\omega_I t + (3k \pm 1)M(t)\}}{3k \pm 1}\right) \tag{3.10}$$

where the sign $\pm$ means that each term of index k should be taken twice, once with the upper (positive) signs, and once with the lower (negative) signs. [Compare equation (3.9) to (3.10).] This double sign symbol, with the above meaning, is used throughout this book to reduce the size of lengthy equations.

By the same procedure, a similar expression can be obtained for $v_{O\pi}$ through the use of the complementary existence functions given by equation (3.7):

$$v_{O\pi} = \frac{3\sqrt{3}}{2\pi}V_I\left(\sin M(t) - \sum_{k=1}^{\infty}(-1)^{3k}\frac{\sin\{3k\omega_I t - (3k \pm 1)M(t)\}}{3k \pm 1}\right) \tag{3.11}$$

Inspection of equations (3.10) and (3.11) clearly indicates that, with fixed ω_I, the output voltage wave indices are entirely determined by the modulating function $M(t)$. In the following sections, therefore, the various characters of $M(t)$ and corresponding properties of the output voltage waveforms are investigated. The main objective is the determination of the spectral characteristics of the output voltage waveforms, that is, the frequencies and the amplitudes of the constituent components. To this end, it is usually necessary to express the output waveform as a sum of all constituent components. Examination of the character of the terms, having the general form $\sin\{3k\omega_I t \pm (3k \pm 1)M(t)\}$, in equations (3.10) and (3.11) indicates that the individual components are not, except in special cases, readily obtainable for a given modulating function. For this reason, an alternative form of equations (3.10) and (3.11), from which the constituent components can be determined without excessive mathematical manipulation for all practically important modulating functions is developed. As the first step, equation (3.10) is written, with the use of appropriate trigonometrical formulae for compound angles, in the following form:

$$v_O = \frac{3\sqrt{3}}{2\pi} V_I \left(\sin M(t) + \sum_{k=1}^{\infty} \frac{\sin 3k\omega_I t \cos\{(3k \pm 1)M(t)\} + \cos 3k\omega_I t \sin\{(3k \pm 1)M(t)\}}{3k \pm 1} \right) \tag{3.12}$$

As seen, each term of index k in the previous equations is now expressed as a sum of two products. In order to obtain expressions for these products in terms of discrete sinusoidal components, it is generally necessary to decompose functions $\cos\{(3k \pm 1)M(t)\}$ and $\sin\{(3k \pm 1)M(t)\}$. To accomplish this, however, first the character of $M(t)$ has to be established.

Consider the general expressions obtained for the output voltage wave [equations (3.10) and (3.11)]. Inspection of these expressions indicates that only the first term, that is, $\sin M(t)$, is independent of the input frequency f_I and thus able to provide the wanted component with an arbitrarily chosen output frequency f_O. Therefore, to generate a practically useful a-c output waveform, $\sin M(t)$ must be a periodic function with period $T_O = 1/f_O$, such that $\int_0^{T_O} \sin M(t)\, dt = 0$. This general requirement can be satisfied if either $M(t)$ is a linear function or a generalized staircase-type function—for example, a staircase function constructed from half trapezoids—or a periodic function such that $\int_0^{T_O} M(t)\, dt = 0$. In the first trivial case, decomposition is not necessary, since $\cos\{(3k \pm 1)M(t)\}$ and $\sin\{3k \pm 1)M(t)\}$ become simple trigonometric functions. In the last two cases, functions $\sin M(t)$, $\cos\{(3k \pm 1)M(t)\}$, and $\sin\{(3k \pm 1)M(t)\}$ are periodic, and they can therefore be simply decomposed by Fourier series expansion.

Assume that $M(t)$ is indeed such a nontrivial function—that is, one that is not given in the form of $M(t) = \omega_O t + \psi$; thus $\sin M(t)$ is periodic with period $T_O = 1/f_O$ and is displaced from the origin ($t = 0$) by time T_d. Let it be further assumed, for convenience, that $M(t)$ is so chosen that $\sin M(t)$ is an *odd* function, having a graph symmetric to the starting point of the period, that is, $\sin\{M(T_d + t)\} = -\sin\{M(T_d - t)\}$. This last condition, of course, implies that $M(t)$ itself is an odd function with respect to the point T_d. It thus further follows that $\sin\{(3k \pm 1)M(t)\}$ is also odd and has a period of T_O, whereas $\cos\{(3k \pm 1)M(t)\}$ is an even function with a period of $T_O/2$. Consequently, these functions may be expanded in the following

Fourier series

$$\cos\{(3k \pm 1)M(t)\} = a_{(3k\pm 1),0} + \sum_{n=1}^{\infty} a_{(3k\pm 1),2n} \cos 2n(\omega_O t + \psi) \quad (3.13)$$

$$\sin M(t) = \sum_{n=1}^{\infty} b_{1,n} \sin n(\omega_O t + \psi) \quad (3.14)$$

$$\sin\{(3k \pm 1)M(t)\} = \sum_{n=1}^{\infty} b_{(3k\pm 1),n} \sin n(\omega_O t + \psi) \quad (3.15)$$

where

$$a_{(3k\pm 1),0} = \frac{1}{\pi}\int_{\psi}^{\pi+\psi} \cos\{(3k \pm 1)M(t)\}\, d(\omega_O t) \quad (3.16)$$

$$a_{(3k\pm 1),2n} = \frac{2}{\pi}\int_{\psi}^{\pi+\psi} \cos\{(3k \pm 1)M(t)\} \cos 2n\omega_O t\, d(\omega_O t) \quad (3.17)$$

$$b_{1,n} = \frac{2}{\pi}\int_{\psi}^{\pi+\psi} \sin M(t) \sin n\omega_O t\, d(\omega_O t) \quad (3.18)$$

$$b_{(3k+1),n} = \frac{2}{\pi}\int_{\psi}^{\pi+\psi} \sin\{(3k \pm 1)M(t)\} \sin n\omega_O t\, d(\omega_O t) \quad (3.19)$$

and $\omega_O = 2\pi/T_O, \psi = \omega_O T_d, k = 1, 2, 3, \ldots$

By substituting equations (3.13)–(3.15) in equation (3.12) and using appropriate trigonometric formulae for products, the following expression is obtained for v_O:

$$\begin{aligned} v_O = \frac{3\sqrt{3}}{2\pi} V_I \Bigg(& \sum_{n=1}^{\infty} \mathrm{b}_{1,n} \sin n(\omega_O t + \psi) \\ & + \sum_{k=1}^{\infty} 2A_{3k,0} \sin 3k\omega_I t \\ & + \sum_{k=1}^{\infty}\sum_{n=1}^{\infty} (A_{3k,2n} \sin\{(3k\omega_I \pm 2n\omega_O)t \pm 2n\psi\} \\ & \pm B_{3k,2n} \sin\{(3k\omega_I \pm n\omega_O)t \pm n\psi\})\Bigg) \end{aligned} \quad (3.20)$$

With the same manipulation, a similar expression may be obtained for $v_{O\pi}$ given by equation (3.11), namely,

$$\begin{aligned} v_{O\pi} = \frac{3\sqrt{3}}{2\pi} V_I \Bigg(& \sum_{n=1}^{\infty} b_{1,n} \sin n(\omega_O t + \psi) \\ & - \sum_{k=1}^{\infty} (-1)^{3k} 2A_{3k,0} \sin 3k\omega_I t \\ & - \sum_{k=1}^{\infty}\sum_{n=1}^{\infty} (-1)^{3k}(A_{3k,2n} \sin\{(3k\omega_I \pm 2n\omega_O)t \pm 2n\psi\} \\ & \mp B_{3k,2n} \sin\{(3k\omega_I \pm n\omega_O)t \pm n\psi\})\Bigg) \end{aligned} \quad (3.21)$$

where

$$\left.\begin{aligned} A_{3k,0} &= \frac{1}{2}\left(\frac{a_{(3k+1),0}}{3k+1} + \frac{a_{(3k+1),0}}{3k-1}\right) \\ A_{3k,2n} &= \frac{1}{2}\left(\frac{a_{(3k+1),2n}}{3k+1} + \frac{a_{(3k-1),2n}}{3k-1}\right) \\ B_{3k,n} &= \frac{1}{2}\left(\frac{b_{(3k+1),n}}{3k+1} + \frac{b_{(3k-1),n}}{3k-1}\right) \end{aligned}\right\} \tag{3.22}$$

Equations (3.20) and (3.21) are alternative expressions to (3.10) and (3.11), which describe the two complementary output voltage waveforms, v_O and $v_{O\pi}$, for the case of a general periodic modulating function satisfying the conditions outlined above.

Before proceeding to a consideration of the synthesis of composite waveforms, we pause to consider an example in which the complementary positive-type and negative-type output waveforms are produced according to a specific *periodic* modulating function, which, for the sake of generality, produces a nonsinusoidal "mean" output voltage wave. Consideration of this example will enable us to proceed to develop the analytical techniques for representing more practically useful composite voltage waveforms, which are synthesized from both the positive-type and negative-type voltage waves.

Assume that the following periodic modulating function

$$M(t) = \begin{cases} \dfrac{9}{5}\omega_O t & -\dfrac{5\pi}{18} < \omega_O t \leqq \dfrac{5\pi}{18} \\ \dfrac{\pi}{2} & \dfrac{5\pi}{18} < \omega_O t \leqq \dfrac{13\pi}{18} \\ \pi - \dfrac{9}{5}\omega_O t & \dfrac{13\pi}{18} < \omega_O t \leqq \pi + \dfrac{5\pi}{18} \\ \dfrac{\pi}{2} & \pi + \dfrac{5\pi}{18} < \omega_O t \leqq 2\pi - \dfrac{5\pi}{18} \end{cases} \tag{3.23}$$

is used to generate the complementary output voltage waveforms. The modulating functions $M(t)$ and $-M(t)$, appearing in the arguments of the two complementary sets of existence functions given by equations (3.6) and (3.7), are illustrated at b and f in Figure 3.2. As previously explained, the modulating function is, in effect, a time-varying angle in the arguments of the existence functions. The present modulating function $M(t)$ thus can be considered as an angle oscillating between $-\pi/2$ and $\pi/2$ in the manner shown at b. The corresponding variation of the repetition rates of the rectangular pulse trains representing the existence functions may be determined by differentiating $M(t)$ with respect to time t, namely,

$$\frac{dM(t)}{dt} = \Omega(t) = \begin{cases} \dfrac{9}{5}\omega_O & -\dfrac{5\pi}{18} < \omega_O t \leqq \dfrac{5\pi}{18} \\ 0 & \dfrac{5\pi}{18} < \omega_O t \leqq \dfrac{13\pi}{18} \\ -\dfrac{9}{5}\omega_O & \dfrac{13\pi}{18} < \omega_O t \leqq \pi + \dfrac{5\pi}{18} \\ 0 & \pi + \dfrac{5\pi}{18} < \omega_O t \leqq 2\pi - \dfrac{5\pi}{18} \end{cases} \tag{3.24}$$

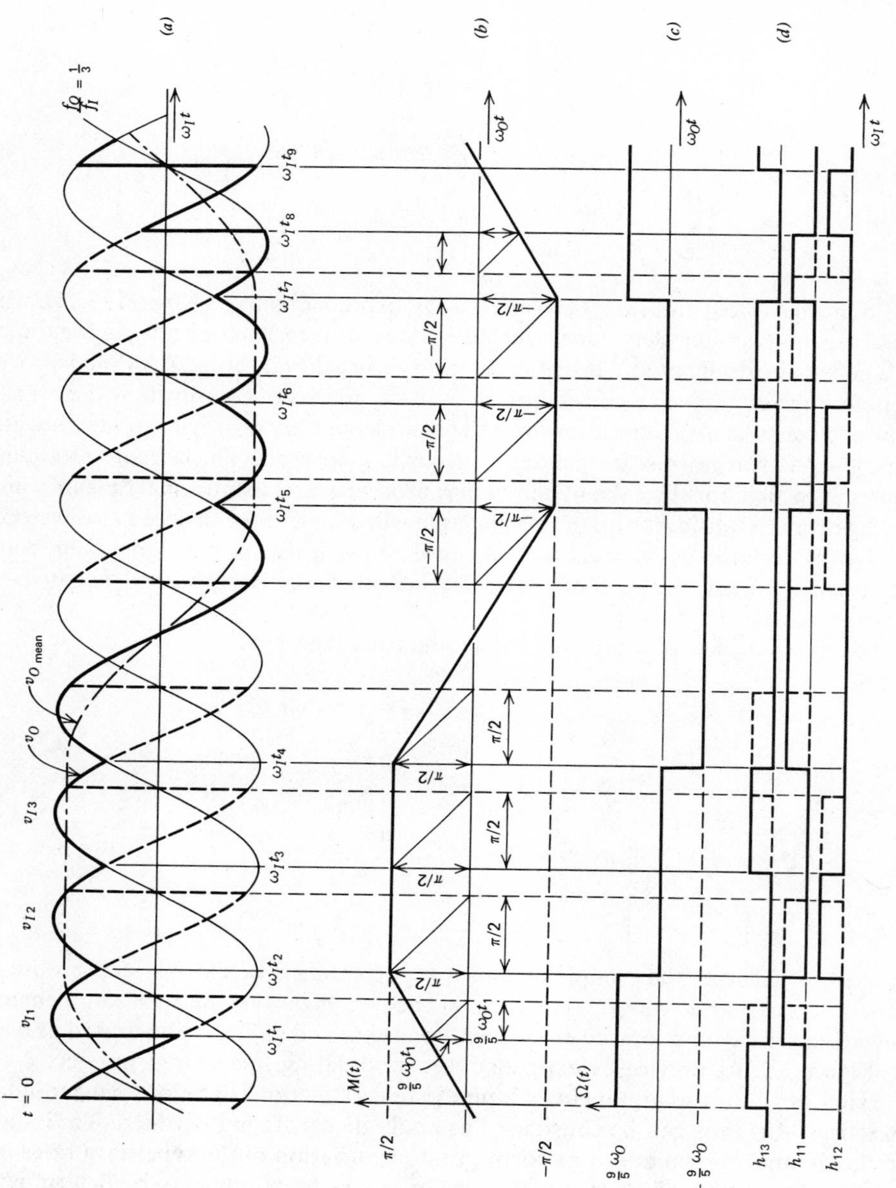

t = 0
v_{I1}
v_{I2}
v_{I3}
v_O
$v_{O\,\mathrm{mean}}$
$\omega_I t_1$
$\omega_I t_2$
$\omega_I t_3$
$\omega_I t_4$
$\omega_I t_5$
$\omega_I t_6$
$\omega_I t_7$
$\omega_I t_8$
$\omega_I t_9$
$\omega_I t$
$\frac{f_O}{f_I} = \frac{1}{3}$
(a)
$M(t)$
$\pi/2$
$-\pi/2$
$\frac{9}{5}\,\omega_O t_1$
$\omega_O t$
(b)
$\Omega(t)$
$\frac{9}{5}\,\omega_O$
$-\frac{9}{5}\,\omega_O$
(c)
h_{13}
h_{11}
h_{12}
(d)

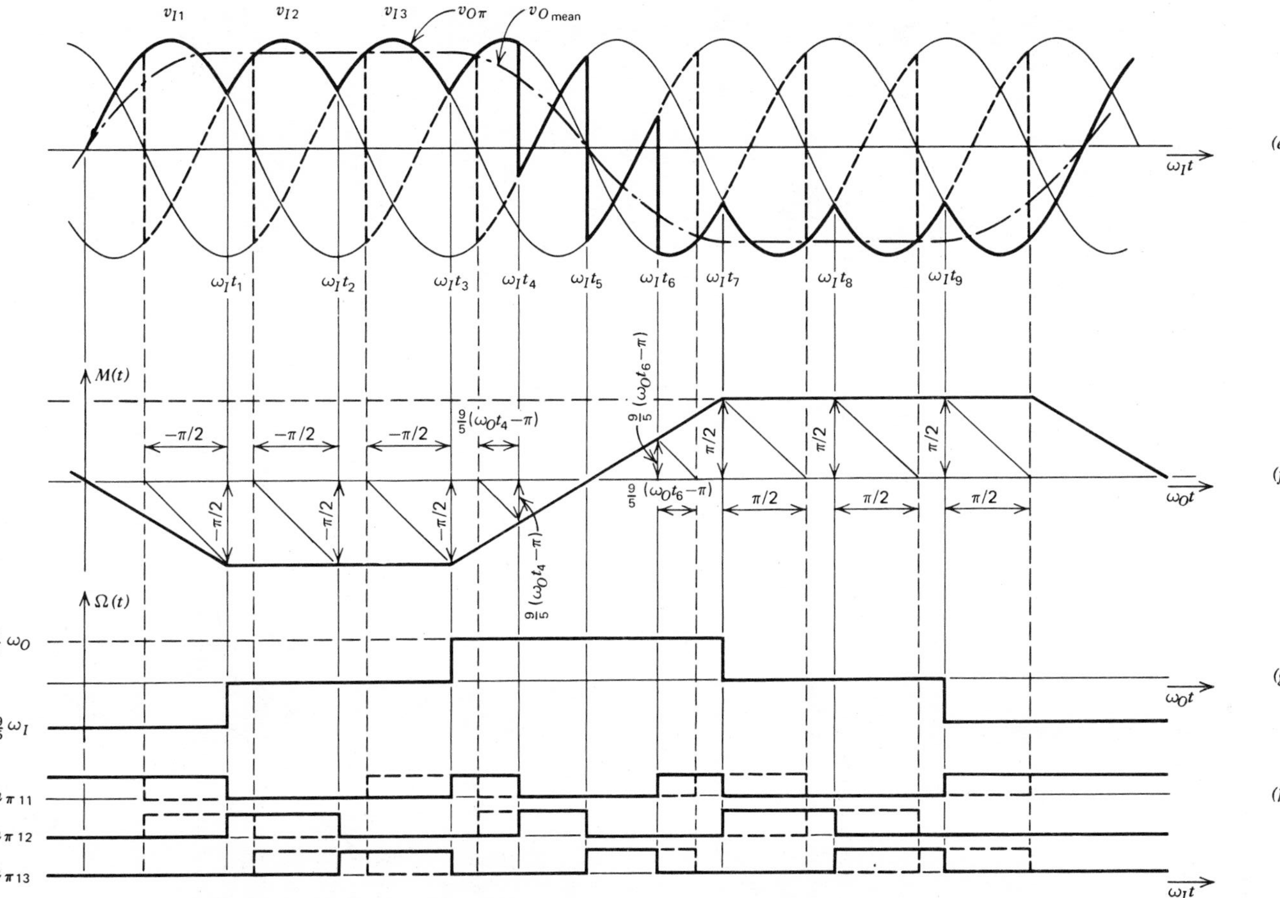

Figure 3.2 Generation of *a* the positive-type and *b* the negative-type complementary output voltage waveforms by a periodic modulating function.

The functions $\Omega(t)$ and $-\Omega(t)$ are shown at *c* and *g*. The graphs of the corresponding existence functions are shown at *d* and *h*, and the generated output waveshapes, together with the sinusoidal input voltage waves, at *a* and *e*. These illustrations clearly show that the two complementary output voltage waveforms, v_O and $v_{O\pi}$, are generated by oscillating the phase positions of the two complementary sets of existence functions, h_{11}, h_{12}, h_{13}, and $h_{\pi 11}$, $h_{\pi 12}$, $h_{\pi 13}$, between $-\pi/2$ and $+\pi/2$ *in opposite directions* to one another, about the quiescent position representing zero output voltage. The opposite phase variation is accompanied with opposite change in the repetition rates of the two sets of existence functions. That is, when the repetition rate of h_{11}, h_{12}, and h_{13} is stepped *up* from the original f_I to $f_I + \frac{9}{5}f_O$ (to change their angle from $-\pi/2$ to $\pi/2$), that of $h_{\pi 11}$, $h_{\pi 12}$, and $h_{\pi 13}$ is stepped *down* from f_I to $f_I - \frac{9}{5}f_O$ (to change their angle from $\pi/2$ to $-\pi/2$), and vice versa. It may also be observed, however, that the mean output voltage wave, $v_{O_{\text{mean}}}$, that is, the output voltage averaged between successive switching points, is the same for both v_O and $v_{O\pi}$.

A general property of the complementary waveforms generated by a periodic modulating function follows directly from the above outlined considerations. The switches of the converter which generates waveform v_O are operated at a *fast* rate of $f_I + cf_O$, $c > 0$ (in a more general case, but not in the specific example under consideration, coefficient c could be a function of time) during the interval when the slope of the mean wave is positive, and they are operated at a *slow* rate of $f_I - cf_O$, when the slope of the mean wave is negative. During the intervals of zero slope, the switches are operated at a constant rate of f_I. Thus it may be expected that the waveform sections with fast switching rates contribute unwanted ripple components with frequencies consisting of *sums* of multiples of f_I and f_O, whereas the intervals with slow switching rates contribute unwanted ripple components with frequencies consisting of differences of multiples of f_I and f_O. The intervals with the constant switching rate of f_I might be expected to contribute ripple components with frequencies that are multiples of f_I. Each complementary waveform, v_O and $v_{O\pi}$, therefore may be expected, in general, to have a frequency spectrum consisting of multiples of the input frequency and both sums and differences of multiples of the input and output frequency, as the general expressions given by equations (3.20) and (3.21) do indeed indicate.

It should be appreciated that certain terms contributed by different waveform sections may cancel each other when combined. This cancellation, as will be seen, is generally dependent upon the pulse number, and it can cause the absence of some families of terms in the expression describing the actual output waveform in question.

3.1.2 General Expressions for Consecutive Composite Waveforms

Because of the identical mean output waves, portions of the complementary waveforms v_O and $v_{O\pi}$ can be pieced together one after the other, or *consecutively*, to synthesize a new output waveshape. The reason why we might wish to do this would be to obtain certain desired operating features—for example, natural commutation of the switches, reduced distortion, or controllable input displacement factor.

The first plausible possibility is to construct an output waveshape from the complementary waveforms such that the switching rate is always the highest or the lowest possible. In the first case, the output frequency spectrum should be improved, as compared with that of either one of the complementary waveforms v_O or $v_{O\pi}$, and in the second, the reduced switching rate might be advantageous from the practical viewpoint of keeping the device switching rate as low as possible. These objectives can be accomplished simply by constructing the output voltage waveform from half-cycle sections of the complementary waves* containing either the fast or slow switching intervals. This is illustrated in Figure 3.3, in which the positive-type and negative-type complementary waves are shown at *a* and *b*, and the corresponding fast switching and slow switching composite waveforms at *e* and *f*. In order to define the waveforms analytically, two periodic existence functions, illustrated by graphs *c* and *d*, are introduced:

$$\left.\begin{aligned} E &= \begin{cases} 1 & -\dfrac{\pi}{2} < \omega_O t \leqq \dfrac{\pi}{2} \\ 0 & \dfrac{\pi}{2} < \omega_O t \leqq \dfrac{3\pi}{2} \end{cases} \\ E_\pi &= \begin{cases} 0 & -\dfrac{\pi}{2} < \omega_O t \leqq \dfrac{\pi}{2} \\ 1 & \dfrac{\pi}{2} < \omega_O t \leqq \dfrac{3\pi}{2} \end{cases} \end{aligned}\right\} \tag{3.25}$$

Then

$$v_{O_{FS}} = Ev_O + E_\pi v_{O\pi} \tag{3.26}$$

and

$$v_{O_{SS}} = Ev_{O\pi} + E_\pi v_O \tag{3.27}$$

where subscripts *FS* and *SS* stand for fast switching and slow switching, respectively.

A different type of consecutive composite waveform can be constructed by piecing together arbitrary but consecutive half-cycle intervals of the complementary waves. Such a waveform can be mathematically defined by making existence functions E and E_π functions of an angle, ρ ($-\pi \leqq \rho \leqq \pi$), measured at the angular frequency ω_O, namely,

$$E(\rho) = \begin{cases} 1 & -\rho < \omega_O t \leqq \pi - \rho \\ 0 & \pi - \rho < \omega_O t \leqq 2\pi - \rho \end{cases} \tag{3.28}$$

and

$$E_\pi(\rho) = \begin{cases} 0 & -\rho < \omega_O t \leqq \pi - \rho \\ 1 & \pi - \rho < \omega_O t \leqq 2\pi - \rho \end{cases} \tag{3.29}$$

With this, the position of E and E_π with respect to the origin ($\omega_O t = 0$) is variable, and a general consecutive composite waveform can be defined as a function of angle ρ

$$v_O(\rho) = E(\rho)v_O + E_\pi(\rho)v_{O\pi} \tag{3.30}$$

The existence functions $E(\rho)$ and $E_\pi(\rho)$, and a corresponding general output voltage waveshape $v_O(\rho)$ are illustrated at *g*, *h*, and *j* in Figure 3.3. Evidently, when $\rho = \phi_O$, where ϕ_O is the phase angle between the mean output voltage and current waves, equation (3.30) describes a naturally commutated type output voltage waveform that is produced by the alternate operation of a unidirectional positive converter circuit,

* It is pointed out that these output waveforms can also be produced by single staircase-type modulating functions previously mentioned. This approach is not pursued for a general case, although it is treated in the next section for sinusoidal mean output waveforms, in which case, however, the staircase function degenerates into a simple linear function of the type $M(t) = \omega_O t + \psi$.

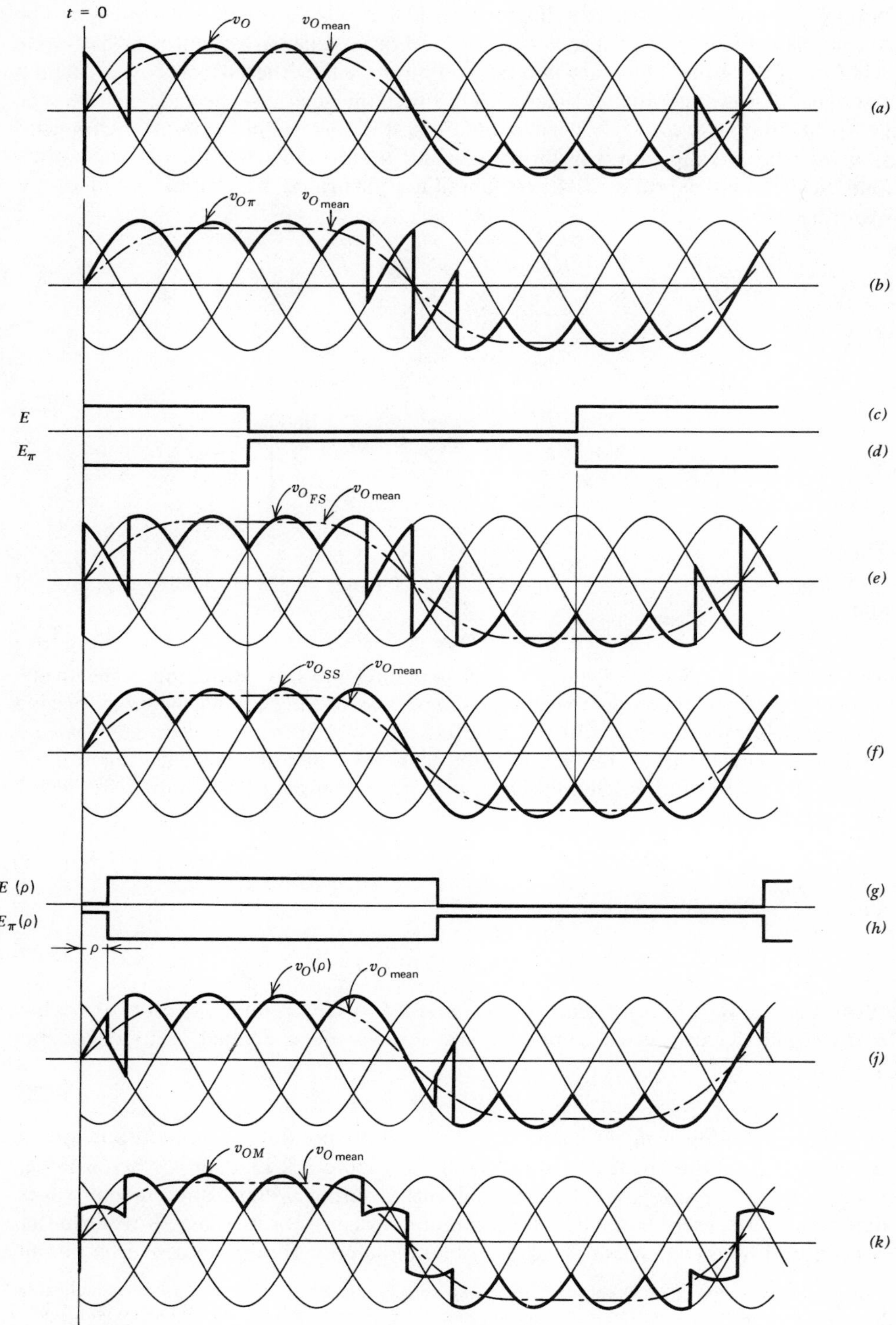

Figure 3.3 Synthesis of different output voltage waveshapes from the positive-type and negative-type complementary waveforms.

working during the positive current half-cycle, and a similar negative converter circuit, working during the negative current half-cycle. Note also that when $\rho = \pi/2$, $E(\rho)$ and $E_\pi(\rho)$ are equal to E and E_π [equation (3.25)], respectively, used to define the fast and slow switching output waveforms.

The mechanism of output voltage waveform construction specified by equation (3.30) can be understood better by substituting in place of v_O and $v_{O\pi}$ the appropriate forms of the basic relationship $[v_O] = [H][v_I]$, that is,

$$v_O(\rho) = E(\rho)\begin{bmatrix} h_{11} & h_{12} & h_{13} \end{bmatrix}\begin{bmatrix} v_{I1} \\ v_{I2} \\ v_{I3} \end{bmatrix} + E_\pi(\rho)\begin{bmatrix} h_{\pi 11} & h_{\pi 12} & h_{\pi 13} \end{bmatrix}\begin{bmatrix} v_{I1} \\ v_{I2} \\ v_{I3} \end{bmatrix} \tag{3.31}$$

or

$$v_O(\rho) = \left(E(\rho)\begin{bmatrix} h_{11} & h_{12} & h_{13} \end{bmatrix} + E_\pi(\rho)\begin{bmatrix} h_{\pi 11} & h_{\pi 12} & h_{\pi 13} \end{bmatrix}\right)\begin{bmatrix} v_{I1} \\ v_{I2} \\ v_{I3} \end{bmatrix} \tag{3.32}$$

Equation (3.32) means that, for an arbitrary ρ, the operation of the bidirectional switches of the power circuit is defined for half output cycle intervals by existence functions h_{11}, h_{12}, and h_{13}, and it is defined for the other half cycle intervals by $h_{\pi 11}$, $h_{\pi 12}$, and $h_{\pi 13}$. If the power circuit is composed of two unidirectional naturally commutated converters (one positive and one negative as shown in Figure 1.24), operated alternately during the positive and negative output current half cycles, then, with $\rho = \phi_O$, product $E(\rho)[h_{11}h_{12}h_{13}]$ describes the operation of the power switches in the positive converter, whereas $E_\pi(\rho)[h_{\pi 11}h_{\pi 12}h_{\pi 13}]$ describes that of the switches in the negative converter. As seen in Chapter 1, the frequency changer operated in this fashion is called a naturally commutated cycloconverter.

To proceed with the development of equation (3.30), periodic existence functions $E(\rho)$ and $E_\pi(\rho)$ are now expanded in the following Fourier series [see definitions (3.28) and (3.29)]:

$$E(\rho) = \frac{1}{2} + \frac{2}{\pi}\sum_{m=1}^{\infty}\frac{1}{2m-1}\sin\{(2m-1)(\omega_O t + \rho)\} \tag{3.33}$$

$$E_\pi(\rho) = \frac{1}{2} - \frac{2}{\pi}\sum_{m=1}^{\infty}\frac{1}{2m-1}\sin\{(2m-1)(\omega_O t + \rho)\} \tag{3.34}$$

Substituting the above equations, together with the general expressions for v_O and $v_{O\pi}$ given by equations (3.20) and (3.21), into (3.30), $v_O(\rho)$ can be written in the form

$$\text{(a)}\quad \begin{aligned} v_O(\rho) = \frac{3\sqrt{3}}{2\pi} V_I \Bigg\{ & \sum_{n=1}^{\infty} b_{1,n} \sin n(\omega_O t + \psi) \\ & + \sum_{k=1}^{\infty} 2A_{3(2k-1),0} \sin\{3(2k-1)\omega_I t\} \\ & + \sum_{k=1}^{\infty}\sum_{n=1}^{\infty}\Big(A_{3(2k-1),2n} \sin\{[3(2k-1)\omega_I \pm 2n\omega_O]t \pm 2n\psi\} \\ & \pm B_{(6k-1),n} \sin\{(6k\omega_I \pm n\omega_O)t \pm n\psi\}\Big)\Bigg\} \end{aligned}$$

$$
\text{(b)}\quad \left[\begin{aligned}
&+\frac{3\sqrt{3}}{2\pi}V_I\left\{\sum_{k=1}^{\infty}2A_{6k,0}\sin 6k\omega_I t\right.\\
&\qquad+\sum_{k=1}^{\infty}\sum_{n=1}^{\infty}\Big(A_{6k,2n}\sin\{(6k\omega_I\pm 2n\omega_O)t\pm 2n\psi\}\\
&\qquad\qquad\left.\pm B_{3(2k-1),n}\sin\{[3(2k-1)\omega_I\pm n\omega_O]t\pm n\psi\}\Big)\right\}\\
&\qquad\times\left(\frac{4}{\pi}\sum_{m=1}^{\infty}\frac{1}{2m-1}\sin\{(2m-1)(\omega_O t+\rho)\}\right)
\end{aligned}\right. \tag{3.35}
$$

Note that part (a) of equation (3.35) is independent of angle ρ. Writing explicitly the odd and even terms of index k, carrying out the indicated multiplications, and using appropriate trigonometrical formulae for products, the output voltage waveform $v_O(\rho)$ may be expressed as follows:

$$
\begin{aligned}
v_O(\rho) = a &- \frac{3\sqrt{3}}{\pi^2}V_I\sum_{k=1}^{\infty}\sum_{m=1}^{\infty}\frac{1}{2m-1}\\
&\times\Big\{\pm 2\,A_{6k,0}\cos\{[6k\omega_I\pm(2m-1)\omega_O]t\pm(2m-1)\rho\}\\
&+\sum_{n=1}^{\infty}\Big(A_{6k,2n}(\pm\cos\{[6k\omega_I\pm\{2(n+m)-1\}\omega_O]t\pm(2m-1)\rho\pm 2n\psi\}\\
&\qquad\mp\cos\{[6k\omega_I\pm\{2(n-m)+1\}\omega_O]t\mp(2m-1)\rho\pm 2n\psi\})\\
&+B_{3(2k-1),n}(\cos\{[3(2k-1)\omega_I\pm(n+2m-1)\omega_O]t\pm(2m-1)\rho\pm n\psi\}\\
&\qquad-\cos\{[3(2k-1)\omega_I\pm(n-2m+1)\omega_O]t\mp(2m-1)\rho\pm n\psi\})\Big)\Big\}
\end{aligned} \tag{3.36}
$$

where a is part (a) of equation (3.35), and coefficients $A_{3(2k-1),0}$, $A_{3(2n-1),2n}$, $B_{(6k-1),n}$ [in part (a)] and $A_{6k,0}$, $A_{6k,2n}$, $B_{3(2k-1),n}$ are defined by equation (3.22).

Equation (3.36) is a general analytical expression for a consecutive composite output voltage wave constructed from alternate half-period sections of the two complementary waves v_O and $v_{O\pi}$.

3.1.3 General Expression for Concurrent Composite Waveform

As shown in Chapter 1, there is a further useful way of constructing an output waveshape from the two complementary waveforms. That is, the output waveshape may be produced by *concurrently* summing or generating the arithmetic mean of the waveforms v_O and $v_{O\pi}$ as illustrated by the waveform at (k) in Figure 3.3. This method requires two converter circuits, operated from a common source and supplying the same load, to be concurrently in conduction during both the positive-and negative-current half-cycles. The advantage of this arrangement is that certain groups of unwanted components appear in phase opposition with one another in the expressions for v_O and $v_{O\pi}$, as inspection of equations (3.20) and (3.21) indicates, and therefore they cancel one another in the composite waveform. This results in an improved frequency spectrum and decreased r.m.s. distortion.

An analytical expression for the waveform v_{OM} (Figure 3.3k) may be obtained from the basic definition

$$v_{OM} = \frac{1}{2}(v_O + v_{O\pi}) \tag{3.37}$$

by substituting the general expressions for v_O and $v_{O\pi}$, given by equations (3.20) and (3.21), and noting that the terms of index k cancel whenever $k = 2\ell$, ($\ell = 1, 2, \ldots$). Thus

$$\text{(a)}\quad \left[\begin{aligned} v_{OM} = \frac{3\sqrt{3}}{2\pi} V_I \Bigg\{ &\sum_{n=1}^{\infty} b_{1,n} \sin n(\omega_O t + \psi) \\ &+ \sum_{k=1}^{\infty} 2A_{3(2k-1),0} \sin\{3(2k-1)\omega_I t\} \\ &+ \sum_{k=1}^{\infty}\sum_{n=1}^{\infty}\Big(A_{3(2k-1),2n} \sin\{[3(2k-1)\omega_I \pm 2n\omega_O]t \pm 2n\psi\} \\ &\pm B_{(6k-1),n} \sin\{(6k\omega_I \pm n\omega_O)t \pm n\psi\}\Big)\Bigg\} \end{aligned}\right. \tag{3.38}$$

Inspection of equation (3.38) indicates that the expression for v_{OM} is identical to part (a) of equation (3.36) obtained for waveform $v_O(\rho)$. Thus it may be concluded that the components given by equation (3.38) are invariably the "basic" constituents of the whole family of output waveforms related to a given periodic modulating function—that is, of the two complementary waveforms, v_O and $v_{O\pi}$, and the corresponding composite waveforms, $v_O(\rho)$ and v_{OM}.

With equation (3.38), our preparatory investigation of output waveform synthesis is completed. The analytical methods described and the general expressions obtained, however, are utilized in the subsequent sections, in which the practically important modulating functions and the corresponding output voltage waveforms are studied.

3.1.4 Summary

Before closing this section, it may be useful to review the final analytical expressions obtained for the output voltage waveforms.

Equations (3.10) and (3.11) are the two fundamental expressions derived with the use of modulated existence functions for the two complementary output voltage waveforms of a frequency changer. Although completely general, these equations do not give the constituent components of the output voltage waveform explicitly unless the modulating function is, in effect, a linear function of time.

Equations (3.20) and (3.21) are derived from the basic expressions (3.10) and (3.11). They give explicitly the components of the two complementary waveforms for any periodic modulating function that can be expanded in a Fourier series. The amplitudes of the components can be computed for a given (periodic) modulating function from the general coefficients defined by equations (3.16)–(3.19).

Equation (3.36) is the general expression for an output voltage waveform constructed from consecutive half-period sections of the two complementary waveforms. This expression also gives the individual constituents of the output waveform, the amplitudes of which are again defined in terms of the same general coefficients given by equations (3.16)–(3.19).

Finally, equation (3.38) is the general expression for the output voltage waveform obtained by generating the arithmetic mean (or sum—in which case, it should of course be multiplied by two) of the two complementary waveforms. It gives explicitly the individual constituent components of the output waveform, whose amplitudes are given again in terms of the general coefficients [equations (3.16)–(3.19)].

From this review, the reader may notice the uniformity of the expressions, which makes actual calculations quite simple. In every "final" equation [(3.20), (3.21), (3.36), (3.38)] the frequencies of the constituent components are explicitly given; they are independent of the modulating function. (Of course, the amplitudes of some of these components may become zero depending on the character of the modulating function.) The amplitudes of the constituent components are, in all cases, defined by the same general coefficients, which can be computed for any practical modulating function from the formulae given. In fact, if the general coefficients corresponding to a given modulating function are once determined, the spectral characteristics (amplitudes, frequencies, and phases) of the components of the different types of output voltage waveforms considered can be determined readily from the above expressions.

The reader might ask why we do not rather analyze the actual output voltage waveform directly by conventional Fourier expansion, if such expansion must in any case be used to determine the general coefficients. The answer is, simply, that the conventional Fourier approach is not suitable for a general analysis of an output voltage waveform produced by a frequency changer. This is, of course, also true for the input current waveform. The reason is that the actual shape of the output voltage wave depends on the ratio between the output and input frequencies; if the output frequency is not an exact integral submultiple, or multiple, of the product of the input frequency and the pulse number, the output waveform does not repeat itself every output cycle. It should be recalled that the terms *output frequency* and *output cycle* are associated with the *wanted component* of the output waveform. For conventional Fourier analysis, it would therefore be necessary first to establish the basic repetition cycle of the output waveshape at a given output to input frequency ratio, and then to compute the Fourier coefficients. For the general case of variable output to input frequency ratio, this computation would have to be repeated many times to cover, in discrete increments, the total range of interest. Such an undertaking would clearly be formidable, and even once it was carried out, the results would have limited usefulness because they would not reveal the general rules governing the spectral characteristic of the output voltage waveform, nor would they show directly how the spectrum is related to the particular technique of output voltage wave construction employed; a general comparison of differently produced waveforms would be practically impossible.

As has been shown, the analytical approach used in this book overcomes these difficulties and enables us to express the output voltage waveform quite generally, as a trigonometric series, in terms of the relevant input/output quantities (e.g., f_I, f_O, V_I, V_O) and the possible variables of the waveform synthesis—for example, ρ—yet the numerical computation does not involve more than the one-time calculation of certain Fourier coefficients. It should perhaps be mentioned, however, that for some modulating functions the numerical computation of these coefficients may be quite laborious.

3.2 SYNTHESIS OF SINUSOIDAL MEAN OUTPUT VOLTAGE WAVEFORMS

Reference is again made to equations (3.10) and (3.11) which show that, in general, only the first term, that is, sin $M(t)$, can provide a sinusoidal component with a frequency that is independent of the input frequency f_I. The wanted component of the output voltage waveform is therefore generally determined only by the expression sin $M(t)$. A *sinusoidal mean* output waveform means, by definition, that the frequencies of the constituent components are generally not, except at certain discrete f_O/f_I ratios, integral multiples of the wanted output frequency f_O. This condition can only be satisfied if

$$\sin M(t) = \sin(\omega_O t + \psi) \tag{3.39}$$

where $\omega_O = 2\pi f_O$ (f_O is the wanted output frequency) and ψ is an arbitrary phase angle. From equation (3.39) it follows that a sinusoidal mean output waveform can be generated only if the modulating function is given by either

$$M(t) = \omega_O t + \psi \tag{3.40}$$

or

$$M(t) = \sin^{-1}\{\sin(\omega_O t + \psi)\} \tag{3.41}$$

where

$$-\frac{\pi}{2} \leqq \sin^{-1}\{\sin(\omega_O t + \psi)\} \leqq \frac{\pi}{2}$$

3.2.1 Linear Modulating Function and Corresponding Output Waveforms

The simplest form of the modulating function is given by equation (3.40), where $M(t)$ is a simple linear function of time. Substituting this modulating function into the two general formulae for v_O and $v_{O\pi}$ given by equations (3.10) and (3.11), obtained through the use of two complementary sets of existence functions containing modulating functions $+M(t)$ and $-M(t)$, respectively, the following expressions for the output voltage waveform may be directly obtained:

$$v_O = \frac{3\sqrt{3}}{2\pi} V_I \left(\sin(\omega_O t + \psi) + \sum_{k=1}^{\infty} \frac{\sin\{[3k\omega_I + (3k \pm 1)\omega_O]t + (3k \pm 1)\psi\}}{3k \pm 1} \right) \tag{3.42}$$

and

$$v_{O\pi} = \frac{3\sqrt{3}}{2\pi} V_I \left(\sin(\omega_O t + \psi) - \sum_{k=1}^{\infty} (-1)^{3k} \frac{\sin\{[3k\omega_I - (3k \pm 1)\omega_O]t - (3k \pm 1)\psi\}}{3k \pm 1} \right) \tag{3.43}$$

Before comparing the above expressions for the two output voltage waveforms, it may be appropriate to examine the related existence functions. From the general expressions given by equations (3.6) and (3.7) it follows that $M(t) = \omega_O t + \psi$ increases the original repetition rate, f_I, of h_{11}, h_{12}, and h_{13} to $f_S = f_I + f_O$, whereas it decreases that of $h_{\pi 11}$, $h_{\pi 12}$, and $h_{\pi 13}$ to $f_{S\pi} = f_I - f_O$. (Recall that the negative of the modulating function, $-M(t)$, appears in the expressions of the complementary existence functions.) It follows therefore that, in the first case, the frequency of the wanted component is simply the difference between the repetition rate of the existence functions and the frequency of the supply voltages, namely,

$$f_O = f_S - f_I, \qquad f_S \geqq f_I \tag{3.44}$$

and in the second case, it is the difference between the frequency of the a-c supply and the repetition rate of the existence functions, namely

$$f_O = f_I - f_{S\pi}, \qquad f_I \geqq f_{S\pi} \tag{3.45}$$

It is clear that equation (3.44) can always be satisfied for any given f_I and wanted f_O; the theoretical range of the output frequency is therefore infinite ($0 \leqq f_O \leqq \infty$). On the other hand, the maximum output frequency defined by equation (3.45) is limited to $f_I (0 \leqq f_O \leqq f_I)$. Pertinent waveforms illustrating the generation of the output waveshape by modulating function $M(t) = \omega_O t$ (ψ is taken to be zero for convenience) for the two sets of complementary existence functions are shown in Figure 3.4*a* and *b*. (The reader may recognize that two-pulse versions of these waveforms are discussed in the introductory examples given in Chapter 2.)

Using the definitions given by equations (2.11)–(2.13), the output voltage wave indices characterizing v_O and $v_{O\pi}$ can readily be obtained from expressions (3.42) and (3.43), respectively.

Thus, the normalized frequencies of the unwanted components present in waveform v_O are given by

$$\nu_{Ok} = (3k \pm 1) + 3k \frac{f_I}{f_O} \tag{3.46}$$

The corresponding normalized amplitudes are

$$\gamma_{Ok} = \frac{1}{3k \pm 1} \tag{3.47}$$

resulting in the following total r.m.s. distortion

$$\mu_O = \sqrt{\sum_{k=1}^{\infty} \frac{1}{(3k \pm 1)^2}} \cong 0.676 \tag{3.48}$$

The output voltage wave indices of $v_{O\pi}$ are given by

$$\nu_{O\pi k} = \left| (3k \pm 1) - 3k \frac{f_I}{f_O} \right| \tag{3.49}$$

$$\nu_{O\pi k} = \frac{1}{3k \pm 1} \tag{3.50}$$

$$\mu_{O\pi} = \sqrt{\sum_{k=1}^{\infty} \frac{1}{(3k \pm 1)^2}} \cong 0.676 \tag{3.51}$$

Evidently $\gamma_{Ok} = \gamma_{O\pi k}$, $\mu_O = \mu_{O\pi}$ and only ν_{Ok} differs from $\nu_{O\pi k}$. However, this difference is very significant from the practical application viewpoint. As may be observed, ν_{Ok} ($k = 1, 2, \ldots$) is *always* greater than unity, converging to a minimum value of two ($k = 1$) as f_O approaches infinity. This means that the frequency of every unwanted component is higher, at any f_O/f_I ratio, than the wanted output frequency. The value of every ν_{Ok}, however, decreases as f_O/f_I increases. The normalized frequency of the most significant unwanted component corresponding to $k = 1$ $[\nu_{O1} = 2 + 3(f_I/f_O)]$ is infinity at $f_O/f_I = 0$, five at $f_O/f_I = 1$, and two at $f_O/f_I = \infty$. The

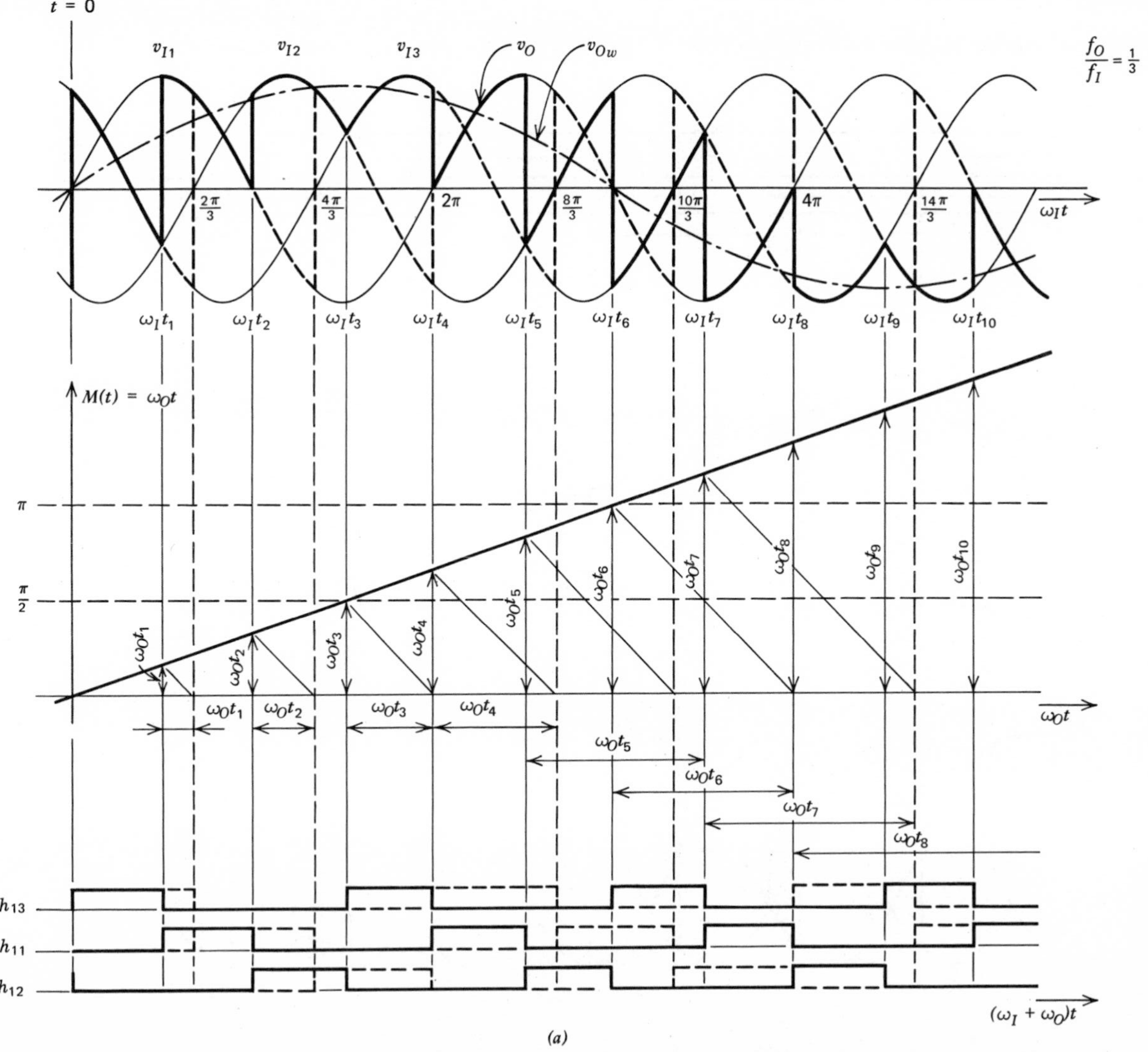

$t = 0$
v_{I1}
v_{I2}
v_{I3}
v_O
v_{Ow}
$\frac{f_O}{f_I} = \frac{1}{3}$
$\frac{2\pi}{3}$
$\frac{4\pi}{3}$
2π
$\frac{8\pi}{3}$
$\frac{10\pi}{3}$
4π
$\frac{14\pi}{3}$
$\omega_I t$
$\omega_I t_1$
$\omega_I t_2$
$\omega_I t_3$
$\omega_I t_4$
$\omega_I t_5$
$\omega_I t_6$
$\omega_I t_7$
$\omega_I t_8$
$\omega_I t_9$
$\omega_I t_{10}$
$M(t) = \omega_O t$
π
$\frac{\pi}{2}$
$\omega_O t_1$
$\omega_O t_2$
$\omega_O t_3$
$\omega_O t_4$
$\omega_O t_5$
$\omega_O t_6$
$\omega_O t_7$
$\omega_O t_8$
$\omega_O t_9$
$\omega_O t_{10}$
$\omega_O t$
h_{13}
h_{11}
h_{12}
$(\omega_I + \omega_O)t$

(a)

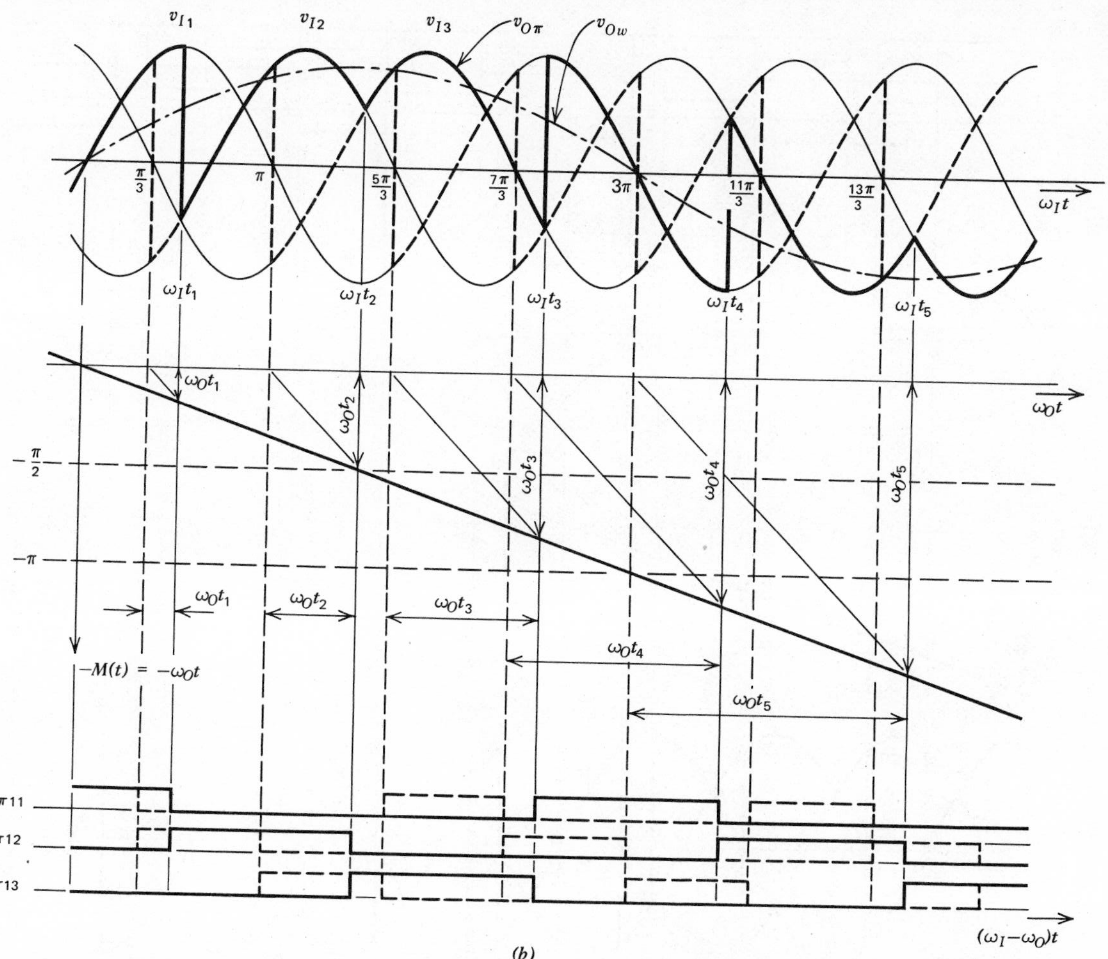

(b)

Figure 3.4 The generation of two complementary output voltage waveforms by linear modulating function $M(t) = \omega_0 t$.

frequency changer controlled to generate waveform v_O given by equation (3.42) thus has an "unrestricted" output frequency range, that is, theoretically any wanted output frequency is obtainable at any given input frequency, for which reason it is termed, as previously indicated, the *unrestricted frequency changer.*

Inspection of equation (3.49), on the other hand, indicates that $v_{O\pi k}$ rapidly decreases with increasing output to input frequency ratio, actually becoming zero at discrete values of f_O/f_I that satisfy the following condition

$$\frac{f_O}{f_I} = \frac{3k}{3k+1}, \qquad \begin{array}{l} k = 1, 2, \ldots \\ f_O \leqq f_I \end{array} \tag{3.52}$$

The frequency of one of the two unwanted components corresponding to $k = 1$, that is, $v_{O\pi 1} = 4 - 3(f_I/f_O)$, becomes zero at $f_O/f_I = 3/4$. This means that at this output to input frequency ratio a d-c component with a relative amplitude of 25% ($\gamma_{O\pi 1} = 0.25$) is generally present in the output. In most applications this amount of d-c content is not tolerable; thus the practical upper limit for the output frequency is generally less than 75% of the input frequency.*

The two complementary output voltage waveforms v_O and $v_{O\pi}$ related to modulating function $M(t) = \omega_O t$ are shown for various output to input frequency ratios in Figure 3.5*a* and *b*, respectively. For clear comparison, the output frequency is kept constant, and the input frequency is varied. These waveforms were synthesized and then plotted from the first 24 components of the series ($k = 1, 2, \ldots, 12$) given by equations (3.42) and (3.43), with the aid of a digital computer.

The brief investigation just carried out already indicates that the output characteristics of the waveform v_O, generated by $M(t) = \omega_O t$, are rather attractive from the practical point of view: the output to input frequency ratio can be chosen freely, because the frequencies of the unwanted components are higher than, and remain well separated from, the output frequency f_O, regardless of the f_O/f_I ratio. In addition, the existence functions retain their original form of rectangular pulse trains with *constant* repetition rate, which allows an extremely simple practical control realization.

3.2.2 Triangular Wave Modulating Function and Corresponding Output Waveforms

The second modulating function resulting in a sinusoidal mean output waveform is given by equation (3.41), namely,

$$M(t) = \sin^{-1}\{\sin(\omega_O t + \psi)\}$$

$$-\frac{\pi}{2} \leqq \sin^{-1}\{\sin(\omega_O t + \psi)\} \leqq \frac{\pi}{2}$$

This is an odd periodic function with respect to point $\omega_O t = \psi$ which may also be defined in the period of 2π by the following expression

$$M(t) = \begin{cases} \omega_O t + \psi & -\dfrac{\pi}{2} - \psi \leqq \omega_O t < \dfrac{\pi}{2} - \psi \\ -(\omega_O t + \psi) + \pi & \dfrac{\pi}{2} - \psi \leqq \omega_O t < \dfrac{3\pi}{2} - \psi \end{cases} \tag{3.53}$$

* These remarks are strictly valid only for a three-pulse converter.

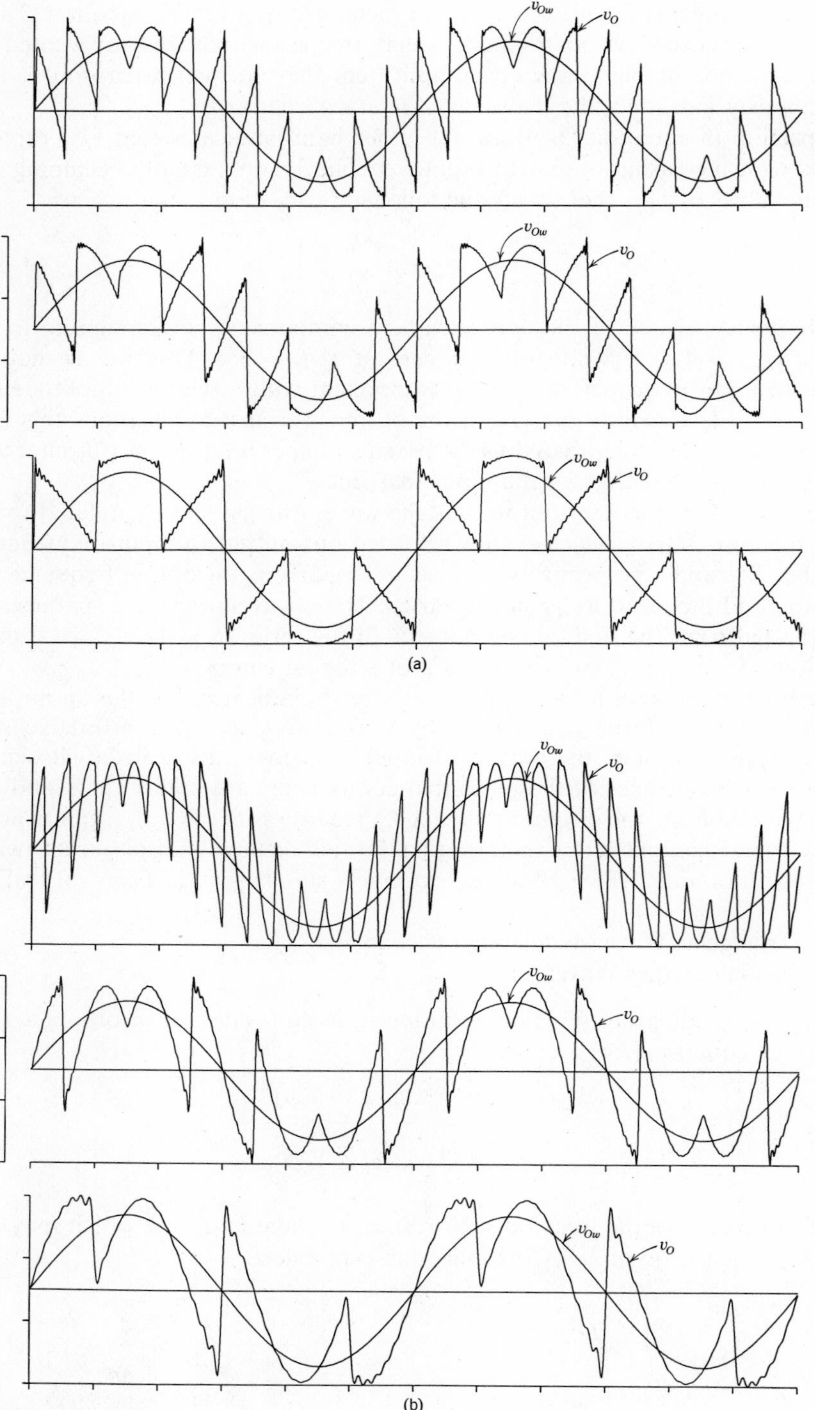

Figure 3.5 Output voltage waveforms with various output to input frequency ratios synthesized from the terms of *a* equation (3.42) ($f_O/f_I = 1/3$, $f_O/f_I = 1/2$, $f_O/f_I = 1$) and *b* equation (3.43) ($f_O/f_I = 1/6$, $f_O/f_I = 1/3$, $f_O/f_I = 1/2$).

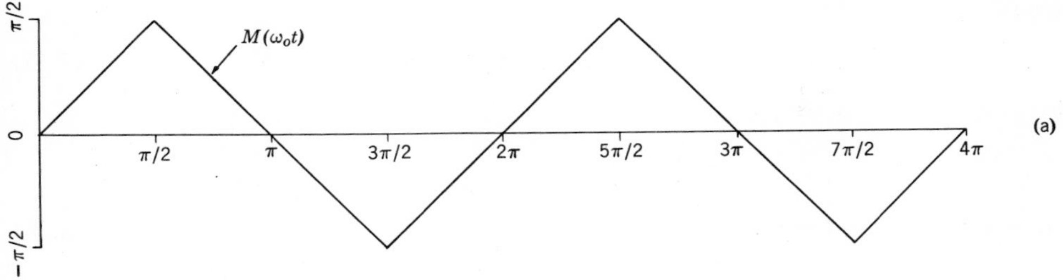

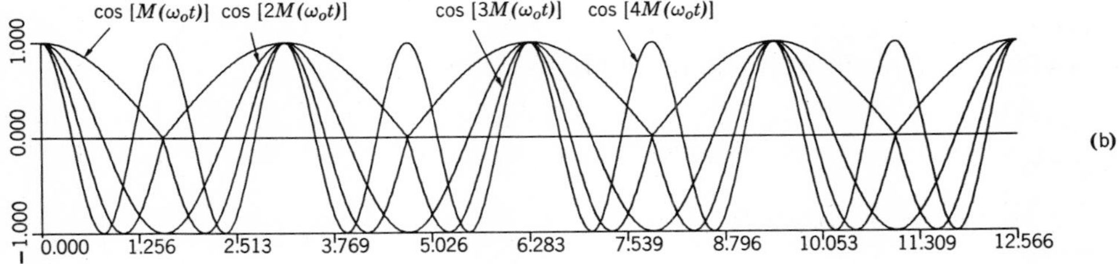

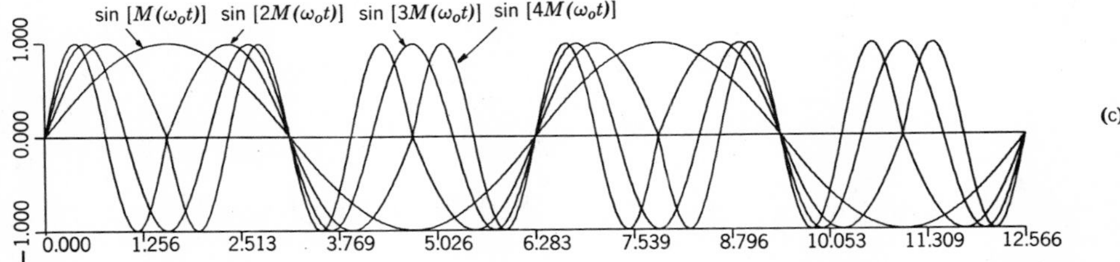

Figure 3.6 Waveforms illustrating the triangular modulating function defined by equation (3.53) and the associated functions given by equations (3.54a) and (3.54b).

Function $M(t)$ is a triangular wave, as illustrated in Figure 3.6*a*. Since it is a periodic function, equations (3.20) and (3.21) may be used in deriving an analytical expression for v_O and $v_{O\pi}$. To find the pertinent coefficients $a_{(3k\pm1),(2n-2)}$, $b_{1,n}$, and $b_{(3k+1),n}$, $k = 1, 2, \ldots$; $n = 1, 2, \ldots$ defined by equations (3.16)–(3.19), the properties of functions $\cos\{(3k \pm 1)M(t)\}$, $\sin M(t)$, and $\sin\{(3k \pm 1)M(t)\}$ have to be established. These functions have the following general form

$$\cos nM(t) = \cos n\{\sin^{-1}[\sin(\omega_O t + \psi)]\} \tag{3.54a}$$

and

$$\sin nM(t) = \sin n\{\sin^{-1}[\sin(\omega_O t + \psi)]\} \tag{3.54b}$$

where $n = 1, 2, 3, \ldots$. Their graphs are shown for various ns at $\psi = 0$ in Figure 3.6*b* and *c*, respectively. Inspection of these graphs indicates that the functions have the following general properties

$$\cos n\{\sin^{-1}[\sin(\omega_O t + \psi)]\} = \cos n(\omega_O t + \psi) \tag{3.55}$$

for $n = 2m$, $m = 1, 2, 3, \ldots$

$$\cos n\{\sin^{-1}[\sin(\omega_O t + \psi)]\} = \begin{cases} \cos n(\omega_O t + \psi) & -\dfrac{\pi}{2} - \psi \leqq \omega_O t < \dfrac{\pi}{2} - \psi \\ -\cos n(\omega_O t + \psi) & \dfrac{\pi}{2} - \psi \leqq \omega_O t < \dfrac{3\pi}{2} - \psi \end{cases} \tag{3.56}$$

for $n = 2m - 1, m = 1, 2, 3, \ldots$

$$\sin n\{\sin^{-1}[\sin(\omega_O t + \psi)]\} = \sin n(\omega_O t + \psi) \tag{3.57}$$

for $n = 2m - 1, m = 1, 2, \ldots$

$$\sin n\{\sin^{-1}[\sin(\omega_O t + \psi)]\} = \begin{cases} \sin n(\omega_O t + \psi) & -\dfrac{\pi}{2} - \psi \leqq \omega_O t < \dfrac{\pi}{2} - \psi \\ -\sin n(\omega_O t + \psi) & \dfrac{\pi}{2} - \psi \leqq \omega_O t < \dfrac{3\pi}{2} - \psi \end{cases} \tag{3.58}$$

for $n = 2m, m = 1, 2, 3, \ldots$

Therefore it follows from equations (3.13)–(3.19) that

$$b_{1,n} = \begin{cases} 1 & n = 1 \\ 0 & n \neq 0 \end{cases} \tag{3.59}$$

$$\left.\begin{aligned} a_{[3(2k-1)\pm 1],0} &= 0 \\ a_{(6k\pm 1),0} &= \frac{1}{\pi}\int_{\psi}^{\psi+\pi} \cos\{(6k \pm 1)\sin^{-1}[\sin(\omega_O t + \psi)]\} \end{aligned}\right\} \tag{3.60}$$

$$\left.\begin{aligned} a_{[3(2k-1)\pm 1],2n} &= \begin{cases} 1 & 2n = 3(2k-1) \pm 1 \\ 0 & 2n \neq 3(2k-1) \pm 1 \end{cases} \\ a_{(6k\pm 1),2n} &= \frac{2}{\pi}\int_{\psi}^{\psi+\pi} \cos\{(6k \pm 1)\sin^{-1}[\sin(\omega_O t + \psi)]\} \end{aligned}\right\} \tag{3.61}$$

$$\left.\begin{aligned} b_{[3(2k-1)\pm 1],2n} &= 0 \\ b_{[3(2k-1)\pm 1],(2n-1)} &= \frac{2}{\pi}\int_{\psi}^{\psi+\pi} \sin\{[3(2k-1) \pm 1]\sin^{-1}[\sin(\omega_O t + \psi)]\} \\ b_{(6k\pm 1),n} &= \begin{cases} 1 & n = 6k \pm 1 \\ 0 & n \neq 6k \pm 1 \end{cases} \end{aligned}\right\} \tag{3.62}$$

The substitution of the above coefficients in equations (3.20) and (3.21) results in the following expressions for v_O and $v_{O\pi}$:

$$\begin{aligned}
\text{(a)}\ \Bigg[\ v_O = {} & \frac{3\sqrt{3}}{2\pi} V_I \Bigg\{ \sin(\omega_O t + \psi) \\
& + \sum_{k=1}^{\infty} \Bigg(\frac{\sin\{[3k\omega_I + (3k \pm 1)\omega_O]t + (3k \pm 1)\psi\}}{2(3k \pm 1)} \\
& - (-1)^{3k} \frac{\sin\{[3k\omega_I - (3k \pm 1)\omega_O]t - (3k \pm 1)\psi\}}{2(3k \pm 1)} \Bigg) \Bigg\} \\
\text{(b)}\ \Bigg[\ & + \frac{3\sqrt{3}}{2\pi} V_I \sum_{k=1}^{\infty} \sum_{n=0}^{\infty} \Big(A_{6k,2n} \sin\{[6k\omega_I \pm 2n\omega_O]t \pm 2n\psi\} \\
& + B_{[3(2k-1)],(2n+1)}(\pm\sin\{[3(2k-1)\omega_I \pm (2n+1)\omega_O]t \pm (2n+1)\psi\}) \Big)
\end{aligned} \tag{3.63}$$

and

$$
\begin{aligned}
&\text{(a)}\quad v_{O\pi} = \frac{3\sqrt{3}}{2\pi} V_I \Bigg\{ \sin(\omega_O t + \psi) \\
&\qquad + \sum_{k=1}^{\infty} \left(\frac{\sin\{[3k\omega_I + (3k \pm 1)\omega_O]t + (3k \pm 1)\psi\}}{2(3k \pm 1)} \right. \\
&\qquad \left. - (-1)^{3k} \frac{\sin\{[3k\omega_I - (3k \pm 1)\omega_O]t - (3k \pm 1)\psi\}}{2(3k \pm 1)} \right) \Bigg\} \\
&\text{(b)}\quad - \frac{3\sqrt{3}}{2\pi} V_I \sum_{k=1}^{\infty} \sum_{n=0}^{\infty} \Big(A_{6k,2n} \sin\{[6k\omega_I \pm 2n\omega_O]t \pm 2n\psi\} \\
&\qquad + B_{[3(2k-1)],(2n+1)} (\pm \sin\{[3(2k-1)\omega_I \pm (2n+1)\omega_O]t \pm (2n+1)\psi\}) \Big)
\end{aligned}
\tag{3.64}
$$

where

$$
\left.
\begin{aligned}
A_{6k,2n} &= \frac{1}{2}\left(\frac{a_{(6k+1),2n}}{6k+1} + \frac{a_{(6k-1),2n}}{6k-1} \right) \\
B_{[3(2k-1)],(2n+1)} &= \frac{1}{2}\left(\frac{b_{[3(2k-1)+1],(2n+1)}}{3(2k-1)+1} + \frac{b_{[3(2k-1)-1],(2n+1)}}{3(2k-1)-1} \right)
\end{aligned}
\right\}
\tag{3.65}
$$

Numerical values of $a_{(6k\pm1),2n}$ and $b_{[3(2k-1)\pm1],(2n+1)}$ are given for $k = 1, 2$ and $n = 0, 1, 2, \ldots 8$ in Tables A.3 and A.4 in the Appendix. (Read values in the row of $r = 1.0$.) The numerical values of the amplitudes $A_{6k,2n}$ and $B_{[3(2k-1)],(2n+1)}$ are given for the dominant terms in Tables 3.1 and 3.2.

Comparison of equation (3.63) with (3.64) shows the previously indicated characteristic of this class of complementary waveforms, namely that the corresponding components of v_O and $v_{O\pi}$ have the same amplitude and frequency, and they are either in phase [part (a)] or in anti phase [part (b)] with each other.

The output voltage waveforms expressed by equations (3.63) and (3.64) have been obtained by a periodic modulating function oscillating linearly between $\pi/2$ and $-\pi/2$. The corresponding variation of the repetition rates of the existence functions can be

TABLE 3.1. Normalized Amplitudes of the Dominant Components in Equation (3.64) with Frequencies of $6kf_I \pm 2nf_O$ $(k = 1, 2; n = 0, 1, \ldots 6)$

$2n$	0	2	4	6	8	10	12
$A_{6,2n}$	0.0124	−0.0162	0.0516	0.1069	0.0261	−0.0414	0.0013
$A_{12,2n}$	−0.0016	0.0016	−0.0019	0.0025	−0.0051	0.0210	0.0528

TABLE 3.2. Normalized Amplitudes of the Dominant Components in Equation (3.64) with Frequencies of $3(2k-1)f_I \pm (2n+1)f_O$ $(k = 1, 2; n = 0, 1, \ldots 6)$

$2n + 1$	1	3	5	7	9	11	13
$B_{3,(2n+1)}$	0.1701	0.2184	0.0404	−0.0051	0.0016	−0.0006	0.0003
$B_{9,(2n+1)}$	−0.0038	0.0045	−0.0080	0.0299	0.0710	0.0191	−0.0032

determined by differentiating $M(t)$ [equation (3.53)] with respect to time. Thus

$$\frac{dM(t)}{dt} = \Omega(t) = \begin{cases} \omega_O & -\frac{\pi}{2} - \psi \leqq \omega_O t < \frac{\pi}{2} - \psi \\ -\omega_O & \frac{\pi}{2} - \psi \leqq \omega_O t < \frac{3\pi}{2} - \psi \end{cases} \tag{3.66}$$

which indicates that the output waveform v_O ($v_{O\pi}$) was produced by the act of periodically stepping up (down) and down (up) the quiescent f_I repetition frequency of the existence functions to $f_I + f_O$ ($f_I - f_O$) and $f_I - f_O$ ($f_I + f_O$), respectively. Pertinent waveforms illustrating the generation of the two complementary waveforms are shown in Figure 3.7*a* and *b*. Note that the output voltage waveshape is, in fact, composed of consecutive half-period sections of the output waveforms shown in Figure 3.4*a* and *b*, in agreement with the findings of the initial general investigation in Section 3.1 (see Figure 3.3).

It is evident from the expressions obtained for v_O and $v_{O\pi}$ [equations (3.63) and (3.64)] that the output voltage wave indices of the two waveforms are identical. Inspection of the terms constituting parts (a) and (b) of these expressions indicates that their frequency and amplitude characteristics are quite different. For this reason, the relevant performance indices, ν_O and μ_O, are expressed separately for each group. Thus, for part (a)

$$\nu_{Ok} = \begin{cases} (3k \pm 1) + 3k\dfrac{f_I}{f_O} & \text{(3.67a)} \\[2ex] \left|(3k \pm 1) - 3k\dfrac{f_I}{f_O}\right| & \text{(3.67b)} \end{cases}$$

$$\gamma_{Ok} = \frac{1}{2}\frac{1}{3k \pm 1} \tag{3.68}$$

and for part (b)

$$\nu_{Ok,n} = \begin{cases} \left|(2n + 1) \pm 3(2k - 1)\dfrac{f_I}{f_O}\right| & \text{(3.69a)} \\[2ex] \left|2n \pm 6k\dfrac{f_I}{f_O}\right| & \text{(3.69b)} \end{cases}$$

$$\gamma_{Ok,n} = \begin{cases} A_{6k,2n} & \text{(3.70a)} \\ B_{[3(2k-1)],(2n+1)} & \text{(3.70b)} \end{cases}$$

$k = 1, 2, \ldots, n = 0, 1, 2, \ldots$.

The total r.m.s. distortion of waveform v_O or $v_{O\pi}$ is

$$\mu_O = \left\{\sum_{k=1}^{\infty}\sum_{n=0}^{\infty}\left(\frac{1}{4}\frac{1}{(3k \pm 1)^2} + A^2_{6k,2n} + B^2_{[3(2k-1)],(2n+1)}\right)\right\}^{\frac{1}{2}} \cong 0.676 \tag{3.71}$$

The following conclusions may be made after examing equations (3.67)–(3.71):

1. The expression for the normalized frequencies, ν_{Ok}, consists of two equations, one of which (3.67a) is identical to that given by (3.46), and the other (3.67b) to that given by (3.49). Thus the observations made there are also valid here. This leads to the conclusion that the significant values of ν_{Ok}, which limit the range of the output

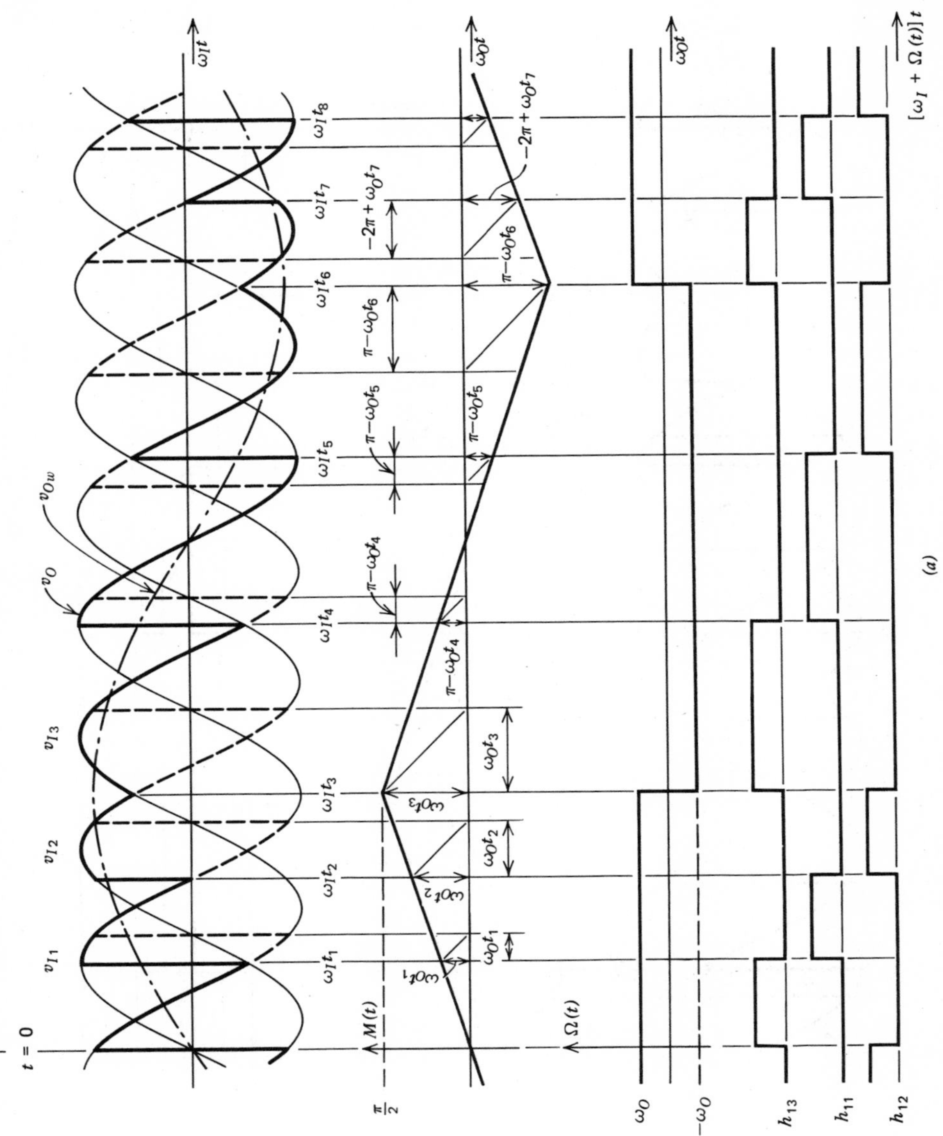

t = 0
v_{I1}
v_{I2}
v_{I3}
v_O
v_{Ow}
ω_I t
ω_I t_1
ω_I t_2
ω_I t_3
ω_I t_4
ω_I t_5
ω_I t_6
ω_I t_7
ω_I t_8
π/2
M(t)
ω_O t_1
ω_O t_2
ω_O t_3
π − ω_O t_4
π − ω_O t_5
π − ω_O t_6
−2π + ω_O t_7
ω_O t
Ω(t)
ω_O
−ω_O
h_13
h_11
h_12
[ω_I + Ω(t)]t

(a)

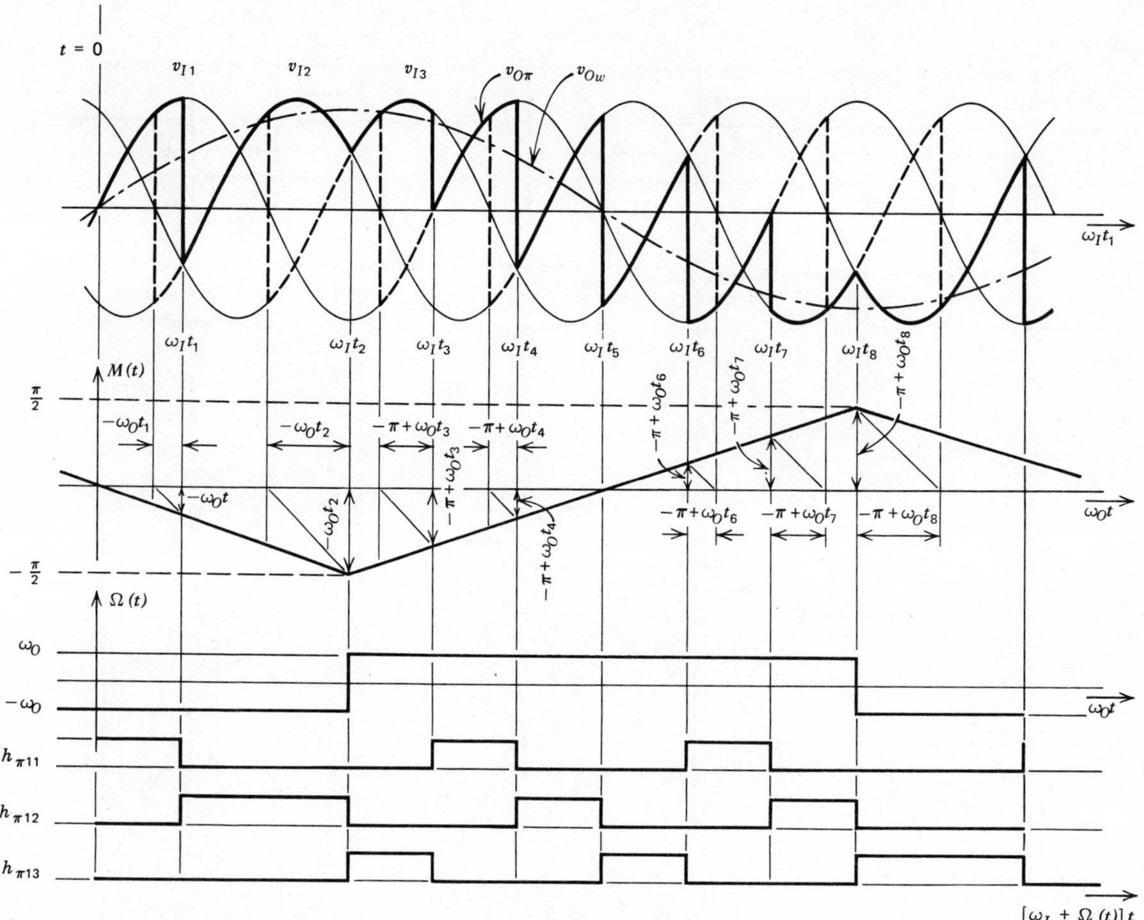

Figure 3.7 Generation of the *a* positive-type and *b* negative-type complementary output voltage waveforms by the triangular modulating function.

frequency, are obtainable from equation (3.67b), and (3.67a) may be completely ignored.

Similarly, from the four expressions given for $v_{Ok,n}$ [contained within (3.69a) and (3.69b)], only the two with negative signs (i.e., $|(2n + 1) - 3(2k - 1)(f_I/f_O)|$ and $|2n - 6k(f_I/f_O)|$ are significant. From equations (3.69a) and (3.69b) it follows that $v_{Ok,n}$ becomes zero whenever the following conditions are satisfied

$$\frac{f_O}{f_I} = \frac{3(2k - 1)}{2n + 1} \tag{3.72a}$$

and

$$\frac{f_O}{f_I} = 3\frac{k}{n} \tag{3.72b}$$

where $k = 1, 2, \ldots; n = 0, 1, 2, \ldots$. Since k and n are independent of each other, it further follows that the output voltage wave will, in general, contain a d-c component at discrete f_O/f_I ratios over the *whole* output frequency range.

2. Since the output voltage waveform generally contains components with lower than the wanted output frequency, the determination of the significant values of $\gamma_{Ok,n}$ (i.e., the normalized amplitudes of the unwanted components) becomes important. The allowed amplitudes of the low-frequency components will set a limit to the maximum obtainable output to input frequency ratio. This limit for the *three-pulse* converter considered is typically not higher than $\frac{1}{3}$.

3. The numerical value of the total r.m.s. distortion is the same as that previously obtained for the other two sinusoidal mean output waveforms [see equations (3.48) and (3.51)].

The output voltage waveforms characterized above are shown at $\psi = 0$ for various output to input frequency ratios in Figures 3.8*a* and *b*. These waveforms were synthesized and then mechanically plotted from the series given by equations (3.63) and (3.64).

3.2.3 Composite Output Waveforms

As was previously indicated, practically important waveforms can be synthesized from a pair of complementary waveforms or selected portions thereof. Two general techniques of synthesis have been described: one in which the output waveform is pieced together from consecutive half-cycle sections of the two complementary waves, and one in which the output waveform is produced concurrently as the arithmetic mean (or sum) of the two complementary waveforms. General analytical expressions for these *composite* output waveforms $v_O(\rho)$ and v_{OM} are derived [equations (3.36) and (3.38)] in Section 3.1.

In each of the previous two sections a pair of complementary waves is analyzed [equations (3.42), (3.43), and (3.63), (3.64)]. Although generated by different modulating functions (linear and triangular), these complementary waves have been shown to be closely related; in fact, the first pair of complementary waves can be constructed from half-period sections of the second pair of waveforms, and vice versa (see Figures 3.4 and 3.7). It follows therefore that identical composite waveforms could be synthesized from either of the two pairs of complementary waves. Although the mathematical expressions for the complementary positive-type and negative-type waves generated by the periodic (triangular) modulating function are relatively complex, we

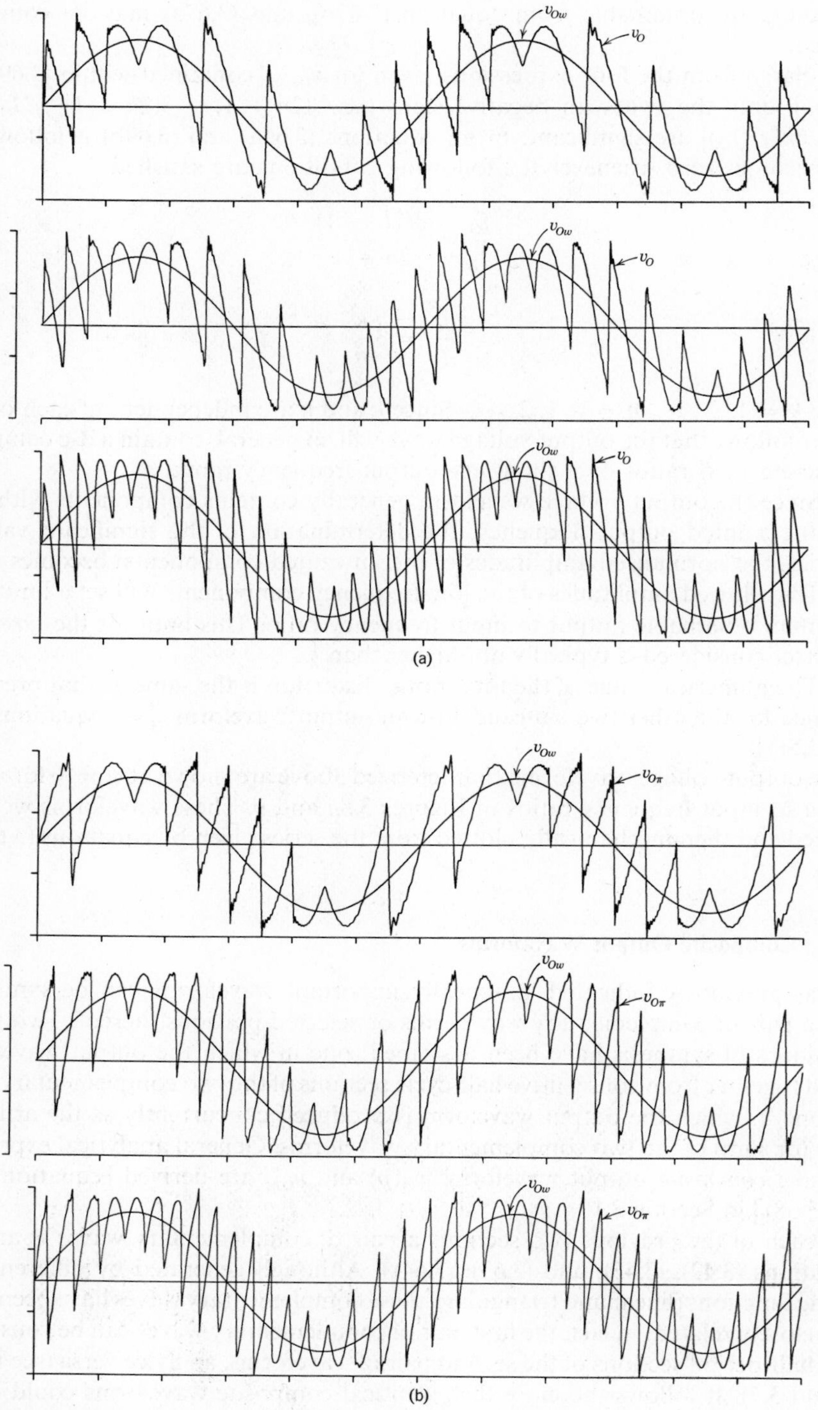

Figure 3.8 *a* Positive-type waveforms and *b* negative-type waveforms with various output to input frequency ratios ($f_O/f_I = 1/3$, $f_O/f_I = 1/4.5$, $f_O/f_I = 1/6$) synthesized from the terms of the series given by equations (3.63) and (3.64), respectively.

shall still, for convenience, use these in the synthesis of composite waveforms. The reason for this is that we have already developed "ready for use" mathematical formulae with these expressions, and, more significantly, these expressions can be generalized later for the practically important case in which the amplitude of the wanted component is variable.

3.2.3.1 *Consecutive Composite Waveforms.* Let us consider first the case in which the composite output voltage waveform is constructed from consecutive half-cycle sections of the complementary waves.

Refer to Figure 3.9. Graphs a and b show the two complementary positive-type and negative-type waveforms v_O and $v_{O\pi}$ related to the periodic modulating function $M(t) = \sin^{-1}(\sin \omega_O t)$. These waveforms are described analytically by equations

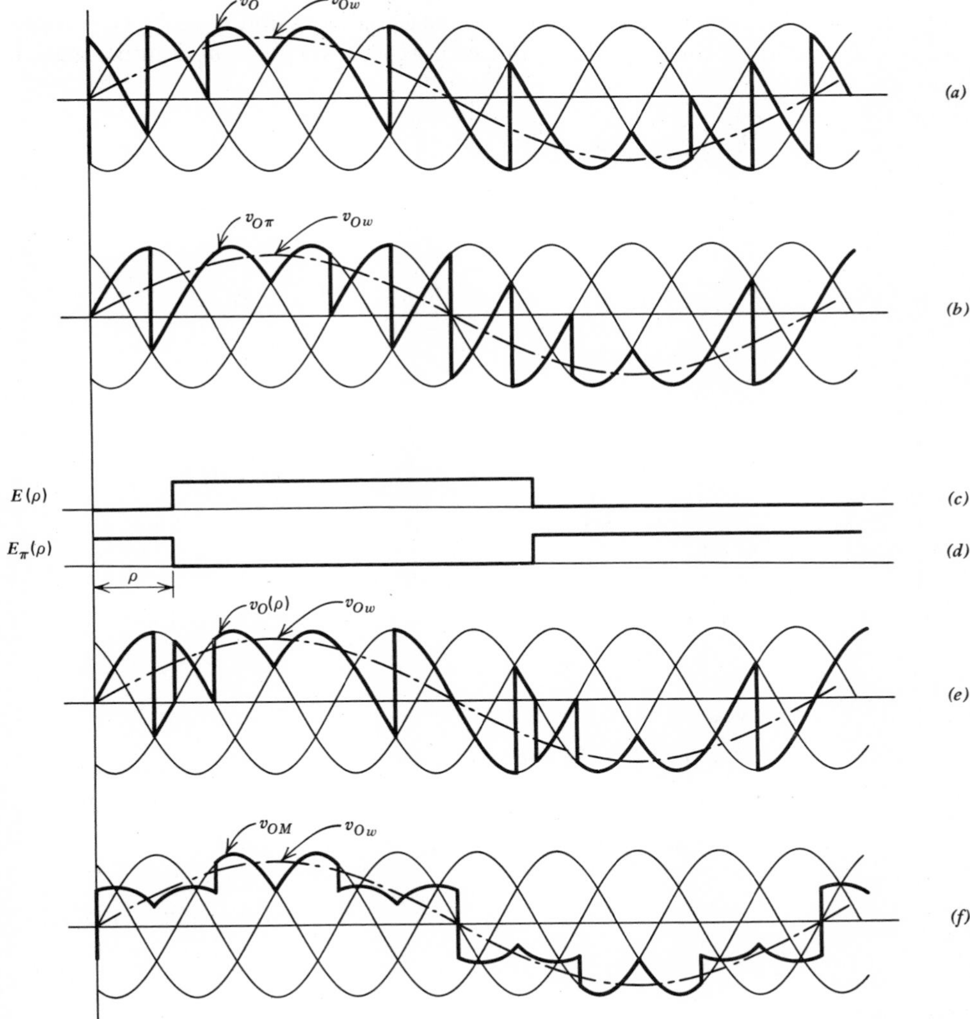

Figure 3.9 Synthesis of output voltage waveforms $v_O(\rho)$ and v_{OM} from the positive-type and negative-type sinusoidal mean complementary waves.

(3.63) and (3.64). A general mathematical definition of an output waveform constructed from consecutive half-period sections of v_O and $v_{O\pi}$ is given by equation (3.30), namely

$$v_O(\rho) = E(\rho)v_O + E_\pi(\rho)v_{O\pi}$$

where $E(\rho)$ and $E_\pi(\rho)$ are existence functions, given by equations (3.28) and (3.29), specifying the half-period intervals of v_O and $v_{O\pi}$ used in the output waveform construction. The graphs of existence functions $E(\rho)$ and $E_\pi(\rho)$ relevant to the present case are shown at *c* and *d* in Figure 3.9. The resultant output waveshape $v_O(\rho)$ appropriate to angle ρ is shown at *e*.

For the case of a periodic modulating function, the composite waveform $v_O(\rho)$ is mathematically described by equation (3.36) in terms of the general Fourier coefficients, $a_{(3k\pm1),2n}$ and $b_{(6k\pm1),n}$, of the complementary waveforms. Thus an analytical expression for the presently considered waveform $v_O(\rho)$ can readily be obtained by substituting the specific coefficients, $a_{(3k\pm1),2n}$ and $b_{(6k\pm1),n}$ [equations (3.59)–(3.62)] derived for modulating function $M(t) = \sin^{-1}(\sin \omega_O t)$ into equation (3.36)

$$\text{(a)}\quad \left[\begin{aligned} v_O(\rho) = \frac{3\sqrt{3}}{2\pi} V_I \Bigg\{ & \sin(\omega_O t + \psi) \\ & + \sum_{k=1}^{\infty} \Bigg(\frac{\sin\{[3k\omega_I + (3k \pm 1)\omega_O]t + (3k + 1)\psi\}}{2(3k \pm 1)} \\ & - (-1)^{3k} \frac{\sin\{[3k\omega_I - (3k \pm 1)\omega_O]t - (3k \pm 1)\psi\}}{2(3k \pm 1)} \Bigg) \Bigg\} \end{aligned}\right.$$

$$\text{(b)}\quad \left[\begin{aligned} & - \frac{3\sqrt{3}}{\pi^2} V_I \sum_{k=1}^{\infty} \sum_{m=1}^{\infty} \frac{1}{2m - 1} \\ & \times \Bigg\{ 2A_{6k,0}(\pm\cos\{[6k\omega_I \pm (2m - 1)\omega_O]t \pm (2m - 1)\rho\}) \\ & + \sum_{n=1}^{\infty} \Bigg(A_{6k,2n} \\ & \qquad \times (\pm\cos\{[6k\omega_I \pm \{2(n + m) - 1\}\omega_O]t \pm (2m - 1)\rho \pm 2n\psi\} \\ & \qquad \mp \cos\{[6k\omega_I \pm \{2(n - m) + 1\}\omega_O]t \mp (2m - 1)\rho \pm 2n\psi\}) \\ & + B_{[3(2k-1)],(2n-1)} \\ & \qquad \times (\cos\{[3(2k - 1)\omega_I \pm 2\{(n + m) - 1\}\omega_O]t \\ & \qquad\qquad \pm (2m - 1)\rho \pm (2n - 1)\psi\} \\ & \qquad - \cos\{[3(2k - 1)\omega_I \pm 2(n - m)\omega_O]t \\ & \qquad\qquad \mp (2m - 1)\rho \pm (2n - 1)\psi\}) \Bigg) \Bigg\} \end{aligned}\right.$$

(3.73)

where $A_{6k,0}$, $A_{6k,2n}$, and $B_{[3(2k-1)],(2n-1)}$, $k = 1, 2, \ldots, n = 1, 2, \ldots$ are defined by equations (3.65), and their numerical values for the most significant *k*s and *n*s are

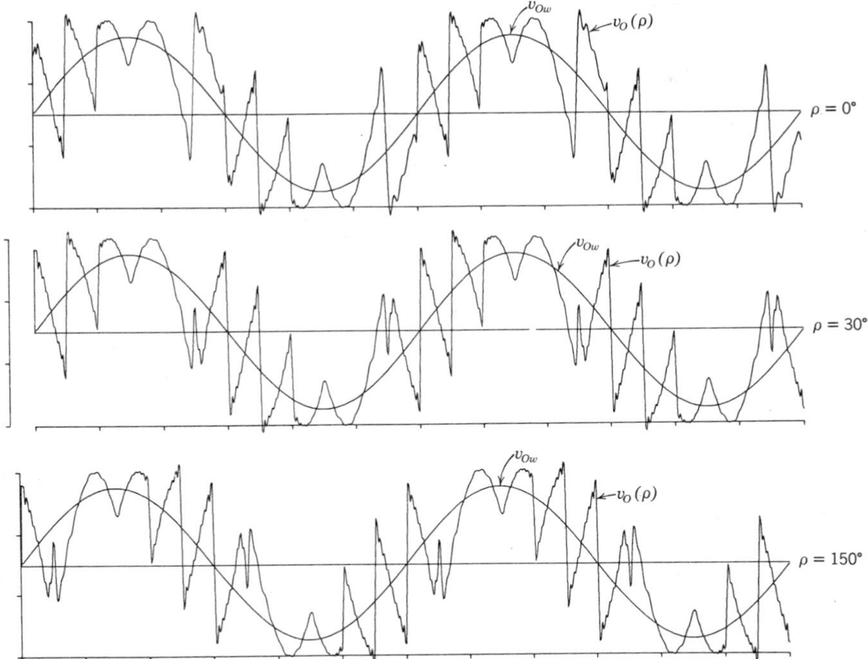

Figure 3.10 Consecutive composite output voltage waveforms synthesized from the terms of equation (3.73) at $\rho = 0$, $30°$, and $150°$, respectively; $f_O/f_I = 1/3$.

tabulated in Tables 3.1 and 3.2. Typical output waveforms synthesized from the terms of equation (3.73) at $\rho = 0$, $30°$, $150°$ are shown in Figure 3.10.

It is noteworthy that part (a) of equation (3.73) is, in agreement with the previous results, the same as that of the component complementary waveforms given by equations (3.63) and (3.64). Part (b) of equation (3.73) is rather complex, and its evaluation is tedious. The problem is that the various terms of indices n and m may repeatedly have the same frequency but different phase angles at appropriate values of integers n and m, and therefore those terms have to be summed to obtain the amplitude of the resultant component. In fact, this process generally requires the summation of an infinite number of terms. Consider, for example, expression $\pm 2(n - m)\omega_O t$ which at $n = m + 1$ gives the fixed value of $\pm 2\omega_O t$ for each m; $m = 1, 2, \ldots, \infty$. Fortunately, the coefficients $a_{(6k\pm1),2n}/(2m - 1)$ and $b_{[3(2k-1)\pm1],(2n-1)}/(2m - 1)$, determining the amplitudes of the constituent terms of the same frequency, decrease rapidly with increasing m and also with increasing n above $2n = 6k$ and $2n - 1 = 3(2k - 1)$ (see Tables in the Appendix), making it possible to compute accurately the resultant amplitudes without undue difficulties.

Inspection of equation (3.73) further indicates that the constituent terms of part (a) have frequencies of $3k\omega_I - (3k \pm 1)\omega_O$ and $3k\omega_I - (3k \pm 1)\omega_O$, and those of part (b) have frequencies of $3(2k - 1)\omega_I \pm 2\ell\omega_O$ and $6k\omega_I \pm (2\ell + 1)\omega_O$, $\ell = 0, 1, 2, \ldots$. Thus whenever $2\ell = 3k \pm 1$ or $2\ell + 1 = 3k \pm 1$, the frequencies of certain terms in part (b) become equal to those of the corresponding terms in part (a), and therefore these terms have to be combined to obtain the amplitudes of the "total" components at these frequencies. Consequently, equation (3.73) can be written in the following simple general form:

$$v_O(\rho) = \frac{3\sqrt{3}}{2\pi} V_I \Bigg(\sin(\omega_O t + \psi) + \sum_{k=1}^{\infty} \sum_{\ell=0}^{\infty} (A_{[3(2k-1)],(\pm 2\ell)}(\rho) \sin\{[3(2k-1)\omega_I \pm 2\ell\omega_O]t - \psi_{[3(2k-1)],(\pm 2\ell)}(\rho)\} + A_{6k,[\pm(2\ell+1)]}(\rho) \sin\{[6k\omega_I \pm (2\ell+1)\omega_O]t - \psi_{6k,[\pm(2\ell+1)]}(\rho)\}) \Bigg) \tag{3.74}$$

where the amplitudes $A(\rho)$ and phase angles $\psi(\rho)$ are functions of angle ρ. The effect of ρ on the amplitudes of the dominant components is shown in Table 3.3, in which the numerical values of $A(\rho)$ are given, for $k = 1$ and for various ℓs, for $\rho = 0$, $\pm\pi/6$, $\pm\pi/3$, and $\pm\pi/2$.

The results in Table 3.3 support the previous statement that the composite waveform $v_O(\rho)$ can be made identical to either one of the two complementary waves obtained through the use of the linear modulating function $M(t) = \omega_O t$ by appropriately setting angle ρ. That is to say, at $\rho = \pi/2$ and $\rho = -\pi/2$, the frequencies and amplitudes shown in Table 3.3 are identical to those of the dominant terms in equations (3.42) and (3.43), which describe analytically the two waveforms generated by $M(t) = \omega_O t$.

Table 3.3 also provides considerable insight into the variation of the spectral characteristic of the waveform $v_O(\rho)$ as angle ρ is varied over the range of $\pi/2$ to $-\pi/2$. Refer to Figure 3.9 and Table 3.3. At $\rho = \pi/2$, the composite waveform is

TABLE 3.3. Normalized Amplitudes of the Dominant Components in Equation (3.74) Given as a Function of Angle ρ.

	ρ	$-\frac{\pi}{2}$	$-\frac{\pi}{3}$	$-\frac{\pi}{6}$	0	$+\frac{\pi}{6}$	$+\frac{\pi}{3}$	$+\frac{\pi}{2}$
$3f_I \pm 2\ell f_O$	$A_{3,0}$	0.000	0.020	0.179	0.318	0.179	0.020	0.000
	$A_{3,+2}$	0.000	0.020	0.167	0.272	0.333	0.486	0.500
	$A_{3,-2}$	0.500	0.486	0.333		0.167	0.020	0.000
	$A_{3,+4}$	0.000	0.019	0.134	0.164	0.274	0.269	0.250
	$A_{3,-4}$	0.250	0.269	0.274		0.134	0.019	0.000
	$A_{3,+6}$, $A_{3,-6}$	0.000	0.017	0.095	0.064	0.095	0.017	0.000
$6f_I \pm (2\ell+1)f_O$	$A_{6,+1}$, $A_{6,-1}$	0.000	0.023	0.018	0.006	0.018	0.023	0.000
	$A_{6,+3}$, $A_{6,-3}$	0.000	0.022	0.045	0.055	0.045	0.022	0.000
	$A_{6,+5}$	0.000	0.021	0.058	0.105	0.150	0.181	0.200
	$A_{6,-5}$	0.200	0.181	0.150		0.058	0.021	0.000
	$A_{6,+7}$	0.000	0.019	0.055	0.100	0.136	0.151	0.143
	$A_{6,-7}$	0.143	0.151	0.136		0.055	0.019	0.000
	$A_{6,+9}$, $A_{6,-9}$	0.000	0.016	0.042	0.055	0.042	0.016	0.000

pieced together from the fast-switching half-cycle sections of the two complementary waves. This results in a simple spectral structure: only those components with frequencies consisting of sums of multiples of f_I and f_O (hereafter called *sum* frequencies), conforming to the expression $3kf_I + (3k \pm 1)f_O$ ($k = 1, 2, \ldots$), are present; their amplitudes are maxima. As ρ moves from $\pi/2$ towards zero, the composite waveform contains increasing intervals of the slow-switching portions of the complementary waves. As a consequence the spectral structure becomes complex. The sum frequency components expand: all components now with frequencies conforming to the expressions $3(2k - 1)f_I + 2\ell f_O$ and $6kf_I + (2\ell + 1)f_O$ ($k = 1, 2, \ldots$; $\ell = 0, 1, 2$) are present. In addition, *difference* frequency components (i.e., components with frequencies consisting of differences of multiples of f_I and f_O), conforming to the expressions $3(2k - 1)f_I - 2\ell f_O$ and $6kf_I - (2\ell + 1)f_O$, appear. The amplitudes of the dominant components having sum frequencies of $3kf_I + (3k - 1)f_O$ rapidly decrease, whereas those of the dominant components with difference frequencies of $3kf_I - (3k \pm 1)f_O$ rapidly increase. At $\rho = 0$, the duration of the fast and slow switching periods in the composite waveform are equal; in consequence, the amplitudes of the corresponding sum and difference components also become equal. As ρ moves towards $-\pi/2$, the durations of the slow-switching periods in the composite waveform increase, and the difference components become increasingly dominant. At $\rho = -\pi/2$, the composite waveform is pieced together entirely from the slow-switching half-cycle sections of the complementary waves. The spectral structure again becomes simple: only components with difference frequencies, conforming to the simple expression $3kf_I - (3k \pm 1)f_O$, are present; their amplitudes, however, are maxima.

It will be recalled from Chapter 1 that the basic motivation behind the concept of piecing selected portions of the complementary waves together to construct the output waveform is either to ensure natural commutation of the switches in the power circuit (naturally commutated cycloconverter) or to provide means for controlling the displacement angle of the input current (controllable displacement factor frequency changer). It may be appropriate to mention here that the previously established conditions for natural commutation are satisfied if angle ρ is made equal to the output phase angle ϕ_O, that is, if the half-cycle sections of v_O and $v_{O\pi}$ used in the synthesis of the composite output waveform are made to coincide with the positive and the negative half-cycles of the a-c output current, respectively. Whatever the motivation, however, the above analysis shows that the price that has to be paid for achieving the objectives sought is the spectral mutation of the output waveform.

The formal output voltage wave indices, characterizing output waveform $v_O(\rho)$, can be written readily from equation (3.74).

The normalized frequencies of the unwanted components are given by

$$v_{Ok,\ell} = \begin{cases} \left|2\ell \pm 3(2k - 1)\dfrac{f_I}{f_O}\right| & \text{(3.75a)} \\[2ex] \left|(2\ell + 1) \pm 6k\dfrac{f_I}{f_O}\right| & \text{(3.75b)} \end{cases}$$

The normalized amplitudes of the unwanted components are given by

$$\gamma_{Ok,\ell}(\rho) = \begin{cases} A_{[3(2k-1)],(\pm 2\ell)}(\rho) & \text{(3.76a)} \\ A_{6k,[\pm(2\ell \pm 1)]}(\rho) & \text{(3.76b)} \end{cases}$$

The total r.m.s. distortion is given by

$$\mu_O = \left(\sum_{k=1}^{\infty} \sum_{\ell=0}^{\infty} (A^2_{[3(2k-1)],(\pm 2\ell)} + A^2_{6k,[+(2\ell \pm 1)]}) \right)^{\frac{1}{2}} \cong 0.676 \tag{3.77}$$

In conclusion, the major characteristics of output voltage waveform $v_O(\rho)$ may be summarized as follows:

1. The output frequency spectrum is, in general, except at $\rho = \pm\pi/2$, independent of angle ρ. The most significant normalized frequencies of the spectrum to be considered in practical applications are again the difference frequencies given by equations (3.75a) and (3.75b), with the negative sign. These expressions provide zero values for $v_{Ok,\ell}$ whenever the following conditions are satisfied:

$$\frac{f_O}{f_I} = \frac{3(2k-1)}{2\ell} \tag{3.78a}$$

and

$$\frac{f_O}{f_I} = \frac{6k}{2\ell + 1} \tag{3.78b}$$

$k = 1, 2, \ldots$; $\ell = 0, 1, 2, \ldots$. Thus the output voltage waveform $v_O(\rho)$ generally contains a d-c component at discrete f_O/f_I ratios over the whole output frequency range.

2. The normalized amplitudes of the unwanted components are dependent upon angle ρ. The amplitudes of the components with frequencies of $3kf_I - (3k \pm 1)f_O$ increase (decrease) and those with frequencies of $3kf_I + (3k \pm 1)f_O$ decrease (increase) as angle ρ varies from zero to $-\pi/2$ ($+\pi/2$). The amplitudes of the terms with frequencies of $3(2k-1)f_I \pm 2\ell f_O$ ($2\ell \neq 3(2k-1) \pm 1$) and $6kf_I \pm (2\ell+1)f_O$ ($2\ell + 1 \neq 6k \pm 1$) are zero at $\rho = \pm\pi/2$.

3. Since the output waveform generally contains components with lower than the wanted output frequency, the amplitudes of which vary with angle ρ (thus, for the naturally commutated cycloconverter, where $\rho = \phi_O$, they vary with the load power factor), the determination and careful evaluation of the worst case values of $\gamma(\rho)_{Ok,\ell}$, which will set a limit to the attainable maximum output to input frequency ratio, is important. This limit is typically lower than $\frac{1}{3}$ for a *three-pulse* converter.

4. The total r.m.s. distortion of the output waveform is constant (0.676) and independent of ρ. Thus the interesting conclusion can be made that the r.m.s. distortion of $v_O(\rho)$ is the same, at any value of ρ, as that of the component waveforms v_O and $v_{O\pi}$.

3.2.3.2 *Concurrent Composite Waveform.* Let us turn now our attention to the *concurrent* type of composite output voltage waveform shown in Figure 3.9*f*. This waveform, v_{OM}, is the arithmetic mean of waveforms v_O and $v_{O\pi}$ shown at *a* and *b* in the figure. The mathematical definition of v_{OM} is given by equation (3.37), and it has been analytically described in terms of the constituent components for the case of a general periodic modulating function by equation (3.38). This equation is, of course, valid for the presently considered modulating function $M(t) = \sin^{-1}(\sin \omega_O t)$ if the relevant coefficients $a_{[3(2k-1)\pm 1],2n}$ and $b_{(6k\pm 1),n}$, as given by equations (3.59)–(3.62), are used. In the present case, however, it is simpler to derive v_{OM} from the basic definition, $v_{OM} = \frac{1}{2}(v_O + v_{O\pi})$, using the "ready" analytical expressions for

v_O and $v_{O\pi}$ [equations (3.63) and (3.64)]. This gives directly the following result:

$$\begin{aligned} v_{OM} = \frac{3\sqrt{3}}{2\pi} V_I \Bigg\{ & \sin(\omega_O t + \psi) \\ & + \sum_{k=1}^{\infty} \left(\frac{\sin\{[3k\omega_I + (3k \pm 1)\omega_O]t + (3k \pm 1)\psi\}}{2(3k \pm 1)} \right. \\ & \left. - (-1)^{3k} \frac{\sin\{[3k\omega_I - (3k \pm 1)\omega_O]t - (3k \pm 1)\psi\}}{2(3k \pm 1)} \right) \Bigg\} \end{aligned} \tag{3.79}$$

Note that equation (3.79) is equal to part (a) of the expressions obtained for v_O and $v_{O\pi}$ [equations (3.63) and (3.64)]. This is because the sign of part (a) is the same and that of part (b) is the opposite in the two expressions.

The performance indices related to waveform v_{OM} are as follows:

$$v_{Ok} = \begin{cases} (3k \pm 1) + 3k\dfrac{f_I}{f_O} & \text{(3.80a)} \\[2ex] \left|(3k \pm 1) - 3k\dfrac{f_I}{f_O}\right| & \text{(3.80b)} \end{cases}$$

$$\gamma_{Ok} = \frac{1}{2}\frac{1}{(3k \pm 1)} \tag{3.81}$$

$$\mu_O = \frac{1}{\sqrt{2}}\sqrt{\sum_{k=1}^{\infty} \frac{1}{(3k \pm 1)^2}} \cong 0.478 \tag{3.82}$$

The above output voltage wave indices lead to the following conclusions:

1. The significant values of v_{Ok} are given by equation (3.80b) which is identical to equation (3.49). Thus, as discussed on pages 86 and 89 in connection with waveform $v_{O\pi}$ obtained with a linear modulating function, the output waveform contains components with frequencies below f_O at f_O/f_I ratios greater than 0.75, which limits the maximum useful output frequency for a *three-pulse* circuit in most applications to about $0.7f_I$.
2. The normalized amplitudes, γ_{Ok}, of the significant unwanted components are only 50% of those obtained for $v_{O\pi}$ with a linear modulating function [see equation (3.50)].
3. The total r.m.s. distortion is only 71% of that obtained with previous sinusoidal mean output waveforms.

Typical output waveforms synthesized from the first 64 components of the series given by equation (3.79) are shown at various output to input frequency ratios in Figure 3.11.

3.3 SYNTHESIS OF NONSINUSOIDAL MEAN OUTPUT VOLTAGE WAVEFORMS

Most a-c loads supplied by frequency changers operate satisfactorily only if the applied voltage or current is reasonably sinusoidal. In other words, only the sinusoidal component of the generated waveform with the wanted frequency can be

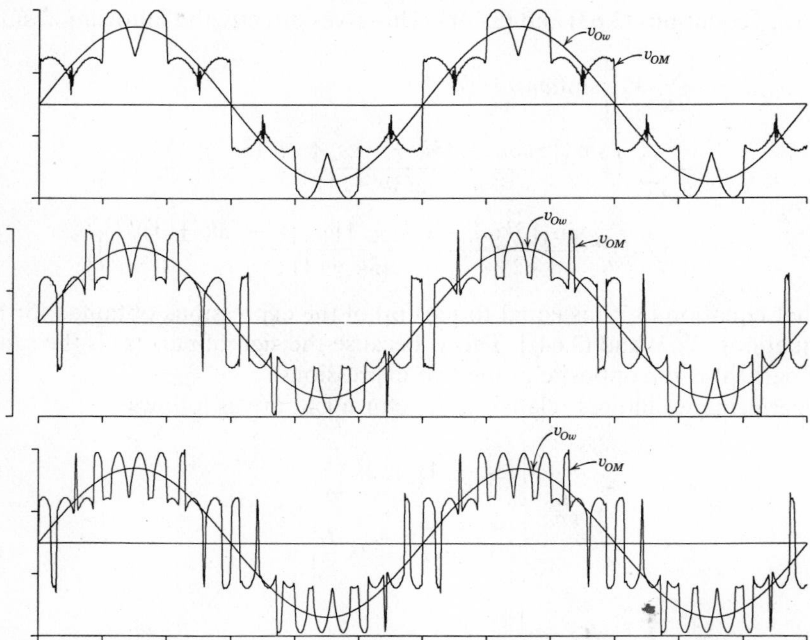

Figure 3.11 Concurrent composite output voltage waveforms synthesized from equation (3.79) at output to input frequency ratios of $f_O/f_I = 1/3$, $f_O/f_I = 1/4.5$, and $f_O/f_I = 1/6$, respectively.

utilized in the output. The remaining components of the voltage waveform are either largely removed by an external filter or attenuated by the inherent inductance of the load—for example, the leakage inductance of an electrical machine. In either case, the closer the output waveform approximates the wanted sinusoidal component, the easier and more economical the external filtering, and the more effective the internal ("natural") filtering of the load becomes. From the results of the previous investigations it should be obvious that the total r.m.s. distortion does not, in general, adequately specify the quality of the output waveform. Indeed, it is necessary to evaluate the spectral characteristics (frequencies and amplitudes) of the output waveforms produced. As was shown, the sinusoidal mean output waveforms have the unique characteristic that the frequencies of the unwanted components generally consist of sums and differences of multiples of both the input and output frequencies. This means that the separation between the wanted and unwanted frequencies is not fixed, but is a function of the f_O/f_I ratio. Consequently, as f_O decreases or f_I increases, the frequencies of the unwanted components, relative to f_O, increase.

Nonsinusoidal mean output waveforms inevitably contain constituent components whose frequencies are integrally related to f_O and are independent of f_I, that is, they are harmonics. The presence of harmonics in the output is, in many applications (for example, variable speed a-c motor drives), less desirable than that of the unwanted components, whose frequencies are dependent upon both f_I and f_O. (The reason for this is that, at low output frequencies, the unwanted frequencies are essentially determined by the input frequency; thus they are generally much higher than the low order harmonics.) It is logical therefore to ask why we consider at all the generation of nonsinusoidal mean output voltage waveforms. The answer is that operation with a nonsinusoidal mean output waveform may offer other benefits. It can provide an increase in the amplitude of the wanted component and, in some cases, an improvement in the input displacement factor. This is particularly beneficial for the naturally commutated cycloconverter.

A wide variety of nonsinusoidal mean output waveforms could obviously be synthesized. In the following two sections, however, we consider just two different waveshapes, one that deviates only slightly from the previously considered sinusoidal mean waveforms, and one that approximates a square wave. Our main intent is to illustrate the analytical technique and the obtainable performance characteristics.

3.3.1 Sinusoidal Modulating Function and Corresponding Output Waveforms

The simple sinusoidal modulating function

$$M(t) = \frac{\pi}{2}\sin(\omega_O t + \psi) \tag{3.83}$$

results in a nonsinusoidal waveform having a wanted component with an amplitude greater than $(3\sqrt{3}/2\pi)V_I$. Since $M(t)$ is a periodic function, equations (3.20) and (3.21) are again applicable. To obtain pertinent analytical expressions for v_O and $v_{O\pi}$, coefficients defined by equations (3.16)–(3.19) must be evaluated for the present modulating function. Thus, substituting equation (3.83) into equations (3.16)–(3.19), we obtain

$$\begin{aligned} a_{(3k\pm1),0} &= \frac{1}{\pi}\int_{\psi}^{\pi+\psi} \cos\{(3k \pm 1)(\pi/2)\sin(\omega_O t + \psi)\}\, d(\omega_O t) \\ &= J_O\{(3k \pm 1)(\pi/2)\} \end{aligned} \tag{3.84}$$

$$\begin{aligned} a_{(3k\pm1),2n} &= \frac{2}{\pi}\int_{\psi}^{\pi+\psi} \cos\{(3k \pm 1)(\pi/2)\sin(\omega_O t + \psi)\}\cos 2n\omega_O t\, d(\omega_O t) \\ &= 2\sum_{n=1}^{\infty} J_{2n}\{(3k \pm 1)(\pi/2)\} \end{aligned} \tag{3.85}$$

$$\begin{aligned} b_{1,(2n-1)} &= \frac{2}{\pi}\int_{\psi}^{\pi+\psi} \sin\{(\pi/2)\sin(\omega_O t + \psi)\}\sin(2n - 1)\omega_O t\, d(\omega_O t) \\ &= 2\sum_{n=1}^{\infty} J_{(2n-1)}(\pi/2) \end{aligned} \tag{3.86}$$

$$b_{1,2n} \equiv 0 \tag{3.87}$$

$$\begin{aligned} b_{(3k\pm1),(2n-1)} &= \frac{2}{\pi}\int_{\psi}^{\pi+\psi} \sin\{(3k \pm 1)(\pi/2)\sin(\omega_O t + \psi)\}\sin(2n - 1)\omega_O t\, d(\omega_O t) \\ &= 2\sum_{n=1}^{\infty} J_{(2n-1)}\{(3k \pm 1)(\pi/2)\} \end{aligned} \tag{3.88}$$

$$b_{(3k\pm1),2n} \equiv 0 \tag{3.89}$$

where $J_n\{(3k \pm 1)(\pi/2)\}$ is the Bessel function of the first kind with order n and argument $(3k \pm 1)(\pi/2)$.

Substitution of equations (3.84)–(3.89) into (3.20), and subsequently into (3.21), results in the following expressions:

$$\begin{aligned} v_O = \frac{3\sqrt{3}}{2\pi} V_I \Bigg\{ & 2J_1(\pi/2)\sin(\omega_O t + \psi) + 2\sum_{n=1}^{\infty} J_{(2n+1)}(\pi/2)\sin\{(2n+1)(\omega_O t + \psi)\} \\ & + \sum_{k=1}^{\infty}\left(\frac{J_O\{(3k+1)(\pi/2)\}}{3k+1} + \frac{J_O\{(3k-1)(\pi/2)\}}{3k-1}\right)\sin 3k\omega_I t \\ & + \sum_{k=1}^{\infty}\sum_{n=1}^{\infty}\left(\frac{J_n\{(3k+1)(\pi/2)\}}{3k+1} + \frac{J_n\{(3k-1)(\pi/2)\}}{3k-1}\right) \\ & \times \left(\begin{matrix}+\\(-1)^n\end{matrix} \sin\{(3k\omega_I \pm n\omega_O)t \pm n\psi\}\right)\Bigg\} \end{aligned} \tag{3.90}$$

and

$$\begin{aligned} v_{O\pi} = \frac{3\sqrt{3}}{2\pi} V_I \Bigg\{ & 2J_1(\pi/2)\sin(\omega_O t + \psi) + 2\sum_{n=1}^{\infty} J_{(2n+1)}(\pi/2)\sin\{(2n+1)(\omega_O t + \psi)\} \\ & - \sum_{k=1}^{\infty}(-1)^{3k}\left(\frac{J_O\{(3k+1)(\pi/2)\}}{3k+1} + \frac{J_O\{(3k-1)(\pi/2)\}}{3k-1}\right)\sin 3k\omega_I t \\ & - \sum_{k=1}^{\infty}\sum_{n=1}^{\infty}(-1)^{3k+n}\left(\frac{J_n\{(3k+1)(\pi/2)\}}{3k+1} + \frac{J_n\{(3k-1)(\pi/2)\}}{3k-1}\right) \\ & \times \left(\begin{matrix}+\\(-1)^n\end{matrix} \sin\{(3k\omega_I \pm n\omega_O)t \pm n\psi\}\right)\Bigg\} \end{aligned} \tag{3.91}$$

Equations (3.90) and (3.91) may be rewritten in the following forms:

$$\begin{aligned} v_O = \frac{3\sqrt{3}}{2\pi} V_I \Bigg(& 1.134\sin(\omega_O t + \psi) + 0.138\sin 3(\omega_O t + \psi) \\ & + 0.0045\sin 5(\omega_O t + \psi) + \cdots \\ & + \sum_{k=1}^{\infty}\sum_{n=0}^{\infty} F \begin{matrix}(+)\\(-1)^n\end{matrix} A_{3k,n}\sin\{(3k\omega_I \pm n\omega_O)t \pm n\psi\}\Bigg) \end{aligned} \tag{3.92}$$

where

$$F = \begin{cases} 1 & \text{for describing equation (3.90)} \\ -(-1)^{3k+n} & \text{for describing equation (3.91)} \end{cases}$$

and $A_{3k,n}$ is given for the dominant terms in Table 3.4.

In order to examine the effect of the modulating function $M(t) = (\pi/2)\sin(\omega_O t + \psi)$ on the repetition frequency of the basic existence functions [equations (3.6) and (3.7)], $M(t)$ is differentiated with respect to t (recall that $M(t)$ is, in effect, a time varying angle):

$$\frac{dM(t)}{dt} = \Omega(t) = \frac{d}{dt}\left(\frac{\pi}{2}\sin(\omega_O t + \psi)\right) = \frac{\pi}{2}\cos(\omega_O t + \psi) \tag{3.93}$$

The above expression clearly indicates that $M(t)$ has the effect of co-sinusoidally varying the repetition frequency of the existence functions about their quiescent frequency f_I. Typical waveforms illustrating the generation of the output waveforms v_O and $v_{O\pi}$ with this method are shown in Figure 3.12*a* and *b*.

TABLE 3.4. Normalized Amplitudes of the Dominant Components in equation (3.92) with frequencies of $3kf_I \pm nf_O$ ($k = 1, 2, 3, 4,; n = 0, 1, \ldots 11$)

n	0	1	2	3	4	5	6	7	8	9	10	11
$A_{3,n}$	−0.097	0.089	0.171	0.174	0.155	0.119	0.077	0.041	0.019	0.007	0.000	0.000
$A_{6,n}$	0.016	0.017	−0.010	−0.025	−0.016	0.009	0.040	0.065	0.074	0.067	0.051	0.033
$A_{9,n}$	0.006	−0.005	−0.007	0.002	0.009	0.006	−0.004	−0.014	−0.014	−0.003	0.016	0.034
$A_{12,n}$	0.003	−0.003	0.002	0.004	0.000	−0.004	−0.003	0.001	0.006	0.005	−0.001	−0.010

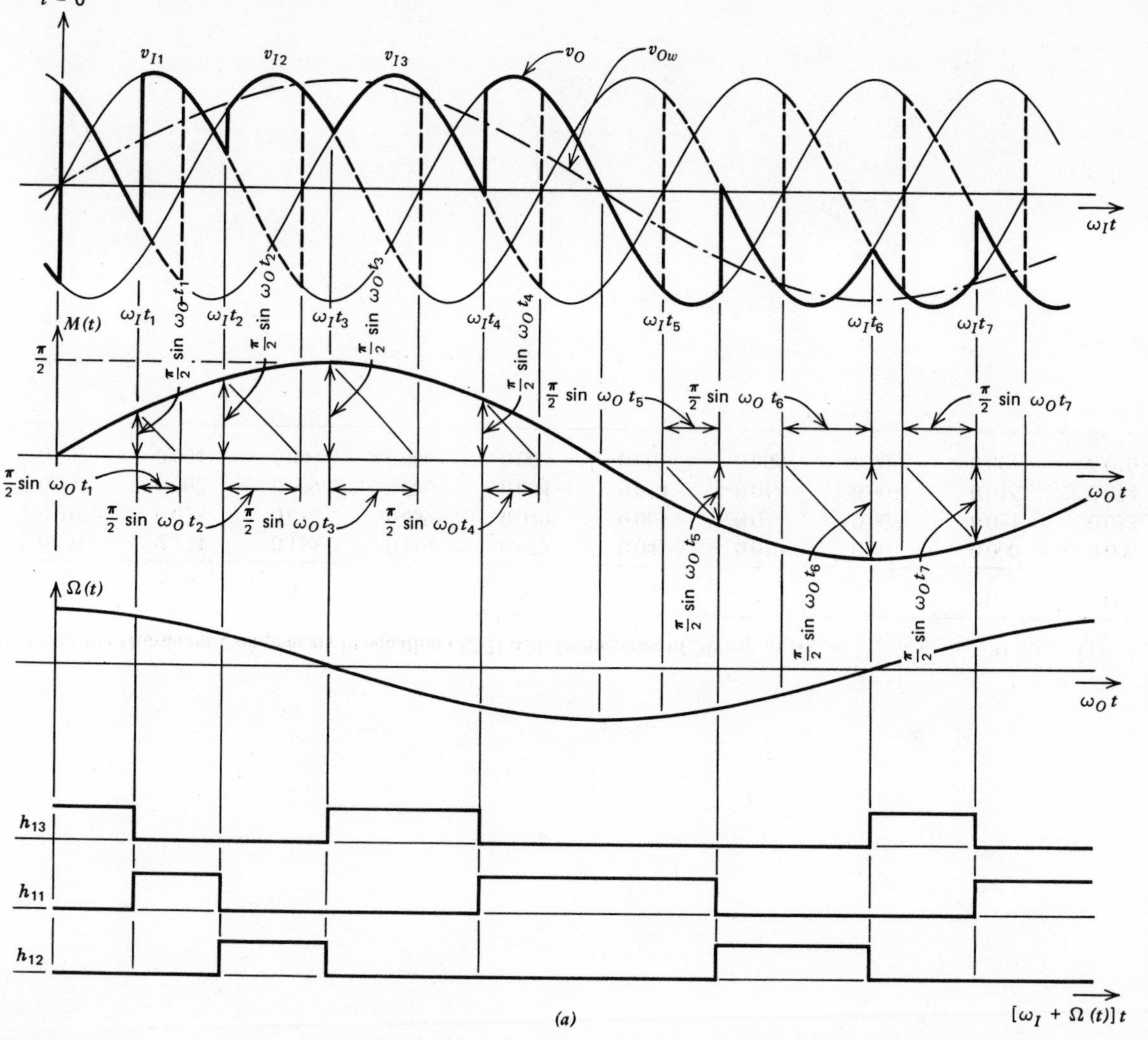

t = 0
v_{I1}
v_{I2}
v_{I3}
v_O
v_{Ow}
$\omega_I t$
$\omega_I t_1$
$\omega_I t_2$
$\omega_I t_3$
$\omega_I t_4$
$\omega_I t_5$
$\omega_I t_6$
$\omega_I t_7$
$M(t)$
$\frac{\pi}{2}$
$\frac{\pi}{2} \sin \omega_O t_1$
$\frac{\pi}{2} \sin \omega_O t_2$
$\frac{\pi}{2} \sin \omega_O t_3$
$\frac{\pi}{2} \sin \omega_O t_4$
$\frac{\pi}{2} \sin \omega_O t_5$
$\frac{\pi}{2} \sin \omega_O t_6$
$\frac{\pi}{2} \sin \omega_O t_7$
$\omega_O t$
$\Omega(t)$
$\omega_O t$
h_{13}
h_{11}
h_{12}
$[\omega_I + \Omega(t)]t$

(a)

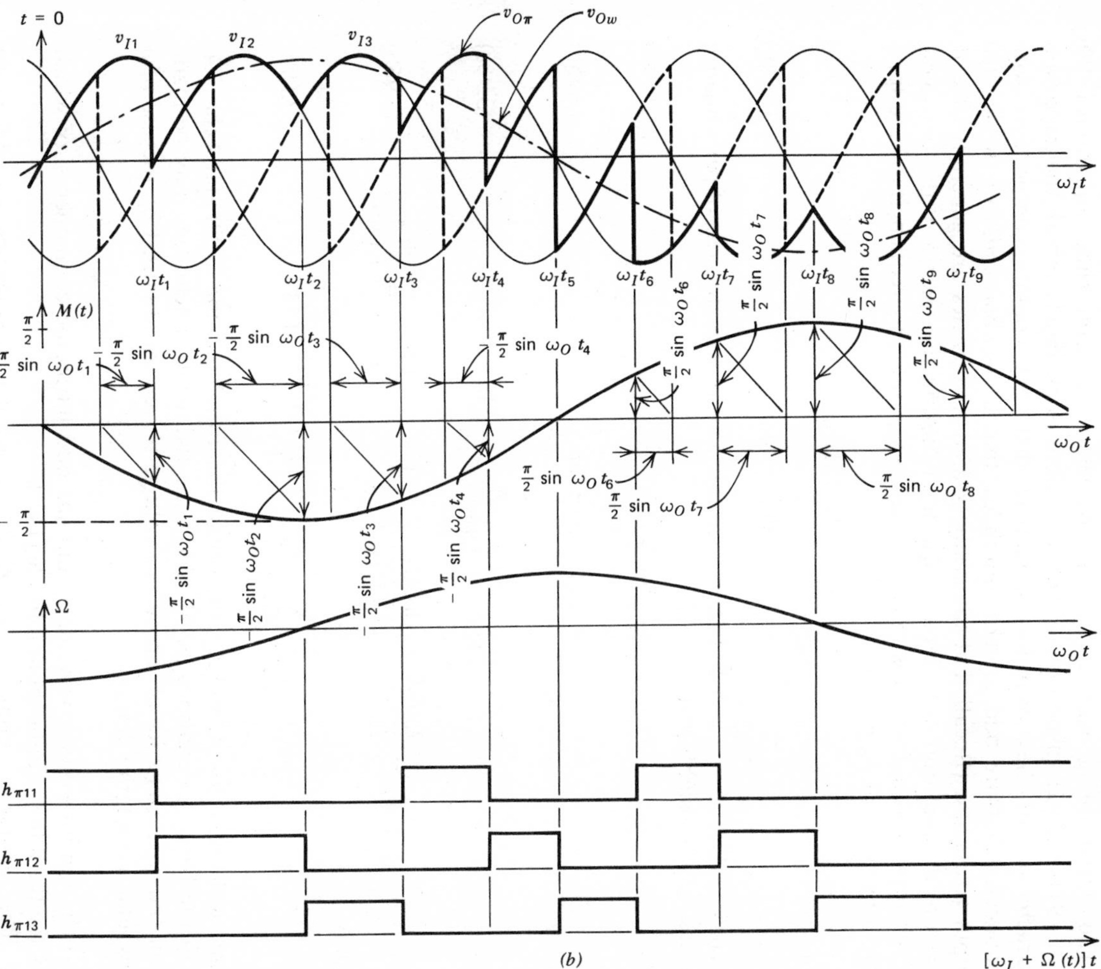

Figure 3.12 Generation of the *a* positive-type and *b* negative-type complementary output voltage waveforms by the sinusoidal modulating function $M(t) = \pi/2 \sin \omega_O t$.

The output voltage wave indices may be determined from either equations (3.90) and (3.91) or (3.92). Inspection of these equations immediately reveals the important characteristic of these waveforms, namely that they contain components with frequencies that are odd integral multiples, that is, *odd-harmonics* of the wanted output frequency. (Recall that integrally related frequencies are generally absent, except at discrete output to input frequency ratios, in the spectra of the sinusoidal mean output waveforms.) It is thus practical to separate the frequencies of the spectrum into two groups, namely,

$$f_n = (2n + 1)f_O \tag{3.94a}$$

and

$$f_{k,n} = 3kf_I \pm nf_O \tag{3.94b}$$

where $k = 1, 2, 3, \ldots; n = 0, 1, 2, \ldots$. In this way, two related sets of performance indices may be established

$$\nu_{On} = 2n + 1 \tag{3.95a}$$

$$\nu_{Ok,n} = n \pm 3k\frac{f_I}{f_O} \tag{3.95b}$$

$$\gamma_{On} = \frac{J_{(2n+1)}(\pi/2)}{J_1(\pi/2)} = A_n \tag{3.96a}$$

$$\gamma_{Ok,n} = \frac{J_n\{(3k+1)(\pi/2)\}}{2(3k+1)J_1(\pi/2)} + \frac{J_n\{(3k-1)(\pi/2)\}}{2(3k-1)J_1(\pi/2)} = \frac{A_{k,n}}{1.134} \tag{3.96b}$$

Finally

$$\mu_O = \sqrt{\sum_{k=1}^{\infty}\sum_{n=0}^{\infty}\left\{A_n^2 + \left(\frac{A_{k,n}}{1.134}\right)^2\right\}} \cong 0.537 \tag{3.97}$$

Numerical values for A_n and $A_{k,n}$ are obtainable from equation (3.92) and Table 3.4.

On the basis of equations (3.94)–(3.97), the following conclusions may be made about the characteristics of the output voltage waveform obtained by the use of a sinusoidal modulating function.

1. The output voltage waveform contains odd harmonic components, of which only the third has significant amplitude (14%).

2. The significant nonintegrally related unwanted frequencies are difference frequencies. It follows from equation (3.95b) that $\nu_{Ok,n}$ becomes zero whenever the following condition is satisfied

$$\frac{f_O}{f_I} = 3\frac{k}{n} \tag{3.98}$$

Consequently, at the above f_O/f_I ratios the output voltage contains a d-c component. Since k and n are independent of each other, components with lower than the wanted frequency are generally present over the whole output frequency range. Note that equation (3.98) is identical to equation (3.72b), and therefore the comments made there about the useful output frequency range (#2 on page 97) are valid also for the present case.

3. The amplitude of the wanted component is 13.4% greater than, and the total r.m.s. distortion only 80% of that of the sinusoidal mean output waveforms previously considered. It should be noted that this relatively lower r.m.s. distortion is largely due to the increased amplitude of the wanted component.

The output voltage waveform v_O discussed above is shown at various f_O/f_I ratios ($\psi = 0$) in Figure 3.13. The waveforms were synthesized from the terms of the series given by equation (3.90).

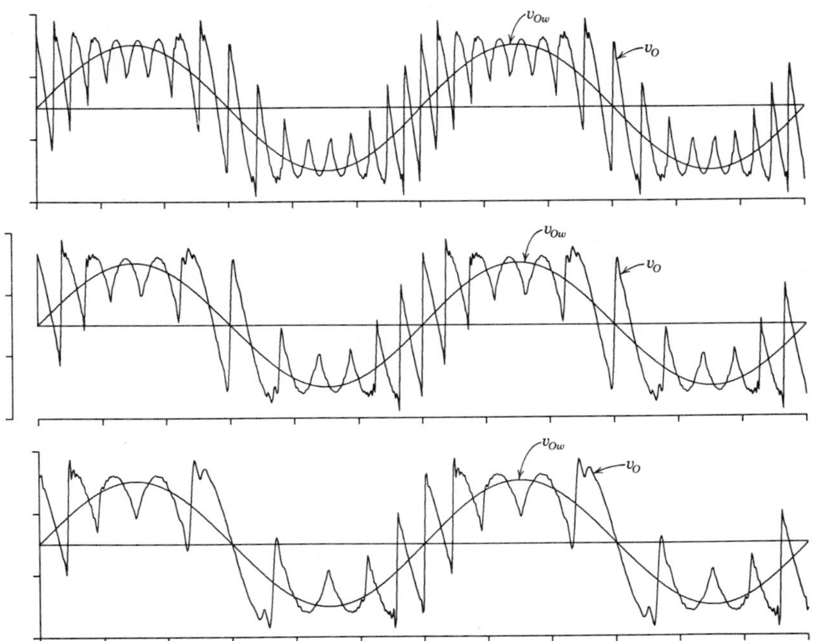

Figure 3.13 Waveforms synthesized from the terms of equation (3.90) at output to input frequency ratios of $f_O/f_I = 1/6$, $f_O/f_I = 1/4$, and $f_O/f_I = 1/3$, respectively.

The complementary waveforms v_O and $v_{O\pi}$ corresponding to modulating function $M(t) = (\pi/2)\sin(\omega_O t + \psi)$ show a strong resemblance to those corresponding to $M(t) = \sin^{-1}\{\sin(\omega_O t + \psi)\}$. (Compare Figure 3.12 with Figure 3.7.) Indeed, with the exception of the presence or absence of harmonic components the two pairs of waveforms exhibit quite similar characteristics.

It would, of course, be possible to derive consecutive and concurrent component output waveshapes from the complementary waveforms generated by the presently considered sinusoidal modulating function. These waveshapes would also have characteristics similar to $v_O(\rho)$ and v_{OM} described in the previous section, except for the presence of harmonics. This possibility will not, however, be pursued here because these waveforms would not, in general, provide practical advantages over their sinusoidal mean counterparts. This exercise, however, might be beneficial to the reader who requires further familiarization with the analytical techniques presented, or who requires to know the precise details of the spectral structure of these composite waves.

3.3.2 Square Wave Modulating Function

Consider the square wave modulating function given by

$$M(t) = \begin{cases} \dfrac{\pi}{2} & -\psi \leqq \omega_O t < \pi - \psi \\ -\dfrac{\pi}{2} & \pi - \psi \leqq \omega_O t < 2\pi - \psi \end{cases} \tag{3.99}$$

The general expressions for the complementary voltage waveforms v_O and $v_{O\pi}$ given by equations (3.20) and (3.21) are still applicable; it is necessary only to evaluate the pertinent coefficients defined by equations (3.16) and (3.19), which can, in the present case, be done quite simply:

$$a_{(3k+1),0} = \frac{1}{\pi}\int_{\psi}^{\pi+\psi} \cos\left((3k \pm 1)\frac{\pi}{2}\right) d(\omega_O t) = \begin{cases} a_{[3(2k-1)+1],0} = -(-1)^{3k} \\ a_{[3(2k-1)-1],0} = \quad (-1)^{3k} \\ a_{(6k+1),0} \quad = \quad 0 \end{cases} \tag{3.100}$$

$$a_{(3k+1),2n} = \frac{2}{\pi}\int_{\psi}^{\pi+\psi} \cos\{(3k \pm 1)(\pi/2)\} \cos 2n\omega_O t \, d(\omega_O t) = 0 \tag{3.101}$$

$$b_{1,n} = \frac{2}{\pi}\int_{\psi}^{\pi+\psi} \sin\frac{\pi}{2} \sin n\omega_O t \, d(\omega_O t) = \begin{cases} b_{1,2n} = 0 \\ b_{1,(2n-1)} = \dfrac{4}{\pi}\dfrac{1}{2n-1} \end{cases} \tag{3.102}$$

$$b_{(3k+1),n} = \frac{2}{\pi}\int_{\psi}^{\pi+\psi} \sin\{(3k \pm 1)(\pi/2)\} \sin n\omega_O t \, d(\omega_O t)$$

$$= \begin{cases} b_{(3k\pm 1),2n} = 0 \\ b_{[3(2k-1)\pm 1],(2n-1)} = 0 \\ b_{(6k\pm 1),(2n-1)} = \pm\dfrac{4}{\pi}\dfrac{(-1)^{3k}}{2n-1} \end{cases} \tag{3.103}$$

$k = 1, 2, \ldots; n = 1, 2, \ldots$

Substitution of equations (3.100)–(3.103) into (3.20) and (3.21) results in the following expression:

$$v_O = v_{O\pi} = \frac{3\sqrt{3}}{2\pi} V_I \Bigg\{ \frac{4}{\pi}\left(\sin(\omega_O t + \psi) + \sum_{n=1}^{\infty} \frac{1}{2n+1} \sin\{(2n+1)(\omega_O t + \psi)\} \right)$$
$$- \sum_{k=1}^{\infty} (-1)^{3k} \left(\frac{1}{3(2k-1)+1} - \frac{1}{3(2k-1)-1} \right) \sin\{3(2k-1)\omega_I t\}$$
$$+ \frac{2}{\pi} \sum_{k=1}^{\infty}\sum_{n=1}^{\infty} \frac{(-1)^{3k}}{2n-1} \left(\frac{1}{6k+1} - \frac{1}{6k-1} \right)$$
$$\times (\pm\sin\{[6k\omega_I \pm (2n-1)\omega_O]t \pm (2n-1)\psi\}) \Bigg\} \tag{3.104}$$

Equation (3.104) may be written in the following form

$$v_O = \frac{3\sqrt{3}}{2\pi} V_I \Bigg\{ 1.272 \sin(\omega_O t + \psi) + \sum_{n=1}^{\infty} A_{(2n+1)} \sin\{(2n+1)(\omega_O t + \psi)\}$$
$$+ \sum_{k=1}^{\infty} (-1)^{3k} \Bigg(A_{3(2k-1)} \sin 3(2k-1)\omega_I t$$
$$\mp \sum_{n=1}^{\infty} A_{6k,(2n-1)} \sin\{[6k\omega_I \pm (2n-1)\omega_O]t \pm (2n-1)\psi\} \Bigg) \Bigg\} \quad (3.105)$$

where $A_{(2n+1)}$, $A_{[3(2k-1)]}$, and $A_{6k,(2n-1)}$ are given for the dominant terms in Table 3.5.

It is evident that the output waveform is generated by the act of alternating the phase positions of the existence functions between $-\pi/2$ and $\pi/2$ about the quiescent point. At the instants of change, the repetition rate of the existence functions is infinite, that is,

$$\frac{dM(t)}{dt} = \Omega(t) = \begin{cases} +\delta(\psi + n2\pi) \\ -\delta\{\psi + (2n+1)\pi\} \end{cases} \quad (3.106)$$

where δ is the Dirac function, and $n = 0, 1, 2, \ldots$. Generation of the output waveshape for a square wave modulating function is shown in Figure 3.14.

The output voltage wave indices relevant to the *harmonic* and *unwanted* components of the output waveforms can be determined from equation (3.104) or (3.105):

$$\nu_{On} = 2n + 1 \quad (3.107a)$$

$$\nu_{Ok} = 3(2k-1)\frac{f_I}{f_O} \quad (3.107b)$$

$$\nu_{Ok,n} = \left|(2n-1) \pm 6k\frac{f_I}{f_O}\right| \quad (3.107c)$$

$$\gamma_{On} = \frac{1}{2n+1} \quad (3.108a)$$

TABLE 3.5. Normalized Amplitudes of the Dominant Components in Equation (3.105) with Frequencies of $(2n+1)f_O$ $(n = 1, 2, \ldots 8)$, $3(2k-1)f_I$ $(k = 1, 2, \ldots 8)$, **and** $6kf_I \pm (2n-1)f_O$ $(k = 1, 2, 3, 4;\ n = 1, 2, \ldots 8)$, **Respectively**

$2n+1$	3	5	7	9	11	13	15	17
$A_{(2n+1)}$	0.424	0.2546	0.1819	0.1415	0.1157	0.0979	0.0848	0.0748
$3(2k-1)$	3	9	15	21	27	33	39	45
$A_{[3(2k-1)]}$	0.2500	0.0250	0.0089	0.0045	0.0027	0.0018	0.0013	0.0009
$2n-1$	1	3	5	7	9	11	13	15
$A_{6,(2n-1)}$	0.0364	0.0121	0.0073	0.0052	0.0040	0.0033	0.0028	0.0021
$A_{12,(2n-1)}$	0.0089	0.0030	0.0018	0.0013	0.0010	0.0008	0.0007	0.0006
$A_{18,(2n-1)}$	0.0039	0.0013	0.0008	0.0006	0.0004	0.0004	0.0003	0.0003
$A_{24,(2n-1)}$	0.0022	0.0007	0.0004	0.0003	0.0002	0.0002	0.0002	0.0001

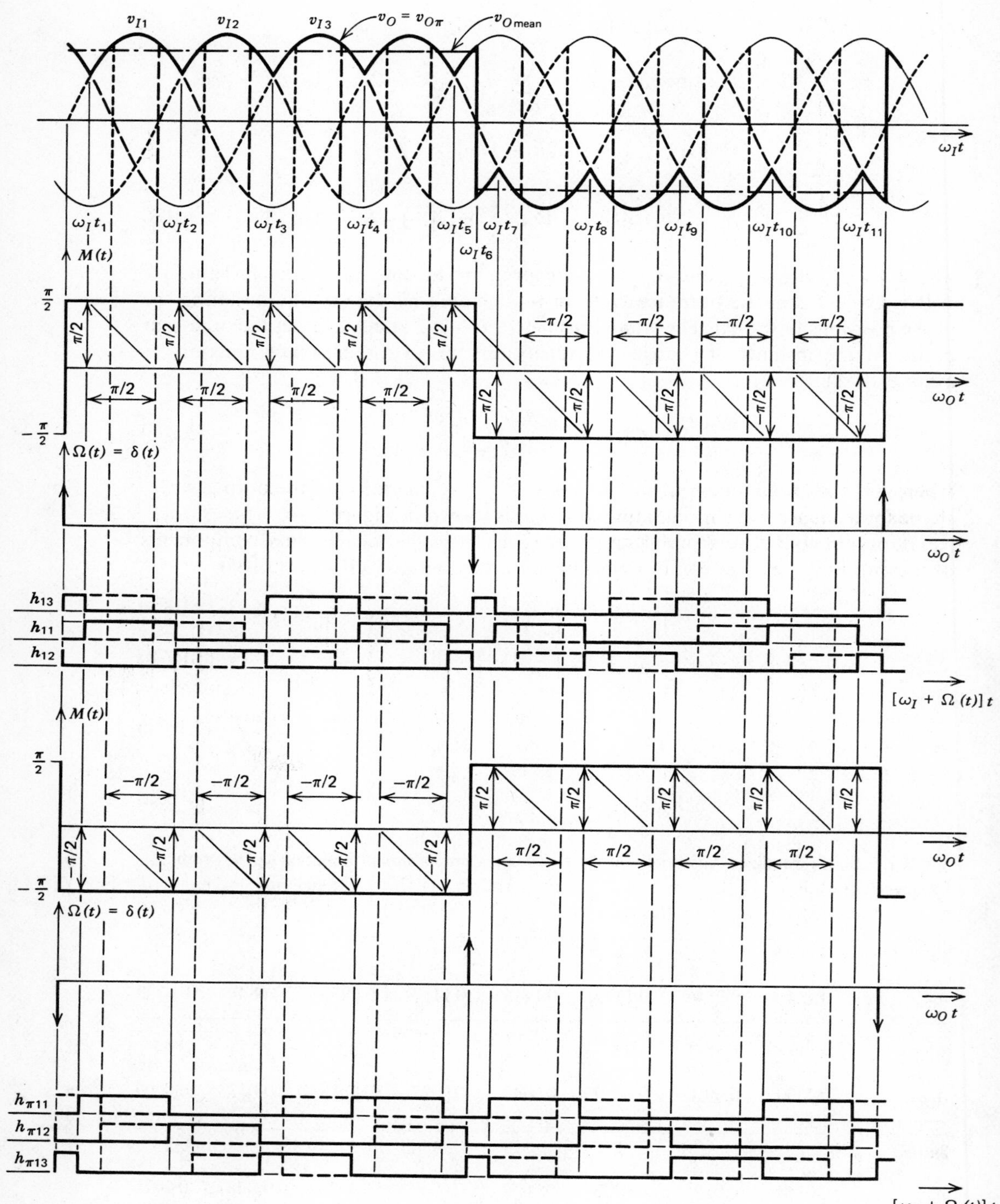

Figure 3.14 Generation of a square wave mean output voltage waveform by modulating function $M(t) = \pm\pi/2$.

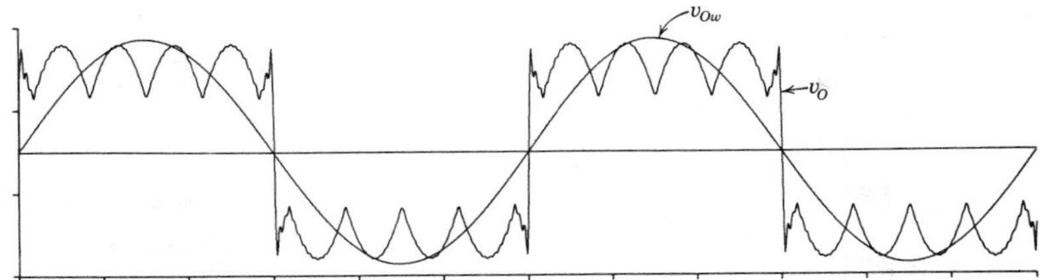

Figure 3.15 Square mean output voltage waveform synthesized from the terms of equation (3.104) at $f_O/f_I = 1/3$.

$$\gamma_{Ok} = \frac{\pi}{4}\left(\frac{1}{3(2k-1)-1} - \frac{1}{3(2k-1)+1}\right) = \frac{\pi}{4}A_{3(2k-1)} \qquad (3.108b)$$

$$\gamma_{Ok,n} = \left|\frac{1}{2(2n-1)}\left(\frac{1}{6k+1} - \frac{1}{6k-1}\right)\right| = \frac{\pi}{4}A_{6k,(2n-1)} \qquad (3.108c)$$

$(k = 1, 2, 3, \ldots; n = 1, 2, 3, \ldots)$ and

$$\mu_O = \left\{\sum_{k=1}^{\infty}\sum_{n=1}^{\infty}\left(\frac{1}{(2n+1)^2} + \frac{\pi^2}{16}(A_{3(2k-1)}^2 + A_{6k,(2n-1)}^2)\right)\right\}^{\frac{1}{2}} \cong 0.512 \qquad (3.109)$$

Inspection of the above indices indicates that the output performance is dominantly determined by the square wave character of the voltage waveform produced. Although components with lower frequency than f_O generally appear in the output at noninteger f_O/f_I ratios, the amplitudes of these components are generally too low to have substantial practical significance. Therefore, the output waveform generated by $M(t) = \pm\pi/2$ approximates well the symmetrical square wave with an amplitude of $(3\sqrt{3}/2\pi)V_I$. (The difference in total r.m.s. distortion is only 8%; i.e., 0.472 versus 0.512.)

A typical output voltage waveform synthesized from the terms of equation (3.104) is shown at $f_O/f_I = 1/3$ in Figure 3.15.

3.4 SUMMARY OF SINUSOIDAL AND NONSINUSOIDAL WAVEFORM SYNTHESIS

The most significant results obtained for sinusoidal and nonsinusoidal three-pulse output voltage waveforms are summarized in Figure 3.16.

3.5 MULTIPULSE OUTPUT VOLTAGE WAVEFORMS

The preceding investigations are restricted to three-pulse output waveforms. The reason for this is that, since virtually all practically important frequency changer circuits are composed of basic three-pulse units (see Chapter 1), it is logical to investigate initially the output waveforms of these elementary circuits; once this has been accomplished, simple rules allow generalization of the analytical expressions for three-pulse waveforms to cover multipulse waveforms in those cases in which the pulse number is an integral multiple of three.

In practice, three-pulse circuits are not often used because of the relatively high *ripple* content of the obtainable output voltage waveforms. The ripple of the output voltage rapidly decreases with increasing pulse number because there are effectively more and more input voltage waves from which to construct the output waveshape; therefore the instantaneous deviation between the desired and the actual waveform

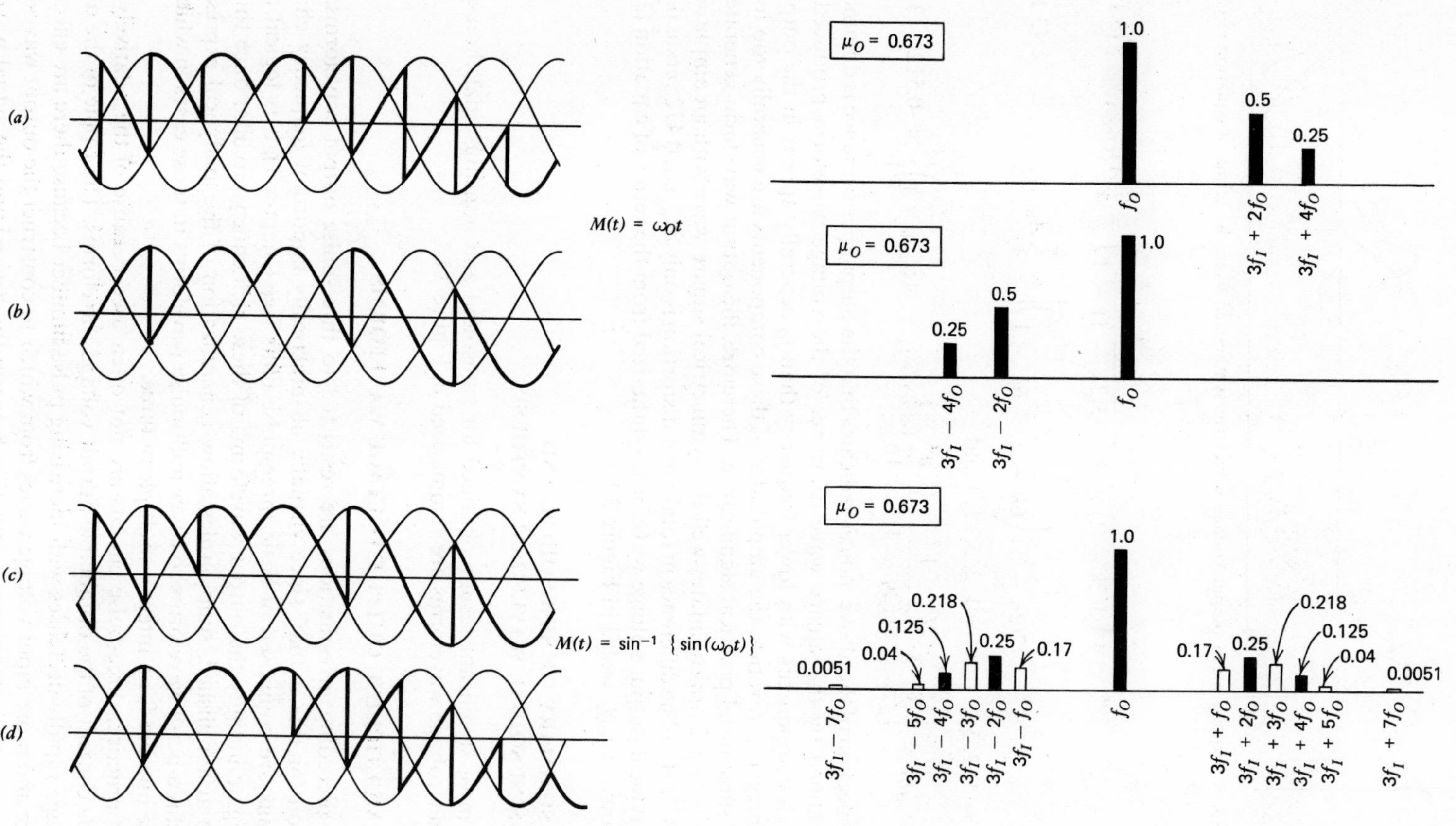

(a)
(b)
(c)
(d)
$M(t) = \omega_O t$
$M(t) = \sin^{-1}\{\sin(\omega_O t)\}$
$\mu_O = 0.673$
1.0
0.5
0.25
f_O
$3f_I + 2f_O$
$3f_I + 4f_O$
$\mu_O = 0.673$
0.25
0.5
1.0
$3f_I - 4f_O$
$3f_I - 2f_O$
f_O
$\mu_O = 0.673$
1.0
0.0051
0.04
0.125
0.218
0.25
0.17
0.17
0.25
0.218
0.125
0.04
0.0051
$3f_I - 7f_O$
$3f_I - 5f_O$
$3f_I - 4f_O$
$3f_I - 3f_O$
$3f_I - 2f_O$
$3f_I - f_O$
f_O
$3f_I + f_O$
$3f_I + 2f_O$
$3f_I + 3f_O$
$3f_I + 4f_O$
$3f_I + 5f_O$
$3f_I + 7f_O$

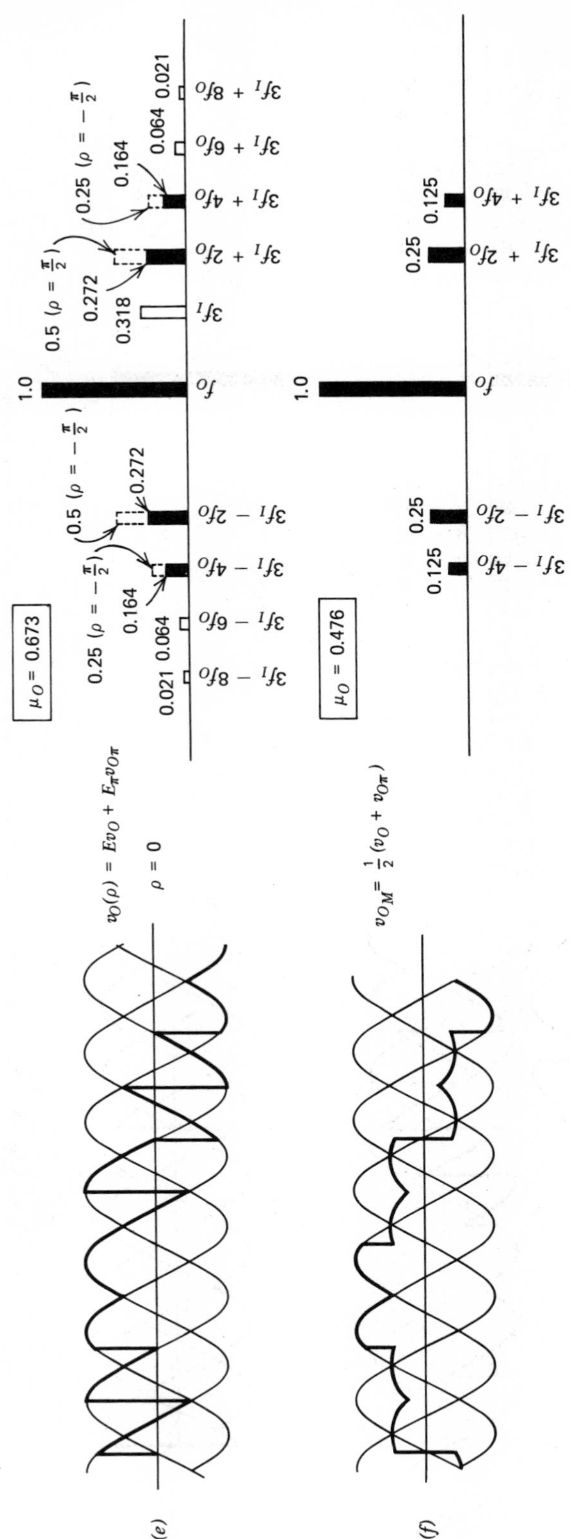

(e)
$v_O(\rho) = Ev_O + E_\pi v_{O\pi}$
$\rho = 0$
$\mu_O = 0.673$
0.021
0.064
0.25 ($\rho = -\frac{\pi}{2}$)
0.164
0.5 ($\rho = -\frac{\pi}{2}$)
0.272
1.0
0.5 ($\rho = \frac{\pi}{2}$)
0.272
0.318
0.25 ($\rho = -\frac{\pi}{2}$)
0.164
0.064
0.021
$3f_I - 8f_O$
$3f_I - 6f_O$
$3f_I - 4f_O$
$3f_I - 2f_O$
f_O
$3f_I$
$3f_I + 2f_O$
$3f_I + 4f_O$
$3f_I + 6f_O$
$3f_I + 8f_O$
(f)
$v_{O_M} = \frac{1}{2}(v_O + v_{O\pi})$
$\mu_O = 0.476$
0.125
0.25
1.0
0.25
0.125
$3f_I - 4f_O$
$3f_I - 2f_O$
f_O
$3f_I + 2f_O$
$3f_I + 4f_O$

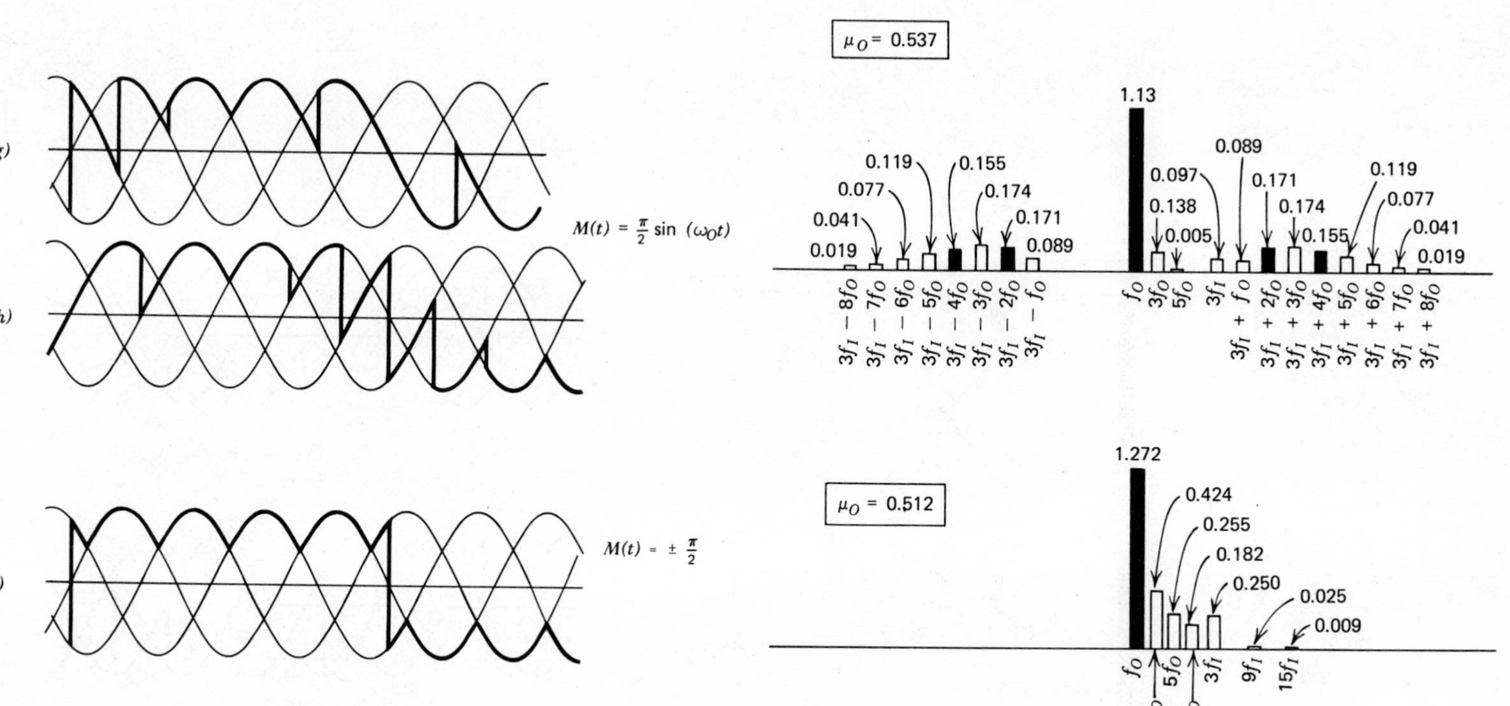

Figure 3.16 Amplitudes of significant components of various sinusoidal (*a–f*) and nonsinusoidal (*g–i*) mean output voltage waveforms. (*a*) "Fast-switching", (*b*) "slow-switching" type waveforms obtained with linear modulating function; (*c*) "positive-type", (*d*) "negative-type", (*e*) "consecutive", (*f*) "concurrent" waveforms obtained with triangular wave modulating function; (*g*) "positive-type", (*h*) "negative-type" complementary waveforms obtained with sinusoidal modulating function; (*i*) waveform obtained with square wave modulating function. (Filled columns indicate components generally present in all types of output voltage waveforms.)

can be made smaller and smaller. On the other hand, an increase in the pulse number means a corresponding increase in the number of switches employed in the power circuit. Note, however, that for switches of given ratings, the obtainable output power of the system increases with increasing number of switches. Multipulse systems of high pulse numbers (12 and above) may therefore be economical only in high-power systems in which the required output power in any case necessitates the use of a relatively large number of switches.

In this section we develop simple rules that enable us to generalize the previously derived three-pulse expressions for multipulse output waveforms.

Consider the six-pulse circuit comprising two three-pulse units, whose outputs are combined by an interphase reactor as shown in Figure 1.26*b*1. Here the output voltage wave is generated by two three-pulse frequency changers operated independently of one another from two sets of three-phase input voltages mutually displaced by $\pi/3$. The output voltage wave is the arithmetic mean of the two constituent three-pulse voltage waveforms, as illustrated for zero output frequency in Figure 1.26*b*3. The single-phase output voltage v_O is defined by

$$v_O = \frac{1}{2}(v_{O(135)} + v_{O(246)}) \tag{3.110}$$

where subscripts (135) and (246) refer to the two groups of three switches generating the two constituent three-pulse waveforms. If the operation of the switches 1, 3, 5 is described by existence functions h_1, h_3, h_5, and that of switches 2, 4, 6 by h_2, h_4, h_6 (see Figure 1.26*b*3), the output voltage can be expressed from the basic relationship $[v_O] = [H][v_I]$ in terms of the input voltages as follows:

$$v_O = \frac{1}{2}\left\{[h_1 \quad h_3 \quad h_5]\begin{bmatrix} v_{I1} \\ v_{I3} \\ v_{I5} \end{bmatrix} + [h_2 \quad h_4 \quad h_6]\begin{bmatrix} v_{I2} \\ v_{I4} \\ v_{I6} \end{bmatrix}\right\} \tag{3.111}$$

where

$$\begin{bmatrix} v_{I1} \\ v_{I3} \\ v_{I5} \end{bmatrix} = \frac{V_I}{2j}\begin{bmatrix} e^{j\omega_I t} - e^{-j\omega_I t} \\ e^{-j\frac{2\pi}{3}}(e^{j\omega_I t} - e^{-j\omega_I t}) \\ e^{-j\frac{4\pi}{3}}(e^{j\omega_I t} - e^{-j\omega_I t}) \end{bmatrix} \tag{3.112}$$

and

$$\begin{bmatrix} v_{I2} \\ v_{I4} \\ v_{I6} \end{bmatrix} = \frac{V_I}{2j}\begin{bmatrix} e^{-j\frac{\pi}{3}}(e^{j\omega_I t} - e^{-j\omega_I t}) \\ e^{-j\pi}(e^{j\omega_I t} - e^{-j\omega_I t}) \\ e^{-j\frac{5\pi}{3}}(e^{j\omega_I t} - e^{-j\omega_I t}) \end{bmatrix} \tag{3.113}$$

Input voltages v_{I1}, v_{I3}, and v_{I5} form a three-phase set identical to that which has hitherto been used exclusively to derive the three-pulse output waveforms [see equation (3.2)]; thus the corresponding modulated existence functions h_1, h_3, and h_5 can also be described by the expressions previously developed [equation (3.6)]. It follows therefore that the three-pulse output waveform $v_{O(135)}$ is mathematically defined, in terms of a general modulating function $M(t)$, by equation (3.10), that is,

$$v_{O(135)} = \frac{3\sqrt{3}}{2\pi} V_I \left(\sin M(t) + \sum_{k=1}^{\infty} \frac{\sin\{3k\omega_I t + (3k \pm 1)M(t)\}}{3k \pm 1}\right) \tag{3.114}$$

As indicated in Figure 1.26*b*3, the existence functions h_2, h_4, and h_6 (just like the input voltages v_{I2}, v_{I4}, and v_{I6}) are displaced by $\pi/3$ with respect to their counterparts, h_1, h_3, and h_5. By similarity with equation (3.6), Fourier expressions for these functions therefore can be written as follows:

$$\left.\begin{aligned} h_2 &= \frac{1}{3} - \sum_{n=-\infty}^{\infty} \frac{\sin n\dfrac{2\pi}{3}}{n\pi} \exp jn\left(\omega_I t + M(t) - \frac{\pi}{3}\right) \\ h_4 &= \frac{1}{3} - \sum_{n=-\infty}^{\infty} \frac{\sin n\dfrac{2\pi}{3}}{n\pi} \exp jn\left(\omega_I t + M(t) - \frac{2\pi}{3} - \frac{\pi}{3}\right) \\ h_6 &= \frac{1}{3} - \sum_{n=-\infty}^{\infty} \frac{\sin n\dfrac{2\pi}{3}}{n\pi} \exp jn\left(\omega_I t + M(t) - \frac{4\pi}{3} - \frac{\pi}{3}\right) \end{aligned}\right\} \quad (3.115)$$

The constituent output voltage, $v_{O(246)}$, can now be expressed in a form similar to that originally derived for v_O in equation (3.8) by substituting equation (3.113) and (3.115) into the second part of equation (3.111):

$$\begin{aligned} v_{O(246)} = {} & \frac{V_I}{2j}\frac{1}{3}\left\{[1\quad 1\quad 1]\begin{bmatrix}1\\a^2\\a\end{bmatrix} e^{j\left(\omega_I t - \frac{\pi}{3}\right)} - [1\quad 1\quad 1]\begin{bmatrix}1\\a\\a^2\end{bmatrix} e^{-j\left(\omega_I t - \frac{\pi}{3}\right)}\right\} \\ & - \frac{V_I}{2j}\sum_{n=1}^{\infty}\frac{\sin n\dfrac{2\pi}{3}}{n\pi}\left\{[1\quad a^{2n}\quad a^n]\begin{bmatrix}1\\a^2\\a\end{bmatrix} e^{j\left\{(n+1)\left(\omega_I t - \frac{\pi}{3}\right) + nM(t)\right\}}\right. \\ & - [1\quad a^n\quad a^{2n}]\begin{bmatrix}1\\a\\a^2\end{bmatrix} e^{-j\left\{(n+1)\left(\omega_I t - \frac{\pi}{3}\right) + nM(t)\right\}} \\ & - [1\quad a^{2n}\quad a^n]\begin{bmatrix}1\\a\\a^2\end{bmatrix} e^{j\left\{(n-1)\left(\omega_I t - \frac{\pi}{3}\right) + nM(t)\right\}} \\ & \left. + [1\quad a^n\quad a^{2n}]\begin{bmatrix}1\\a^2\\a\end{bmatrix} e^{-j\left\{(n-1)\left(\omega_I t - \frac{\pi}{3}\right) + nM(t)\right\}}\right\} \end{aligned} \quad (3.116)$$

where $a = \exp j(2\pi/3)$, $a^2 = \exp j(4\pi/3)$, $a^n = \exp jn(2\pi/3)$, and $a^{2n} = \exp jn(4\pi/3)$.

Comparison of equation (3.116) with (3.8) shows that equation (3.8) becomes identical to (3.116) if $\omega_I t$ is replaced by $(\omega_I t - \pi/3)$. Therefore, the output voltage $v_{O(246)}$ can be expressed readily from equation (3.10) simply by replacing $\omega_I t$ with $(\omega_I t - \pi/3)$, namely,

$$v_{O(246)} = \frac{3\sqrt{3}}{2\pi} V_I\left(\sin M(t) + \sum_{k=1}^{\infty}\frac{\sin\{3k(\omega_I t - \pi/3) + (3k \pm 1)M(t)\}}{3k \pm 1}\right) \quad (3.117)$$

Observing that $-3k(\pi/3)$ $(=-k\pi)$ in the arguments of the sine functions causes an alteration in the signs of the terms, $v_{O(246)}$ may be rewritten in the following form:

$$v_{O(246)} = \frac{3\sqrt{3}}{2\pi} V_I \left(\sin M(t) + \sum_{k=1}^{\infty} (-1)^{3k} \frac{\sin\{3k\omega_I t + (3k \pm 1)M(t)\}}{3k \pm 1} \right) \quad (3.118)$$

Comparison of equation (3.118), describing $v_{O(246)}$, with equation (3.114), describing $v_{O(135)}$, indicates that the similar terms in the two expressions are either in phase (k is even) or in anti phase (k is odd) with one another. Since the final output voltage v_O is given as the arithmetic mean of the constituent voltages $v_{O(135)}$ and $v_{O(246)}$ [equation (3.110)], it follows that the terms of odd k cancel each other in the output, whereas those of even k add together. Therefore

$$v_O = \frac{3\sqrt{3}}{2\pi} V_I \left(\sin M(t) + \sum_{k=1}^{\infty} \frac{\sin\{6k\omega_I t + (6k \pm 1)M(t)\}}{6k \pm 1} \right) \quad (3.119)$$

It can be shown easily that this general expression is valid, except for a constant scaling factor, for both midpoint and bridge six-pulse circuits.

Inspection of the expressions for three-pulse and six-pulse waveforms, given by equations (3.10) and (3.119), respectively, indicates a rather interesting characteristic, namely that the constant multiplying coefficient of integer k ($k = 1, 2, 3, \ldots$) in both cases is equal to the pulse number P—that is, it is 3 in equation (3.10) and 6 in equation (3.119). It can be shown that this characteristic holds for output voltage waveforms of any pulse number, and therefore the general expression for a P-pulse output voltage waveform can be given in terms of the modulating function $M(t)$ in the following universal form:

$$v_O = S\frac{3\sqrt{3}}{2\pi} V_I \left(\sin M(t) + \sum_{k=1}^{\infty} \frac{\sin\{Pk\omega_I t + (Pk \pm 1)M(t)\}}{Pk \pm 1} \right) \quad (3.120)$$

where P is the pulse number ($P = 3, 6, 9, \ldots$), and S is a circuit-dependent scaling factor (for example, $S = 1$ for circuits shown in Figures 1.25*a*, *c*, 1.26*b*1, *b*2, 1.27*b*1, *b*2, 1.28*b*1, *b*2, $S = 2$ for 1.26*c*1, *c*2, 1.29*b*1, *b*2; $S = 4$ for 1.29*a*1, *a*2; $S = 2/\sqrt{3}$ for 1.26*a*1, *a*2; $S = 2.05/\sqrt{3}$ for 1.27*a*1, *a*2; $S = 2.07/\sqrt{3}$ for 1.28*a*1, *a*2.)

It was seen in the previous analyses that all expressions for three-pulse output waveforms corresponding to specific modulating functions have been derived from the general equation (3.10). Since equation (3.10) is a special case ($P = 3$) of equation (3.120), it follows that an expression for any multipulse ($P > 3$) output voltage waveform corresponding to a specific modulating function can be derived from equation (3.120) by methods similar to those employed for the three-pulse waveforms. However, the simple relationship between the basic three-pulse and the P-pulse expressions indicates that this is really unnecessary, and the previously derived three-pulse equations, relevant to the various modulating functions considered, can in fact be readily modified to describe the corresponding multipulse output voltage waveforms.

Equation (3.120) shows that the only effect of the increased pulse number is that whole "families" of components that are functions of the input frequency f_I simply disappear from the output. At $P = 3$, all "families" of components with frequencies comprising multiples of $3f_I$ are present. As P is increased to 6, the "families" of components with frequencies comprising *odd* multiples of $3f_I$ disappear, and only those with frequencies that comprise multiples of $6f_I$—that is, *even* multiples of $3f_I$—remain.

In general, at pulse number P, only those "families" of components will be present whose frequencies comprise multiples of Pf_I. Therefore, it follows that if product $3k$, present in the expressions of three-pulse output voltage waveforms, is simply replaced by Pk, ($P = 3, 6, 9, \ldots$ and $k = 1, 2, 3, \ldots$), these equations will precisely describe the relevant output voltage waveforms for any given pulse number.

In using the above simple rule for generalizing the expressions for three-pulse voltage waveforms, some caution must be exercised. If the arguments of all input frequency-dependent terms contain the product $3k\omega_I$, there is no difficulty; product $3k$ can be replaced routinely by Pk to obtain the expression sought. However, if the arguments of certain terms contain products $3(2k - 1)\omega_I$ and/or $6k\omega_I$, this direct replacement is not permissible. The reason is that, in separating the terms according to whether their arguments contain only the *odd* or the *even* multiples of product $3\omega_I$, we changed the original structure of these equations; this change was really the consequence of the fact that the terms with nonconforming frequencies have zero coefficient (amplitude) and therefore are not present in the output. If these terms were formally included with zero coefficients in the expressions, of course the substitution of $3k$ with Pk would provide the right expressions. For the simplified equations containing terms with frequencies comprising $3(2k - 1)\omega_I$ and $6k\omega_I$ the basic rule however has to be applied differently to obtain the correct results: in products $3k$, replace 3 with P; in products $3(2k - 1)$ replace 3 with P only if P is *odd* (i.e., $P = 3, 9, 15 \ldots$), otherwise leave the terms whose arguments contain the product $3(2k - 1)\omega_I$ completely out of the expression; in products $6k$, replace 6 with P if P is even ($P = 6, 12, 18, \ldots$), and replace 6 with $2P$ if P is *odd.*

The above outlined generalization of the three-pulse expressions is illustrated by some examples.

As the first example, consider the three-pulse output voltage waveform v_O described by equation (3.42) for the linear modulating function $M(t) = \omega_O t + \psi$—that is, the waveform of the unrestricted frequency changer. By substituting Pk for $3k$, this equation becomes:

$$v_O = \frac{3\sqrt{3}}{2\pi} V_I \left(\sin(\omega_O t + \psi) + \sum_{k=1}^{\infty} \frac{\sin\{Pk\omega_I t + (Pk \pm 1)(\omega_O t + \psi)\}}{Pk \pm 1} \right) \tag{3.121}$$

Waveforms synthesized from the terms of equation (3.121) are shown at $f_O/f_I = \frac{1}{3}$ in Figure 3.17 for $P = 6, 9$, and 12.

As a second example, consider expression (3.63), which describes the output voltage waveform for the triangular wave modulating function $M(t) = \sin^{-1}\{\sin(\omega_O t + \psi)\}$. First let P be equal to 6, then, by using the above rules, $v_{O,P=6}$ can be written as follows:

$$\begin{aligned} v_{O,P=6} = \frac{3\sqrt{3}}{2\pi} V_I \Bigg\{ &\sin(\omega_O t + \psi) \\ &+ \sum_{k=1}^{\infty} \left(\frac{\sin\{[6k\omega_I + (6k \pm 1)\omega_O]t + (6k \pm 1)\psi\}}{2(6k \pm 1)} \right. \\ &\left. - \frac{\sin\{[6k\omega_I - (6k \pm 1)\omega_O]t - (6k \pm 1)\psi\}}{2(6k \pm 1)} \right) \\ &+ \sum_{k=1}^{\infty} \sum_{n=0}^{\infty} A_{6k,2n} \sin\{[6k\omega_I \pm 2n\omega_O]t \pm 2n\psi\} \Bigg\} \end{aligned} \tag{3.122}$$

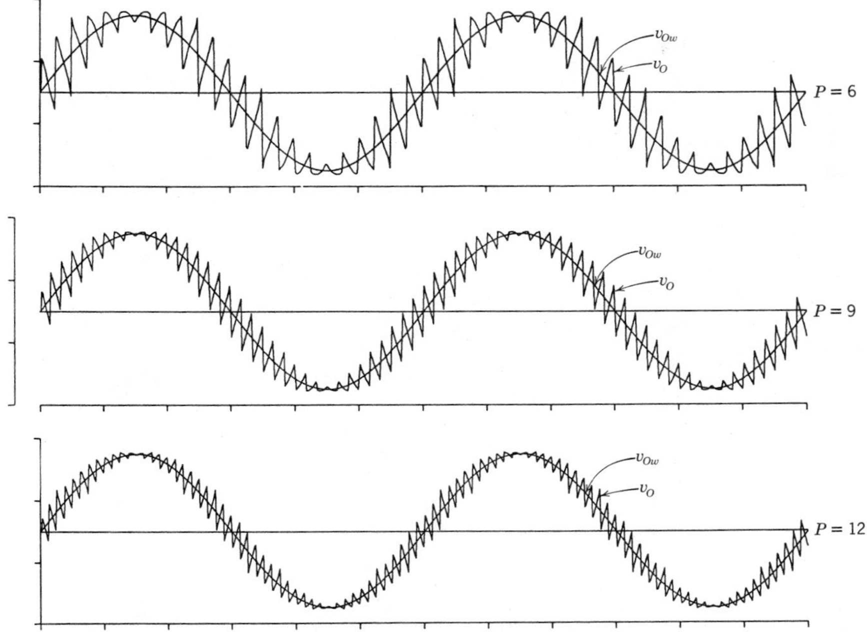

Figure 3.17 Typical six-, nine-, and twelve-pulse UFC output voltage waveforms synthesized from the terms of equation (3.121) at $f_O/f_I = 1/3$.

Now let P be equal to 9, then

$$\begin{aligned} v_{O,P=9} = \frac{3\sqrt{3}}{2\pi} V_I \Bigg\{ & \sin(\omega_O t + \psi) \\ & + \sum_{k=1}^{\infty} \left(\frac{\sin\{[9k\omega_I + (9k \pm 1)\omega_O]t + (9k \pm 1)\psi\}}{2(9k \pm 1)} \right. \\ & \left. - (-1)^{9k} \frac{\sin\{[9k\omega_I - (9k \pm 1)\omega_O]t - (9k \pm 1)\psi\}}{2(9k \pm 1)} \right) \\ & + \sum_{k=1}^{\infty} \sum_{n=0}^{\infty} \Big(A_{18k,2n} \sin\{[18k\omega_I \pm 2n\omega_O]t \pm 2n\psi\} \pm B_{[9(2k-1)],(2n+1)} \\ & \times \sin\{[9(2k - 1)\omega_I \pm (2n + 1)\omega_O]t \pm (2n + 1)\psi\} \Big) \Bigg\} \end{aligned} \tag{3.123}$$

Waveforms synthesized from the terms of the above equations with $P = 6, 9$, and 12 at $f_O/f_I = \frac{1}{3}$ are shown in Figure 3.18.

As a final example, consider the composite output voltage waveform, v_{OM}, described by equation (3.79). Substituting $3k$ with Pk, this equation becomes:

$$\begin{aligned} v_{OM} = \frac{3\sqrt{3}}{2\pi} V_I \Bigg\{ & \sin(\omega_O t + \psi) \\ & + \sum_{k=1}^{\infty} \left(\frac{\sin\{[Pk\omega_I + (Pk \pm 1)\omega_O]t + (Pk \pm 1)\psi\}}{2(Pk \pm 1)} \right. \\ & \left. - (-1)^{Pk} \frac{\sin\{[Pk\omega_I - (Pk \pm 1)\omega_O]t - (Pk \pm 1)\psi\}}{2(Pk \pm 1)} \right) \Bigg\} \end{aligned} \tag{3.124}$$

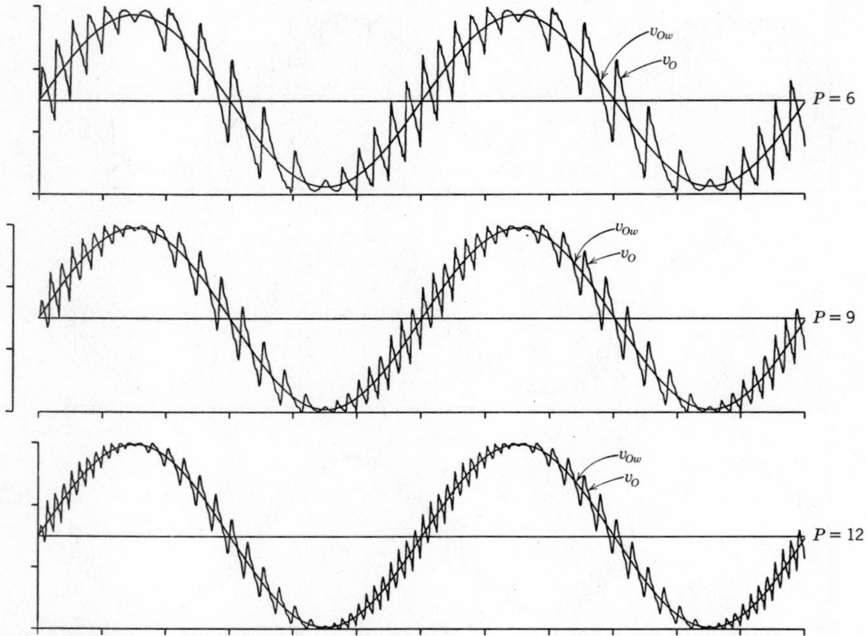

Figure 3.18 Typical six-, nine-, and twelve-pulse positive-type sinusoidal mean output voltage waveforms synthesized from the terms of equations (3.122) and (3.123) at $f_O/f_I = 1/3$.

Waveforms synthesized from the terms of equation (3.124) are shown for $P = 6, 9$, and 12 at $f_O/f_I = \frac{1}{3}$ in Figure 3.19.

From the preceding treatment it is obvious that the output voltage wave indices, that is, the normalized frequencies and amplitudes of the unwanted components, obtained for the three-pulse waveforms can also be generalized by appropriately replacing $3k$ with Pk ($P = 3, 6, 9, \ldots$), $3(2k - 1)$ with $P(2k - 1)$ ($P = 3, 9, 15, \ldots$), and $6k$ with Pk ($P = 6, 12, 18, \ldots$), or with $2Pk$ ($P = 3, 9, 15, \ldots$). For example, from equations (3.46) and (3.47) the output voltage wave indices of a P-pulse unrestricted frequency changer $[M(t) = \omega_O t + \psi]$ are given by

$$\nu_{Ok} = (Pk \pm 1) + Pk\frac{f_I}{f_O} \tag{3.125}$$

$$\gamma_{Ok} = \frac{1}{Pk \pm 1} \tag{3.126}$$

It is evident that the output voltage wave indices progressively improve with increasing pulse number, indicating that the approximation of the desired voltage wave becomes closer.

Before concluding this section, data on total r.m.s. distortion of the output waveforms of different pulse numbers may be illustrative. Generally the r.m.s. distortion of the output voltage waveform is dependent upon the modulating function. However, it was shown that for sinusoidal mean three-pulse (noncomposite) output waveforms, the total r.m.s. distortion is invariably about 0.68, regardless of the modulating function. The total r.m.s. distortion of sinusoidal mean multipulse output voltage waveforms of the same pulse number as one another is, of course, also independent

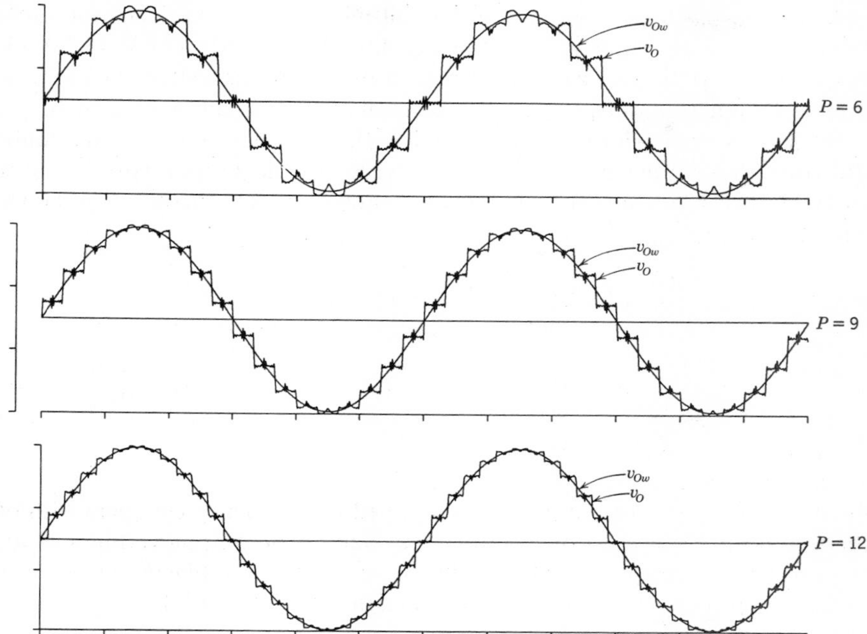

Figure 3.19 Typical six-, nine-, and twelve-pulse concurrent composite output voltage waveforms synthesized from the terms of equation (3.124) at $f_O/f_I = 1/3$.

of the modulating function; it is about 0.30 for six-pulse, 0.18 for nine-pulse, and 0.13 for twelve-pulse waveforms.

3.6 THREE-PHASE OUTPUT VOLTAGE WAVEFORMS

A frequency changer with three-phase output generally comprises three identical power circuits, one for each output phase. The input power is usually supplied by a common source to all three circuits. Each circuit is controlled to generate an output voltage waveform with a wanted component displaced by $2\pi/3$ with respect to the other two wanted outputs. The three wanted components thus form a balanced set of three-phase voltages.

It has also been shown that the phase position of the desired output wave and that of the wanted component are completely determined by the phase position of the corresponding modulating function. That is to say, if the phase position of the modulating function is defined by angle ψ with respect to a chosen reference point, the desired wave of the generated output voltage will also be displaced by the same angle ψ from the reference point. It follows therefore that the three modulating functions defining the operation of the power switches in the three circuits of a frequency changer with three-phase output must be displaced by $2\pi/3$ with respect to each other in order to produce a balanced set of three wanted output voltages.

It is obvious from the preceding discussion that the analytical expressions for the three output waveforms must be identical except for the phase angles of the constituent terms. Therefore, the expressions previously derived for one (single-phase) output voltage can easily be modified to describe any one of the three voltages constituting a three-phase output.

Consider the basic expressions for the output voltage waveform for different modulating functions—that is, equations (3.42), (3.43), (3.63), (3.64), (3.73), (3.79), (3.90), (3.91), (3.104). In each case the wanted component—as well as the modulating function—is a function of $\omega_O t + \psi$. Therefore, if angle ψ is substituted by 0, $-2\pi/3$ and $-4\pi/3$, three expressions describing each of the three output phases are obtained. To illustrate this simple procedure, let us write up the output voltages of a P-pulse, three-phase unrestricted frequency changer in a general form [refer to equation (3.121)]

$$v_{Op} = \frac{3\sqrt{3}}{2\pi} V_I \left(\sin\left(\omega_O t - (p-1)\frac{2\pi}{3}\right) + \sum_{k=1}^{\infty} \frac{\sin\left\{Pk\omega_I t + (Pk \pm 1)\left(\omega_O t - (p-1)\frac{2\pi}{3}\right)\right\}}{Pk \pm 1} \right) \tag{3.127}$$

$p = 1, 2, 3.$

Obviously, the above technique can be applied for frequency changers with other numbers of output phases. For example, any one of the output voltages of an m-phase unrestricted frequency changer can be obtained by replacing $(p - 1)(2\pi/3)$, $p = 1, 2, 3$, with $(p - 1)(2\pi/m)$, $p = 1, 2, \ldots m$, in equation (3.127).

CHAPTER FOUR

CONTROL OF THE OUTPUT VOLTAGE

The primary function of a frequency changer is to provide some constant or variable frequency a-c power when energized by an a-c source having frequency characteristics incompatible with the output requirements. In the previous investigation of output waveform synthesis, the magnitude of the desired a-c output voltage was not directly controllable; it was always proportional to the input source voltage. In many practical applications, however, the amplitude of the mean a-c output voltage—that is, the amplitude of the desired output voltage wave—has to be controllable independently of the amplitude of the input source voltage. For example, when a frequency changer is used to control the speed of an a-c machine, the mean a-c output voltage is normally varied with the output frequency in order to keep the ratio of the stator voltage to frequency, and thereby the air-gap flux, constant. In other applications, independent control of each output phase voltage may be required to provide a precisely regulated a-c power supply with unbalanced loads on each output phase.

In this section various methods for controlling the mean a-c output voltage of static frequency changers are investigated. It has already been shown that the output voltage waveform is generated by judicious control of the duration and sequence of the switch closures, which are mathematically described by appropriately modulated existence functions. The output voltage waveforms are, for a given input source and pulse number, determined by the character of the existence functions. It follows, therefore, that an appropriate mathematical modification in the character of the previously defined existence functions is necessary to make the mean a-c output voltage variable, independent of the input source. Since the unmodulated existence functions by definitions generate zero mean output voltage, it may be expected that the amplitude of the desired voltage wave can be varied by judiciously controlling the *depth* of the applied frequency modulation. An alternative means for varying the mean a-c output voltage is to control the unit value intervals of the existence functions—that is, the conduction intervals of the corresponding switches in the power circuit—while maintaining their repetition rate the same as for full output voltage. While the first procedure requires only the generalization of the modulating function (to make the modulation process amplitude dependent), the second makes it necessary to express the basic, unmodulated existence functions as *pulse-width-modulated* rectangular waves.

The output voltage of a frequency changer composed of a number of elementary three-pulse circuits may also be varied by the indirect method of phase shifting the constituent wanted components with respect to each other, thereby altering their vectorial sum at the output.

The objective of the present investigation is to find out in what way the above methods of output voltage control affect the spectral characteristic of the output voltage waveforms previously considered. The *quality* of the output waveshapes has been measured by the relevant output voltage wave indices. In the present case these indices become functions of the amplitude of the mean a-c output voltage wave. Thus the character of these functions will show the relative merit of the corresponding voltage control technique and its compatibility with the original *full* output voltage waveform.

In the following three sections the three possible methods of output voltage control—pulse-width modulation, amplitude-dependent frequency modulation, and phase shift—are analyzed in detail.

4.1 OUTPUT VOLTAGE CONTROL BY PULSE-WIDTH MODULATION OF THE EXISTENCE FUNCTIONS

The possibility of applying the technique of pulse-width modulation to the control of the mean output voltage exists for all frequency changer circuits except the NCC.

As we have seen, the output voltage waveform is constructed by successively connecting the input voltage waves, via an array of bidirectional switches, to the output. The conduction time of each switch is controlled by the corresponding existence function. Suppose now that each conduction period is subdivided into two intervals and the switches are closed during one subinterval only—the *active* interval. During the other subinterval—the *passive* interval—the output is effectively disconnected from the input source, and a separate "freewheeling" path is provided for the output current, which generally will continue to flow due to reactive elements in the load circuit. The output voltage waveform thus obtained consists of successive segments of the input voltage waves, separated by intervals of zero voltage. By controlling the relative duration of the active and passive intervals within the original conduction period, or *time frame*, the mean a-c output voltage can be varied continuously from maximum to zero, independently of the output frequency.

The above form of pulse-width modulation lends itself more naturally to bridge circuits than midpoint circuits. In bridge circuits, the switches make connections to both ends of the load, and thus a freewheeling path for the load current during the passive interval can be provided through a chosen *leg* of the circuit. Midpoint circuits, on the other hand, do not offer this facility, although it is always possible to provide a separate freewheeling switch across the output terminals. An approach applicable to midpoint circuits with three-phase, three-wire loads, which does not require a separate shorting switch, is presented in Chapter 6.

A somewhat different principle is also possible, however, that allows the basic frequency changer circuit to be used without modification. The essence of this method is to control the mean output voltage of each elementary three-pulse circuit by connecting its output during the passive interval to another input wave. This can be accomplished by *stepping ahead*; that is, preceding each active interval within each time frame, the output is connected for the duration of the passive interval to the input phase that will be used during the active interval in the next time frame.

The following analysis will again be carried out for a three-pulse circuit. It will be seen, however, as with previous results, that the analytical expressions derived are directly applicable to complex multipulse circuits.

Consider Figure 4.1, in which the derivation of the basic ($f_O \equiv 0$) pulse-width-modulated existence functions for an elementary three-pulse circuit is illustrated.

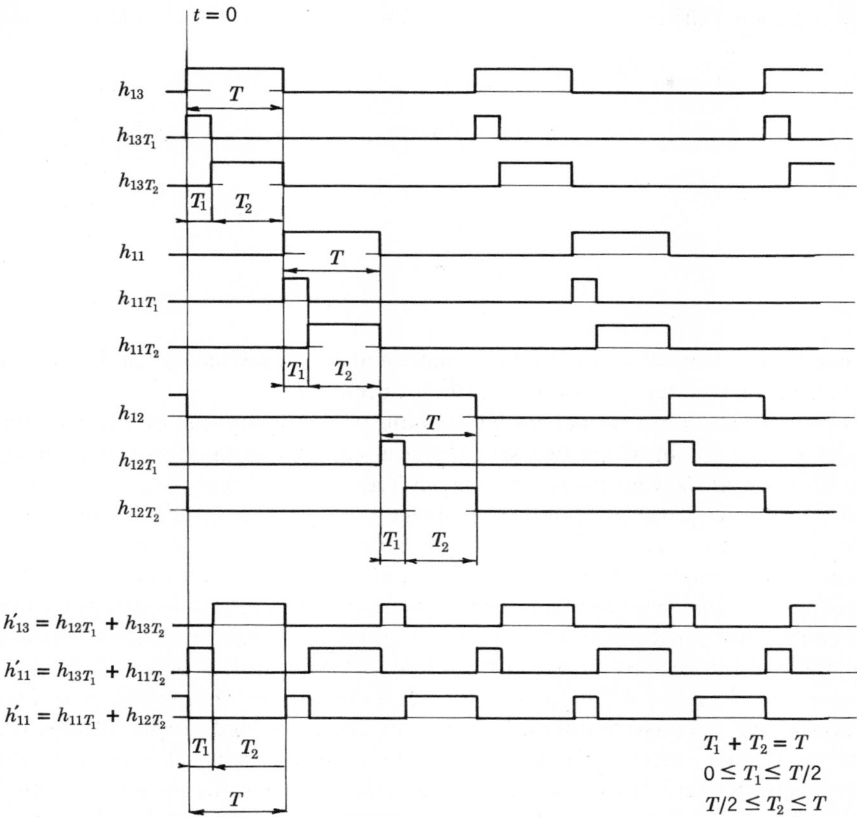

Figure 4.1 Waveforms illustrating the derivation of pulse-width modulated existence functions.

The conduction period T ($T = 1/3f_I$) of the three existence functions, h_{11}, h_{12}, and h_{13}, is subdivided into a passive interval T_1 and an active interval T_2. The output voltage waveform corresponding to the active intervals, designated by $v_{O_{T2}}$, is defined as before

$$v_{O_{T2}} = [h_{11_{T2}} \quad h_{12_{T2}} \quad h_{13_{T2}}] \begin{bmatrix} v_{I1} \\ v_{I2} \\ v_{I3} \end{bmatrix} \tag{4.1}$$

where $h_{11_{T2}}$, $h_{12_{T2}}$, $h_{13_{T2}}$ are the existence functions representing the switch closures during active intervals, and v_{I1}, v_{I2}, v_{I3} are the input voltages.

As stipulated, the output voltage during the passive intervals, designated $v_{O_{T1}}$, is defined in the following way:

$$v_{O_{T1}} = [h_{13_{T1}} \quad h_{11_{T1}} \quad h_{12_{T1}}] \begin{bmatrix} v_{I1} \\ v_{I2} \\ v_{I3} \end{bmatrix} \tag{4.2}$$

where $h_{11_{T1}}$, $h_{12_{T1}}$, and $h_{13_{T1}}$ are the existence functions representing the switch closures during passive intervals.

The complete output waveform, v_O, is of course the sum of (4.1) and (4.2), namely

$$v_O = v_{O_{T1}} + v_{O_{T2}}$$

$$= [(h_{13_{T1}} + h_{11_{T2}}) \ (h_{11_{T1}} + h_{12_{T2}}) \ (h_{12_{T1}} + h_{13_{T2}})] \begin{bmatrix} v_{I1} \\ v_{I2} \\ v_{I3} \end{bmatrix} \tag{4.3}$$

or

$$v_O = [h'_{11}\ h'_{12}\ h'_{13}] \begin{bmatrix} v_{I1} \\ v_{I2} \\ v_{I3} \end{bmatrix} \tag{4.4}$$

Existence functions h'_{11}, h'_{12}, and h'_{13}, representing the switch closures during both active and passive intervals, are illustrated in Figure 4.1.

In order to acquire a deeper understanding of this technique of voltage control, consider Figure 4.2, in which two sets of pulse-width-modulated existence functions and related output waveforms at zero output frequency and zero mean output voltage are shown for six-pulse midpoint and bridge circuits. For future convenience, the passive intervals are represented by angle β measured, in the case of zero output frequency, at ω_I angular frequency, and the pulse-width modulation of the existence functions is executed symmetrically about the time zero axis, as indicated in Figure 4.2. This symmetrical pulse-width modulation is convenient mathematically because the phase angle of the desired output voltage remains independent of β.

Inspection of Figure 4.2 indicates that each constituent three-pulse waveform is not zero during the passive intervals. However, the combined output voltage is zero during the passive intervals for both types of six-pulse circuits. It is perhaps worthwhile to examine here, before beginning the actual analysis, the means whereby zero output voltage and a corresponding zero-impedance current path is achieved in the two types of six-pulse circuits.

Consider Figure 4.2. At time t_1 (an instant of an active interval) the switches represented by h'_{11a} and, h'_{13b} are closed. The output voltage obtained from the parallel configuration—at the output of the summing symbol M—is $\frac{1}{2}(v_{I1} - v_{I2})$; that obtained from the series configuration—that is, the bridge circuit—is $(v_{I1} - v_{I2})$. In the first circuit the output current flows from phases 1 and -2 via the load back to the neutral, and in the second one it flows from phase 1 via the load to phase 2 (heavy lines). At time t_2 (an instant of a passive interval), the switches represented by existence functions h'_{11a} and h'_{12b} are closed. The voltage at the output terminals of both circuits is zero. However, the output current of the parallel configuration, assuming a reactive load, still flows through the source (from phase 1, via the load, to phase -1). The load of the bridge circuit, on the other hand, is actually *shorted* by the two switches; consequently, the current in the input source is zero. It should be noted that, if the six-phase source for the parallel combination is produced by a phase-splitting transformer, the load current would only circulate through the appropriate secondary windings and would not flow in the input source during the passive intervals.

To proceed with the analysis, consider the basic set of three pulse-width-modulated existence functions shown in Figure 4.2 (h'_{11a}, h'_{12a}, h'_{13a}). These functions can be expanded into similar Fourier series as given by equation (3.4). By introducing the modulating function $M(t)$ into the arguments of these Fourier expressions, the pulse-width-modulated version of the existence functions, analogous to those given

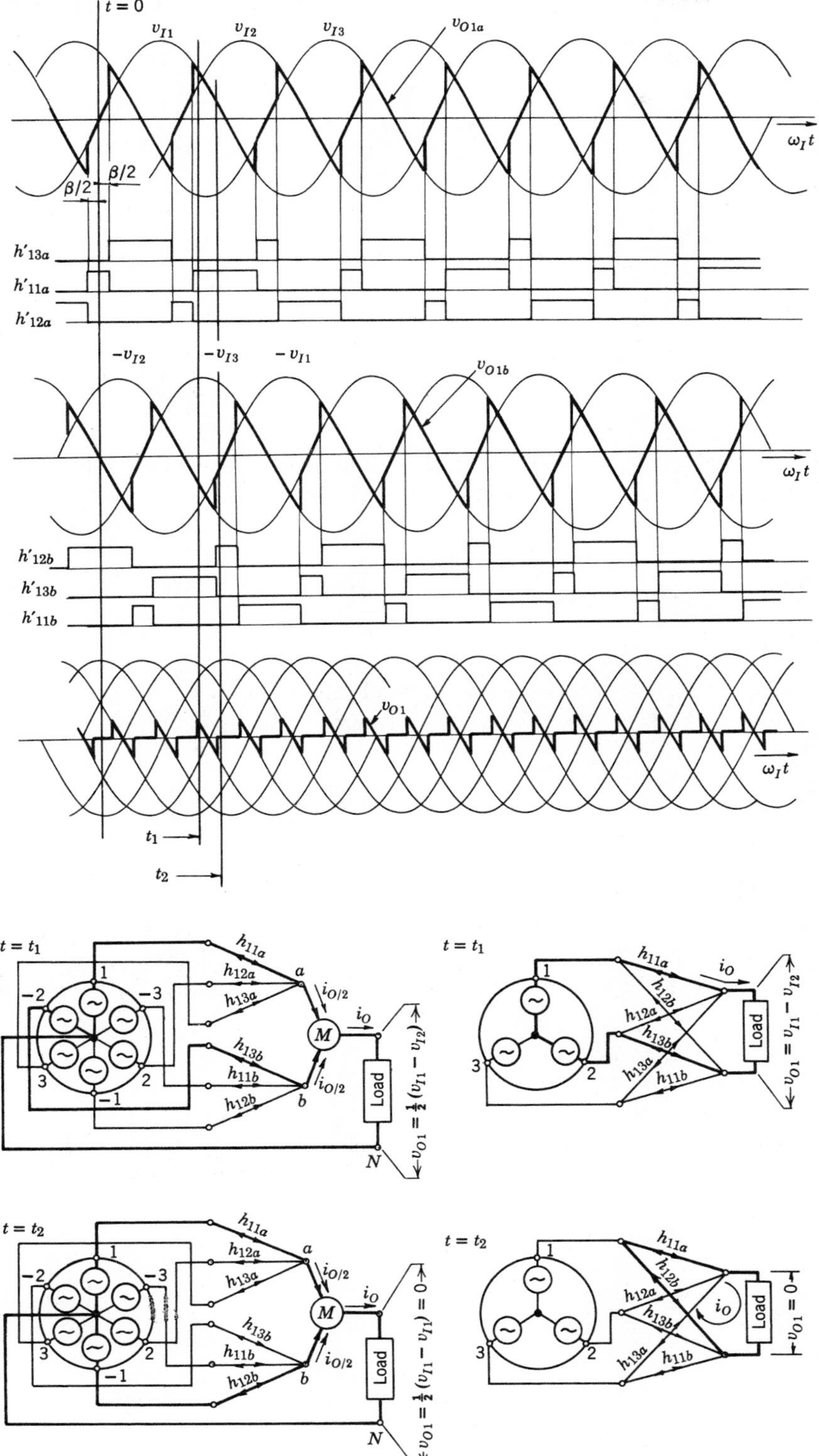

Figure 4.2 Pulse-width modulated existence functions and related output voltage waveforms for six-pulse midpoint and bridge circuits at zero output frequency.

by equation (3.6), is obtained, namely

$$
\begin{aligned}
h'_{11}(\beta) &= \frac{1}{3} - \sum_{n=-\infty}^{\infty} \frac{2 \sin n\dfrac{\pi}{3}}{n\pi} \cos n\left(\frac{\pi}{3} + \frac{\beta}{2}\right) \exp jn\{\omega_I t + M(t)\} \\
h'_{12}(\beta) &= \frac{1}{3} - \sum_{n=-\infty}^{\infty} \frac{2 \sin n\dfrac{\pi}{3}}{n\pi} \cos n\left(\frac{\pi}{3} + \frac{\beta}{2}\right) \exp jn\left\{\omega_I t - \frac{2\pi}{3} + M(t)\right\} \qquad (4.5) \\
h'_{13}(\beta) &= \frac{1}{3} - \sum_{n=-\infty}^{\infty} \frac{2 \sin n\dfrac{\pi}{3}}{n\pi} \cos n\left(\frac{\pi}{3} + \frac{\beta}{2}\right) \exp jn\left\{\omega_I t - \frac{4\pi}{3} + M(t)\right\}
\end{aligned}
$$

where $0 \leqq \beta \leqq \pi/3$.

The complementary set of pulse-width-modulated existence functions, analogous to those given by equation (3.7), can be similarly obtained:

$$
\begin{aligned}
h'_{\pi 11}(\beta) &= \frac{1}{3} + \sum_{n=-\infty}^{\infty} \frac{2 \sin n\dfrac{2\pi}{3}}{n\pi} \cos n\left(\frac{\pi}{3} + \frac{\beta}{2}\right) \exp jn\{\omega_I t - M(t)\} \\
h'_{\pi 12}(\beta) &= \frac{1}{3} + \sum_{n=-\infty}^{\infty} \frac{2 \sin n\dfrac{2\pi}{3}}{n\pi} \cos n\left(\frac{\pi}{3} + \frac{\beta}{2}\right) \exp jn\left\{\omega_I t - \frac{2\pi}{3} - M(t)\right\} \qquad (4.6) \\
h'_{\pi 13}(\beta) &= \frac{1}{3} + \sum_{n=-\infty}^{\infty} \frac{2 \sin n\dfrac{2\pi}{3}}{n\pi} \cos n\left(\frac{\pi}{3} + \frac{\beta}{2}\right) \exp jn\left\{\omega_I t - \frac{4\pi}{3} - M(t)\right\}
\end{aligned}
$$

Comparison of equations (4.5) and (4.6) with the corresponding expressions for the original existence functions given by equations (3.6) and (3.7) indicates that only the coefficients of the terms are different. Therefore, the basic expression written for the three-pulse output waveform [equation (3.8)] will remain valid for the pulse-width-modulated existence functions if coefficient $\sin n(2\pi/3)$ is replaced by $2 \sin n(\pi/3) \cos n(\pi/3 + \beta/2)$. Recognizing that

$$
-2 \sin n\frac{\pi}{3} \cos n\left(\frac{\pi}{3} + \frac{\beta}{2}\right) = \begin{cases} -(-1)^{3k}\sqrt{3} \cos\left\{(3k+1)\left(\dfrac{\pi}{3} + \dfrac{\beta}{2}\right)\right\}, & k = 0, 1, 2, \ldots \\ (-1)^{3k}\sqrt{3} \cos\left\{(3k-1)\left(\dfrac{\pi}{3} + \dfrac{\beta}{2}\right)\right\}, & k = 1, 2, \ldots \end{cases} \qquad (4.7a)
$$

and

$$
2 \sin n\frac{2\pi}{3} \cos n\left(\frac{\pi}{3} + \frac{\beta}{2}\right) = \begin{cases} \sqrt{3} \cos\left\{(3k+1)\left(\dfrac{\pi}{3} + \dfrac{\beta}{2}\right)\right\}, & k = 0, 1, 2, \ldots \\ -\sqrt{3} \cos\left\{(3k-1)\left(\dfrac{\pi}{3} + \dfrac{\beta}{2}\right)\right\}, & k = 1, 2, \ldots \end{cases} \qquad (4.7b)
$$

the following fundamental expressions for the two complementary output voltage waveforms, v_O and $v_{O\pi}$, which are analogous to equations (3.10) and (3.11), can be obtained:

$$v_O(\beta) = \frac{3\sqrt{3}}{\pi} V_I \left(\cos\left(\frac{\pi}{3} + \frac{\beta}{2}\right) \sin M(t) + \sum_{k=1}^{\infty} (-1)^{3k} \frac{\cos\left\{(3k \pm 1)\left(\frac{\pi}{3} + \frac{\beta}{2}\right)\right\}}{3k \pm 1} \sin\{3k\omega_I t + (3k \pm 1)M(t)\} \right) \tag{4.8}$$

$$v_{O\pi}(\beta) = \frac{3\sqrt{3}}{\pi} V_I \left(\cos\left(\frac{\pi}{3} + \frac{\beta}{2}\right) \sin M(t) - \sum_{k=1}^{\infty} \frac{\cos\left\{(3k \pm 1)\left(\frac{\pi}{3} + \frac{\beta}{2}\right)\right\}}{3k \pm 1} \sin\{3k\omega_I t - (3k \pm 1)M(t)\} \right) \tag{4.9}$$

where $0 \leqq \beta \leqq \pi/3$.

Evidently the amplitude of the desired output voltage wave sin $M(t)$ is a function of angle β; it is equal to $(3\sqrt{3}/2\pi)V_I$ at $\beta = 0$, and becomes zero at $\beta = \pi/3$. The reduction of the output voltage may be expressed by the *output voltage ratio*, r, defined here as the ratio of the amplitude of the actual (sinusoidal) wanted component to the maximum amplitude of the wanted component obtained at $\beta = 0$, namely,

$$r = \frac{V_O}{V_{O\max}} = 2\cos\left(\frac{\pi}{3} + \frac{\beta}{2}\right) \tag{4.10}$$

Equations (4.8) and (4.9) explicitly show that the frequencies of the components constituting the output voltage waveform are, as previously, functions only of $M(t)$ and not of β. On the other hand, the amplitudes of the constituent components are now functions of β. This means of course that the amplitudes of the unwanted components corresponding to a given modulating function will generally vary as the amplitude of the wanted component is varied by pulse-width modulation.

Since the difference between the original [equations (3.10) and (3.11)] and the pulse-width-modulated versions [equations (4.8) and (4.9)] of the two expressions for the complementary waveforms is only in the coefficients of the terms, it follows that it is not necessary to go through lengthy mathematical manipulations for finding the pulse-width-modulated counterparts of the expressions previously derived for various modulating functions. In fact, it is enough to replace the multipliers $1/(3k \pm 1)$ with

$$\frac{(-1)^{3k} 2\cos\left\{(3k \pm 1)\left(\frac{\pi}{3} + \frac{\beta}{2}\right)\right\}}{3k \pm 1}$$

in the original equations to obtain the corresponding pulse-width-modulated expressions. It should also be noted that the previously established rules for modifying the expressions of three-pulse waveforms for multipulse waveforms will remain valid for the pulse-width-modulated expressions. For example, by making the above specified replacement for the relevant multipliers in equation (3.121), an expression for the pulse-width-modulated version of the P-pulse UFC $[M(t) = \omega_O t]$ output

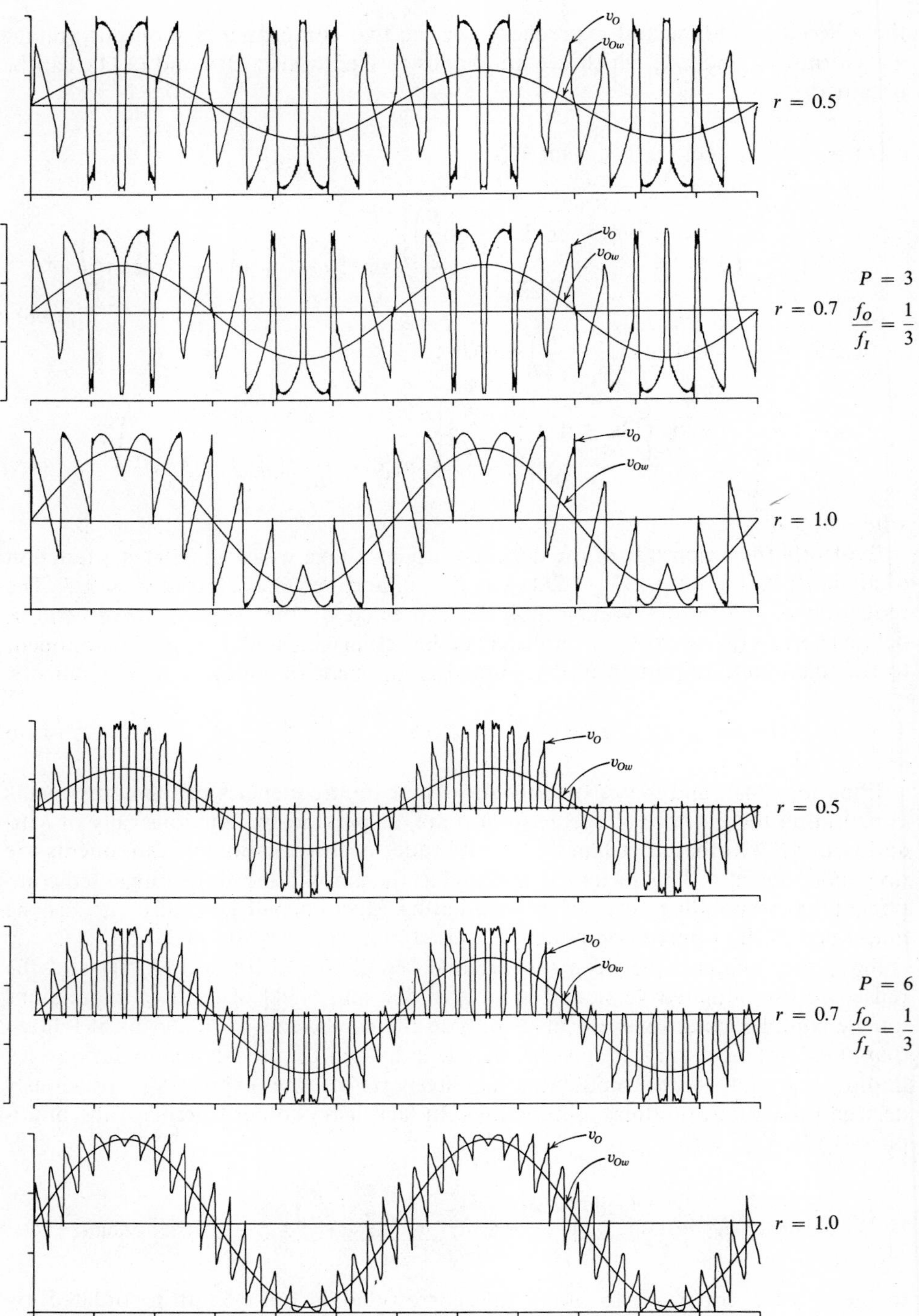
v_O
v_{Ow}
$r = 0.5$
$P = 3$
$r = 0.7$
$\frac{f_O}{f_I} = \frac{1}{3}$
$r = 1.0$
$r = 0.5$
$P = 6$
$r = 0.7$
$\frac{f_O}{f_I} = \frac{1}{3}$
$r = 1.0$

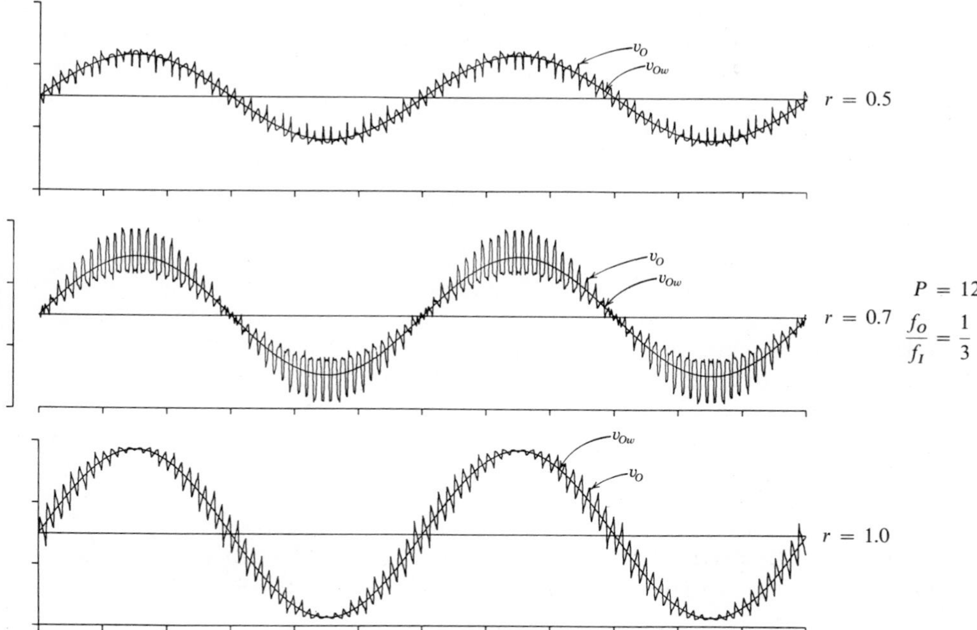

Figure 4.3 Typical three-, six-, and twelve-pulse output voltage waveforms synthesized at output voltage ratios of $r = 0.5$, $r = 0.7$, and $r = 1.0$ from the terms of equation (4.11); $f_O/f_I = 1/3$.

voltage waveform is obtained (at $\psi = 0$):

$$v_O(\beta) = \frac{3\sqrt{3}}{\pi} V_I \left(\cos\left(\frac{\pi}{3} + \frac{\beta}{2}\right) \sin \omega_O t \right.$$
$$\left. + \sum_{k=1}^{\infty} (-1)^{Pk} \frac{\cos\left\{(Pk \pm 1)\left(\frac{\pi}{3} + \frac{\beta}{2}\right)\right\}}{Pk \pm 1} \sin\{Pk\omega_I + (Pk \pm 1)\omega_O\}t \right) \quad (4.11)$$

where $P = 3, 6, 9, 12, \ldots; 0 \leqq \beta \leqq \pi/3$. Typical output waveforms synthesized from the terms of equation (4.11) at various output voltage ratios, $r = (V_O/V_{O\max}) = V_O/(3\sqrt{3}V_I/2\pi)$, are shown for pulse numbers 3, 6, and 12 in Figure 4.3.

The characteristics of the pulse-width-modulated output voltage waveforms, and hence the advantages and disadvantages of this method of output voltage control, can readily be established from the two basic expressions given by equations (4.8) and (4.9); these are summarized below:

1. The most important, and—as will be seen—unique, characteristic of the pulse-width-modulation voltage control method is the fact that the frequencies of the unwanted components are independent of the amplitude of the wanted output voltage wave; in other words, no new unwanted components are introduced as the mean output voltage is reduced. This property is particularly significant for the unrestricted frequency changer, the unique feature of which is the *unrestricted* output frequency range obtainable at full output voltage, on account of the appropriate separation of the unwanted frequencies from the wanted frequency, which feature can thus be preserved as the output voltage is reduced.

2. The amplitudes of the unwanted components, and thus the r.m.s. distortion of the output voltage waveform, vary as a function of the output voltage ratio, $r = 2\cos(\pi/3 + \beta/2)$. The variation of the normalized amplitudes is determined for any general P-pulse output waveform by the multiplier $2\cos\{(Pk \pm 1)(\pi/3 + \beta/2)\}$. Since the maximum value of this multiplier is 2, it follows that at certain values of β (i.e., at certain output voltage ratios at which $\cos\{(Pk \pm 1)(\pi/3 + \beta/2)\}$ is unity) the amplitude of every unwanted component becomes twice as large as its value at full voltage—although its relative value, of course, will be more than twice that obtained at full voltage.

3. The technique of pulse-width modulation makes it necessary to operate the power switches at double rate, as indicated by the existence functions in Figure 4.2. The increased switching rate may be objectionable in some practical applications, particularly if the frequency of the input source is high, because of the correspondingly increased losses of the power circuit. Also, in practical frequency changers some loss of voltage control range will be obtained because the passive and active intervals, respectively, cannot be made infinitely small.

4.2 OUTPUT VOLTAGE CONTROL BY AMPLITUDE-DEPENDENT FREQUENCY MODULATION OF THE EXISTENCE FUNCTIONS

In the course of investigating ways of synthesizing different output voltage waveforms it has been found that the desired output voltage wave has always been obtained from the same general expression $\sin M(t)$, where $M(t)$ is the modulating function defining the angular variation of the pertinent existence functions. This suggests that a convenient and universally applicable way of controlling the amplitude of the mean output voltage wave may be provided by the modulating function itself. A modulating function suitable for voltage control should, of course, have two independent variables, one for controlling the *frequency*, and one for controlling the *amplitude* of the desired output voltage. To examine the requirements of this generalized modulating function, let us simply assume here that the modulation of the existence functions can indeed be controlled by two independent variables, that is, the modulating function takes the general form $M = M(\kappa, t)$ in which κ defines the amplitude of the desired output voltage, and t is the time. This assumption implies that such a modulating function will inevitably be a *periodic* function of time. To see this, consider for example our "popular" nonperiodic modulating function $M = \omega_O t$. This can only be made a function of κ if ω_O itself becomes a function κ, that is, $\omega_O = \omega_O(\kappa)$. It follows from the basic term $\sin\{M(t)\} = \sin\{\omega_O(\kappa)t\}$ that the desired output voltage wave will be periodic, as originally stipulated, only if $\omega_O(\kappa)$ is constant or itself is a periodic function. Since $\omega_O(\kappa)$ by definition is not constant, consequently it must be periodic.

In order to avoid unnecessary complications without giving up the possibility of handling any desired output voltage wave of practical importance, we may further assume here that $M(\kappa, t)$ will satisfy the following condition:

$$\begin{gathered} \sin M(\kappa, t) = \kappa F_D(\omega_O t) \\ -1 \leqq F_D(\omega_O t) \leqq 1 \end{gathered} \tag{4.12}$$

where $F_D(\omega_O t)$ is the function describing the desired output voltage wave (which is usually the sinusoidal wanted component), and κ is its normalized amplitude. Since the maximum amplitude of the desired output voltage wave is limited by that of the input voltage waves—for a three-pulse circuit, for example, the amplitude of the desired output voltage wave cannot exceed $(3\sqrt{3}/2\pi)V_I$—it follows that the character of the desired output voltage wave can be reproduced only in the range $0 \leqq \kappa \leqq 1$. This range may thus be termed the linear operating range of the frequency changer, because the amplitude of the desired output voltage wave, and the wanted component thereof,* is directly proportional to κ. However, it is sometimes useful to operate a frequency changer outside this range; for this reason function $\sin M(\kappa, t)$ is defined for the range $\kappa > 1$ as follows:

$$\left.\begin{aligned} \sin M(\kappa, t) &= \kappa F_D(\omega_O t) && \text{for} \quad 0 \leqq |\kappa F_D(\omega_O t)| \leqq 1 \\ \sin M(\kappa, t) &= 1 && \text{for} \quad \kappa F_D(\omega_O t) > 1 \\ \sin M(\kappa, t) &= -1 && \text{for} \quad \kappa F_D(\omega_O t) < -1 \end{aligned}\right\} \tag{4.13}$$

where $1 < \kappa \leqq \infty$.

This operating mode is of course nonlinear; the mean output wave becomes similar to that obtainable from an ordinary limiter (i.e., the portions of the wave above $+1$ and below -1 are "clipped" off). The operating range $\kappa > 1$ may be useful in practice to increase the amplitude of the *wanted* component above that of the input voltage wave (of course, at the cost of increased distortion). Consider, for example, the case of $F_D(\omega_O t) = \kappa \sin \omega_O t$; the mean output voltage wave is sinusoidal in the range $0 \leqq \kappa \leqq 1$, and it becomes pseudo-trapezoidal—that is, a sine wave with the peaks levelled off as κ increases above unity, approaching a square-wave as κ tends to infinity.

Before proceeding further, it may be useful to clarify the definition of κ and establish its relationship with the output voltage ratio, r, defined earlier. As has been stipulated, the amplitude of the desired output voltage wave becomes maximum at $\kappa = 1$. Thus, in the range $0 \leqq \kappa \leqq 1$, κ represents the ratio of the amplitude of the *actual* desired output voltage wave to that obtained at $\kappa = 1$. In the range $1 < \kappa \leqq \infty$, on the other hand, κ represents the ratio of the amplitude of the *fictitious* desired output voltage wave $\kappa F_D(\omega_O t)$—which is not obtainable from the frequency changer due to "saturation"—to the amplitude of the desired output voltage wave obtained at $\kappa = 1$. The output voltage ratio, r, on the other hand, is defined as the ratio of the amplitude of the sinusoidal *wanted* component to the maximum amplitude obtainable with sinusoidal mean output voltage—that is, with a sinusoidal desired output voltage wave. It follows therefore that, for $F_D(\omega_O t) = \sin \omega_O t$, $r = \kappa$ in the range $0 \leqq \kappa \leqq 1$.

The conditions specified in equations (4.13) can be satisfied if the modulating function $M(\kappa, t)$ is defined as follows:

$$\left.\begin{aligned} M(\kappa, t) &= \sin^{-1}\{\kappa F_D(\omega_O t)\} && \text{for} \quad 0 \leqq |\kappa F_D(\omega_O t)| \leqq 1 \\ M(\kappa, t) &= \frac{\pi}{2} && \kappa F_D(\omega_O t) > 1 \\ M(\kappa, t) &= -\frac{\pi}{2} && \kappa F_D(\omega_O t) < 1 \end{aligned}\right\} \tag{4.14}$$

* Again, we draw the reader's attention to the distinction between what we call the desired output voltage wave, and the wanted component of output voltage. The former is the mean wave that the control attempts to produce and may or may not be sinusoidal; the latter, by definition, is the sinusoidal component of the output voltage wave at the wanted output frequency.

It may be recognized that, for sinusoidal mean output voltage wave, that is, $F_D(\omega_O t) = \sin(\omega_O t + \psi)$, the modulating function given in (4.14) is a generalized form of the previously considered "triangular wave" modulating function $M(t) = \sin^{-1}\{\sin(\omega_O t + \psi)\}$ defined by equation (3.41). Practical ways of deriving the modulating function of equation (4.14) and the associated existence functions are described in Chapter 7.

Since the general, amplitude-dependent modulating function, $M(\kappa, t)$, is periodic (the period is $T_O = 1/f_O$), it follows that there is really no new theory or mathematical expression to be developed; the formulae derived at the beginning of Chapter 3 for periodic modulating functions of fixed amplitude are readily applicable. The only difference between the present and the previous case is that the set of Fourier coefficients, $a_{(3k\pm1),0}$, $a_{(3k\pm1),2n}$, $b_{1,n}$, and $b_{(3k\pm1),n}$ given in equations (3.16)–(3.19), which appear in the general expressions of the differently constructed output voltage waveforms, are now functions of the normalized amplitude κ because $M(\kappa, t)$ is a function of κ. Therefore they have to be computed separately for each value of κ of interest.

To recapitulate the relevant ideas, consider the basic expression given for one of the complementary waveforms (v_O) in equation (3.12). This expression is rewritten here, with the substitution of $M(t) = M(\kappa, t)$ for convenience:

$$v_O(\kappa) = \frac{3\sqrt{3}}{2\pi} V_I \left(\sin M(\kappa, t) + \sum_{k=1}^{\infty} \frac{\sin 3k\omega_I t \cos\{(3k \pm 1)M(\kappa, t)\} + \cos 3k\omega_I t \sin\{(3k \pm 1)M(\kappa, t)\}}{3k \pm 1} \right) \tag{4.15}$$

As explained previously, in order to develop this equation further, it is necessary to decompose functions $\cos\{(3k \pm 1)M(\kappa, t)\}$ and $\sin\{(3k \pm 1)M(\kappa, t)\}$. For periodic modulating functions, this can be accomplished by Fourier expansion, namely,

$$\cos\{(3k \pm 1)M(\kappa, t)\} = a_{(3k\pm1),0}(\kappa) + \sum_{n=1}^{\infty} a_{(3k\pm1),2n}(\kappa) \cos 2n(\omega_O t + \psi) \tag{4.16}$$

$$\sin M(\kappa, t) = \sum_{n=1}^{\infty} b_{1,n}(\kappa) \sin n(\omega_O t + \psi) \tag{4.17}$$

$$\sin\{(3k \pm 1)M(\kappa, t)\} = \sum_{n=1}^{\infty} b_{(3k\pm1),n}(\kappa) \sin n(\omega_O t + \psi) \tag{4.18}$$

The above series are of course defined only at fixed values of κ; this is quite natural since every value of κ defines a different modulating function of similar character. For this reason, each coefficient becomes an indirect function of κ and is defined for a given value of κ as before:

$$a_{(3k\pm1),0}(\kappa) = \frac{1}{\pi} \int_{\psi}^{\pi+\psi} \cos\{(3k \pm 1)M(\kappa, t)\}\, d(\omega_O t) \tag{4.19}$$

$$a_{(3k\pm1),2n}(\kappa) = \frac{2}{\pi} \int_{\psi}^{\pi+\psi} \cos\{(3k \pm 1)M(\kappa, t)\} \cos 2n\omega_O t\, d(\omega_O t) \tag{4.20}$$

$$b_{1,n}(\kappa) = \frac{2}{\pi} \int_{\psi}^{\pi+\psi} \sin M(\kappa, t) \sin n\omega_O t \, d(\omega_O t) \tag{4.21}$$

$$b_{(3k\pm 1),n}(\kappa) = \frac{2}{\pi} \int_{\psi}^{\pi+\psi} \sin\{(3k \pm 1)M(\kappa, t)\} \sin n\omega_O t \, d(\omega_O t) \tag{4.22}$$

The basic similarity between the original (κ is absent) and the present equations—that is, between equations (4.15)–(4.22) and (3.12)–(3.19)—makes it evident that the general expressions given previously for different output voltage waveforms in equations (3.20), (3.21), (3.36), and (3.38) will remain valid at any given value of κ, provided that the Fourier coefficients are computed for the relevant modulating function $M(\kappa, t) = M(\kappa_{\text{given}}, t)$.

The computation of the Fourier coefficients is usually quite involved and time consuming; for this reason the numerical values of these coefficients, computed for the practically most important modulating function $M(\kappa, t) = \sin^{-1}(\kappa \sin \omega_O t)$, which produces sinusoidal mean output voltage waveforms, at ten discrete values of κ in the range $0 \leqq \kappa \leqq 1$, are tabulated in the Appendix. In the above important case, which is the only one considered further in this and the following chapter, κ is identical to the output voltage ratio r; this fact will be emphasized from here on by writing all relevant equations in terms of r rather than κ.

It may be appropriate here to reinforce the understanding of the previously developed theory revealing the close relationship between the different complementary and composite output voltage waveforms of a given periodic modulating function by elaborating further on the general Fourier coefficients for the most important case of sinusoidal mean output voltage waves. For this purpose, let the modulating function $M(r, t)$ be given by

$$M(r, t) = \sin^{-1}\{r \sin(\omega_O t + \psi)\} \qquad \text{for } 0 \leqq r \leqq 1 \tag{4.23}$$

and, for convenience, let ψ be equal to zero.

The evaluation of equation (4.17) is simple: $\sin M(r, t) = r \sin \omega_O t$. To find the relevant Fourier coefficients of the series given by equations (4.16) and (4.18), let us examine first the specific functions in question:

$$\cos\{(3k \pm 1) \sin^{-1}(r \sin \omega_O t)\} \tag{4.24}$$

$$\sin\{(3k \pm 1) \sin^{-1}(r \sin \omega_O t)\} \tag{4.25}$$

It can be shown analytically that these functions may be represented either by trigonometric polynomials of finite order or by trigonometric series (infinite terms), depending upon whether multiplier $(3k \pm 1)$ is an even or an odd number. More specifically, functions

$$\cos\{[3(2k - 1) \pm 1] \sin^{-1}(r \sin \omega_O t)\} \tag{4.26}$$

and

$$\sin\{(6k \pm 1) \sin^{-1}(r \sin \omega_O t)\} \tag{4.27}$$

are in fact trigonometric polynomials of orders $[3(2k - 1) \pm 1]$ and $(6k \pm 1)$, respectively, whereas functions

$$\cos\{(6k \pm 1) \sin^{-1}(r \sin \omega_O t)\} \tag{4.28}$$

and

$$\sin\{[3(2k - 1) \pm 1] \sin^{-1}(r \sin \omega_O t)\} \tag{4.29}$$

can be represented only by infinite trigonometric series. Graphs of the functions given by equations (4.26) and (4.27) are shown in Figure 4.4 for $r = 0.5$ and $k = 1, 2, 3, 4$; those of the functions (4.28) and (4.29) are shown in Figure 4.5 for the same values of r and k. Note that the cosine functions, given by equations (4.26) and (4.28), have a period of $1/2f_O$, whereas the period of the sine functions, given by equations (4.27) and (4.29), is $1/f_O$.

The above assertions indicate that it will be convenient to split expressions (4.16) and (4.18) into two parts in order to separate the two different kinds of coefficients—that is, to separate the coefficients of a trigonometric polynomial from those of a trigonometric series. Thus

$$\cos\{[3(2k-1) \pm 1] \sin^{-1}(r \sin \omega_O t)\} = a_{[3(2k-1)\pm 1],0} + \sum_{n=1}^{2n=3(2k-1)\pm 1} a_{[3(2k-1)\pm 1],2n} \cos 2n\omega_O t \quad (4.30)$$

$$\sin\{(6k \pm 1) \sin^{-1}(r \sin \omega_O t)\} = \sum_{n=1}^{2n-1=6k\pm 1} b_{(6k\pm 1),(2n-1)} \sin(2n-1)\omega_O t \quad (4.31)$$

and

$$\cos\{(6k \pm 1) \sin^{-1}(r \sin \omega_O t)\} = a_{(6k\pm 1),0} + \sum_{n=1}^{\infty} a_{(6k\pm 1),2n} \cos 2n\omega_O t \quad (4.32)$$

$$\sin\{[3(2k-1) \pm 1] \sin^{-1}(r \sin \omega_O t)\} = \sum_{n=1}^{\infty} b_{[3(2k-1)\pm 1],(2n-1)} \sin(2n-1)\omega_O t \quad (4.33)$$

where all the coefficients $a_{[3(2k-1)\pm 1],2n}$, $a_{(6k\pm 1),2n}$, $b_{[3(2k-1)\pm 1],(2n-1)}$, and $b_{(6k\pm 1),(2n-1)}$ are defined by the appropriate Fourier integrals given in equations (4.19)–(4.22).

The reader probably realizes at this point that a large number of coefficients are needed for the quantitative evaluation of the output waveform, since four different functions are defined by every integer k ($k = 1, 2, \ldots \infty$) for every discrete value of r ($0 \leq r \leq 1$). Thus there will be four families of coefficients for each value of r, two of which terminate with k, and two of which are infinite for any k. (See Tables in the Appendix.) Fortunately, in the usual practical cases of three-, six-, and twelve-pulse output waveforms, it is enough to consider only two values of k ($k = 1$, $k = 2$) and perhaps nine values of n ($n = 1, \ldots 9$). Note that n is limited by k in the case of the trigonometric polynomials.

Having established the different categories of coefficients relevant to the modulating function $M(r, t) = \sin^{-1}(r \sin \omega_O t)$, it may be instructive to rewrite the general expression [equation (3.20)] for the positive-type output voltage waveform, v_O, for the present case of variable mean output voltage, namely,

$$\text{(a)} \quad \left[\begin{aligned} v_O(r) = \frac{3\sqrt{3}}{2\pi} V_I \Bigg\{ & r \sin \omega_O t + \sum_{k=1}^{\infty} 2A_{[3(2k-1)],0} \sin\{3(2k-1)\omega_I t\} \\ & + \sum_{k=1}^{\infty} \Bigg(\sum_{n=1}^{2n=3(2k-1)+1} A_{[3(2k-1)],2n} \sin\{[3(2k-1)\omega_I \pm 2n\omega_O]t\} \\ & \pm \sum_{n=1}^{2n-1=6k+1} B_{6k,(2n-1)} \sin\{[6k\omega_I \pm (2n-1)\omega_O]t\} \Bigg) \Bigg\} \end{aligned} \right.$$

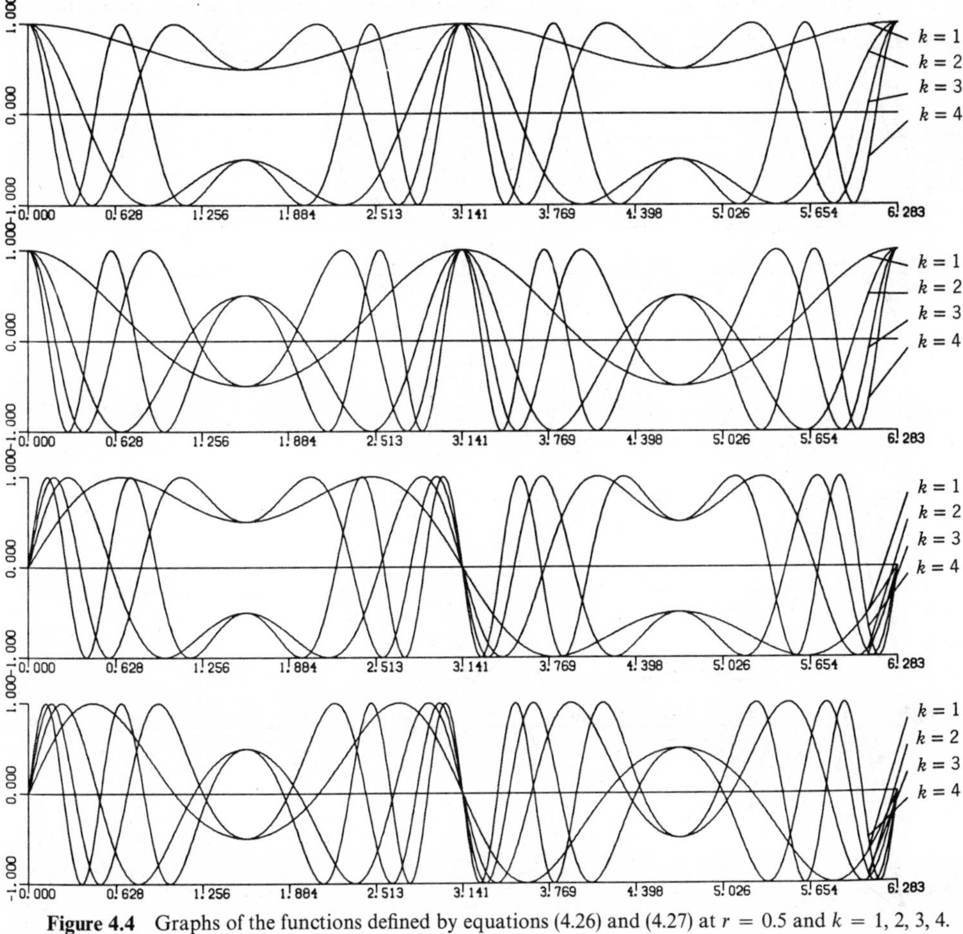

Figure 4.4 Graphs of the functions defined by equations (4.26) and (4.27) at $r = 0.5$ and $k = 1, 2, 3, 4$.

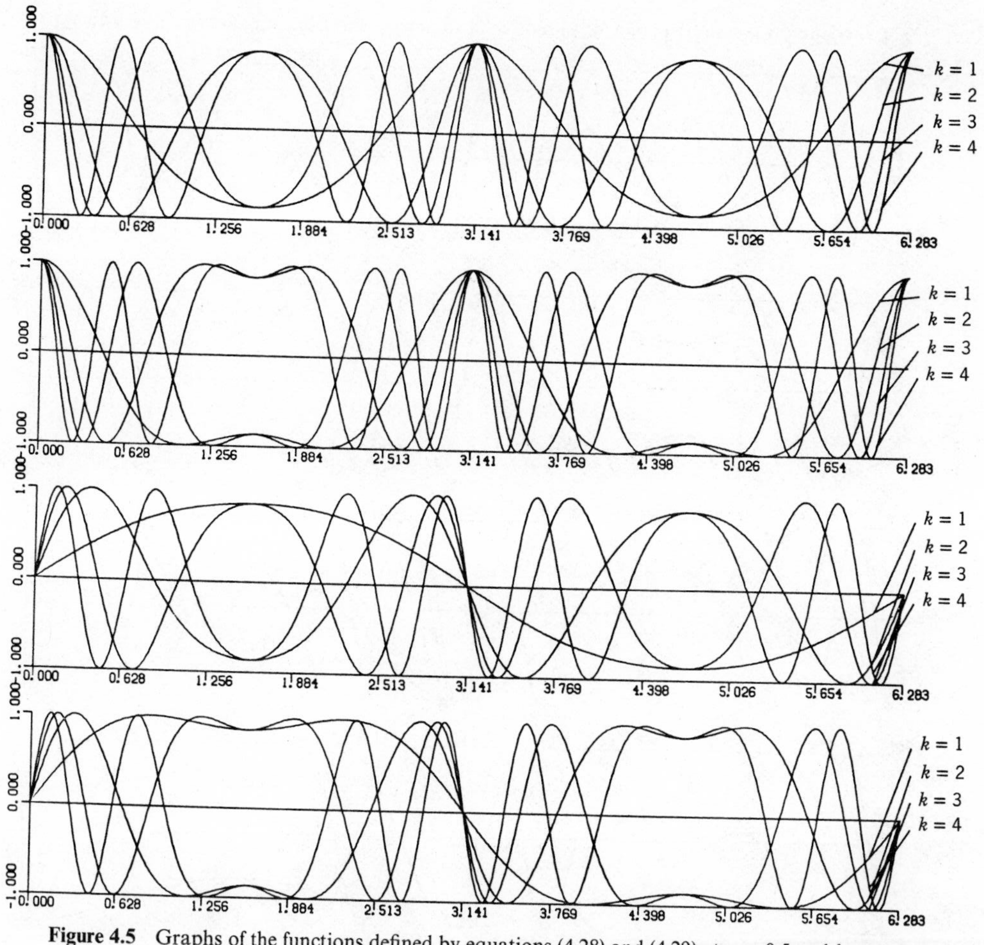

Figure 4.5 Graphs of the functions defined by equations (4.28) and (4.29) at $r = 0.5$ and $k = 1, 2, 3, 4$.

$$\text{(b)}\quad \left[\begin{aligned} &+\frac{3\sqrt{3}}{2\pi}V_I\left\{\sum_{k=1}^{\infty} 2A_{6k,0}\sin 6k\omega_I t\right.\\ &+\sum_{k=1}^{\infty}\sum_{n=1}^{\infty}\Big(A_{6k,2n}\sin\{[6k\omega_I \pm 2n\omega_O]t\}\\ &\left.\pm B_{[3(2k-1)],(2n-1)}\sin\{[3(2k-1)\omega_I \pm (2n-1)\omega_O]t\}\Big)\right\} \end{aligned}\right. \tag{4.34}$$

where

$$A_{[3(2k-1)],0} = \frac{1}{2}\left(\frac{a_{[3(2k-1)+1],0}}{3(2k-1)+1} + \frac{a_{[3(2k-1)-1],0}}{3(2k-1)-1}\right) \tag{4.35a}$$

$$A_{[3(2k-1]),2n} = \frac{1}{2}\left(\frac{a_{[3(2k-1)+1],2n}}{3(2k-1)+1} + \frac{a_{[3(2k-1)-1],2n}}{3(2k-1)-1}\right) \tag{4.36a}$$

$$B_{6k,(2n-1)} = \frac{1}{2}\left(\frac{b_{(6k+1),(2n-1)}}{6k+1} + \frac{b_{(6k-1),(2n-1)}}{6k-1}\right) \tag{4.37a}$$

$$A_{6k,0} = \frac{1}{2}\left(\frac{a_{(6k+1),0}}{6k+1} + \frac{a_{(6k-1),0}}{6k-1}\right) \tag{4.35b}$$

$$A_{6k,2n} = \frac{1}{2}\left(\frac{a_{(6k+1),2n}}{6k+1} + \frac{a_{(6k-1),2n}}{6k-1}\right) \tag{4.36b}$$

$$B_{[3(2k-1)],(2n-1)} = \frac{1}{2}\left(\frac{b_{[3(2k-1)+1],(2n-1)}}{3(2k-1)+1} + \frac{b_{[3(2k-1)-1],(2n-1)}}{3(2k-1)-1}\right) \tag{4.37b}$$

Note that all of the above coefficients are functions of the output voltage ratio r.

Expression (4.34) may be written symbolically in the following form:

$$v_O(r) = a + b \tag{4.38}$$

where a is part (a), and b is part (b) of equation (4.34).

In a similar way, the general expression given for the negative-type output voltage waveform $v_{O\pi}$ may be written for modulating function $M(r, t) = \sin^{-1}(r \sin \omega_O t)$ as follows:

$$v_{O\pi}(r) = a - b \tag{4.39}$$

Equations (4.38) and (4.39) thus give, with the proper substitution for a and b, the general expressions for the positive-type and negative-type sinusoidal mean complementary output voltage waveforms with variable amplitude. With the use of these two expressions and the auxiliary equations given by (4.35a)–(4.37b), the consecutive and concurrent composite sinusoidal mean output voltage waveforms, $v_O(\rho)$ and v_{OM}, with variable amplitude can be written readily on the basis of the original expressions given by equations (3.36) and (3.38).

Recall, first of all, that part (a) of the expressions obtained for the complementary waveforms is invariant; it appears unaltered in both composite waveforms. In fact, v_{OM} is *equal* to part (a) of the expression of either complementary waveform. Thus

$$v_{OM}(r) = a \tag{4.40}$$

Using the "not quite final" general expression for $v_O(\rho)$ given by equation (3.35), this composite waveform with variable amplitude may be written in the following symbolic form:

$$v_O(\rho, r) = a + b\left(\frac{4}{\pi}\sum_{m=1}^{\infty}\frac{1}{2m-1}\sin\{(2m-1)(\omega_O t + \rho)\}\right) \tag{4.41}$$

It may be observed that this equation becomes, after the substitution of the actual expressions for a and b, formally identical to the general expression for $v_O(\rho)$ given by equation (3.36), except that in the present case coefficients $B_{6k,n}$ and $B_{3(2k-1),n}$ are zero whenever integer n is even. This of course indicates only the simple fact that the presently considered modulating function is an odd-harmonic function, that is, $M(t + T_O/2) = -M(t)$, which condition has not been imposed on the original general modulating function.*

It has already been mentioned that the modulating function $M(r, t) = \sin^{-1}(r \sin \omega_O t)$ is a generalized form of the *triangular wave* modulating function $M(t) = \sin^{-1}(\sin \omega_O t)$ considered earlier. Consequently, equations (4.34), (4.39), (4.40), and (4.41) are also generalized versions of the corresponding *full voltage* expressions given by equations (3.63), (3.64), (3.79), and (3.73), respectively. It may thus be interesting to compare the corresponding equations to see the effect of the presently considered method of voltage control. Actually a glance will show that they do not substantially differ; part (a) of the "full" voltage expressions is somewhat simpler, containing fewer terms than the "variable" voltage expressions; on the other hand, part (b) of the corresponding pairs of equations is identical in structure. To illustrate the actual effect of the reduction of the wanted output voltage upon the spectral characteristics of these expressions, the variation of coefficients $A_{[3(2k-1)],2n}$, $B_{6k,(2n-1)}$ and $A_{6k,2n}$, $B_{[3(2k-1)],2n}$ with the output voltage ratio is shown in Figures 4.6 and 4.7, respectively, for $k = 1$ and for an appropriate number of ns. Recall that for the first pair of coefficients, index n is *naturally* terminated at $2n = 3(2k-1) + 1$ (A coefficients) and $2n - 1 = 6k + 1$ (B coefficients). Inspection of Figure 4.6 indicates that coefficients $A_{3,0}$, $B_{6,1}$, and $B_{6,3}$ become zero precisely at $r = 1$. This confirms that all A coefficients except those with indeces $3(2k-1)$, $[3(2k-1) \pm 1]$, and all B coefficients except those with indeces $6k$, $(6k \pm 1)$, become zero at $r = 1$.

It is relevant to ask here what the practical significance of all this is, from the viewpoint of the output voltage distortion. To answer this let us identify first the part coefficients A and B play in the expressions of the complementary and composite waveforms and estimate the effect of their variation.

Inspection of equation (4.34) indicates that the coefficients A and B are in fact the *amplitudes* of the unwanted components of the complementary waveforms. That is, coefficients $A_{[3(2k-1)],2n}$, $B_{6k,(2n-1)}$ and $A_{6k,2n}$, $B_{[3(2k-1)],(2n-1)}$ are the amplitudes† of the components with the frequencies $3(2k-1)\omega_I \pm 2n\omega_O$, $6k\omega_I \pm (2n+1)\omega_O$, and $6k\omega_I \pm 2n\omega_O$, $3(2k-1)\omega_I \pm (2n+1)\omega_O$, respectively ($k = 1, 2, \ldots$; $n = 0, 1, 2, \ldots$). Examining in this light the graphs showing the variations of the coefficients A and B with r, one can conclude that the reduction of the mean output voltage does not have a very significant effect upon the spectral characteristics—the frequencies and amplitudes—of the complementary waveforms. The most noticeable and the most plausible change is that, as r approaches zero, the coefficient $A_{3k,0}$ rapidly increases,

* The reader is reminded that originally $M(t)$ was only stipulated to be a periodic *odd* function, $M(t) = -M(-t)$, which condition did not restrict the order number of terms in the Fourier series.

† Actually, for index $n = 0$, coefficients A and B are, as indicated in equation (4.34), equal to half of the amplitudes of the corresponding components.

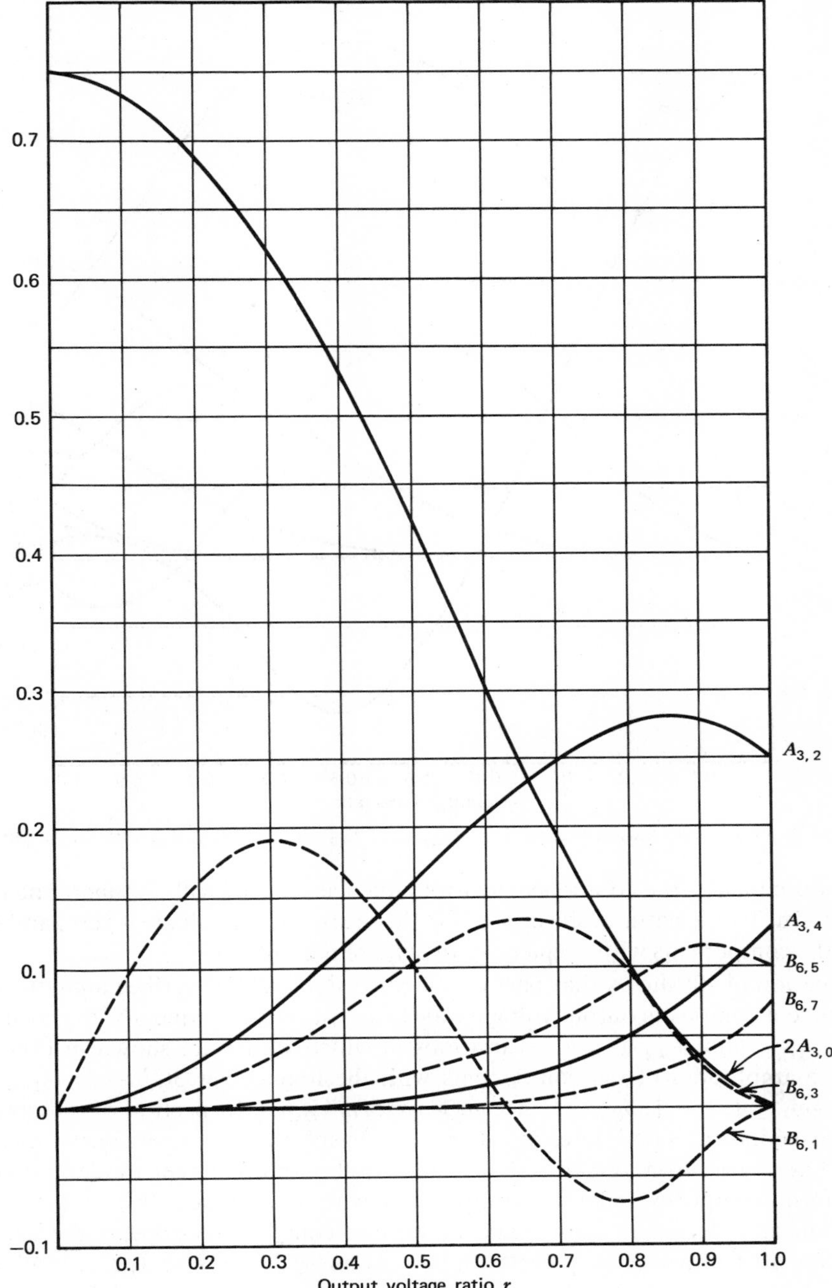

Figure 4.6 Variation of the coefficients $2A_{3,0}$, $A_{3,2}$, $A_{3,4}$, and $B_{6,1}$, $B_{6,3}$, $B_{6,5}$ with the output voltage ratio r.

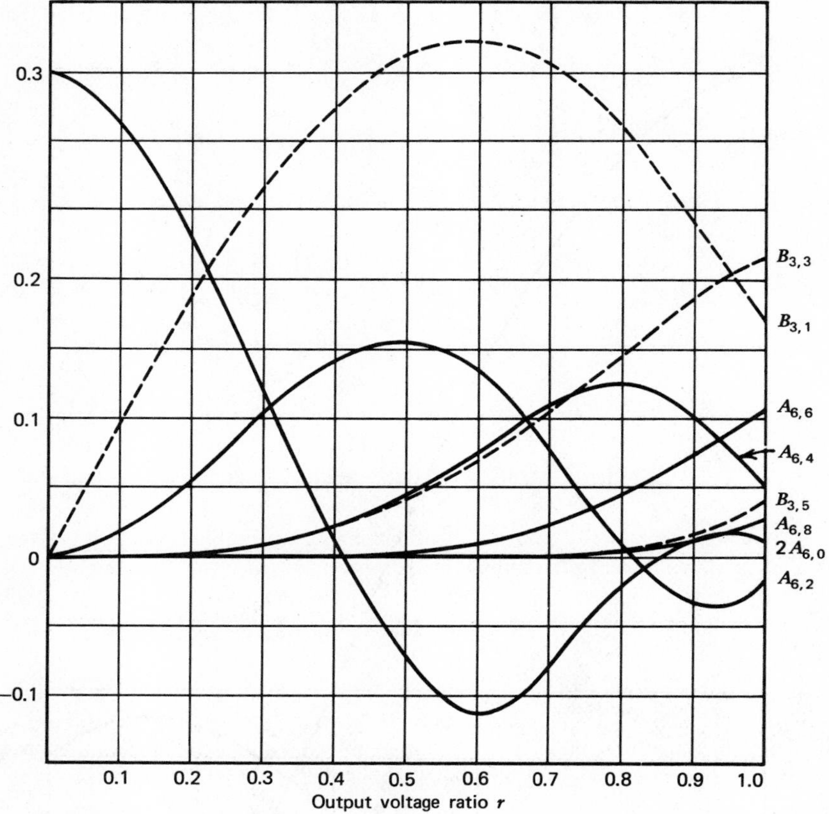

Figure 4.7 Variation of the coefficients $A_{6,0}$, $A_{6,2}$, $A_{6,4}$, $A_{6,8}$ and $B_{3,1}$, $B_{3,3}$, $B_{3,5}$ with the output voltage ratio r.

and consequently the components with frequencies of $3kf_I$ will dominate the output waveform. This is natural, since at $r = 0$, the mean output voltage is zero, and in fact only the components with frequencies of $3kf_I$ are present.

Equation (4.40) shows that part (a) of expression (4.34) describes analytically the concurrent composite output voltage waveform $v_{OM}(r)$. Consequently, the coefficients $A_{[3(2k-1)],2n}$ and $B_{6k,(2n-1)}$, the variations of which with r are shown in Figure 4.6, are the amplitudes of the components with the frequencies $3(2k-1)\ \omega_I \pm 2n\omega_O$ and $6k\omega_I \pm (2n-1)\omega_O$ contained in waveform $v_{OM}(r)$. Inspection of the graphs in Figure 4.6 indicates an interesting change in the spectral characteristics of waveform $v_{OM}(r)$ as r varies from one to zero. At $r = 1$ (full output voltage), the output voltage waveform comprises only the components with frequencies $3k\omega_I \pm (3k \pm 1)\omega_O$. As soon as r decreases from unity, additional components appear; the spectrum contains all families of frequencies $3(2k-1)\ \omega_I \pm 2n\omega_O$ $[k = 1, 2, \ldots; n = 0, 1, 2, \ldots, 3(2k-1)+1]$ and $6k\omega_I \pm (2n-1)\omega_O$ $(k = 1, 2, 3, \ldots; n = 1, 2, \ldots, 6k+1)$. It is important to note however that the "new" frequencies in each family, obtained at each value of integer k, are higher than the lowest, and lower than the highest frequency of the "permanently existing" components in that group. For example, at $r = 1$, the lowest frequency of the "family" of $k = 1$ in the spectrum is $3\omega_I - 4\omega_O$, and the highest is $3\omega_I + 4\omega_O$. The new member of this family at reduced r is $3\omega_I$; clearly, $3\omega_I - 4\omega_O \leqq 3\omega_I \leqq 3\omega_I + 4\omega_O$. Thus, we may draw the conclusion that the new components appearing in the output waveform at $r < 1$ do not influence the attainable output to input frequency ratio established previously for full output voltage.

It is also interesting to note that only the odd multiples of $3f_I$, that is, $3(2k-1)f_I$, are present in the spectrum. This means that the components with these frequencies are present in the output only if the pulse number is odd; for even pulse numbers they are absent—which implies that at $r=0$ the output voltage waveform has no unwanted components. This is of course true, since the net output voltage is in fact continuously zero under this condition.

To illustrate the effect of the presently discussed output voltage control, typical waveforms of $v_{OM}(r)$ synthesized at $f_O/f_I = \frac{1}{3}$ from the terms of part (a) of equation (4.34) are shown at various output voltage ratios in Figure 4.8 for a three-pulse circuit and in Figure 4.9 for a six-pulse circuit.

Let us consider last the composite output waveform $v_O(\rho, r)$ given in a symbolic form by equation (4.41). The full voltage counterpart is defined by equation (3.73). The difference between part (a) of these equations has just been established. The structure of part (b) is identical in both expressions. On this basis, and because of the fact that the spectrum of $v_O(\rho)$ is already so "dense" that it would hardly be possible to make it any more so, one could already conclude that the basic characteristics of the waveform will not generally change significantly with varying r. In spite of this intuitive deduction, it may still be worthwhile to consider equation (4.41), together with (4.34) and (3.73), to get a better understanding of this rather complex expression.

As seen in equation (4.34), part (a) of the expression contains sine terms with the following frequencies: $3(2k-1)\omega_I$, $3(2k-1)\omega_I \pm 2n\omega_O$ and $6k\omega_I \pm (2n-1)\omega_O$. Inspection of equation (3.73) indicates that cosine terms with the same frequencies are present, at particular values of integers n and m, in part (b) of the expression for

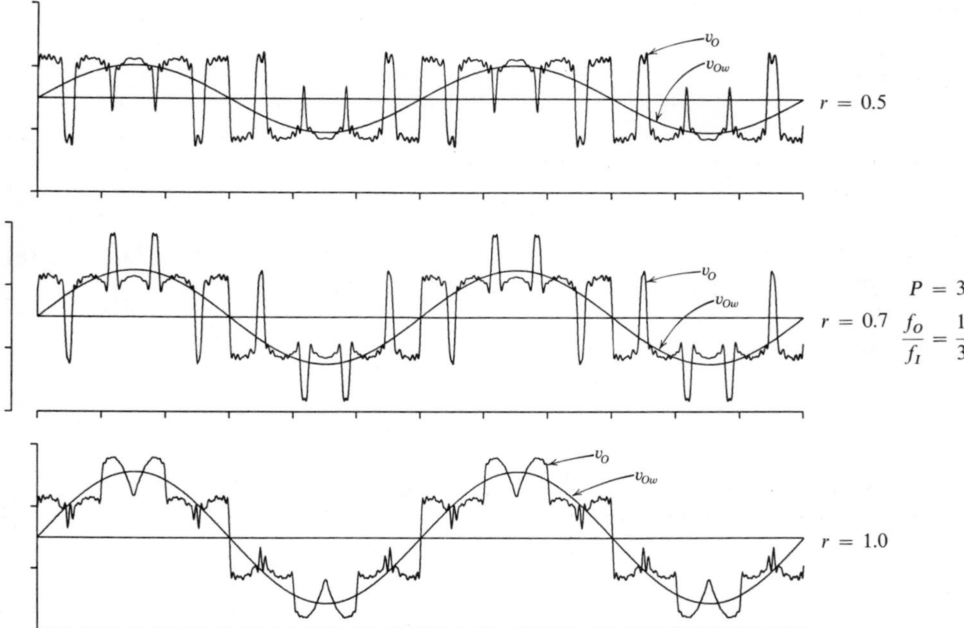

Figure 4.8 Three-pulse concurrent composite output voltage waveforms synthesized from the terms of part (a) of equation (4.34) at output voltage ratios of $r = 0.5$, $r = 0.7$, and $r = 1.0$; $f_O/f_I = 1/3$.

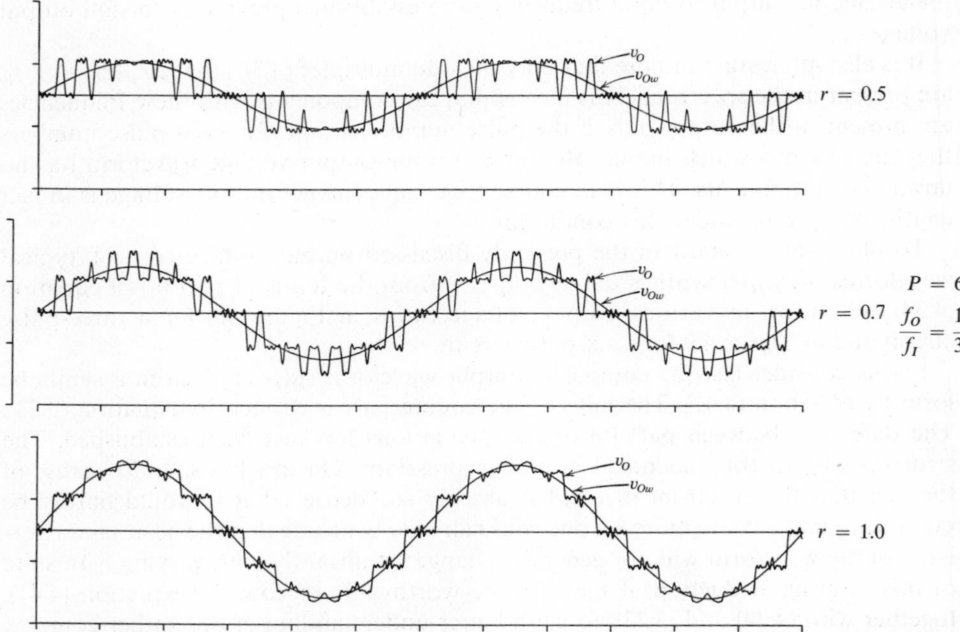

Figure 4.9 Six-pulse concurrent composite output voltage waveforms synthesized from the terms of part (a) of equation (4.34) at output voltage ratios of $r = 0.5$, $r = 0.7$, and $r = 1.0$; $f_O/f_I = 1/3$.

$v_O(\rho, r)$. As has been previously indicated, each general term in part (b) may actually provide an infinite number of components of the same frequency as n and m tend to infinity. Moreover, each component has a phase angle that is a function of angle ρ and integer m. However, the coefficients of these components decrease rapidly with increasing m—that is, as $1/(2m - 1)$ decreases—and n—that is, coefficients $A_{6k,2n}$ and $B_{[3(2k-1)],(2n-1)}$ decrease (see Figure 4.7). It follows therefore that neither the coefficients A and B in part (a) nor those in part (b) represent the actual amplitudes of the unwanted components. The amplitude of each unwanted component is obtained by vectorially summing the coefficient of all terms, both in part (a) and (b), with the same frequency.

Consider, as a simple example, the component with the frequency $3\omega_I$. Per equation (4.34), part (a) contributes one term: $A_{3,0} \sin 3\omega_I t$. Per equation (3.73), part (b) contributes the following terms (the bottom row at $n = m$):

$$-\frac{2}{\pi}\sum_{n=1}^{\infty} \frac{1}{2n-1} B_{3,(2n-1)}[\cos\{3\omega_I t - (2n-1)\rho\} + \cos\{3\omega_I t + (2n-1)\rho\}]$$

$$= -\frac{2}{\pi}\sum_{n=1}^{\infty} \frac{B_{3,(2n-1)}}{2n-1} \cos(2n-1)\rho \cos 3\omega_I t$$

Thus the unwanted component with frequency $3\omega_I$ present in the waveform $v_O(\rho, r)$ may be written in the following form:

$$D \sin(3\omega_I t + \Psi)$$

where

$$D = \sqrt{A_{3,0}^2 + \frac{4}{\pi^2}\left(\sum_{n=1}^{\infty} \frac{B_{3,(2n-1)}}{2n-1} \cos(2n-1)\rho\right)^2}$$

and

$$\Psi = \tan^{-1}\left(\frac{-\dfrac{2}{\pi}\displaystyle\sum_{n=1}^{\infty}\frac{B_{3,(2n-1)}}{2n-1}\cos(2n-1)\rho}{A_{3,0}}\right)$$

This simple example illustrates the complexity of the actual computation, particularly when it is remembered that $A_{3,0}$ and $B_{3,(2n-1)}$ are functions of r, and angle ρ is an independent variable in the range $-\pi \leqq \rho \leqq \pi$. Still, due to the practical importance of the waveform $v_O(\rho, r)$, the normalized amplitudes of its most significant constituent (unwanted) components have been computed for ten discrete values of r (0.1, 0.2, ... 1.0) at four values of ρ (0°, ±30°, ±60°, ±90°) and are presented in Chapter 6.

Here, as an illustration, typical six-pulse output voltage waveforms synthesized from the terms of the expanded form of equation (4.41) at $\rho = 0, -30°$, and 90° are shown for various output voltage ratios at (a), (b), and (c), respectively, in Figure 4.10.

It has been shown before and can be observed in Figure 4.10*c*, that the consecutive composite voltage waveform $v_O(\rho) = v_O(\rho, r)_{r=1}$ is, at $\rho = \pi/2$, identical to the output voltage waveform of the unrestricted frequency changer ($M(t) = \omega_O t$). However, Figure 4.10*c* also indicates that the width of the voltage segments that constitute the output waveform become uneven at reduced values of r ($0 < r < 1.0$). This is a consequence of the fact that the repetition frequency of the existence functions, when modulated by $M(r, t) = \sin^{-1}(r \sin \omega_O t)$, varies continuously over the period $1/f_O$ at any value of r different from unity. (Recall that $M(r, t) = \sin^{-1}(r \sin \omega_O t)$ becomes, at $r = 1.0$, a triangular wave modulating function that results in constant "fast" and "slow" repetition rates for the existence functions over consecutive half period intervals. This property has been used to construct the UFC output voltage waveform from half-cycle sections of the complementary waveforms.) It may therefore be expected, and is confirmed by the data in Chapter 6,* that the unique frequency spectrum of the UFC cannot be maintained at reduced output voltage with this type of voltage control. This leads to the conclusion that the method of voltage control considered here is not compatible with the UFC.

Let us finally summarize the essential points of this section:

1. The amplitude of the mean output voltage can be varied by means of controlling the "depth" of frequency modulation applied to the existence functions. This is achieved by a periodic modulating function of the general character $M(\kappa, t) = \sin^{-1}\{\kappa F_D(\omega_O t)\}$ where $F_D(\omega_O t)$ is the desired output voltage wave, and κ is its normalized amplitude.
2. The wanted component of the output voltage waveform may be slightly increased at the expense of increased distortion by increasing κ above unity. As κ tends to infinity, the mean output voltage approaches a square wave, regardless of the character of the desired output voltage wave $F_D(\omega_O t)$.
3. The instantaneous deviation of the output voltage waveform from the mean output voltage remains the minimum obtainable in the total range of κ ($0 \leqq \kappa \leqq \infty$). Consequently the total r.m.s. distortion of the output voltage waveform remains the minimum obtainable for a given pulse number.
4. Although the frequency spectrum is generally the simplest at full output voltage ($\kappa = r = 1$), the spectral characteristics of the sinusoidal mean output waveforms

* This confirmation is indirect, since this type of voltage control method for the UFC is not specifically considered in Chapter 6. However, the data given for the NCC with $\phi_0 = \pi/2$ are in fact applicable.

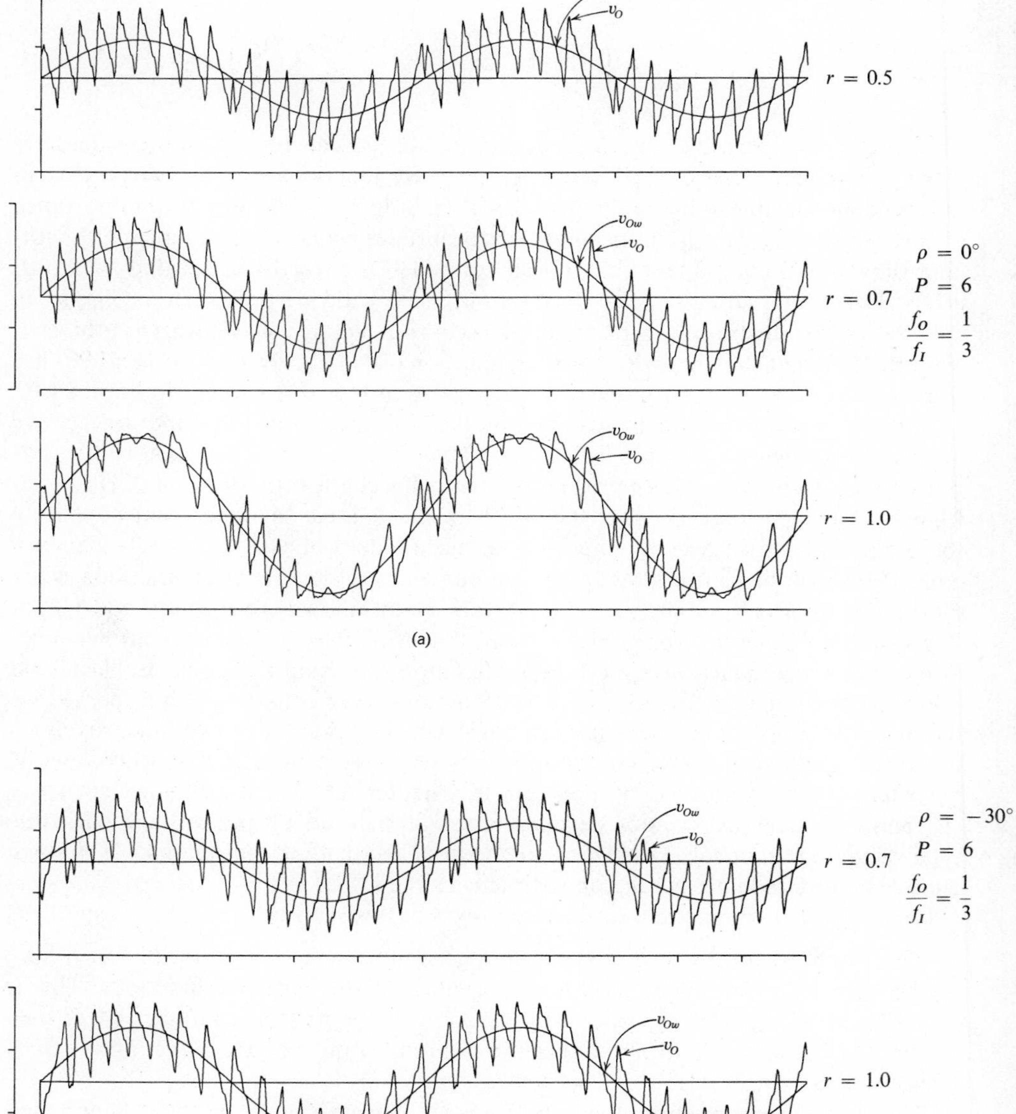

v_{Ow}
v_O
$r = 0.5$
$r = 0.7$
$r = 1.0$
$\rho = 0°$
$P = 6$
$\frac{f_O}{f_I} = \frac{1}{3}$
(a)
$\rho = -30°$
$P = 6$
$\frac{f_O}{f_I} = \frac{1}{3}$
$r = 0.7$
$r = 1.0$
$r = 0.5$
(b)

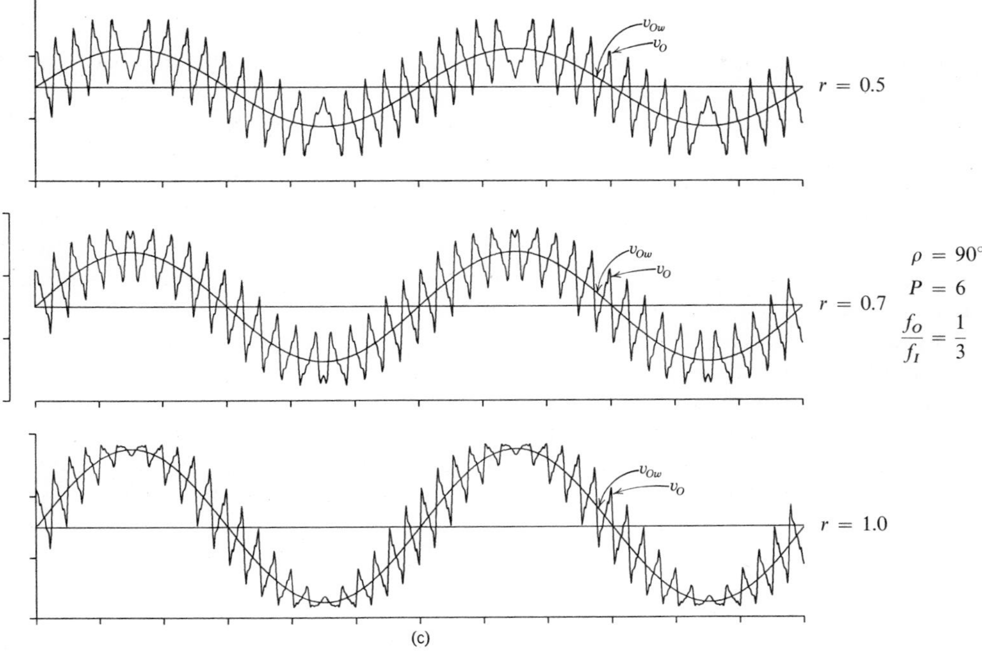

Figure 4.10 Six-pulse consecutive composite output voltage waveforms synthesized from the terms of equation (4.44) at output voltage ratios of $r = 0.5$, $r = 0.7$, and $r = 1.0$ for (a) $\rho = 0°$, (b) $\rho = -30°$, and (c) $\rho = 90°$; $f_O/f_I = 1/3$.

(v_O, $v_{O\pi}$, $v_O(\rho)$, and v_{OM}) corresponding to the periodic modulating function $M(r,t) = \sin^{-1}(r \sin \omega_O t)$ do not change significantly with the output voltage ratio in the range $0 \leqq r \leqq 1$. Thus, the attainable output to input frequency ratio is not generally affected as the amplitude of the desired output voltage wave is decreased from unity to zero. This method of output voltage control is therefore compatible with (and in fact the "best" available for) the UDFFC (v_{OM}), CDFFC $[v_O(\rho)]$, and NCC $[v_O(\rho = \phi_O)]$.

5. The frequency spectrum of the UFC output voltage waveform, when produced as a special case of the consecutive composite waveform $v_O(\rho)$, changes significantly as the output voltage ratio is reduced. Families of components with *difference* frequencies (i.e., frequencies that are *differences* between multiples of the output and input frequencies) absent at $r = 1$ appear in the spectrum as r becomes less than unity. For this reason, the method of output voltage control considered in this section is not really compatible with the UFC, and therefore its practical use for the UFC would be restricted to special applications in which only small adjustments in the output voltage are required.

4.3 OUTPUT VOLTAGE CONTROL BY PHASE SHIFT

This method of voltage control is conceptually very simple: two similar output waveforms with controllable relative phase displacement are produced, and these are summed (or their arithmetic mean is generated) in the output. Assuming that the amplitudes of the wanted components of the two constituent waveforms are identical, the amplitude of the wanted component of the resultant output waveform will vary from maximum to zero as the phase displacement between them is increased from zero to π.

This method of voltage control obviously requires two separate groups of switches. Since most practical multipulse circuits ($P > 3$) are composed of an even number of three-pulse elementary units, this requirement can usually be met; that is, the relative phase position of the output waveforms of two basic constituent circuits—viewed as separate units—can be controlled to achieve the desired amplitude reduction of the net wanted component in the output. It should be pointed out, however, that series (bridge) circuits generally lend themselves much more readily to this voltage control technique then do midpoint circuits, because in the latter parallel arrangements an interphase reactor is required that must support an increasing component of voltage at the wanted frequency as the amplitude of the wanted component of the output voltage is decreased.

Consider the simple six-pulse frequency changer circuit shown for single-phase output in Figure 4.11. The voltage waveform of this circuit is analyzed in Section 3.5. Assume that the wanted components generated by the two three-pulse groups, (135) and (246), of the circuit can be phase shifted with respect to a chosen time reference, by suitable control. Suppose, for example, that the phase angle of the wanted component produced by group (135) is controllable from zero to $-\pi/2$, and that

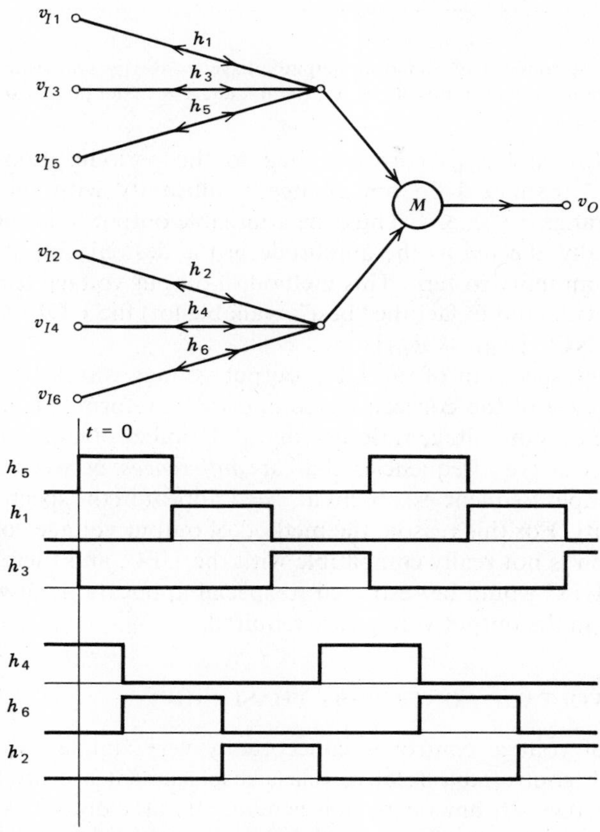

Figure 4.11 Schematic of a six-pulse midpoint circuit composed of two three-pulse groups and corresponding basic existence functions.

produced by group (246) from zero to $+\pi/2$. Then, since the output voltage is the arithmetic mean of the two constituent waveforms $v_{O(135)}$ and $v_{O(246)}$, the amplitude of the wanted component in the output is variable from maximum to zero.

As has been shown previously, the phase position of the wanted component is completely specified by that of the modulating function $M(t) = M(\omega_O t)$; for the modulating functions considered in this book, the phase angle of the wanted component, with respect to a chosen reference, is the same as that of $M(\omega_O t)$. It follows therefore that the phase positions of the two similar modulating functions generating $v_{O(135)}$ and $v_{O(246)}$ must be made variable to implement the output voltage control considered. From the relevant relationships given in equations (3.110) and (3.111),

$$v_O = \frac{1}{2}(v_{O(135)} + v_{O(246)}) = \frac{1}{2}\left\{[h_1 \quad h_3 \quad h_5]\begin{bmatrix} v_{I1} \\ v_{I3} \\ v_{I5} \end{bmatrix} + [h_2 \quad h_4 \quad h_6]\begin{bmatrix} v_{I2} \\ v_{I4} \\ v_{I6} \end{bmatrix}\right\}$$

it follows that this can be accomplished by introducing a variable angle ξ (measured at ω_O angular frequency), with appropriate sign, into the argument of the modulating function $M(\omega_O t)$ associated with the two sets of existence functions h_1, h_3, h_5 and h_2, h_4, h_6 [refer to equations (3.6) and (3.115)], namely,

$$\left.\begin{aligned}
h_{11}(\xi) &= \frac{1}{3} - \sum_{n=-\infty}^{\infty} \frac{\sin n\dfrac{2\pi}{3}}{n\pi} \exp jn\{\omega_I t + M(\omega_O t - \xi)\} \\
h_{13}(\xi) &= \frac{1}{3} - \sum_{n=-\infty}^{\infty} \frac{\sin n\dfrac{2\pi}{3}}{n\pi} \exp jn\left\{\omega_I t - \frac{2\pi}{3} + M(\omega_O t - \xi)\right\} \\
h_{15}(\xi) &= \frac{1}{3} - \sum_{n=-\infty}^{\infty} \frac{\sin n\dfrac{2\pi}{3}}{n\pi} \exp jn\left\{\omega_I t - \frac{4\pi}{3} + M(\omega_O t - \xi)\right\}
\end{aligned}\right\} \tag{4.42}$$

and

$$\left.\begin{aligned}
h_{12}(\xi) &= \frac{1}{3} - \sum_{n=-\infty}^{\infty} \frac{\sin n\dfrac{2\pi}{3}}{n\pi} \exp jn\left\{\omega_I t - \frac{\pi}{3} + M(\omega_O t + \xi)\right\} \\
h_{14}(\xi) &= \frac{1}{3} - \sum_{n=-\infty}^{\infty} \frac{\sin n\dfrac{2\pi}{3}}{n\pi} \exp jn\{\omega_I t - \pi + M(\omega_O t + \xi)\} \\
h_{16}(\xi) &= \frac{1}{3} - \sum_{n=-\infty}^{\infty} \frac{\sin n\dfrac{2\pi}{3}}{n\pi} \exp jn\left\{\omega_I t - \frac{5\pi}{3} + M(\omega_O t + \xi)\right\}
\end{aligned}\right\} \tag{4.43}$$

Using the above expressions and the definitions given for v_{I_1}, v_{I_3}, v_{I_5} [equation (3.112)] and v_{I_2}, v_{I_4}, v_{I_6} [equation (3.113)], the two constituent output voltage waveforms $v_{O(135)}$ and $v_{O(246)}$ can readily be written in the forms analogous to those given by expressions (3.114) and (3.118), namely,

$$v_{O(135)} = \frac{3\sqrt{3}}{2\pi} V_I \left(\sin M(\omega_O t - \xi) + \sum_{k=1}^{\infty} \frac{\sin\{3k\omega_I t + (3k \pm 1)M(\omega_O t - \xi)\}}{3k \pm 1} \right) \tag{4.44}$$

and

$$v_{O(246)} = \frac{3\sqrt{3}}{2\pi} V_I \left(\sin M(\omega_O t + \xi) + \sum_{k=1}^{\infty} (-1)^{3k} \frac{\sin\{3k\omega_I t + (3k \pm 1)M(\omega_O t + \xi)\}}{3k \pm 1} \right) \tag{4.45}$$

where $0 \leqq \xi \leqq \pi/2$.

The two constituent voltages are expressed in terms of the modulating function, the phase position of which is defined by angle ξ. To obtain an actual expression for the output voltage waveform $v_O(\xi)$, $[v_O(\xi) = \frac{1}{2}(v_{O(135)} + v_{O(246)})]$, it is necessary first to define the character of $M(\omega_O t)$. It has been shown that the modulating functions of interest are either linear functions of time in the form $M(t) = \omega_O t + \psi$ or they are periodic (odd) functions with period time $2\pi/\omega_O$. The present analysis is restricted only to the first (and simpler) case. The reason is, first, that this method of voltage control does not offer any advantage; in fact it is disadvantageous in most respects, for output waveforms generated by periodic modulating functions, over the more "natural" method—that is, amplitude-dependent frequency modulation—discussed in the previous section. Second, the pertinent characteristics of this voltage control method can be established from the results obtained with the simple linear modulating function. The interested reader can, however, derive a general expression for the output voltage waveform with *phase-shift* control with a periodic modulating function: equations (4.44) and (4.45) should first be decomposed by the process demonstrated at the beginning of Chapter 3 [equations (3.12)–(3.20)], and then the two equations should be combined to show explicitly the dependence of the constituent terms upon the angle ξ.

Considering, then, the specific case of $M(\omega_O t) = \omega_O t$, the two phase-displaced modulating functions can be expressed as $M(\omega_O t - \xi) = \omega_O t - \xi$ and $M(\omega_O t + \xi) = \omega_O t + \xi$. Substituting these expressions into equations (4.44) and (4.45) and using the basic relationship $v_O = \frac{1}{2}(v_{O(135)} + v_{O(246)})$, the output voltage waveform may be expressed as a function of ξ in the following form:

$$\begin{aligned} v_O(\xi) = \frac{3\sqrt{3}}{2\pi} V_I \Bigg\{ &\cos\xi \sin\omega_O t \\ &+ \sum_{k=1}^{\infty} \left(\frac{-\sin\{[3(2k-1) \pm 1]\xi\}}{3(2k-1) \pm 1} \cos\{[3(2k-1)\omega_I + (3(2k-1) \pm 1)\omega_O]t\} \right. \\ &\left. + \frac{\cos\{(6k \pm 1)\xi\}}{6k \pm 1} \sin\{[6k\omega_I + (6k \pm 1)\omega_O]t\} \right) \Bigg\} \end{aligned} \tag{4.46}$$

where $0 \leqq \xi \leqq \pi/2$.

Inspection of equation (4.46) leads to the following general conclusions:

1. The amplitude of the wanted component varies co-sinusoidally with ξ; the output voltage ratio is given by

$$r = \frac{V_O}{V_{O\max}} = \cos\xi \tag{4.47}$$

2. The frequency spectrum of the output voltage wave contains, in general, all frequencies that are present in the spectrum of the *constituent* waveforms.

3. The frequencies $3(2k - 1)\omega_I + [3(2k - 1) \pm 1]\omega_O$ are absent only if

$$\xi = \frac{2n}{3(2k - 1) \pm 1}\frac{\pi}{2}$$

and (4.48)

$$0 \leqq \frac{2n}{3(2k - 1) \pm 1} \leqq 1 \qquad \text{for} \begin{array}{l} n = 0, 1, 2, \ldots \\ k = 1, 2, 3, \ldots \end{array}$$

4. The frequencies $6k\omega_I + (6k \pm 1)\omega_O$ are absent only if

$$\xi = \frac{2n + 1}{6k \pm 1}\frac{\pi}{2}$$

and (4.49)

$$0 \leqq \frac{2n + 1}{6k \pm 1} \leqq 1 \qquad \text{for} \begin{array}{l} n = 0, 1, 2, \ldots \\ k = 1, 2, 3, \ldots \end{array}$$

5. Expression (4.46) remains valid for two identical constituent power circuits each of which has pulse number P ($P = 3, 6, 9, \ldots$)—that is, the overall circuit pulse number at *full* output voltage is $2P$—if multipliers containing index k are appropriately changed; that is, $3(2k - 1)$ changed to $P(2k - 1)$, $3(2k - 1) \pm 1$ is changed to $P(2k - 1) \pm 1$, $6k$ is changed to $2Pk$, and $6k \pm 1$ is changed to $2Pk \pm 1$.

Typical output voltage waveforms synthesized from the terms of equations (4.46) at $f_O/f_I = \frac{1}{3}$ are shown for three-pulse constituent circuits in Figure 4.12 and for six-pulse constituent circuits in Figure 4.13.

Detailed data on the spectral characteristics of the UFC output voltage waveform $[M(t) = \omega_O t]$ pertinent to phase-shift voltage control are given in Chapter 6. Without

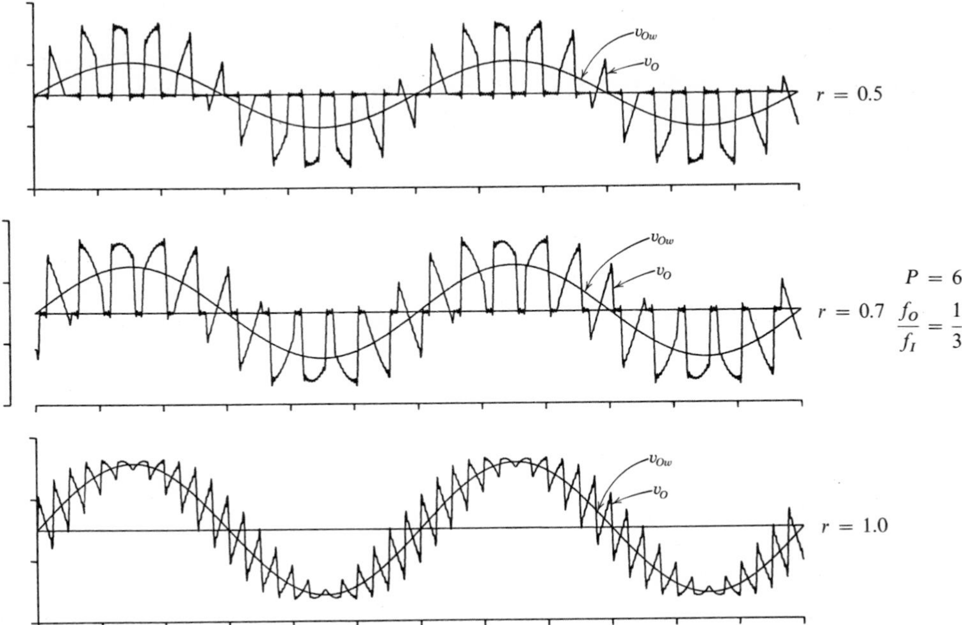

Figure 4.12 Six-pulse UFC output voltage waveforms, with phase-shift-type voltage control, synthesized from the terms of equation (4.49) at output voltage ratios of, $r = 0.5$, $r = 0.7$, and $r = 1.0$; $f_O/f_I = 1/3$.

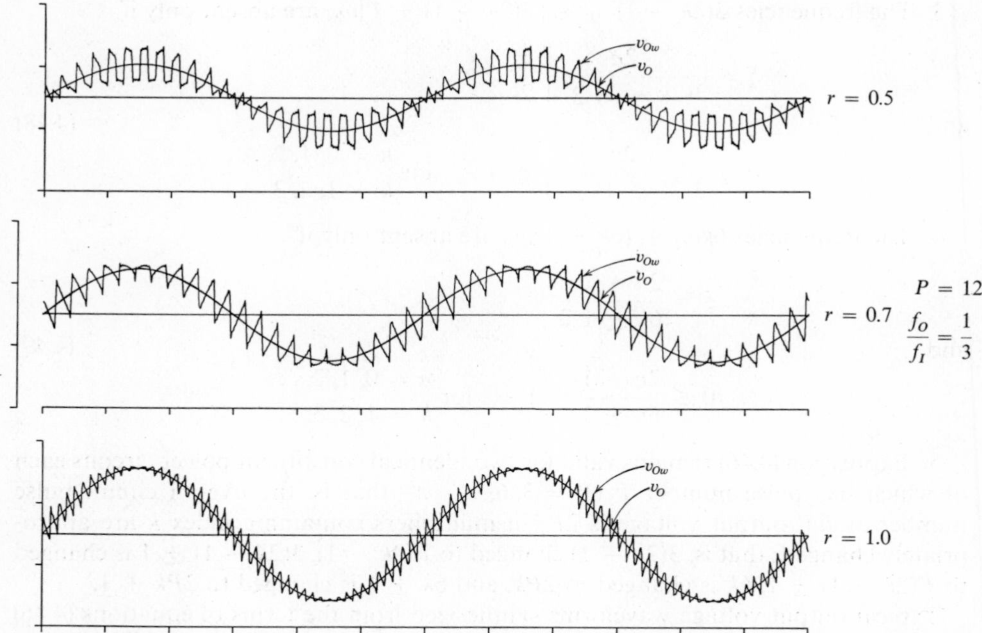

Figure 4.13 Twelve-pulse UFC output voltage waveforms with phase-shift-type voltage control, synthesized from the terms of equation (4.49) at output voltage ratios of $r = 0.5$, $r = 0.7$, and $r = 1.0$; $f_O/f_I = 1/3$.

reference to these results, it is clear that the most important characteristic of the UFC—that is, its unrestricted output frequency range—will *not* be negated by this method of voltage control, since the frequencies of the unwanted components in each constituent group are always higher than the wanted output frequency. The basic disadvantage of this technique, which is true for any modulating function, is the general degradation of the frequency spectrum obtained at full output voltage to that of the component waveforms, each of which has half of the "overall" circuit pulse number.

CHAPTER FIVE
THE INPUT CURRENT WAVE

In Chapters 3 and 4 the topic of output voltage waveform synthesis is discussed. Possible methods of output voltage wave construction are described, and analytical expressions for various waveshapes of potential practical importance are derived and evaluated.

In this chapter the properties of the input current waveforms are examined. It has already been indicated in Chapters 1 and 2 that the waveshape of the input current, drawn by the frequency changer from the a-c source, and the output voltage waveform are uniquely related; both are determined by the pattern of operation of the switches in the power circuit and thus by the method of output waveform construction. The generation of the output voltage and input current waveforms may thus be viewed analogously. The output voltage waveform is constructed from segments of successive input voltage waves supplied by the multiphase input source; the waveform of current in a given input line is composed of segments of the current wave(s) flowing in a single- or multi-phase load at the output. The lengths of the corresponding voltage and current segments are determined by the duration of closures of the relevant switches. The input current waveform, similarly to the output voltage waveform, can be represented as an ensemble of sinusoidal constituents, comprising the fundamental and extrabasal components, the frequencies of which are generally not integrally related.

The purpose of the present investigation is the derivation of analytical expressions for the input current waveforms of the most important frequency changers and a comparative evaluation between them in terms of the input current wave indices—that is, the input displacement factor, input current distortion factor, input power factor, and the normalized amplitudes and frequencies of the extrabasal components. The frequency changers analyzed are the UFC and SSFC, whose output voltage waveforms are generated by the linear modulating function $M(t) = \omega_O t$, the UDFFC, CDFFC, and NCC, whose output voltage waveforms are composed of the positive and negative type complementary waveforms generated by the periodic modulating function $M(r, t) = \sin^{-1}(r \sin \omega_O t)$.

As was stipulated in Chapter 1, the analysis of the input current waveform is based upon the assumption that the frequency changer supplies a set of "smooth" sinusoidal currents. This assumption is not strictly valid, since the output current inevitably contains superimposed "ripple" components; still this approach provides sufficiently accurate results for practical purposes.

In this chapter, frequency changers with single-phase and balanced three-phase loads are considered. Also, in order to exclude secondary effects and corresponding mathematical complications, the a-c input source is assumed to have zero internal impedance. The interested reader may consult reference 48, in which the effects of the source impedance and unbalanced loads are analyzed in a manner compatible with the methods used in this book.

The forthcoming analysis again assumes an elementary three-pulse circuit; however, the results will be generalized to multipulse circuits that are constructed from three-pulse units and have pulse number of $3n$ ($n = 1, 2, \ldots$).

5.1 DERIVATION OF GENERAL EXPRESSIONS FOR THE COMPLEMENTARY INPUT CURRENT WAVES

The set of three input currents drawn from the a-c source by the frequency changer is expressed in terms of the output currents and the existence functions, by the basic relationship given in equation (2.28), namely,

$$[i_I] = [H]^T[i_O]$$

or

$$\begin{bmatrix} i_{I1} \\ i_{I2} \\ i_{I3} \end{bmatrix} = \begin{bmatrix} h_{11} & h_{21} & h_{31} \\ h_{12} & h_{22} & h_{32} \\ h_{13} & h_{23} & h_{33} \end{bmatrix} \begin{bmatrix} i_{O1} \\ i_{O2} \\ i_{O3} \end{bmatrix} \tag{5.1}$$

where each output current, i_{Op} ($p = 1, 2, 3$), is given by equation (2.27)

$$i_{Op} = I_O \sin\left(\omega_O t + \phi_O - (p-1)\frac{2\pi}{3}\right) \qquad p = 1, 2, 3 \tag{5.2}$$

and functions h_{pq} ($p = 1, 2, 3$; $q = 1, 2, 3$) are the elements of the existence matrix $[H]$ describing the operation of the three-pulse power circuit.

For the generation of the output voltage waveforms, two sets of complementary existence functions ($h_{11}, h_{12}, \ldots; h_{\pi 11}, h_{\pi 12}, \ldots$) were introduced. These were expressed in terms of the angular input frequency, ω_I, and a common modulating function, $M(t)$, in equations (3.6) and (3.7). Subsequently, the coefficients of the original existence functions were generalized to describe output voltage control by pulse-width modulation in equations (4.5) and (4.6). To accommodate ordinary and pulse-width-modulated existence functions in one and the same analysis, h_{pq} and $h_{\pi pq}$ are defined here by a general coefficient, namely,

$$h_{pq} = \frac{1}{3} + \sum_{n=-\infty}^{\infty} \frac{K_n}{\pi} \exp jn\left(\omega_I t - (q-1)\frac{2\pi}{3} + M_p(t)\right) \tag{5.3}$$

and

$$h_{\pi pq} = \frac{1}{3} + \sum_{n=-\infty}^{\infty} \frac{K_{\pi n}}{\pi} \exp jn\left(\omega_I t - (q-1)\frac{2\pi}{3} - M_p(t)\right) \tag{5.4}$$

$$\text{where } K_n = \begin{cases} \dfrac{\sin n\dfrac{2\pi}{3}}{n} & \text{(ordinary)} \\[2ex] \dfrac{2\sin n\dfrac{\pi}{3}}{n}\cos n\left(\dfrac{\pi}{3} + \dfrac{\beta}{2}\right) & \text{(pulse-width-modulated)} \end{cases} \tag{5.5}$$

and

$$K_{\pi n} = \begin{cases} \dfrac{\sin n \dfrac{\pi}{3}}{n} & \text{(ordinary)} \\[2ex] \dfrac{2 \sin n \dfrac{2\pi}{3}}{n} \cos n \left(\dfrac{\pi}{3} + \dfrac{\beta}{2} \right) & \text{(pulse-width-modulated)} \end{cases} \tag{5.6}$$

$M_p(t)$ $(p = 1, 2, 3)$ is a general modulating function used to generate the output voltage waveform v_{Op} $(p = 1, 2, 3)$. It may be dependent on the output voltage ratio: $M_p(t) = M_p(r, t)$. Note that for balanced three-phase output, modulating functions $M_1(t)$, $M_2(t)$, and $M_3(t)$ are identical except for a mutual phase displacement of $2\pi/3$ at the wanted output frequency.

Substituting the first expression for the existence functions given by (5.3), together with equation (5.2) which defines the output currents, into equation (5.1), the set of input currents can be written as follows:

$$\begin{aligned}
\begin{bmatrix} i_{I1} \\ i_{I2} \\ i_{I3} \end{bmatrix} = \frac{I_O}{6j} & \left\{ \begin{bmatrix} 1 & 1 & 1 \\ 1 & 1 & 1 \\ 1 & 1 & 1 \end{bmatrix} \begin{bmatrix} 1 \\ a^2 \\ a \end{bmatrix} e^{j(\omega_O t + \phi_O)} - \begin{bmatrix} 1 & 1 & 1 \\ 1 & 1 & 1 \\ 1 & 1 & 1 \end{bmatrix} \begin{bmatrix} 1 \\ a \\ a^2 \end{bmatrix} e^{-j(\omega_O t + \phi_O)} \right\} \\
- \frac{I_O}{2\pi j} \sum_{n=1}^{\infty} K_n & \left\{ [a(-n)] \begin{bmatrix} e^{jnM_1(t)} \\ e^{j\left(nM_2(t) - \frac{2\pi}{3}\right)} \\ e^{j\left(nM_3(t) - \frac{4\pi}{3}\right)} \end{bmatrix} e^{j\{(n\omega_I + \omega_O)t + \phi_O\}} \right. \\
& - [a(n)] \begin{bmatrix} e^{-jnM_1(t)} \\ e^{-j\left(nM_2(t) - \frac{2\pi}{3}\right)} \\ e^{-j\left(nM_3(t) - \frac{4\pi}{3}\right)} \end{bmatrix} e^{-j\{(n\omega_I + \omega_O)t + \phi_O\}} \\
& - [a(-n)] \begin{bmatrix} e^{jnM_1(t)} \\ e^{j\left(nM_2(t) + \frac{2\pi}{3}\right)} \\ e^{j\left(nM_3(t) + \frac{4\pi}{3}\right)} \end{bmatrix} e^{j\{(n\omega_I - \omega_O)t - \phi_O\}} \\
& \left. + [a(n)] \begin{bmatrix} e^{-jnM_1(t)} \\ e^{-j\left(nM_2(t) + \frac{2\pi}{3}\right)} \\ e^{-j\left(nM_3(t) + \frac{4\pi}{3}\right)} \end{bmatrix} e^{-j\{n\omega_I - \omega_O)t - \phi_O\}} \right\}
\end{aligned} \tag{5.7}$$

where matrix $[a(n)]$ is given by

$$[a(n)] = \begin{bmatrix} 1 & 1 & 1 \\ \exp jn \dfrac{2\pi}{3} & \exp jn \dfrac{2\pi}{3} & \exp jn \dfrac{2\pi}{3} \\ \exp jn \dfrac{4\pi}{3} & \exp jn \dfrac{4\pi}{3} & \exp jn \dfrac{4\pi}{3} \end{bmatrix} \tag{5.8}$$

From equation (5.7) the three input currents can be expressed in the following simple form:

$$i_{Iq} = \frac{I_O}{3}\sum_{p=1}^{3} \sin\left(\omega_O t + \phi_O - (p-1)\frac{2\pi}{3}\right)$$
$$+\frac{I_O}{\pi}\sum_{p=1}^{3}\sum_{n=1}^{\infty} K_n\left\{\sin\left[n\left(\omega_I t - (q-1)\frac{2\pi}{3}\right)+\left(\omega_O t + \phi_O - (p-1)\frac{2\pi}{3}\right)+nM_p(t)\right]\right.$$
$$\left.-\sin\left[n\left(\omega_I t - (q-1)\frac{2\pi}{3}\right)-\left(\omega_O t + \phi_O - (p-1)\frac{2\pi}{3}\right)+nM_p(t)\right]\right\} \tag{5.9}$$

where $q = 1, 2, 3$.

In a similar manner, the complementary set of input currents corresponding to the complementary existence functions of equation (5.4) can be written as follows:

$$i_{I\pi q} = \frac{I_O}{3}\sum_{p=1}^{3} \sin\left(\omega_O t + \phi_O - (p-1)\frac{2\pi}{3}\right)$$
$$+\frac{I_O}{\pi}\sum_{p=1}^{3}\sum_{n=1}^{\infty} K_{\pi n}\left\{\sin\left[n\left(\omega_I t - (q-1)\frac{2\pi}{3}\right)\right.\right.$$
$$\left.+\left(\omega_O t + \phi_O - (p-1)\frac{2\pi}{3}\right)-nM_p(t)\right]$$
$$\left.-\sin\left[n\left(\omega_I t - (q-1)\frac{2\pi}{3}\right)-\left(\omega_O t + \phi_O - (p-1)\frac{2\pi}{3}\right)-nM_p(t)\right]\right\} \tag{5.10}$$

where $q = 1, 2, 3$.

Inspection of equations (5.9) and (5.10) leads to the following general conclusions:

1. The structure of the three input current waveforms obtained with successive substitution of $q = 1$, $q = 2$, and $q = 3$ are substantially the same. Therefore it is enough to analyze only one of them, for simplicity, i_{I1} ($i_{I\pi 1}$). For this reason, the expressions for the input current wave will, in future, always be derived for input phase 1, and for brevity subscript 1 will be omitted. The expression of i_{I1} ($i_{I\pi 1}$) can simply be modified to describe i_{I2} ($i_{I\pi 2}$) and i_{I3} ($i_{I\pi 3}$) by replacing $\omega_I t$ with $\omega_I t - 2\pi/3$ and $\omega_I t - 4\pi/3$, respectively.

2. Equations (5.9) and (5.10) have been derived on the assumption that the frequency changer supplies a balanced set of three output currents. This condition is indicated by the summation for p ($p = 1, 2, 3$). It follows, therefore, that the input current corresponding to any one of the output currents can be obtained by substituting the appropriate value for p—that is, $p = 1$ for output phase 1, $p = 2$ for output phase 2, and $p = 3$ for output phase 3—and omitting the summation for p. This means simply that the input current of the frequency changer supplying a three-phase load may be resolved into three components, each corresponding to one of the three output currents. For example, the current in input phase 1 may be given as a sum of three components, that is,

$$i_{I1} = i_{I11} + i_{I12} + i_{I13} \tag{5.11}$$

where, per equation (5.1),

$$\left.\begin{aligned} i_{I11} &= h_{11} i_{O1} \\ i_{I12} &= h_{21} i_{O2} \\ i_{I13} &= h_{31} i_{O3} \end{aligned}\right\} \tag{5.12}$$

are the components contributed by the output currents i_{O1}, i_{O2}, and i_{O3}, respectively.

Equations (5.9) and (5.10) describe the input current in terms of the output current(s) and a general modulating function for the two basic complementary operating modes of the frequency changer represented by the complementary existence functions. These fundamental expressions are the *duals* of the basic expressions for the output voltage given by equations (3.10) and (3.11). They will be the starting point of the forthcoming specific analytical derivation of the input current waveforms, for those modulating functions used in Chapters 3 and 4, for generating the practically important output voltage waveforms.

As will be seen, the analytical expressions for the input current waves are generally larger and more complex than those describing the output voltage waveforms. For this reason, the analysis here will be restricted to those frequency changers that are considered to be of the greatest general interest. Specifically, the input current waveforms related only to the linear modulating function $M(t) = \omega_O t$, and the periodic modulating function $M(\kappa, t) = \sin^{-1}(\kappa \sin \omega_O t)$, $0 \leqq \kappa \leqq \infty$, are analyzed. In the case of the linear modulating function, pulse-width modulation and phase-shift output voltage control methods are considered; for the periodic modulating function, the natural technique of amplitude-dependent frequency modulation is assumed.

5.2 UFC AND SSFC INPUT CURRENT WAVEFORMS

The input current waves of the UFC and SSFC can be expressed by substituting the linear modulating function $M_p(t) = \omega_O t - (p - 1)2\pi/3$ $(p = 1, 2, 3)$ into equations (5.9) and (5.10), respectively. Considering first the UFC, the input current may be written as follows:

$$\begin{aligned} i_I = {} & \frac{I_O}{3} \sum_{p=1}^{3} \sin\left(\omega_O t + \phi_O - (p-1)\frac{2\pi}{3}\right) \\ & + \frac{I_O}{\pi} \sum_{p=1}^{3} \sum_{n=1}^{\infty} K_n \left\{ \sin\left([n\omega_I + (n+1)\omega_O]t + \phi_O - (n+1)(p-1)\frac{2\pi}{3}\right) \right. \\ & \left. - \sin\left([n\omega_I + (n-1)\omega_O]t - \phi_O - (n-1)(p-1)\frac{2\pi}{3}\right)\right\} \end{aligned} \tag{5.13}$$

Before proceeding further it is useful to establish the value of K_n as a function of n. Since

$$\frac{-\sin n\dfrac{2\pi}{3}}{n} = \begin{cases} 0 & \text{for } n = 3k, \quad k = 1, 2, \ldots \\ -\dfrac{\sqrt{3}}{2}\dfrac{1}{n} & \text{for } n = 3k + 1, \quad k = 0, 1, \ldots \\ \dfrac{\sqrt{3}}{2}\dfrac{1}{n} & \text{for } n = 3k - 1, \quad k = 1, 2, \ldots \end{cases}$$

and

$$-\frac{2\sin n\frac{\pi}{3}}{n}\cos n\left(\frac{\pi}{3}+\frac{\beta}{2}\right)$$

$$=\begin{cases} 0 & \text{for } n = 3k, \quad k = 1, 2, \ldots \\ (-1)^n\sqrt{3}\,\frac{1}{n}\cos n\left(\frac{\pi}{3}+\frac{\beta}{2}\right) & \text{for } n = 3k+1, \quad k = 0, 1, \ldots \\ -(-1)^n\sqrt{3}\,\frac{1}{n}\cos n\left(\frac{\pi}{3}+\frac{\beta}{2}\right) & \text{for } n = 3k-1, \quad k = 1, 2, \ldots \end{cases}$$

coefficient K_n can be expressed simply as

$$K_n = \begin{cases} -\frac{\sqrt{3}}{2}\,w(0) & (k = 0) \\ -\frac{\sqrt{3}}{2}\,\frac{w(+)}{3k+1} & k = 1, 2, \ldots \\ \frac{\sqrt{3}}{2}\,\frac{w(-)}{3k-1} & k = 1, 2, \ldots \end{cases} \tag{5.14}$$

where $w(0)$, $w(+)$, and $w(-)$ are unity for ordinary existence functions, and

$$\left.\begin{aligned} w(0) &= 2\cos\left(\frac{\pi}{3}+\frac{\beta}{2}\right) \\ w(+) &= (-1)^{3k}\,2\cos\left\{(3k+1)\left(\frac{\pi}{3}+\frac{\beta}{2}\right)\right\} \\ w(-) &= (-1)^{3k}\,2\cos\left\{(3k-1)\left(\frac{\pi}{3}+\frac{\beta}{2}\right)\right\} \end{aligned}\right\} \tag{5.15}$$

for pulse-width-modulated existence functions.

Substituting equation (5.14) into (5.13), the input current i_I becomes:

$$\begin{aligned}
\text{I}\quad & i_I = \frac{\sqrt{3}}{2\pi} I_O \sum_{p=1}^{3} \Bigg(w(0)\sin\{\omega_I t - \phi_O - (p-1)2\pi\} \\
& \quad + \sum_{k=1}^{\infty} \frac{w(\pm)}{3k\pm 1} \sin\{[(3k\pm 1)\omega_I + 3k\omega_O]t \mp \phi_O - k(p-1)2\pi\}\Bigg) \\
\text{II}\quad & - \frac{\sqrt{3}}{2\pi} I_O \sum_{p=1}^{3} \Bigg\{ w(0)\sin\left((\omega_I + 2\omega_O)t + \phi_O + (p-1)\frac{2\pi}{3}\right) \\
& \quad + \sum_{k=1}^{\infty} \frac{w(\pm)}{3k\pm 1} \sin\Bigg([(3k\pm 1)\omega_I + (3k\pm 2)\omega_O]t \pm \phi_O \\
& \qquad - (3k\pm 2)(p-1)\frac{2\pi}{3}\Bigg)\Bigg\} \\
\text{III}\quad & + \frac{I_O}{3}\sum_{p=1}^{3} \sin\left(\omega_O t + \phi_O - (p-1)\frac{2\pi}{3}\right)
\end{aligned} \tag{5.16}$$

where, as before, the double sign means that the expressions in the relevant brackets should be taken twice, once with the upper signs and once with the lower signs.

Equation (5.16) is the general expression for the input current i_I when the three-pulse output voltage waveform is generated by the linear modulating function $M(t) = \omega_O t$. In other words, this equation describes the input current waveform of the unrestricted frequency changer.

As has already been stated, the general expression for the input current wave derived here is valid for single-phase or balanced three-phase output currents. Actually it is also applicable for the more special case, not considered here, of two output currents displaced by 120 degrees. For single-phase output current, index p should of course be replaced by, for example, one, and the summation for p should be omitted. In this case, equation (5.16), comprising parts I, II, and III, remains essentially unchanged; the coefficients remain as indicated, and the phase angles take the values relevant to $p = 1$.

Inspection of equation (5.16) shows, however, that for balanced three-phase output, the analytical expression for the input current becomes considerably simpler and, from the practical point of view, much more desirable. This is because under this condition the similar terms corresponding to the three output currents ($p = 1, 2, 3$) form balanced three-phase sets in parts II and III, which become zero as the summation for p is carried out. On the other hand, the sum of each set of three terms in part I is three times the value of the individual term, since these are in phase with one another. Putting it simply, for balanced three-phase output currents the terms cancel each other in parts II and III, and they reinforce each other in part I of equation (5.16). Therefore, for balanced three-phase output, i_I can be written in the following simple form:

$$i_I = \frac{3\sqrt{3}}{2\pi} I_O \left(w(0) \sin(\omega_I t - \phi_O) + \sum_{k=1}^{\infty} \frac{w(\pm)}{3k \pm 1} \sin\{[(3k \pm 1)\omega_I + 3k\omega_O]t \mp \phi_O\} \right) \tag{5.17}$$

where $w(0)$, $w(-)$, and $w(+)$ are unity for ordinary existence functions (i.e., for full output voltage), and they are defined by equation (5.15) for pulse-width-modulated existence functions.

Equations (5.16) and (5.17) can, in the usual manner, be generalized for multipulse frequency changer circuits. In equation (5.17) it is enough to make the usual replacement of $3k$ with Pk, where P is the pulse number. In parts I and II of equations (5.16) the same replacement is to be made; part III of the equation should be completely omitted if P is even (i.e., $P = 6, 12, 18, \ldots$), and the coefficient $I_O/3$ should be replaced with I_O/P if P is odd, i.e., $P = 3, 9, 15, \ldots$ It should be noted that the zero sequence current component given in part III can always be eliminated from the input source by supplying the frequency changer via a network that provides an "artificial" neutral point, for example, a transformer whose secondary windings are connected in "zig-zag."

It may also be appropriate to point out here that the expressions for multipulse current waveforms describe the input current in the three *primary* windings of the transformer feeding the frequency changer. This means that a three-phase input source is assumed for all multipulse circuits, with the understanding that a phase-splitting transformer is used, when required, to provide the necessary multiphase input voltages for the frequency changer.

Returning now to the specific three-pulse expressions presently under consideration, inspection of equations (5.16) and (5.17) reveals the fundamental difference between the input current waves obtained with single-phase and balanced three-phase output. To see this clearly, let us assume that the pulse number is very large, so that $P \to \infty$. Then, because $1/(Pk \pm 1) \to 0$, the input current waves relevant to single- and balanced three-phase outputs can be written as follows:

For single-phase output ($p = 1$)

$$i_I = \frac{\sqrt{3}}{2\pi} I_O w(0) \{\sin(\omega_I t - \phi_O) - \sin[(\omega_I + 2\omega_O)t + \phi_O]\} \tag{5.18}$$

For balanced three-phase output ($p = 1, 2, 3$)

$$i_I = \frac{3\sqrt{3}}{2\pi} I_O w(0) \sin(\omega_I t - \phi_O) \tag{5.19}$$

The conclusion can therefore be made that the extrabasal current component with the frequency of $\omega_I + 2\omega_O$ *will* appear in the input with the same amplitude as the fundamental component, regardless of the circuit configuration and pulse number, for a single-phase (or unbalanced) output current. A current component with the output frequency will also appear in the input (unless cancelled by the input network), for a single-phase (or unbalanced) output, for circuits of odd pulse number. As will be seen later, the input current wave of all frequency changers exhibits similar (but not identical) characteristics to those demonstrated by equations (5.18) and (5.19).

For those applications in which the frequency changer supplies a single-phase output, the input source—or appropriate input filters—must be able to supply the large and inevitable extrabasal current component(s). However, most practical applications require three-phase output, and in this case the input current of the frequency changer does not contain undue amounts of extrabasal components.

The input current waveform can be quantitatively characterized by the input current wave indices. Considering only the more important case of balanced three-phase output, these indices can be established readily from equation (5.17). They are, as are the output voltage wave indices, generally functions of the amplitude of the desired output voltage wave and therefore are dependent upon the method of output voltage control. However, in order to provide a uniform basis for the evaluation and comparison of input current waves corresponding to different output voltage waveforms, the input current wave indices as such will be considered only at full output voltage in this chapter. Detailed data related to the input current with a varying output voltage ratio are presented in Chapter 6.

The input current wave indices of the three-pulse UFC at full output voltage $[w(0) = w(-) = w(+) = 1]$ can be written directly from equation (5.17) using the basic definitions given by equations (2.30)–(2.34):

The current distortion factor is

$$\mu_I = \frac{1}{\sqrt{1 + \sum_{k=1}^{\infty} \frac{1}{(3k \pm 1)^2}}} \cong 0.83 \tag{5.20}$$

The input displacement factor is

$$\delta_I = \cos \phi_I = \cos(-\phi_O) \tag{5.21}$$

The input power factor is

$$\lambda_I = \mu_I \, \delta_I \cong 0.83 \cos(-\phi_O) \tag{5.22}$$

The normalized frequencies of the extrabasal components are

$$\nu_{Ik} = (3k \pm 1) + 3k\frac{f_O}{f_I} \qquad k = 1, 2, \ldots \tag{5.23}$$

And the normalized amplitudes of the extrabasal components are

$$\gamma_{Ik} = \frac{1}{3k \pm 1} \qquad k = 1, 2, \ldots \tag{5.24}$$

Equations (5.20)–(5.24) lead to the following conclusions concerning the input current waveform of the UFC:

1. The input distortion factor is independent of the phase angle of the output (load) current.
2. The input displacement angle ϕ_I is the *negative of the output* (*load*) *phase angle* ϕ_O; therefore an inductive load at the output is "seen" by the input source as a capacitive load, and vice versa.
3. The extrabasal frequencies are always higher than the input frequency. All ν_{Ik}s ($k = 1, 2, \ldots$) are minimum when $f_O = 0$, and they increase with increasing f_O.
4. The relative amplitudes of the extrabasal components are the same at all f_O/f_I ratios (at a given output voltage ratio).

It is interesting to note the relationship between the relevant input current and output voltage wave indices: γ_{Ik} is equal to γ_{Ok} [compare equation (5.24) to (3.47)]; ν_{Ik} exhibits a reciprocal characteristic to that of ν_{Ok}, that is, ν_{Ik} is maximum when ν_{Ok} is minimum (at $f_O/f_I = \infty$) and vice versa, ν_{Ok} is maximum when ν_{Ik} is minimum (at $f_O/f_I = 0$); ν_{Ok} and ν_{Ik} are equal when $f_O/f_I = 1$ [see equations (5.23) and (3.46)]. This of course is the consequence of the fact that the analytical expressions for the output voltage and input current waveforms are, for three-phase output, similar [compare equation (5.17) with (3.42)]; in fact, the output voltage and input current waveforms are identical at reciprocal f_O/f_I ratios—that is, the waveshape of the output voltage at f_O/f_I is the same as that of the input current at f_I/f_O. This is a general consequence of the symmetrical and orthogonal property of the existence matrix $[H\{M(t)\}]$ for the linear modulating function, $[H\{M(t)\}] = [H(\omega_O t)]$, namely $[H(\omega_O t)] = [H(\omega_O t)]^T$ and $[H(\omega_O t)][H(\omega_O t)]^T = [1]$. Therefore, the input and output terminals of this frequency changer are mathematically interchangeable:

$$\left.\begin{aligned} [v_O] &= [H][v_I] \text{ (and } [v_I] = [H]^T[v_O] = [H][v_O]) \\ [i_I] &= [H]^T[i_O] = [H][i_O] \text{ (and } [i_O] = [H][i_I]) \end{aligned}\right\} \tag{5.25}$$

Input current waveforms synthesized from the terms of equation (5.17) with $w(0) = w(-) = w(+) = 1$ at various output to input frequency ratios are shown for $\phi_O = 0$ in Figure 5.1. It is interesting to compare these waveforms to those shown for the output voltage in Figure 3.5*a*.

Turning now to the input current wave of the SSFC, this can be obtained, by substituting $M(t) = \omega_O t$ into the general expression given for $i_{I\pi}$ in equation (5.10),

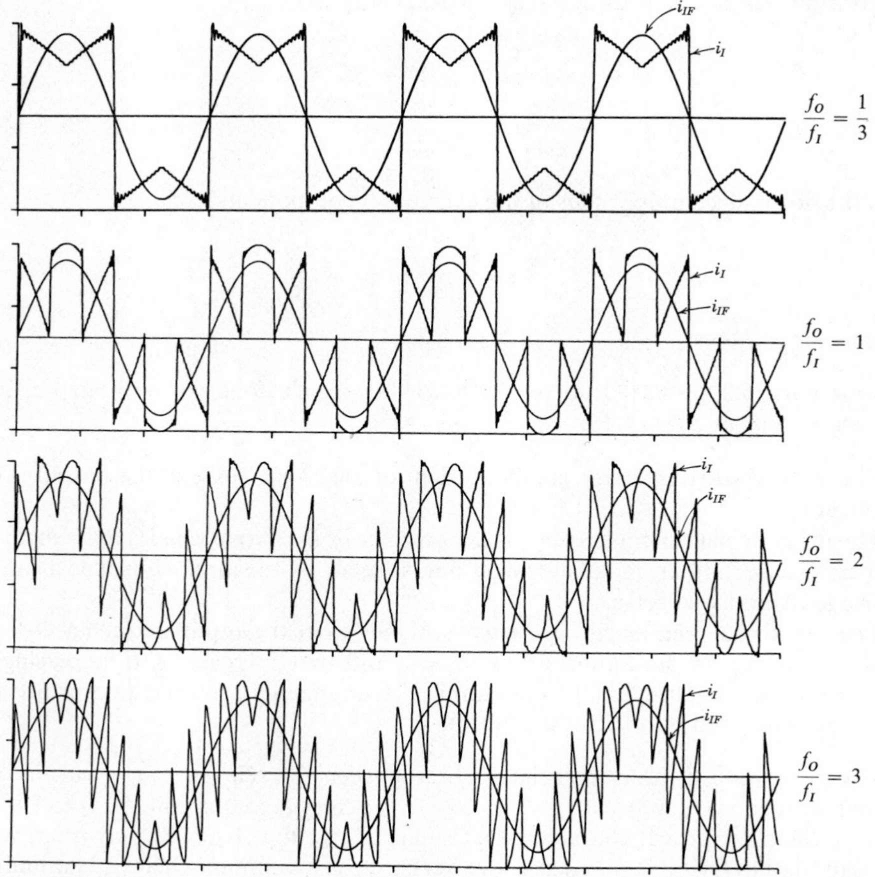

Figure 5.1 Typical three-pulse UFC input current waveforms synthesized at $\phi_O = 0$ from the terms of equation (5.17) for output to input frequency ratios of $f_O/f_I = 1/3$, $f_O/f_I = 1$, $f_O/f_I = 2$, $f_O/f_I = 3$.

in the following form:

$$\text{I}\left[\begin{aligned} i_{I\pi} = \frac{\sqrt{3}}{2\pi} I_O \sum_{p=1}^{3} \Bigg(& w(0) \sin\{\omega_I t + \phi_O - (p-1)2\pi\} \\ & + \sum_{k=1}^{\infty} (-1)^{3k} \frac{w(\pm)}{3k \pm 1} \sin\{[(3k \pm 1)\omega_I - 3k\omega_O]t \pm \phi_O - k(p-1)2\pi\}\Bigg) \end{aligned}\right.$$

$$\text{II}\left[\begin{aligned} & -\frac{\sqrt{3}}{2\pi} I_O \sum_{p=1}^{3} \Bigg\{ w(0) \sin\left((\omega_I - 2\omega_O)t - \phi_O - (p-1)\frac{2\pi}{3}\right) \\ & + \sum_{k=1}^{\infty} (-1)^{3k} \frac{w(\pm)}{3k \pm 1} \sin\Bigg([(3k \pm 1)\omega_I - (3k \pm 2)\omega_O]t \mp \phi_O \\ & \qquad + (3k \pm 2)(p-1)\frac{2\pi}{3}\Bigg)\Bigg\} \end{aligned}\right.$$

$$\text{III}\left[\; + \frac{I_O}{3} \sum_{p=1}^{3} \sin\left(\omega_O t + \phi_O - (p-1)\frac{2\pi}{3}\right)\right. \tag{5.26}$$

where again, $w(0)$, $w(-)$, and $w(+)$ are unity for ordinary existence functions, and they are defined by equation (5.15) for pulse-width-modulated existence functions.

For balanced three-phase output parts II and III of equation (5.26) are again zero, and $i_{I\pi}$ may be expressed in the simple form:

$$i_{I\pi} = \frac{3\sqrt{3}}{2\pi} I_O \left(w(0) \sin(\omega_I t + \phi_O) + \sum_{k=1}^{\infty} (-1)^{3k} \frac{w(\pm)}{3k \pm 1} \sin\{[(3k \pm 1)\omega_I - 3k\omega_O]t \pm \phi_O\} \right) \tag{5.27}$$

The input current wave indices of $i_{I\pi}$ may be written for balanced three-phase output at full output voltage $[w(0) = w(-) = w(+) = 1]$ from equation (5.27) as follows:

$$\mu_{I\pi} = \frac{1}{\sqrt{1 + \sum_{k=1}^{\infty} \frac{1}{(3k \pm 1)^2}}} \cong 0.83 \tag{5.28}$$

$$\delta_{I\pi} = \cos \phi_I = \cos \phi_O \tag{5.29}$$

$$\lambda_{I\pi} = \mu_{I\pi} \delta_{I\pi} \cong 0.83 \cos \phi_O \tag{5.30}$$

$$\nu_{I\pi k} = \left| (3k \pm 1) - 3k \frac{f_O}{f_I} \right| \qquad f_O \leqq f_I \quad \text{and} \quad k = 1, 2, \ldots \tag{5.31}$$

$$\gamma_{I\pi k} = \frac{1}{3k \pm 1} \qquad k = 1, 2, \ldots \tag{5.32}$$

Comparing the analytical expressions for $i_{I\pi}$ [equations (5.26) and (5.27)] and the related input current indices [equations (5.28)–(5.32)] with the relevant complementary expressions [equations (5.16) and (5.17) and equations (5.20)–(5.24)], the following significant *differences*, besides the obvious similarities, should be noticed:

1. The input displacement angle ϕ_I is now *the same* as the output (load) phase angle. Previously ϕ_I was equal to the negative of ϕ_O.
2. The extrabasal components have frequencies that are the differences between multiples of the input and output frequencies, whereas previously they were expressed as sums of multiples of the input and output frequencies. The frequencies of certain extrabasal components can therefore be lower than f_I, and they may become zero at appropriately large f_O/f_I ratios. For balanced three-phase output, $\nu_{I\pi k} < 1$ if $f_O/f_I > (3k - 2)/3k$ and $\nu_{I\pi k} = 0$ if $f_O/f_I = (3k - 1)/3k$, $k = 1, 2, \ldots$
3. In the case of single-phase output, the frequency of the inevitable *pulse-number-independent* extrabasal component is $f_I - 2f_O$, whereas previously it was $f + 2f_O$.
4. Although there is an apparent similarity between the analytical expressions for $i_{I\pi}$ and $v_{O\pi}$—compare equation (5.27) with (3.43)—the corresponding waveforms are always different, because f_O is not interchangeable with f_I, due to the restriction $f_I \geqq f_O$ [equation (3.45)].

A typical three-pulse waveform $i_{I\pi}$, synthesized from the terms of equation (5.27), for a balanced three-phase output at $\phi_O = 0$, is shown for $f_O/f_I = \frac{1}{6}$ in Figure 5.2; typical multipulse waveforms for $f_O/f_I = \frac{1}{3}$ are shown in Figure 5.3.

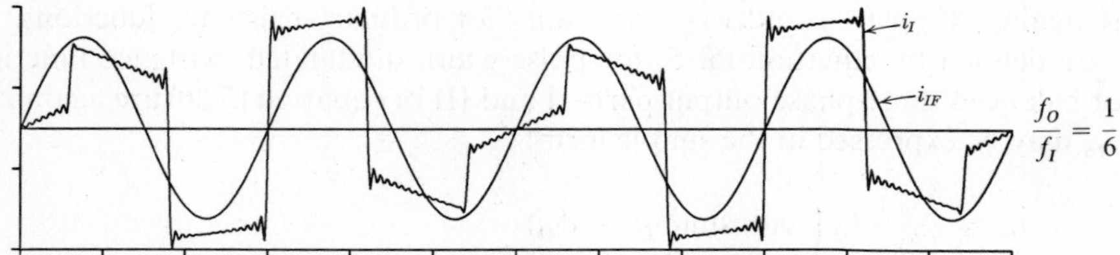

Figure 5.2 A typical three-pulse SSFC input current waveform synthesized from the terms of equation (5.27) at $f_O/f_I = 1/6$.

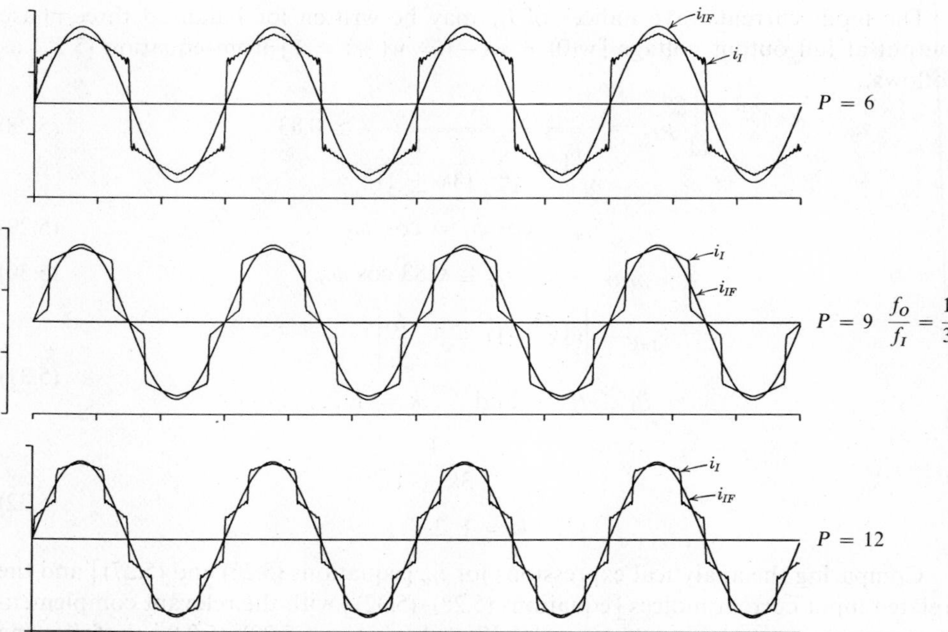

Figure 5.3 Typical six-, nine-, and twelve-pulse SSFC input current waveforms synthesized from the terms of equation (5.27) at $f_O/f_I = 1/3$.

Before concluding this section we briefly consider the effect of output voltage control on the general expression for the input current wave of the UFC. The effect is similar on the complementary input current wave of the SSFC, defined by equation (5.27). It was established in Chapter 4 that only two methods of voltage control—that is, pulse-width modulation and phase shift—provide output voltage wave indices at reduced output voltage ratios that are compatible with those obtained at full output voltage. Therefore only these two methods are considered.

The general expression for the input current wave of the UFC has, in fact, already been derived for pulse-width-modulated existence functions and is given, for balanced three-phase output, by equation (5.17), with coefficients defined by equation (5.15). Detailed data calculated from these equations are given as functions of the output voltage ratio in Chapter 6. Here, typical three-, six-, and twelve-pulse UFC input current waveforms, synthesized from the terms of equation (5.17), using the coefficients given by equation (5.15), are shown for various voltage ratios at $\phi_O = 0$ in Figure 5.4.

The input current wave of the UFC utilizing phase-shift voltage control can be derived easily by recalling that with this method two independent circuits (Figure

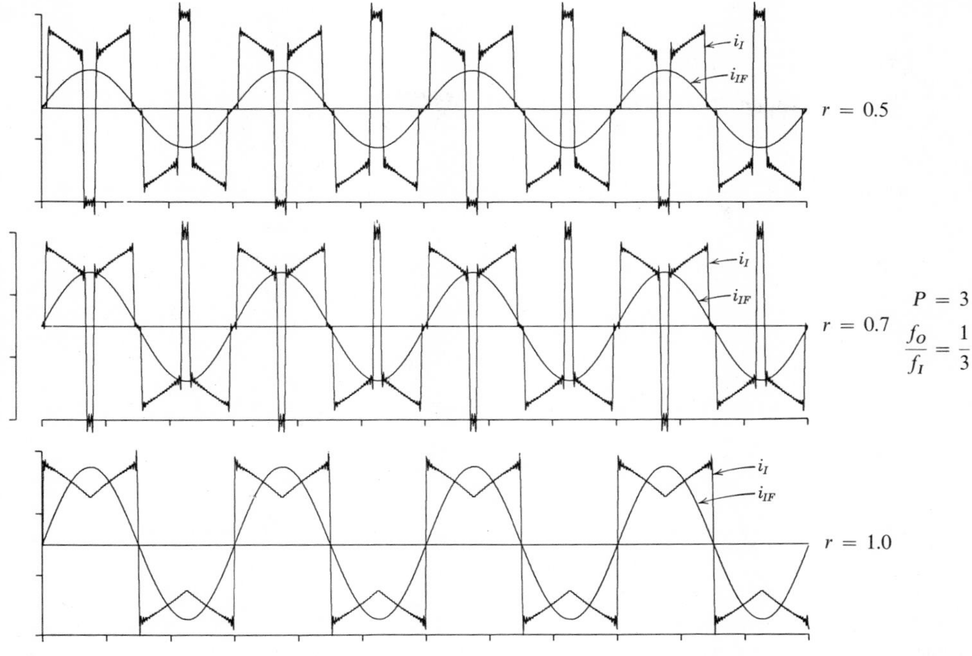

i_I
i_{IF}
$r = 0.5$
i_I
i_{IF}
$r = 0.7$
$P = 3$
$\frac{f_O}{f_I} = \frac{1}{3}$
i_I
i_{IF}
$r = 1.0$

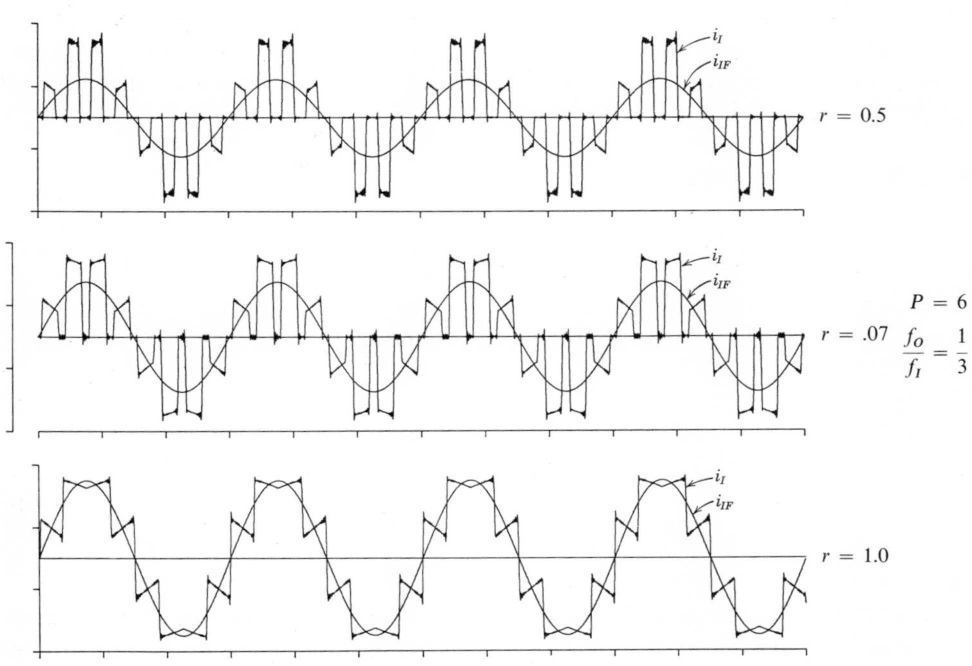

i_I
i_{IF}
$r = 0.5$
i_I
i_{IF}
$r = .07$
$P = 6$
$\frac{f_O}{f_I} = \frac{1}{3}$
i_I
i_{IF}
$r = 1.0$

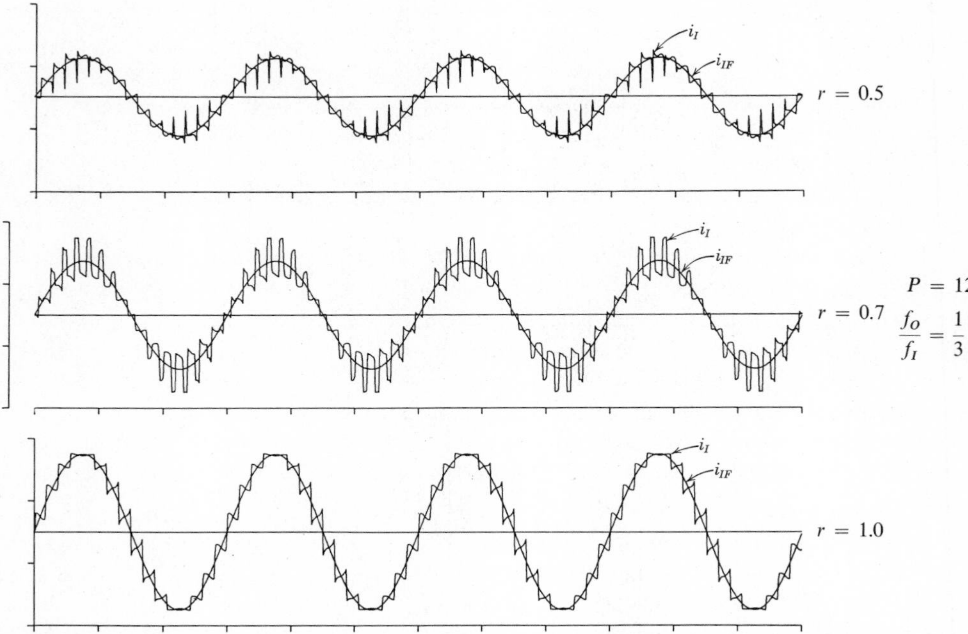

Figure 5.4 Typical three-, six-, and twelve-pulse UFC input current waveforms, with pulse-width modulation type voltage control, synthesized from the terms of equation (5.17) at output voltage ratios of $r = 0.5$, $r = 0.7$, $r = 1.0$; $f_O/f_I = 1/3$.

4.11), each with a pulse number of 3, 6, . . . etc., are employed. The voltage control is achieved by phase shifting the modulating function of one circuit by angle ξ, and that of the other circuit by $-\xi$. Using the techniques demonstrated for the output voltage in Chapter 4, the input current wave i_I for the more important case of balanced three-phase output can be expressed readily as a function of angle ξ, for a system composed of two three-pulse circuits, in the following form:

$$i_I(\xi) = \frac{3\sqrt{3}}{2\pi} I_O \left\{ \cos\xi \sin(\omega_I t - \phi_O) + \sum_{k=1}^{\infty} \left(A_{[3(2k-1)\pm 1]}(\xi) \cos\{([3(2k-1) \pm 1]\omega_I + 3(2k-1)\omega_O)t \mp \phi_O\} + B_{(6k\pm 1)}(\xi) \sin\{[(6k \pm 1)\omega_I + 6k\omega_O]t \mp \phi_O\} \right) \right\} \tag{5.33}$$

where

$$\left. \begin{aligned} A_{[3(2k-1)\pm 1]}(\xi) &= \frac{-\sin\{[3(2k-1) \pm 1]\xi\}}{3(2k-1) \pm 1} \\ B_{(6k\pm 1)}(\xi) &= \frac{\cos\{(6k \pm 1)\xi\}}{6k \pm 1} \end{aligned} \right\} \tag{5.34}$$

and $0 \leqq \xi < \pi/2$

Inspection of equation (5.33) indicates that, similarly to the output voltage waveform, the components with frequencies characteristically present in the three-pulse current waveform do not, in general, cancel each other, except at certain values of ξ given by equation (4.48). On the other hand, components with frequencies of

$(6k \mp 1)f_I + 6kf_O$, which are typical for six-pulse waveforms, also cancel each other whenever condition (4.49) is satisfied.

Equation (5.33) can be modified for two identical circuits of any pulse number P by the following rules: replace $3(2k - 1)$ by $P(2k - 1)$, replace $[3(2k - 1) \pm 1]$ by $[P(2k - 1) \pm 1]$, replace $6k$ by $2Pk$, and replace $(6k \pm 1)$ by $(2Pk \pm 1)$.

Typical current waveforms synthesized from the terms of equation (5.33), with $\phi_O = 0$, for $P = 3$ and $P = 6$, are shown at various output voltage ratios in Figure 5.5*a* and *b*, respectively.

The conclusion for phase-shift voltage control reached in Chapter 4 for the output voltage waveform is essentially valid for the input current wave; that is, the frequency spectrum of the P-pulse input current wave obtained at full output voltage is, in general, degraded to that of the constituent $P/2$ pulse current waveforms. For example, the spectrum of the input current wave of a circuit of overall pulse number six, comprised of two three-pulse elementary circuits, will generally be similar to that characterizing a three-pulse current waveform. It is important to note that the input phase angle—and thus the input displacement factor—is independent of the output voltage ratio. Thus $\phi_I = -\phi_O$, and $\delta_I = \cos\phi_I = \cos(-\phi_O)$ at any value of ξ.

5.3 POSITIVE-TYPE AND NEGATIVE-TYPE INPUT CURRENT WAVEFORMS

In this section input current waves related to the positive-type and negative-type output voltage waveforms obtained with the periodic modulating function $M(\kappa, t) = \sin^{-1}\{\kappa \sin[\omega_O t - (p - 1)(2\pi/3)]\}$, $(p = 1, 2, 3)$ are considered. Hereafter we will refer to these as *positive-type* and *negative-type current waveforms*, respectively.

The analysis is not extended to the range of *saturation* (i.e., $\kappa > 1$), and thus in general κ will be equal to the output voltage ratio r and will be written as such. Data corresponding to $\kappa > 1$ for the naturally commutated cycloconverter is presented in Chapter 6.

It was demonstrated in Chapter 4 that the analytical approach is essentially the same for a periodic modulating function, regardless of its actual character. Therefore, once the following analysis has been understood, the reader may quite easily undertake a similar analysis for a modulating function other than the one specified above.

The present analysis is based upon the two basic complementary expressions (with $q = 1$) given by equations (5.9) and (5.10). Thus, by substituting $M(r, t)$ first into equation (5.9) and applying appropriate trigonometric identities for the purpose of separating $M(r, t)$ from the other variables, the positive-type current wave, i_I, may be expressed in the following form:

$$i_I = \frac{I_O}{3}\sum_{p=1}^{3}\sin\left(\omega_O t + \phi_O - (p-1)\frac{2\pi}{3}\right) + \frac{I_O}{\pi}\sum_{p=1}^{3}\sum_{n=1}^{\infty}K_n\left\{\pm\sin\left([n\omega_I \pm \omega_O]t \pm \phi_O \mp (p-1)\frac{2\pi}{3}\right)\cos\{nM_p(r,t)\} \pm \cos\left([n\omega_I \pm \omega_O]t \pm \phi_O \mp (p-1)\frac{2\pi}{3}\right)\sin\{nM_p(r,t)\}\right\} \quad (5.35)$$

Recall that K_n is equal to zero for $n = 3k$ $(k = 1, 2, \ldots)$, and the functions $\sin\{nM_p(r, t)\}$ and $\cos\{nM_p(r, t)\}$ can be expanded into appropriate Fourier series

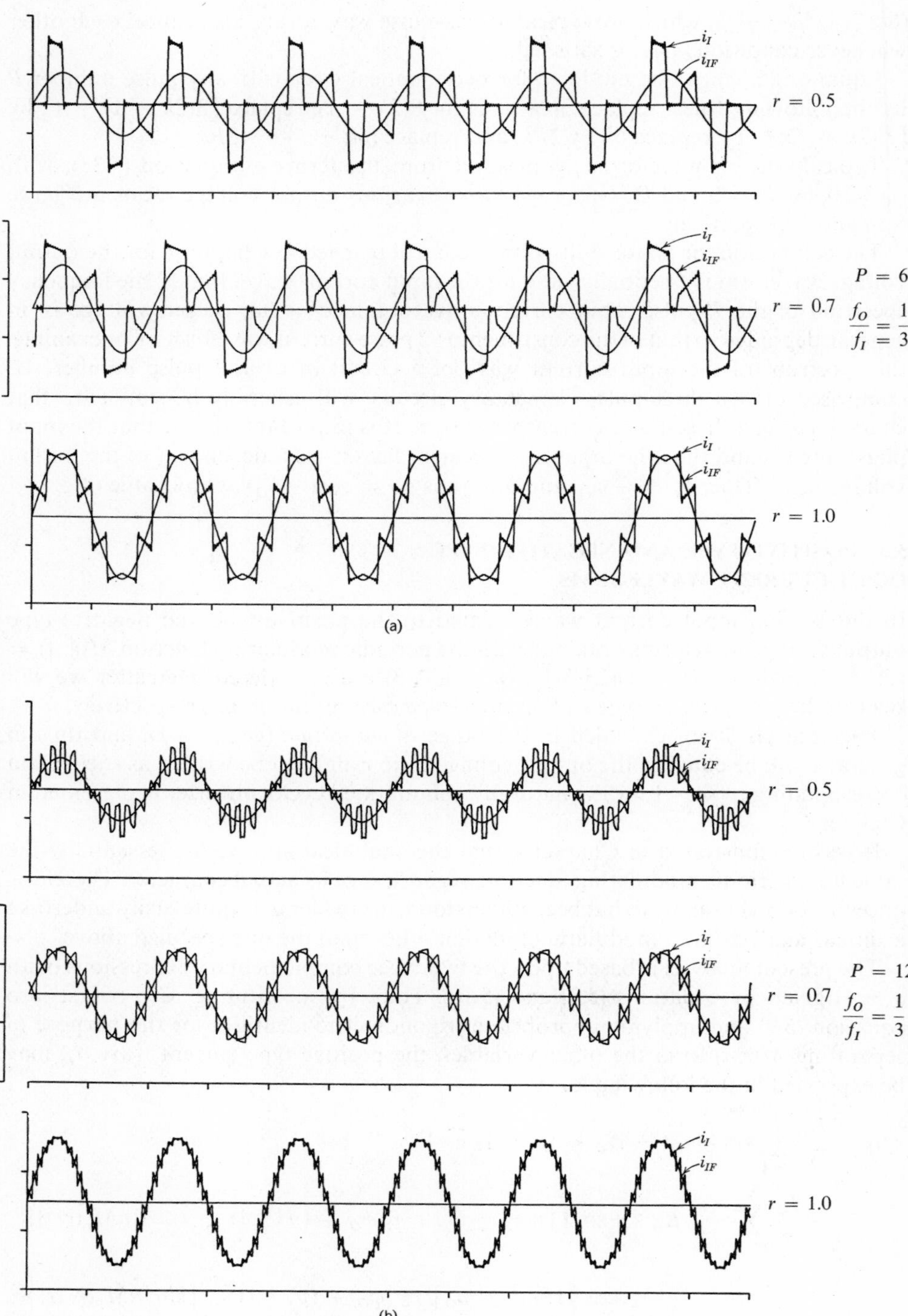

Figure 5.5 Typical input current waveforms of *a* an overall six-pulse and *b* an overall twelve-pulse UFC with phase-shift-type voltage control, synthesized from the terms of equation (5.33) at output voltage ratios of $r = 0.5$, $r = 0.7$, $r = 1.0$; $f_O/f_I = 1/3$.

[see definitions (4.16)–(4.22)]. The results given for the present modulating function in equations (4.30)–(4.33) may be used if $\omega_O t$ is replaced by $\omega_O t - (p-1)(2\pi/3)$. Recall also that the presently considered modulating function sets the amplitude of the output voltage through the output voltage ratio r. Therefore, pulse-width modulation-type voltage control need not be considered, and K_n can be taken for $-(\sqrt{3}/2)$ $(n = 3k+1,\ k = 0, 2, \ldots)$ and $+(\sqrt{3}/2)$ $(n = 3k-1,\ k = 1, 2, \ldots)$. Thus, substituting for $\sin\{nM_p(r,t)\}$, $\cos\{nM_p(r,t)\}$, and K_n as specified above, the input current wave can be expressed as follows:

$$
\begin{aligned}
&\text{(a)}\ \ \text{I}\quad i_I = \frac{\sqrt{3}}{2\pi} I_O r \cos\phi_O \sum_{p=1}^{3} \sin\{\omega_I t - (p-1)2\pi\} \\
&\text{II}\quad - \frac{\sqrt{3}}{4\pi} I_O r \sum_{p=1}^{3} \sin\left((\omega_I \pm 2\omega_O)t \pm \phi_O \pm (p-1)\frac{2\pi}{3}\right) \\
&\text{III}\quad + \frac{I_O}{3} \sum_{p=1}^{3} \sin\left(\omega_O t + \phi_O - (p-1)\frac{2\pi}{3}\right) \\
&\text{IV}\quad + \frac{\sqrt{3}}{2\pi} I_O \sum_{p=1}^{3} \sum_{u=-1}^{1} \sum_{k=1}^{\infty} \Bigg\{ \sum_{n=0}^{2n=3(2k-1)-u} \frac{a_{[3(2k-1)-u],2n}}{3(2k-1)-u}(\pm u) \\
&\quad \times \sin\left(\{[3(2k-1)-u]\omega_I \pm \omega_O\}t \pm \phi_O \mp (p-1)\frac{2\pi}{3}\right) \\
&\quad \times \cos\left(2n\left[\omega_O t - (p-1)\frac{2\pi}{3}\right]\right) + \sum_{n=0}^{2n+1=6k-u} \frac{b_{(6k-u),(2n+1)}}{6k-u}(\pm u) \\
&\quad \times \cos\left([(6k-u)\omega_I \pm \omega_O]t \pm \phi_O \mp (p-1)\frac{2\pi}{3}\right) \\
&\quad \times \sin\left((2n+1)\left[\omega_O t - (p-1)\frac{2\pi}{3}\right]\right)\Bigg\} \\
&\text{(b)}\ \ \text{V}\quad + \frac{\sqrt{3}}{2\pi} I_O \sum_{p=1}^{3} \sum_{n=0}^{\infty} a_{1,2n} \Bigg\{ \mp \sin\left([\omega_I \pm \omega_O]t \pm \phi_O \mp (p-1)\frac{2\pi}{3}\right) \\
&\quad \times \cos\left(2n\left[\omega_O t - (p-1)\frac{2\pi}{3}\right]\right)\Bigg\} \\
&\text{VI}\quad + \frac{\sqrt{3}}{2\pi} I_O \sum_{p=1}^{3} \sum_{u=-1}^{1} \sum_{k=1}^{\infty} \sum_{n=0}^{\infty} \Bigg\{ \frac{b_{[3(2k-1)-u],(2n+1)}}{3(2k-1)-u}(\pm u) \\
&\quad \times \cos\left(\{[3(2k-1)-u]\omega_I \pm \omega_O\}t \pm \phi_O \mp (p-1)\frac{2\pi}{3}\right) \\
&\quad \times \sin\left((2n+1)\left[\omega_O t - (p-1)\frac{2\pi}{3}\right]\right) + \frac{a_{(6k-u),2n}}{6k-u}(\pm u) \\
&\quad \times \sin\left([(6k-u)\omega_I \pm \omega_O]t \pm \phi_O \mp (p-1)\frac{2\pi}{3}\right) \\
&\quad \times \cos\left(2n\left[\omega_O t - (p-1)\frac{2\pi}{3}\right]\right)\Bigg\}
\end{aligned}
\tag{5.36}
$$

where the general coefficients are the same as those used in the expression for the related output voltage waveform, given by equation (4.34), and are defined by equations (4.19)–(4.22). Numerical values of these coefficients are given tabulated in the Appendix.

For brevity, the terms in parts IV, V, and VI of equation (5.36) are given in the form of sine–cosine products. Each of these products represents two families of extrabasal components, one having *sum* and the other *difference* frequencies. For example, a typical product in part IV

$$\sin\left(\{[3(2k-1)\pm 1]\omega_I+\omega_O\}t+\phi_O-(p-1)\frac{2\pi}{3}\right)\cos\left(2n\left[\omega_O t-(p-1)\frac{2\pi}{3}\right]\right)$$

can be decomposed in the following form:

$$\frac{1}{2}\left\{\sin\left(\{[3(2k-1)\pm 1]\omega_I+(2n+1)\omega_O\}t+\phi_O-(2n+1)(p-1)\frac{2\pi}{3}\right)\right.$$
$$\left.+\sin\left(\{[3(2k-1)\pm 1]\omega_I-(2n-1)\omega_O\}t+\phi_O+(2n-1)(p-1)\frac{2\pi}{3}\right)\right\} \tag{5.37}$$

The general expression given for the three-pulse positive-type input current wave in equation (5.36) can, of course, be generalized for multipulse waveforms by following the previously established simple rules, namely: parts I, II, and V remain unchanged; omit part III if P is even ($P = 6, 12, 18, \ldots$) and replace $I_O/3$ with I_O/P if P is odd ($P = 3, 9, 15, \ldots$); replace $[3(2k-1)\pm 1]$ with $[P(2k-1)\pm 1]$ and $(6k \pm 1)$ with $(2Pk \pm 1)$ in parts IV and VI *if P is odd* ($P = 3, 5, 15, \ldots$), or omit terms with coefficients $a_{[3(2k-1)\pm 1],2n}$ and $b_{[3(2k-1)\pm 1],(2n+1)}$ and substitute $(6k \pm 1)$ with $(Pk \pm 1)$ *if P is even* ($P = 6, 12, 18, \ldots$).

Inspection of equation (5.36) reveals the following general characteristics of i_I.

1. Parts I, II, and V of the expression are independent of the pulse number. However, the presence or absence of certain terms in parts III, IV, and VI is dependent upon the pulse number, as indicated above.
2. Part I provides the only component with the frequency of the input source, f_I. This component is *always* in phase with the corresponding source voltage, regardless of the output phase angle ϕ_O. The input source therefore supplies only the real power consumed by the output load and supplies no reactive power. This means that when the output load is purely reactive, there is no fundamental component of input current.
3. For single-phase (or unbalanced) output the *pulse-number-independent* components have frequencies of both $f_I + 2f_O$ and $f_I - 2f_O$.
4. For balanced three-phase output, the amplitude of the fundamental component (part I) is multiplied by three; the pulse-number-independent extrabasal components (parts II and III) cancel.
5. All components in parts IV, V, and VI generally have nonzero amplitude for single-phase output. For balanced three-phase output, however, the amplitudes of certain components become zero. This cancellation is dependent upon the value of index n. Thus, three similar components will cancel each other in the input, when summed for index p, ($p = 1, 2, 3$) at the value of index n at which the angular expression $\pm(p-1)(2\pi/3)$ in effect prevails; conversely, these three components

will reinforce each other at the value of n at which the above angular expression is, in effect, transformed to $\pm(p-1)2\pi$. For example, the angular expression $(2n+1)(p-1)(2\pi/3)$ in equation (5.37) transforms to $(p-1)(2\ell-1)2\pi$ ($\ell = 1, 2, 3\ldots$) when $(2n+1) = 3(2\ell-1)$ or $n = 3\ell - 2$. Consequently, the expression $\sin\{[(3(2k-1)\pm 1)\omega_I + (2n+1)\omega_O]t + \phi_O - (2n+1)(p-1)(2\pi/3)\}$ can be rewritten in the simpler form $\sin\{[(3(2k-1)\pm 1)\omega_I + 3(2n+1)\omega_O]t + \phi_O\}$ for three-phase output.

6. As usual, index k takes all integer values from one to infinity in parts IV, V, and VI. By contrast, integer n is bounded by the value of k in part IV, but it takes all integer values regardless of the value of k from 0 to infinity in parts V and VI.

Despite the complexity of the input current related to the periodic modulating function $M(r, t)$, we write it in the expanded form, showing all components explicitly, for the practically more important and fortunately less space-consuming case of balanced three-phase output:

$$
\begin{aligned}
&\text{(a)}\quad i_I = \frac{3\sqrt{3}}{2\pi} I_O \Bigg\{ r\cos\phi_O \sin\omega_I t \\
&\quad + \frac{1}{2}\sum_{u=-1}^{1}\sum_{k=1}^{\infty}\Bigg(\sum_{n=1}^{6n-4=3(2k-1)-u} \frac{a_{[3(2k-1)-u],(6n-4)}}{3(2k-1)-u}(\pm u) \\
&\quad \times \sin\{([3(2k-1)-u]\omega_I \pm 3(2n-1)\omega_O)t \pm \phi_O\} \\
&\qquad + \sum_{n=1}^{6n-2=3(2k-1)-u} \frac{a_{[3(2k-1)-u],(6n-2)}}{3(2k-1)-u}(\mp u) \\
&\quad \times \sin\{([3(2k-1)-u]\omega_I \pm 3(2n-1)\omega_O)t \mp \phi_O\} \\
&\quad + \sum_{n=1}^{6n-1=6k-u} \frac{b_{(6k-u),(6n-1)}}{6k-u}(\pm u)\sin\{[(6k-u)\omega_I \pm 6n\omega_O]t \pm \phi_O\} \\
&\quad + \sum_{n=0}^{6n+1=6k-u} \frac{b_{(6k-u),(6n+1)}}{6k-u}(\mp u)\sin\{[(6k-u)\omega_I \pm 6n\omega_O]t \mp \phi_O\}\Bigg)\Bigg\} \\
&\text{(b)}\quad + \frac{3\sqrt{3}}{4\pi} I_O \Bigg\{ \mp a_{1,(6n-4)} \sin\{[\omega_I \pm 3(2n-1)\omega_O]t \pm \phi_O\} \\
&\qquad \pm a_{1,(6n-2)} \sin\{[\omega_I \pm 3(2n-1)\omega_O]t \mp \phi_O\} \\
&\quad + \sum_{u=-1}^{1}\sum_{k=1}^{\infty}\Bigg(\sum_{n=1}^{\infty} \frac{b_{[3(2k-1)-u],(6n-1)}}{3(2k-1)-u}(\pm u) \\
&\qquad \times \sin\{([3(2k-1)-u]\omega_I \pm 6n\omega_O)t \pm \phi_O\} \\
&\quad + \sum_{n=0}^{\infty} \frac{b_{[3(2k-1)-u],(6n+1)}}{3(2k-1)-u}(\mp u)\sin\{([3(2k-1)-u]\omega_I \pm 6n\omega_O)t \mp \phi_O\} \\
&\quad + \sum_{n=1}^{\infty} \frac{a_{(6k-u),(6n-4)}}{6k-u}(\pm u)\sin\{[(6k-u)\omega_I \pm 3(2n-1)\omega_O]t \pm \phi_O\} \\
&\quad + \sum_{n=1}^{\infty} \frac{a_{(6k-u),(6n-2)}}{6k-u}(\mp u)\sin\{[(6k-u)\omega_I \pm 3(2n-1)\omega_O]t \mp \phi_O\}\Bigg)\Bigg\}
\end{aligned}
\tag{5.38}
$$

The complementary negative-type input current waveform, $i_{I\pi}$, related to modulating function $M(r, t) = \sin^{-1}(r \sin \omega_O t)$, can be derived analytically in a similar fashion from the general expression given by equation (5.10). Fortunately, the input current waves i_I and $i_{I\pi}$, similarly to the corresponding output voltage waveforms v_O and $v_{O\pi}$, are closely related; thus $i_{I\pi}$ can be expressed simply from the two constituent parts, (a) and (b), of equations (5.36) or (5.38), namely,

$$i_{I\pi} = a - b \tag{5.39}$$

where a is part (a) and b is part (b) of equation (5.36) for single-phase output, and of equation (5.38) for balanced three-phase output.

The relationship between i_I and $i_{I\pi}$, that is, $i_I = a + b$ and $i_{I\pi} = a - b$, expresses an important property of the complementary input current waves associated with periodic modulating functions, which will become evident during the investigation of the composite waveforms.

For the purpose of later comparisons, the three-pulse input current wave indices of i_I (or $i_{I\pi}$) for balanced three-phase output [equations (5.38) and (5.39)] at full output voltage ($r = 1$) are now determined. Since the amplitude of the fundamental component is a function of the output (load) displacement factor, it follows that all the amplitude-related indices also depend upon ϕ_O. For simplicity, therefore, the input current wave indices are given here only at $\phi_O = 0$.

The current distortion factor is

$$\mu_{I,\phi_O=0} = \mu_{I\pi,\phi_O=0} \cong 0.81 \tag{5.40}$$

The input displacement factor is

$$\delta_I = \delta_{I\pi} = \cos \phi_I = 1 \tag{5.41}$$

The input power factor is

$$\left.\begin{aligned} \lambda_I &= \lambda_{I\pi} = \mu_I \, \delta_I = \mu_I \\ \lambda_{I,\phi_O=0} &\cong 0.81 \end{aligned}\right\} \tag{5.42}$$

The normalized frequencies of the extrabasal components are

$$\nu_{Ik} = \nu_{I\pi k} = \begin{cases} (3k \pm 1) + 3n\dfrac{f_O}{f_I} \\[2ex] \left|(3k \pm 1) - 3n\dfrac{f_O}{f_I}\right| \end{cases} \tag{5.43}$$

The normalized amplitudes of the extrabasal components are, at $\phi_O \equiv 0$, proportional to differences of appropriate a and b coefficients, as seen in equation (5.38). Tabulated values of these coefficients are given in the Appendix.

Equations (5.41) and 5.42) state the important fact, predicted in Chapter 1 by qualitative reasoning, that the input displacement factor is invariably unity. This is the most important characteristic of the input current waveform obtained with either a positive-type or negative-type output voltage wave. Actually, for these basic output voltage waveform types, the characteristic is preserved with any periodic modulating function, regardless of its particular character. The capability of the frequency changer to maintain unity input displacement factor independently of the load power factor is discussed further later in this chapter; the phenomenon is illustrated graphically here in Figure 5.6. In Figure 5.6a the input voltage waves, the

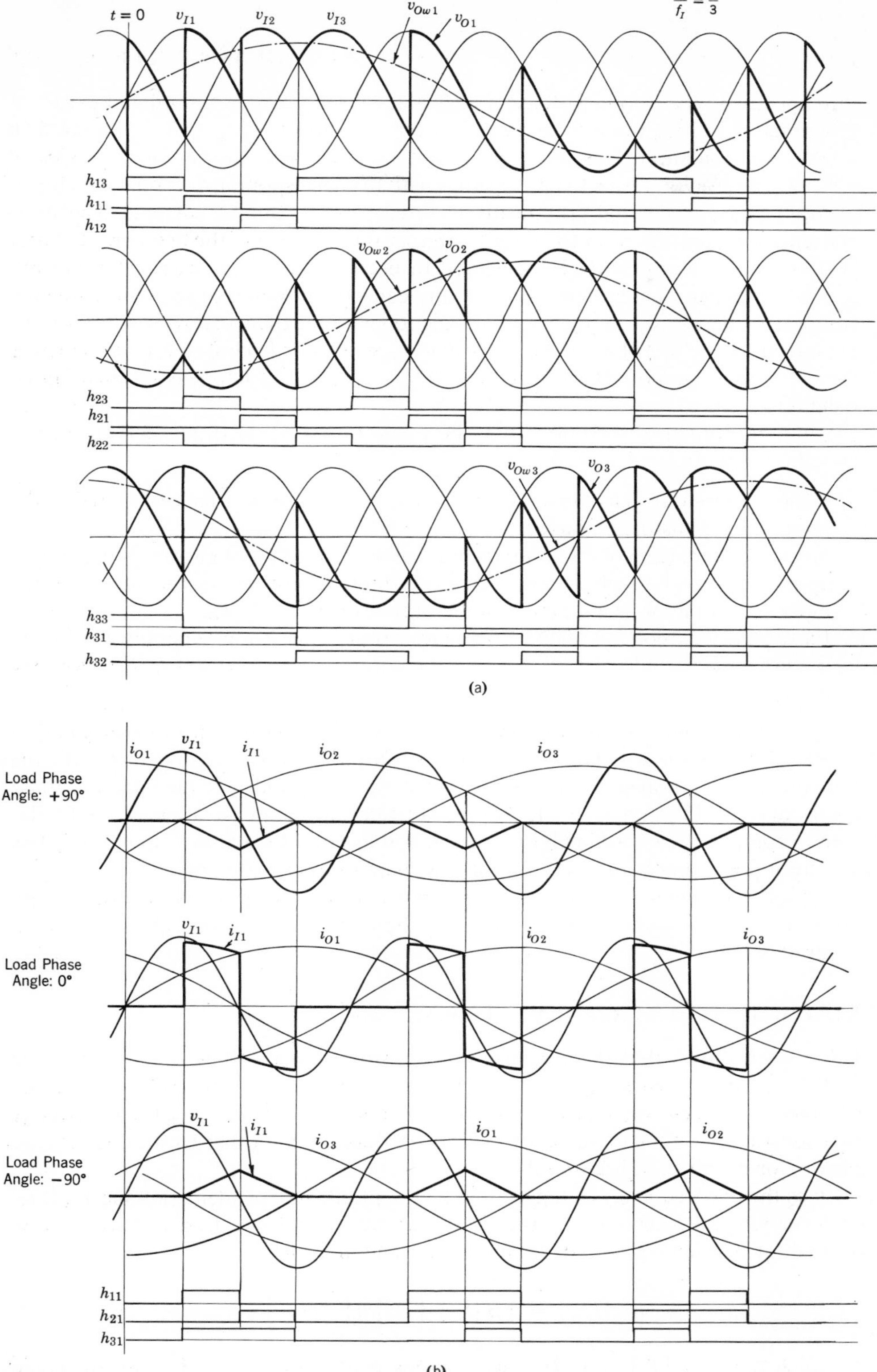

Figure 5.6 Derivation of input current waveforms appropriate to the positive-type output voltage wave with modulating function $M(r,t) = \sin^{-1}(\sin \omega_O t)$, from balanced sets of output current with $+90°$, $0°$, and $-90°$ phase angles.

three positive-type output voltage waveforms, and the related modulated existence functions of a three-pulse frequency changer are shown for $f_O/f_I = \frac{1}{3}$. Figure 5.6*b* shows three balanced sets of three output currents with displacement angles of $+90°$, $0°$, and $-90°$, respectively, together with the corresponding current waveforms of input phase 1, derived graphically from each set of output currents. The three existence functions relevant to phase 1—that is, the elements of the first row of matrix $[H]^T$—are also repeated at *b* for reference. Inspection of the input current waveforms, shown for displacement angles of $\pm 90°$, indicates the presence of some fundamental component, which is seemingly in contradiction with the theory; however, this can be explained by the fact that at the particular f_O/f_I ratio of $\frac{1}{3}$, chosen for convenience, the extrabasal component with frequency $2f_I - 3f_O$ in fact happens to have fundamental frequency.

Some additional observations may be made on equation (5.38), and the corresponding input current wave indices:

1. Since the input displacement factor is unity, the input power factor is equal to the input current distortion factor.
2. Since the amplitude of the fundamental component of input current is dependent upon the output displacement factor, the input distortion factor, and thus the input power factor, is a function of the output phase angle ϕ_O.
3. Extrabasal components with frequencies lower than f_I are generally present in the input. These may degenerate into d-c components at certain f_O/f_I ratios [see equation (5.43)].

Typical three-pulse input current waveforms synthesized from the terms of equation (5.38)—which is for a balanced three-phase output—are shown together with the fundamental component i_{IF} in Figure 5.7 at $f_O/f_I = \frac{1}{6}$ and $r = 1.0$ for load phase angles of $0°$, $-45°$, and $+45°$. It may be noticed that the phase angle of the fundamental component is zero in all three cases, and its amplitude is correspondingly less at output phase angles of $\pm 45°$ than it is with an output phase angle of $0°$.

Typical six-, nine-, and twelve-pulse input current waveforms synthesized from the terms of the same equation are also shown at $r = 1.0$, but at $f_O/f_I = \frac{1}{3}$, in Figure 5.8.

5.4 UDFFC INPUT CURRENT WAVEFORM

It has been shown that the concurrent composite output voltage waveform of the UDFFC is generated simply as the arithmetic mean (or the sum) of two complementary constituent waveforms v_O and $v_{O\pi}$, that is, $v_{OM} = \frac{1}{2}(v_O + v_{O\pi})$. This requires two constituent circuits, one controlled to produce v_O, the other to produce $v_{O\pi}$, as shown, for example, in Figure 1.14.

Since the two frequency changers operate essentially independently of one another, each carrying an equal current, the input current drawn from the a-c source can be defined for parallel connected circuits in the general form:

$$[i_{IM}] = ([H]^T + [H_\pi]^T)\left(\frac{1}{2}[i_O]\right) \tag{5.44}$$

in which matrices $[H]$ and $[H_\pi]$ are composed of the modulated complementary existence functions given by equations (5.3) and (5.4), respectively, and $[i_O]$ is the set of output currents defined by equation (5.2).

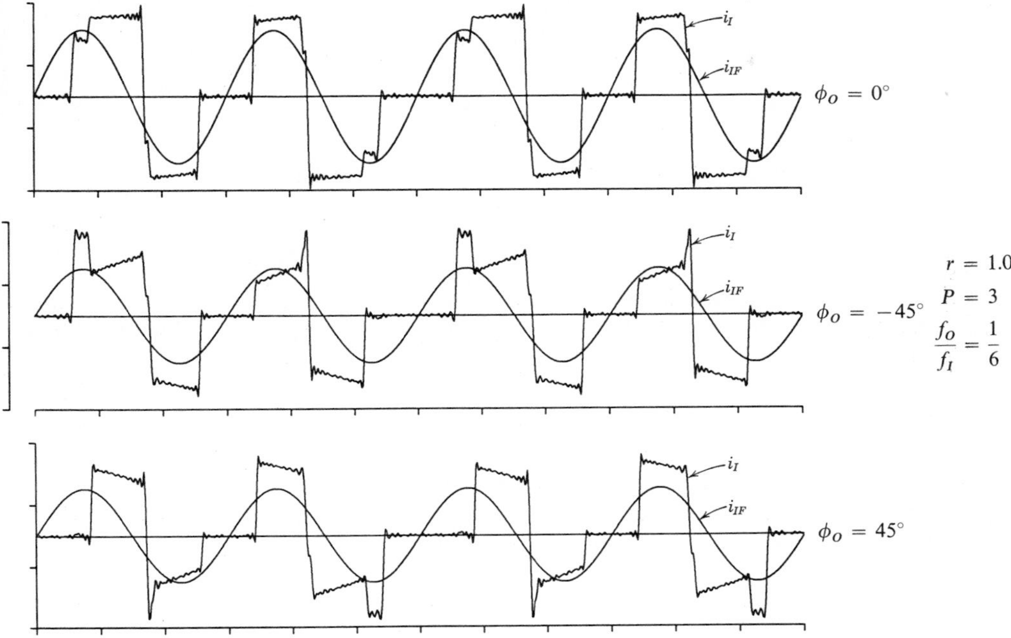

Figure 5.7 Typical three-pulse input current waveforms appropriate to the positive-type output voltage wave with modulating function $M(r,t) = \sin^{-1}(r \sin \omega_O t)$, synthesized from the terms of equation (5.38), for $\phi_O = 0°$, $\phi_O = -45°$, and $\phi_O = 45°$ ($r = 1.0$, and $f_O/f_I = 1/6$).

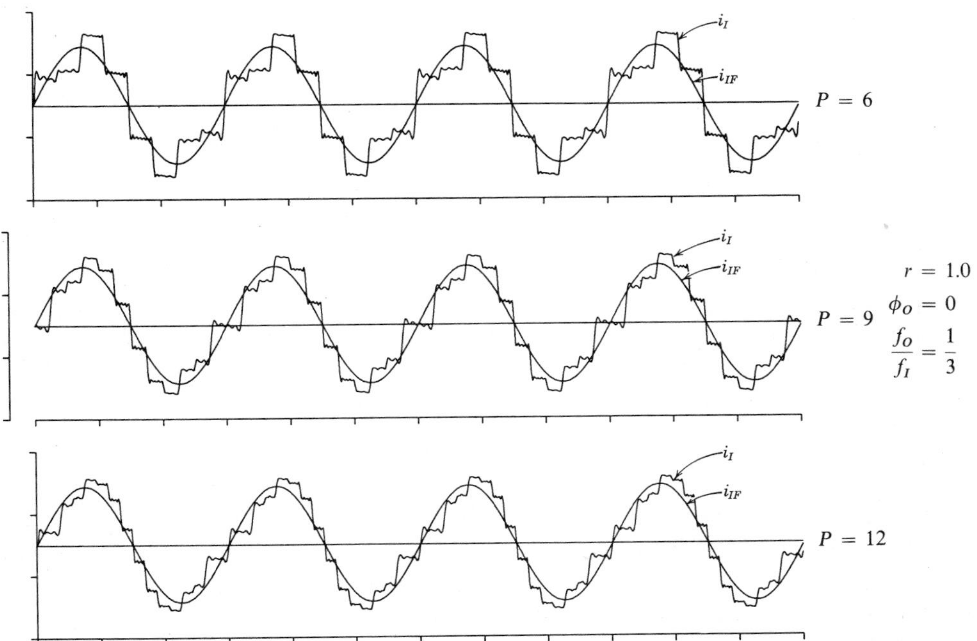

Figure 5.8 Typical six-, nine-, and twelve-pulse input current waveforms appropriate to the positive-type output voltage wave with modulating function $M(r,t) = \sin^{-1}(r \sin \omega_O t)$, synthesized from the terms of equation (5.38); $f_O/f_I = 1/3$, $r = 1.0$, $\phi_O = 0$.

It follows from equation (5.44) that the input current is simply the arithmetic mean of the currents drawn by the two circuits, namely

$$i_{IM} = \frac{1}{2}(i_I + i_{I\pi}) \tag{5.45}$$

Since $i_I = a + b$ [equation (5.36)] and $i_{I\pi} = a - b$ [equation (5.39)], consequently

$$i_{IM} = a \tag{5.46}$$

where a is part (a) of general equation (5.36) valid for single-phase output ($p = 1$, or $p = 2$, or $p = 3$), as well as for balanced three-phase output. Input current i_{IM} is expressed in a more concise form for balanced three-phase output by part (a) of equation (5.38).

The input current wave indices of i_{IM}, for balanced three-phase output, can be readily determined from equation (5.38). Here again only the case of a three-pulse circuit, full output voltage ($r = 1$) and unity power factor load ($\phi_O = 0$), is considered for the purpose of comparison. Comprehensive data characterizing this type of input current waveform are give in Chapter 6.

The current distortion factor can be shown to be

$$\mu_{IM,\phi_O=0} = \frac{1}{\sqrt{1 + \sum_{k=1}^{\infty} \frac{1}{4(3k \pm 1)^2}}} \cong 0.9 \tag{5.47}$$

The input displacement factor is of course unity

$$\delta_{IM} = 1 \tag{5.48}$$

The input power factor is

$$\left.\begin{aligned} \lambda_{IM} &= \mu_{IM}\delta_{IM} = \mu_{IM} \\ \lambda_{IM,\phi_O=0} &\cong 0.9 \end{aligned}\right\} \tag{5.49}$$

The normalized frequencies of the extrabasal components at $r = 1$ are given by

$$\nu_{IMk} = \begin{cases} (3k \pm 1) + 3k\dfrac{f_O}{f_I} \\ \left|(3k \pm 1) - 3k\dfrac{f_O}{f_I}\right| \end{cases} \tag{5.50}$$

The normalized amplitudes of the extrabasal components for $r = 1$ take the simple form

$$\gamma_{IMk} = \frac{1}{2(3k \pm 1)} \tag{5.51}$$

The following conclusions follow from equations (5.47)–(5.51):

1. The input displacement factor is unity independent of ϕ_O.
2. The current distortion and power factors for a three-pulse circuit are both 0.9; this is closer to unity than any μ_I and λ_I previously obtained.
3. The frequencies of the extrabasal components can be lower than f_I if f_O/f_I is greater than $\frac{1}{3}$.

4. The relative amplitudes of the extrabasal components are independent of the f_O/f_I ratio and of ϕ_O; they are generally smaller than those previously obtained.

In general, then, the input characteristics of the frequency changer producing the composite output waveform v_{OM} are, from the practical viewpoint, more advantageous than those of the other frequency changers considered. The reader will no doubt recall that this type of frequency changer is the one we call the unity displacement factor frequency changer, and its essential properties are deduced qualitatively in Chapter 1. It is interesting to note here that, besides its unity input displacement factor, this frequency changer exhibits near-unity input *power* factor for pulse numbers greater than three because of its low current distortion factor. For example, the input power factor of six-, nine-, and twelve-pulse UDFFCs at $\phi_O = 0$ are 0.977, 0.990, and 0.995, respectively.

A typical three-pulse waveform of i_{IM}, synthesized from the terms of part (a) of equation (5.38) at $\phi_O = 45°$, is shown for $f_O/f_I = \frac{1}{6}$ in Figure 5.9. Typical six-, nine-, and twelve-pulse waveforms are shown at $\phi_O = 0$ for $f_O/f_I = \frac{1}{3}$ in Figure 5.10.

5.5 CDFFC AND NCC INPUT CURRENT WAVEFORMS

For a frequency changer with three-phase output, the set of three consecutive composite output voltage waveforms $v_{O1}(\rho)$, $v_{O2}(\rho)$, and $v_{O3}(\rho)$ can be defined mathematically by generalizing equation (3.32) in the following matrix form:

$$[v_O(\rho)] = \{[E(\rho)][H] + [E_\pi(\rho)][H_\pi]\}[v_I] \tag{5.52}$$

with

$$[E(\rho)] = \begin{bmatrix} E_1(\rho) & 0 & 0 \\ 0 & E_2(\rho) & 0 \\ 0 & 0 & E_3(\rho) \end{bmatrix} \tag{5.53}$$

$$[E_\pi(\rho)] = \begin{bmatrix} E_{\pi 1}(\rho) & 0 & 0 \\ 0 & E_{\pi 2}(\rho) & 0 \\ 0 & 0 & E_{\pi 3}(\rho) \end{bmatrix} \tag{5.54}$$

where the periodic existence functions, $E_p(\rho)$ and $E_{\pi p}(\rho)$, defining the half-period sections of the complementary waves used to construct the output waveform, can be obtained from equations (3.33) and (3.34) by replacing $\omega_O t$ with $\omega_O t - (p - 1)(2\pi/3)$, $p = 1, 2, 3$; $[H]$ and $[H_\pi]$ are composed of the modulated complementary existence functions given by equations (5.3) and (5.4) with $M_p(t) = \sin^{-1}\{r \sin[\omega_O t - (p - 1)(2\pi/3)]\}$, and $[v_I]$ is composed of the set of input voltages given by equation (3.2).

Using the general definition $[i_I] = [H]^T[i_O]$, the input current matrix $[i_I(\rho)]$ corresponding to the consecutive composite output voltage matrix $[v_O(\rho)]$ may be defined as follows:

$$[i_I(\rho)] = (\{[E(\rho)][H]\}^T + \{[E_\pi(\rho)][H_\pi]\}^T)[i_O] \tag{5.55}$$

where $[i_O]$ is the output current matrix whose elements are defined by equation (5.2).

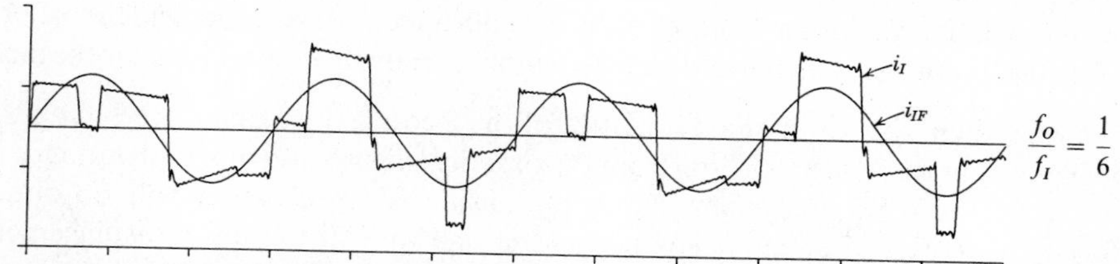

Figure 5.9 A typical three-pulse UDFFC input current waveform synthesized from the terms of equation (5.38) at $r = 1.0$ and $\phi_O = 45°$; $f_O/f_I = 1/6$.

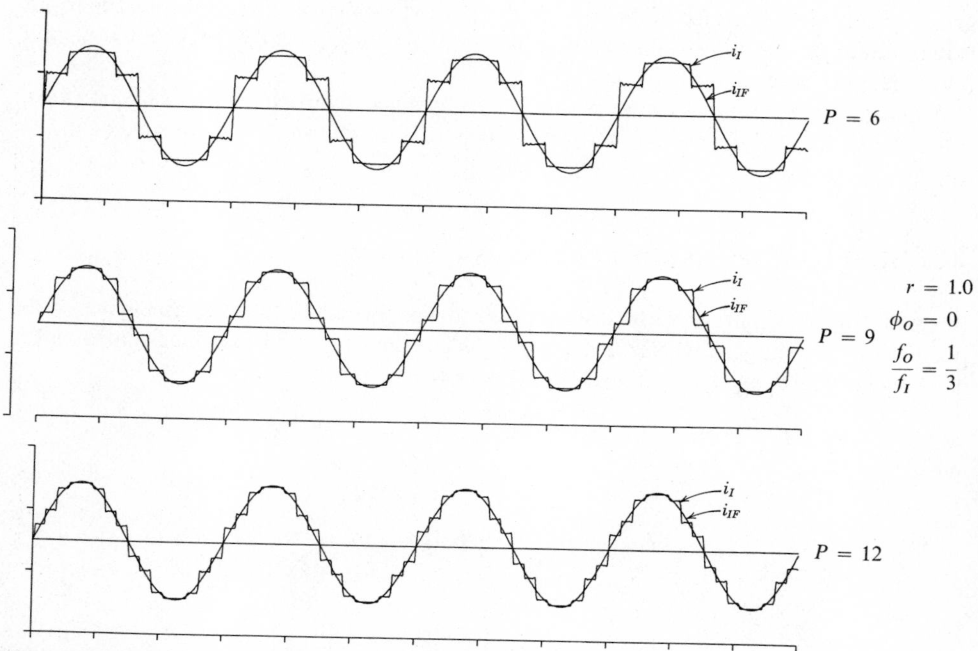

Figure 5.10 Typical six-, nine-, and twelve-pulse UDFFC input current waveforms synthesized from the terms of part (a) of equation (5.38) at $r = 1.0$ and $\phi_O = 0$; $P = 6$, $P = 9$, $P = 12$; $f_O/f_I = 1/3$.

Considering again only the current wave in input phase 1, $i_{I1}(\rho)$,* equation (5.55) can be written in the form

$$i_{I1}(\rho) = E_1 h_{11} i_{O1} + E_2 h_{21} i_{O2} + E_3 h_{31} i_{O3} + E_{\pi 1} h_{\pi 11} i_{O1} + E_{\pi 2} h_{\pi 21} i_{O2} + E_{\pi 3} h_{\pi 31} i_{O3} \tag{5.56}$$

In this equation, the separate constituents of the input current wave contributed by each of the three output currents can be recognized easily. Using the symbols introduced in equation (5.12), $i_{I1}(\rho)$ may also be written as follows:

$$i_{I1}(\rho) = E_1 i_{I11} + E_2 i_{I12} + E_3 i_{I13} + E_{\pi 1} i_{I\pi 11} + E_{\pi 2} i_{I\pi 12} + E_{\pi 3} i_{I\pi 13} \tag{5.57}$$

* In the following four equations subscript 1 is, for clarity, reinstated to describe variables corresponding to input phase 1.

where the constituent input currents i_{I11}, i_{I12}, and i_{I13} are defined by the general input current expression (with $p = 1, p = 2$, and $p = 3$, respectively) given for the presently considered modulating function $Mp(t) = \sin^{-1}\{r \sin[\omega_O t - (p - 1)(2\pi/3)]\}$ in equation (5.36), and constituent input currents $i_{I\pi 11}$, $i_{I\pi 12}$, and $i_{I\pi 13}$ are symbolically defined by parts (a) and (b) of the general expression (5.36) by equation (5.39). Using the same symbolic notation again, equation (5.57) may be written in the following form:

$$\begin{aligned} i_{I1}(\rho) = {} & E_1(a_{p=1} + b_{p=1}) + E_2(a_{p=2} + b_{p=2}) + E_3(a_{p=3} + b_{p=3}) \\ & + E_{\pi 1}(a_{p=1} - b_{p=1}) + E_{\pi 2}(a_{p=2} - b_{p=2}) + E_{\pi 3}(a_{p=3} - b_{p=3}) \end{aligned} \tag{5.58}$$

where $a_{p=1}, a_{p=2}, a_{p=3}$ is part (a) of equation (5.36) at $p = 1, p = 2$, and $p = 3$, respectively;

$b_{p=1}, b_{p=2}, b_{p=3}$ is part (b) of equation (5.36) at $p = 1, p = 2$, and $p = 3$, respectively.

After substituting E_1, E_2, E_3, and $E_{\pi 1}$, $E_{\pi 2}$, $E_{\pi 3}$ given by equations (3.33) and (3.34) into (5.58), $i_{I1}(\rho)$ can be expressed simply as follows:

$$i_{I1}(\rho) = a + b\left\{\frac{4}{\pi}\sum_{m=0}^{\infty}\frac{1}{2m+1}\sin\left((2m+1)\left[\omega_O t + \rho - (p-1)\frac{2\pi}{3}\right]\right)\right\} \tag{5.59}$$

where again a is part (a), and b is part (b) of equation (5.36). Observe that this equation is analogous to equation (4.41) derived for the consecutive composite voltage waveform $v_{O1}(\rho)$.

Equations (5.36), (5.39), (5.46), and (5.59) show that the complementary and composite input current waveforms are related in a similar manner as the corresponding voltage waveforms. Thus a family of extrabasal components, defined by part (a) of equation (5.36), is invariably present in each of the complementary current waveforms i_I and $i_{I\pi}$ and in each of the composite current waveforms i_{IM} and $i_I(\rho)$. Additional components in these current waveforms are either given by, or can be derived from, the family of extrabasal components defined by part (b) of equation (5.36).

Thus each of the four types of input current waveforms can be expressed symbolically as follows:

$$\begin{aligned} i_I &= a + b \\ i_{I\pi} &= a - b \\ i_{IM} &= a \\ i_I(\rho) &= a + b\left\{\frac{4}{\pi}\sum_{m=0}^{\infty}\frac{1}{2m+1}\sin\left((2m+1)\left[\omega_O t + \rho - (p-1)\frac{2\pi}{3}\right]\right)\right\} \end{aligned}$$

where a is part (a), and b is part (b) of equation (5.36).

Let us now continue the investigation of the composite current waveform, $i_I(\rho)$ with the objective of determining its spectral characteristics. The definition of $i_I(\rho)$, in which a complex expression, b, is multiplied by an infinite series, suggests that the final explicit mathematical expression for this waveform is involved. Let us temporarily ignore part (a), the characteristics of which have already been established, and concentrate on the second part of the expression, which will be denoted as $i_{Ib}(\rho)$, namely,

$$i_{Ib}(\rho) = b\left\{\frac{4}{\pi}\sum_{m=0}^{\infty}\frac{1}{2m+1}\sin\left((2m+1)\left[\omega_O t + \rho - (p-1)\frac{2\pi}{3}\right]\right)\right\} \quad (5.60)$$

Recall that only part (a) contains a fundamental (in-phase) component, and part (b) is entirely composed of extrabasal components of different families. One family, marked V in equation (5.36), has components with frequencies that are sums and differences between the input frequency f_I and *odd* multiples of the output frequency f_O. The other one, marked VI, has components that are sums and differences between multiples of the input frequency f_I and multiples of the output frequency f_O. The terms of the series that multiplies b in equation (5.60), on the other hand, have frequencies that are simply odd multiples of f_O. It can therefore be expected that the multiplications of these terms with the terms of part VI in b will result in new components that again have similar spectral characteristics as part VI itself—that is, their frequencies will be sums and differences between the same multiples of the input frequency and different multiples of the output frequency. Similarly, we would expect that the multiplication of part V will give new components, the frequencies of which will be sums and differences between the input frequency and *even* multiples of the output frequency. The fact that sums and differences between f_I and the *even* multiples of f_O appear can lead to a result of great significance, that is, to the production of an *additional* fundamental component. This, of course, cannot violate the condition of equal input and output power. Since the fundamental in-phase component in part (a) already accounts for the total *real* power consumed by the load, the production of an additional fundamental *in-phase* component can be ruled out. The production of a fundamental component that is *in quadrature* with the in-phase component would not violate any physical law; in fact it would be in agreement with the results of our qualitative investigation in Chapter 1, which predicted the existence of a quadrature component for the presently considered composite waveform.

Carrying out the multiplication indicated in equation (5.60) and using appropriate trigonometrical formulae for products, a general expression for the current $i_{Ib}(\rho)$ may be written as follows:

$$\text{V}\left[\begin{aligned} & i_{Ib}(\rho) \\ &= \frac{\sqrt{3}}{2\pi^2} I_O \sum_{p=1}^{3}\left\{\sum_{n=0}^{\infty}\sum_{m=0}^{\infty}\frac{a_{1,2n}}{2m+1}\right. \\ &\quad \times\left[-\cos\left([\omega_I \pm 2(n-m)\omega_O]t \pm \phi_O \mp (2m+1)\rho \mp 2(n-m)(p-1)\frac{2\pi}{3}\right)\right. \\ &\quad + \cos\left([\omega_I \pm 2(n-m-1)\omega_O]t \mp \phi_O \mp (2m+1)\rho \mp 2(n-m-1)(p-1)\frac{2\pi}{3}\right) \\ &\quad - \cos\left([\omega_I \pm 2(n+m)\omega_O]t \mp \phi_O \pm (2m+1)\rho \mp 2(n+m)(p-1)\frac{2\pi}{3}\right) \\ &\quad \left. + \cos\left([\omega_I \pm 2(n+m+1)\omega_O]t \pm \phi_O \pm (2m+1)\rho \mp 2(n+m+1)(p-1)\frac{2\pi}{3}\right)\right]\end{aligned}\right.$$

VI

$$
\begin{aligned}
&+ \sum_{u=-1}^{1} \sum_{k=1}^{\infty} \sum_{n=0}^{\infty} \sum_{m=0}^{\infty} \frac{1}{2m+1} \left[\frac{b_{[3(2k-1)-u],(2n+1)}}{3(2k-1)-u} u \right. \\
&\times \left\{ \pm \cos \left(\{[3(2k-1)-u]\omega_I \pm [2(n-m)+1]\omega_O\} t \right. \right. \\
&\qquad \left. \pm \phi_O \mp (2m+1)\rho \mp [2(n-m)+1](p-1)\frac{2\pi}{3} \right) \\
&\quad \mp \cos \left(\{[3(2k-1)-u]\omega_I \pm [2(n+m+1)+1]\omega_O\} t \right. \\
&\qquad \left. \pm \phi_O \pm (2m+1)\rho \mp [2(n+m+1)-1](p-1)\frac{2\pi}{3} \right) \\
&\quad \pm \cos \left(\{[3(2k-1)-u]\omega_I \pm [2(n+m+1)-1]\omega_O\} t \right. \\
&\qquad \left. \mp \phi_O \pm (2m+1)\rho \mp [2(n+m+1)+1](p-1)\frac{2\pi}{3} \right) \\
&\quad \mp \cos \left(\{[3(2k-1)-u]\omega_I \pm [2(n-m)-1]\omega_O\} t \right. \\
&\qquad \left. \left. \mp \phi_O \mp (2m+1)\rho \mp [2(n-m)-1](p-1)\frac{2\pi}{3} \right) \right\} \\
&\qquad + \frac{a_{(6k-u),2n}}{6k-u} u \\
&\times \left\{ \pm \cos \left([(6k-u)\omega_I \pm 2(n-m)\omega_O] t \right. \right. \\
&\qquad \left. \pm \phi_O \mp (2m+1)\rho \mp 2(n-m)(p-1)\frac{2\pi}{3} \right) \\
&\quad \mp \cos \left([(6k-u)\omega_I \pm 2(n+m+1)\omega_O] t \right. \\
&\qquad \left. \pm \phi_O \pm (2m+1)\rho \mp 2(n+m+1)(p-1)\frac{2\pi}{3} \right) \\
&\quad \mp \cos \left([(6k-u)\omega_I \pm 2(n+m)\omega_O] t \right. \\
&\qquad \left. \mp \phi_O \pm (2m+1)\rho \mp 2(n+m)(p-1)\frac{2\pi}{3} \right) \\
&\quad \pm \cos \left([(6k-u)\omega_I \pm 2(n-m-1)\omega_O] t \right. \\
&\qquad \left. \left. \left. \mp \phi_O \mp (2m+1)\rho \mp 2(n-m-1)(p-1)\frac{2\pi}{3} \right) \right\} \right] \Bigg\}
\end{aligned}
\tag{5.61}
$$

where the two parts corresponding to parts V and VI in equation (5.36) are marked by the same numerals.

Consider first part VI of equation (5.61). Since k, m, and n may each take the value of any positive integer, it is seen that the frequencies of the first family of components can generally be expressed for single-phase output ($p = 1$ or 2 or 3) in the following forms:

$$\begin{aligned}&\{3(2k - 1) \pm 1\}f_I + (2\ell + 1)f_O\\&\{3(2k - 1) \pm 1\}f_I - (2\ell + 1)f_O\end{aligned} \tag{5.62}$$

where $k = 1, 2, 3, \ldots$; $\ell = 0, 1, 2, \ldots$.

The frequencies of the second family of components can generally be expressed for single-phase output as follows:

$$\begin{aligned}&(6k \pm 1)f_I + 2\ell f_O\\&(6k \pm 1)f_I - 2\ell f_O\end{aligned} \tag{5.63}$$

where $k = 1, 2, 3, \ldots$; $\ell = 0, 1, 2, \ldots$.

For balanced three-phase output, three similar components (fixed k, m, and n) of index p ($p = 1, 2, 3$), each corresponding to one output phase current, are summed in the input. These similar components either cancel or reinforce each other, depending upon the values of m and n; that is, these components cancel each other at the values of m and n at which the angular expression $\pm(p - 1)(2\pi/3)$ in effect prevails. Conversely, they reinforce each other at the values of m and n at which the above angular expression becomes in effect equal to $\pm(p - 1)2\pi$. Consequently, only the components with the following frequencies are present in part VI of equation (5.61) for balanced three-phase output:

$$\begin{aligned}&\{3(2k - 1) \pm 1\}f_I + 3(2\ell + 1)f_O\\&\{3(2k - 1) \pm 1\}f_I - 3(2\ell + 1)f_O\end{aligned} \tag{5.64}$$

and

$$\begin{aligned}&(6k \pm 1)f_I + 6\ell f_O\\&(6k \pm 1)f_I - 6\ell f_O\end{aligned} \tag{5.65}$$

where again $k = 1, 2, 3, \ldots$; $\ell = 0, 1, 2, \ldots$.

The amplitudes of the extrabasal components in equation (5.61), besides being functions of indices k, m, and n, are also a complex function of angles ϕ_O and ρ. The reason for this is the same as that given in connection with the related expression for the output voltage [equation (4.41)]. That is, particular values of indices m and n, at each value of index k, result in a series of terms with identical frequencies but different phase angles, depending upon ϕ_O and ρ. The summation of all terms of the same frequency of course gives the net extrabasal component of that frequency. For example, in equation (5.61) the expression

$$\cos\left([(6k - 1)\omega_I \pm 2(n - m)]\omega_O t \pm \phi_O \mp (2m + 1)\rho \mp 2(n - m)(p - 1)\frac{2\pi}{3}\right)$$

provides an infinite number of terms, each with the common frequency of $(6k - 1)\omega_I$, for those values of m and n that satisfy the condition of $m = n$. However, the phase angle of each of these terms is a function of ϕ_O, index m, and angle ρ and is equal to

$\pm \phi_O \mp (2n + 1)\rho$. Similarly, the expression

$$\cos\left([(6k-1)\omega_I \pm 2(n-m-1)]\omega_O t \mp \phi_O \mp (2m+1)\rho \mp 2(n-m-1)(p-1)\frac{2\pi}{3}\right)$$

also provides an infinite series of terms of the same frequency $(6k - 1)\omega_I$, under the condition of $m = n - 1$; however, the phase angle of each of these terms is equal to $\mp \phi_O \mp (2n - 1)\rho$. The sum of all terms (each generally with a different amplitude and phase angle) of the two infinite series provides the extrabasal component of frequency $(6k - 1)\omega_I$.

We now leave the investigation of part VI and examine part V of equation (5.61). Inspection of this expression indicates that the multipliers of frequency ω_O do indeed become zero, as anticipated earlier, in the arguments of the first two general terms, under the following conditions:

$$m = n \tag{5.66}$$

and

$$m = n - 1 \tag{5.67}$$

As a result of summing the relevant terms satisfying the above conditions, part V of equation (5.61) yields a fundamental quadrature component of frequency f_I, the amplitude of which is a function of angles ϕ_O and ρ.

Note that with the above conditions, the multipliers of $2\pi/3$ in the arguments of the first two terms of part V also become zero, indicating that the fundamental quadrature component yielded by this expression is present for both single-phase and balanced three-phase outputs.

All the terms of part V, at indices m and n not satisfying conditions (5.66) and (5.67), result in extrabasal components with frequencies of

$$f_I \pm 2\ell f_O \tag{5.68}$$

for single-phase output and

$$f_I \pm 6\ell f_O \tag{5.69}$$

for balanced three-phase output, in which $\ell = 0, 1, 2, \ldots$. The amplitudes of these extrabasal components are also generally a function of both ϕ_O and ρ.

The fundamental quadrature component in equation (5.61), which will be designated as $i_{IQ}(\rho)$, can be expressed explicitly by using conditions (5.66) and (5.67), namely,

$$i_{IQ}(\rho) = \frac{\sqrt{3}}{\pi^2} I_O \sum_{p=1}^{3} \sum_{n=0}^{\infty} a_{1,2n} \left(\frac{\cos\{\phi_O + (2n-1)\rho\}}{2n-1} - \frac{\cos\{\phi_O - (2n+1)\rho\}}{2n+1}\right)$$
$$\times \cos\{\omega_I t - (p-1)2\pi\} \tag{5.70}$$

The magnitude and *polarity* of i_{IQ} is a function of the output voltage ratio r (because $a_{1,2n}$ is a function of r), the output phase angle, and the waveform switching angle ρ.

The total fundamental component of $i_I(\rho)$ is evidently constituted from two components: one is an in-phase or real component, $i_{IR}(\rho)$, given in part (a) of equation (5.36), and the other is a quadrature or reactive component, $i_{IQ}(\rho)$, given by equation (5.70). Thus, the real component is contributed entirely by part (a), whereas the quadrature component originates from part (b) of the expression derived for the complementary input current waves. The total fundamental input current $i_{IF}(\rho)$ can therefore be written for single-phase output from equations (5.36) and (5.70) in the following form:

$$i_{IF}(\rho) = i_{IR}(\rho) + i_{IQ}(\rho)$$
$$= \frac{\sqrt{3}}{2\pi} I_O \left\{ r \cos \phi_O \sin \omega_I t \right.$$
$$\left. + \frac{2}{\pi} \sum_{n=0}^{\infty} a_{1,2n} \left(\frac{\cos\{\phi_O + (2n - 1)\rho\}}{2n - 1} - \frac{\cos\{\phi_O - (2n + 1)\rho\}}{2n + 1} \right) \cos \omega_I t \right\} \tag{5.71}$$

For balanced three-phase output, expression (5.71) has to be multiplied by three.

The input displacement angle $\phi_I(\rho)$, that is, the angle between the fundamental input current and the corresponding line-to-neutral input voltage, can be expressed from equation (5.71) as follows:

$$\phi_I(\rho) = \tan^{-1} \left\{ \frac{\frac{2}{\pi} \sum_{n=0}^{\infty} a_{1,2n} \left(\frac{\cos\{\phi_O + (2n - 1)\rho\}}{2n - 1} - \frac{\cos\{\phi_O - (2n + 1)\rho\}}{2n + 1} \right)}{r \cos \phi_O} \right\} \tag{5.72}$$

Clearly, the input displacement angle is generally a rather complex function of the output voltage ratio r, the output phase angle ϕ_O, and the waveform switching angle ρ. It is evident that for given values of ϕ_O and r the input phase angle can be controlled by varying the waveform switching angle ρ, which theoretically is a free variable. The property that the input displacement angle ϕ_I, and thus the input displacement factor $\cos \phi_I$, could be made variable, independent of the load phase angle ϕ_O, was predicted by qualitative reasoning in Chapter 1. We call the frequency changer that utilizes this particular property the controllable displacement factor frequency changer. Curves showing the variation of the input phase angle and the quadrature component of the input current with the output phase angle, the output voltage ratio, and the waveform switching angle are presented in Chapter 6.

There are a few special cases related to the input displacement angle that are worthy of further considerations. The first and most important is that of the naturally commutated cycloconverter. As is explained in Chapter 3, the output voltage waveform of the NCC is composed of alternate half-cycle sections of the complementary voltage waveforms in such a way that the positive-type voltage wave v_O is produced whenever the output current is positive, and the negative-type voltage wave $v_{O\pi}$ is produced whenever the output current is negative. Consequently, the NCC is analytically a special case of the CDFFC, under which it operates with the waveform switching angle ρ equal to the output phase angle ϕ_O. The fundamental component of the input current wave and the input phase angle of the NCC can therefore be obtained directly from equations (5.71) and (5.72), respectively, by replacing ρ with ϕ_O, namely,

$$i_{I,\text{NCC}} = A \frac{\sqrt{3}}{2\pi} I_O \left(r \cos \phi_O \sin \omega_I t + \frac{4}{\pi} \sum_{n=0}^{\infty} \frac{a_{1,2n} \cos 2n\phi_O}{4n^2 - 1} \cos \omega_I t \right) \tag{5.73}$$

where A is one for single-phase output and three for balanced three-phase output.

Since $a_{1,0}$ (i.e., $a_{1,2n}$ at $n = 0$) is greater than $\sum_{n=1}^{\infty} a_{1,2n}/(4n^2 - 1)$ (see Table A.3 in the Appendix), it follows that the coefficient of $\cos \omega_I t$ is always *negative*, and consequently the quadrature component of the fundamental input current of the NCC is always lagging. Therefore, the input phase angle

$$\phi_{I,\mathrm{NCC}} = \tan^{-1}\left(\frac{\dfrac{4}{\pi}\sum_{n=0}^{\infty}\dfrac{a_{1,2n}\cos 2n\phi_O}{4n^2-1}}{r\cos\phi_O}\right) \tag{5.74}$$

obtained from equation (5.72) is always lagging, regardless of whether ϕ_O is lagging or leading. Curves showing the variation of the input phase angle of the NCC as a function of the output phase angle at various values of r are presented in Chapter 6.

Next let us consider the case in which the frequency changer is operated in a mode that is the *inverse* of that of the NCC; in other words, ρ is made equal to $\phi_O + \pi$. In this case, the quadrature component of the input current, and thus the input phase angle, will be the exact opposite of those of the NCC, namely,

$$i_{I,\mathrm{INCC}} = A\frac{\sqrt{3}}{2\pi}I_O\left(r\cos\phi_O\sin\omega_I t - \frac{4}{\pi}\sum_{n=0}^{\infty}\frac{a_{1,2n}\cos 2n\phi_O}{4n^2-1}\cos\omega_I t\right) \tag{5.75}$$

and

$$\phi_{I,\mathrm{INCC}} = -\tan^{-1}\left(\frac{\dfrac{4}{\pi}\sum_{n=0}^{\infty}\dfrac{a_{1,2n}\cos 2n\phi_O}{4n^2-1}}{r\cos\phi_O}\right) \tag{5.76}$$

where subscript INCC stands for *inverted NCC*.

The significance of this result is that an NCC ($\rho = \phi_O$) and an inverted NCC ($\rho = \phi_O + \pi$) could be combined to make an overall frequency changer with unity displacement factor. In fact, this arrangement is analytically equivalent to the unity displacement factor frequency changer described previously, but it would have the practical advantage that only one of the two frequency changer circuits, handling half of the total output power, needs to be force commutated.

The final case we consider concerning the input displacement angle is a rather interesting one, although perhaps practically not very important. At any rate, it can be established easily that if $\rho \equiv 0$, $\phi_I(\rho)$ is *constant* and negative (lagging) at any given value of the output voltage ratio r, independently of ϕ_O. Similarly, if $\rho \equiv \pi$, $\phi_I(\rho)$ is constant and positive (leading) at any given value r, regardless of ϕ_O. To show this, substitute $\rho \equiv 0$ and, subsequently $\rho \equiv \pi$, into equation (5.72). Then

$$\phi_{I,\rho\equiv 0} = \tan^{-1}\left(\frac{4}{\pi r}\sum_{n=0}^{\infty}\frac{a_{1,2n}}{4n^2-1}\right) \tag{5.77}$$

and

$$\phi_{I,\rho\equiv\pi} = -\tan^{-1}\left(\frac{4}{\pi r}\sum_{n=0}^{\infty}\frac{a_{1,2n}}{4n^2-1}\right) \tag{5.78}$$

Returning now to a general consideration of the input current waveform $i_I(\rho)$, let us recapitulate the main results of the preceding investigation. The composite current waveform $i_I(\rho)$ is defined for an arbitrary waveform switching angle ρ by equation (5.59). The first part, a, of this equation is independent of the waveform switching angle ρ; it is given explicitly in terms of its constituent components by part (a) of equation (5.36). The second part, denoted as $i_{Ib}(\rho)$, is defined by equation (5.60). The evaluation of this equation showed that $i_{Ib}(\rho)$ is composed of a fundamental *quadrature* component and a complex combination of extrabasal components, the frequencies of which are defined for single-phase output by equations (5.62), (5.63), and (5.68), and for balanced three-phase output by equations (5.64), (5.65), and (5.69). We established that the amplitudes of the components constituting $i_{Ib}(\rho)$ are generally a complex function of the output phase angle ϕ_O and the waveform switching angle ρ.

In order to obtain a comparison with the previously considered input current waveforms, the input current wave indices of $i_I(\rho)$ for the special case of full output voltage ($r = 1.0$), unity load power factor ($\phi_O = 0$) and zero waveform switching angle ($\rho = 0$) are given below. These data thus really characterize the naturally commutated cycloconverter ($\rho = \phi_O = 0$), or its inverse ($\rho = \pi$, $\phi_O = 0$), supplying a unity power factor load.

The current distortion factor is given by

$$\mu_{I,\rho=\phi_O=0} \cong 0.9 \tag{5.79}$$

The input displacement factor is given by

$$\delta_{I,\rho=\phi_O=0} = \cos\phi_{I,\rho=\phi_O=0} \cong 0.843 \tag{5.80}$$

The input power factor is given by

$$\lambda_{I,\rho=\phi_O=0} = \mu_{I,\rho=\phi_O=0}\,\delta_{I,\rho=\phi_O=0} \cong 0.759 \tag{5.81}$$

The normalized frequencies of the extrabasal components are given by

$$\nu_{Ik,\ell} = \begin{cases} 1 \pm 6(\ell + 1)\dfrac{f_O}{f_I} \\[2ex] \{3(2k-1) \pm 1\} + 3(2\ell + 1)\dfrac{f_O}{f_I} \\[2ex] \{3(2k-1) \pm 1\} - 3(2\ell + 1)\dfrac{f_O}{f_I} \\[2ex] (6k \pm 1) + 6\ell\dfrac{f_O}{f_I} \\[2ex] (6k \pm 1) - 6\ell\dfrac{f_O}{f_I} \end{cases} \tag{5.82}$$

$$k = 1, 2, \ldots;\ \ell = 0, 1, 2, \ldots$$

The normalized amplitudes of the extrabasal components are given in Tables 6.7–6.11 at $\rho = \phi_O = 0$ in Chapter 6.

It should be noted that the relatively good current distortion factor of 0.9 is partly the result of the increased fundamental current, due to the added quadrature component which, in the case considered, is 63.7% of the in-phase component.

Comparison of the input current wave indices of $i_I(\rho)$ [equations (5.79)–(5.82)] with those of the basic complementary current waves i_I and $i_{I\pi}$ [equations (5.40)–(5.43)] indicates that there is no substantial difference except for the input displacement factor. As has been mentioned, the input current indices at $\rho = \phi_O$ really characterize the naturally commutated cycloconverter. The lagging input displacement factor of 0.843 substantiates the qualitative deduction made in Chapter 1 that the price of natural commutation is an invariably lagging input displacement factor.

5.6 PHYSICAL EXPLANATIONS FOR RELATIONSHIPS BETWEEN INPUT AND OUTPUT CURRENTS

From the preceding analysis it is seen that the input current waves generally comprise a fundamental *real* component, a fundamental *quadrature* component, and families of different types of *extrabasal* components.

The fundamental real component is a consequence of the basic physical law that for a lossless frequency changer, the real input power must be equal to the real output power. Thus, the real input current component is directly proportional to the product of the real component of output current and the output voltage ratio, and it is independent of the manner in which the output voltage wave is constructed.

The fundamental quadrature component, on the other hand, does depend upon the method of output waveform construction, and it may be a function of the load phase angle. A quadrature component of current may be obtained at the input when there is no quadrature component of current at the output, and vice versa, depending upon the particular type of frequency changer.

The extrabasal components are generally dependent upon the method of waveform construction, the output displacement angle, the pulse number, and the number of output phases. The extrabasal frequencies can be categorized in two groups, which we call *pulse-number-dependent* and *pulse-number-independent*.

The presence or absence of *whole* families of *pulse-number-dependent* components, as the name implies, depends strictly upon the pulse number of the frequency changer; however, certain component *members* within the family are eliminated as the number of output phases is increased. For example, the principal family of pulse-number-dependent components in the input current of a six-pulse frequency changer with single-phase output generally may have frequencies of $(6 \pm 1)f_I \pm nf_O$, where n has values that depend on the method of output voltage waveform construction; with a balanced three-phase output, however, only the $(6 \pm 1)f_I \pm 3nf_O$ members of the family are present. More generally—although we do not specifically draw attention to this in the preceding analysis—with a balanced p-phase output, only the $(6 \pm 1)f_I \pm pnf_O$ components are present. Note that even if we make the hypothetical assumption that the number of output phases is infinite, still the predominant $5f_I$ and $7f_I$ components remain. On the other hand, this particular family of extrabasal components can be eliminated en bloc, regardless of the number of output phases, by increasing the pulse number of the frequency changer beyond six. Thus, a hypothetical frequency changer with infinite pulse number would contain no pulse-number-dependent extrabasal components of input current, regardless of the number of output phases.

The presence or absence of members of the second pulse-number-independent group of extrabasal components, again as the name implies, is independent of the pulse number but is determined only by the number of balanced output phases. This group comprises two types of components. The first has frequencies given by

$f_I \pm 2f_O$, and these terms are present only for a single-phase (or unbalanced) output. The second type has frequencies given by $f_I \pm nf_O$, where n has values that depend upon the method of output voltage waveform construction. Again, although we do not specifically draw attention to this in the preceding analysis, for a p-phase output the frequencies of these latter terms are given by $f_I \pm pnf_O$. Thus, a hypothetical frequency changer with infinite number of output phases would contain no pulse-number-independent components, regardless of the circuit pulse number. As a practical matter, however, the pulse-number-independent components present in the input current of a frequency changer with just three balanced phases are already sufficiently small that they can be neglected.

Having made this brief general summary of the main analytical findings, we now attempt to provide simple physical explanations for the presence of the various principal components of currents at the input.

The key to the explanation resides in the fact that the process of energy transfer through the frequency changer is absolutely direct, and thus it is inherent that *the net instantaneous power at the input terminals must always be equal to the net instantaneous power at the output terminals* (assuming that the losses in the switches can be neglected).

Consider a frequency changer producing a single-phase output from a three-phase input. In order to simplify the discussion, we assume that this frequency changer has infinite pulse number. Such a hypothetical frequency changer would have no pulse-number-dependent extrabasal components and would produce a purely sinusoidal voltage $V_O \sin \omega_O t$ at its output terminals. We further assume that the corresponding output current is $I_O \sin(\omega_O t + \phi_O)$.

The instantaneous power at the output terminals consists of a steady component and a component oscillating at twice the output frequency:

$$P_O = V_O \sin \omega_O t \, I_O \sin(\omega_O t + \phi_O) = \underbrace{\frac{V_O I_O}{2} \cos \phi_O}_{\text{Steady component}} - \underbrace{\frac{V_O I_O}{2} \cos(2\omega_O t + \phi_O)}_{\text{Oscillatory component}} \tag{5.83}$$

Note that the amplitude of the steady component is proportional to the cosine of the output displacement angle, but the amplitude of the oscillatory component does not depend on this angle. Each of the above components of power at the output terminals must be balanced by a corresponding power component at the input.

The steady component must be balanced by the fundamental real component of input current, since this is the one and only component of current at the input capable of so doing:

$$\begin{aligned}\text{Steady component of input power} &= V_I \sin \omega_I t \, I_{IR} \sin \omega_I t \\ &\quad + V_I \sin\left(\omega_I t - \frac{2\pi}{3}\right) I_{IR} \sin\left(\omega_I t - \frac{2\pi}{3}\right) \\ &\quad + V_I \sin\left(\omega_I t - \frac{4\pi}{3}\right) I_{IR} \sin\left(\omega_I t - \frac{4\pi}{3}\right) \\ &= \frac{3V_I I_{IR}}{2} = \frac{V_O I_O}{2} \cos \phi_O\end{aligned} \tag{5.84}$$

The component of input current required to supply the oscillatory component of power in equation (5.83) could in general have a frequency either of $f_I + 2f_O$ or $f_I - 2f_O$; an input component with either of these frequencies would yield an oscillatory *difference* component of input power at frequency $2f_O$. This, then, is the fundamental explanation for the presence of these principal pulse-number-independent components in the input current of the frequency changer supplying a single-phase output. It is evident, moreover, that since the amplitude of the oscillatory component of power at the output is at least as large as the steady component, the amplitude of the principal pulse-number-independent extrabasal component or components is comparable with that of the fundamental component. This indeed is borne out by our analytical results.

An explanation for the remaining higher-order pulse-number-independent components, which generally have frequencies of $f_I \pm pnf_O$, whose presence is revealed by the analytical results, is appropriate at this stage. These components would not be predicted on the basis of equality between the instantaneous input and output power, nor, on this basis, can they be capable of making any contribution to the net instantaneous input power. Computation of the net instantaneous power at the input due to these higher-order components shows that this indeed is zero. The simple explanation for the presence of these components is that they are, in effect, purely "parasites" that contribute nothing to the power balance between the input and output terminals. They are entirely the consequence of the method of waveform construction and in fact are not always present, as is the case for the UFC and SSFC. At all events for a balanced three-phase output, the amplitudes of these components are sufficiently small that they can be neglected for all types of frequency changers.

Consider now the situation with a balanced three-phase output. The sum of the instantaneous powers of all three output phases is constant:

$$\begin{aligned} P_O &= V_O \sin \omega_O t \, I_O \sin(\omega_O t + \phi_O) \\ &\quad + V_O \sin\left(\omega_O t - \frac{2\pi}{3}\right) I_O \sin\left(\omega_O t + \phi_O - \frac{2\pi}{3}\right) \\ &\quad + V_O \sin\left(\omega_O t - \frac{4\pi}{3}\right) I_O \sin\left(\omega_O t + \phi_O - \frac{4\pi}{3}\right) \\ &= \frac{3V_O I_O}{2} \cos \phi_O \end{aligned} \tag{5.85}$$

This steady component of power is of course three times that due to each individual output phase; thus the net fundamental in-phase component of input current will be three times that given by equation (5.84), which applies just to a single-phase output.

Since there is no longer a net oscillatory component of power at the output, the presence of the pulse-number-independent extrabasal components in the net input current wave of the frequency changers supplying all three output phases is no longer to be expected. Again, this conclusion is verified by the results of our detailed analysis.

The situation is further illustrated by reference to the equivalent diagram in Figure 5.11 for a frequency changer supplying a three-phase load. A set of balanced currents, i_{I1}, i_{I2}, and i_{I3}, flow at the input. Each of these currents in general comprises the fundamental real and quadrature components; they may also generally include higher-order members of the pulse-number-independent group. However, as we have

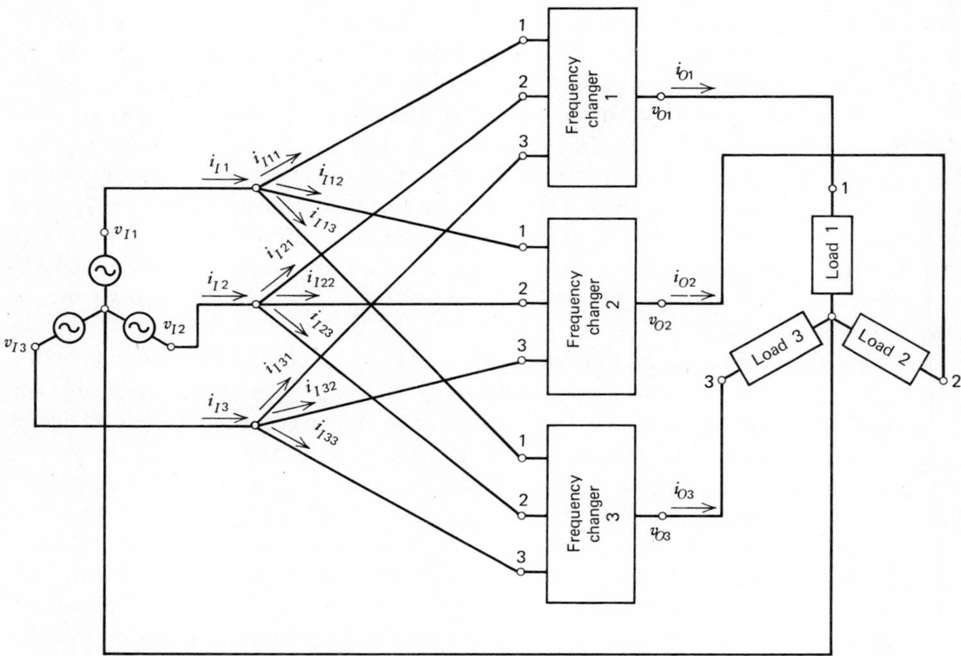

Figure 5.11 Current distribution in a frequency changer with three output phases.

implied, these "parasite" components are generally negligible for a balanced three-phase output and can be ignored. Thus, the input currents i_{I1}, i_{I2}, and i_{I3} can be assumed to be sinusoidal and comprised entirely of the real and quadrature components.

Since each frequency changer circuit, supplying each of the three output phases, functions independently of the others, as if it were a frequency changer with a single-phase load, the current flowing into any one of the input terminals of any of the three frequency changers is not a sine wave; it is composed of segments of the relevant output current wave, as illustrated in general form in Figure 1.15. From the analytical results we have obtained we know, for the presently considered case of high pulse number, that each of these current waveforms can be resolved into a fundamental component and a family of pulse-number-independent extrabasal components:

$$i_{Ipq} = i_{IF_{pq}} + \sum_{n=1}^{\infty} i_{E_{pq,n}}$$

$$p = 1, 2, 3; \qquad q = 1, 2, 3$$

where in practice only the lower-order terms $(f_I \pm 2f_O)$ have significance.

As is illustrated in Figure 5.11, each of the input current waves drawn from the source is the sum of three component current waves flowing into the terminals of the individual frequency changer circuits. Thus

$$\left.\begin{aligned} i_{I1} &= i_{I11} + i_{I12} + i_{I13} \\ i_{I2} &= i_{I21} + i_{I22} + i_{I23} \\ i_{I3} &= i_{I31} + i_{I32} + i_{I33} \end{aligned}\right\} \tag{5.86}$$

or

$$\left.\begin{aligned}
i_{I1} &= i_{IF_{11}} + i_{IF_{12}} + i_{IF_{13}} + \sum_{n=1}^{\infty} i_{E_{11,n}} + \sum_{n=1}^{\infty} i_{E_{12,n}} + \sum_{n=1}^{\infty} i_{E_{13,n}} \\
i_{I2} &= i_{IF_{21}} + i_{IF_{22}} + i_{IF_{23}} + \sum_{n=1}^{\infty} i_{E_{21,n}} + \sum_{n=1}^{\infty} i_{E_{22,n}} + \sum_{n=1}^{\infty} i_{E_{23,n}} \\
i_{I3} &= i_{IF_{31}} + i_{IF_{32}} + i_{IF_{33}} + \sum_{n=1}^{\infty} i_{E_{31,n}} + \sum_{n=1}^{\infty} i_{E_{32,n}} + \sum_{n=1}^{\infty} i_{E_{33,n}}
\end{aligned}\right\} \tag{5.87}$$

Since the input currents i_{I1}, i_{I2}, and i_{I3} are sinusoids of the source frequency f_I, it follows that

$$\left.\begin{aligned}
i_{I1} &= i_{IF_{11}} + i_{IF_{12}} + i_{IF_{13}} \\
i_{I2} &= i_{IF_{21}} + i_{IF_{22}} + i_{IF_{23}} \\
i_{I3} &= i_{IF_{31}} + i_{IF_{32}} + i_{IF_{33}}
\end{aligned}\right\} \tag{5.88}$$

and

$$\left.\begin{aligned}
\sum_{n=1}^{\infty} i_{E_{11,n}} + \sum_{n=1}^{\infty} i_{E_{12,n}} + \sum_{n=1}^{\infty} i_{E_{13,n}} &= 0 \\
\sum_{n=1}^{\infty} i_{E_{21,n}} + \sum_{n=1}^{\infty} i_{E_{22,n}} + \sum_{n=1}^{\infty} i_{E_{23,n}} &= 0 \\
\sum_{n=1}^{\infty} i_{E_{31,n}} + \sum_{n=1}^{\infty} i_{E_{32,n}} + \sum_{n=1}^{\infty} i_{E_{33,n}} &= 0
\end{aligned}\right\} \tag{5.89}$$

The condition expressed by equation (5.89) can only be generally satisfied if the sum of each set of the three components with identical frequencies is also zero, namely,

$$\left.\begin{aligned}
i_{E_{11,n}} + i_{E_{12,n}} + i_{E_{13,n}} &= 0 \\
i_{E_{21,n}} + i_{E_{22,n}} + i_{E_{23,n}} &= 0 \\
i_{E_{31,n}} + i_{E_{32,n}} + i_{E_{33,n}} &= 0
\end{aligned}\right\} \tag{5.90}$$

$$n = 1, 2, 3, \ldots$$

Equation (5.90) simply states that the pulse-number-independent extrabasal components generated by a frequency changer supplying a balanced three-phase load cancel one another in the input lines.* Thus these components flow directly between the input terminals of the frequency changer circuit supplying the three output phases and by-pass the input source.

We have now explained the presence of the real component of current at the input and the presence or absence of the principal pulse-number-independent extrabasal components, according to whether the frequency changer supplies a single-phase or balanced three-phase output.

A further question needs a physical explanation, and this concerns the phenomena predicted in Chapter 1 and confirmed by the analytical results of this chapter relating

* Again, it is pointed out that for all practical purposes, although not strictly theoretically, this is true.

to reactive components of current at the input and output sides of the frequency changer. It will be recalled, for example, that it is possible for a reactive component of current to flow at the output terminals with no reactive component of current at the input, and vice versa. This phenomenon is explained qualitatively in Chapter 1 by showing that the phase positions of segments of the output current wave, which are supplied by any one of the input phases, depend on the method of output waveform construction. Consequently, the input source may "see" the output load with lagging, leading, or unity displacement factor, independent of its actual phase angle.

Consider first a frequency changer producing either a positive-type or a negative-type output voltage waveform. As the analytical results show, the reactive component of current at the input of this type of frequency changer is zero, regardless of whether there is a reactive component of current at the output. The question to be answered, therefore, is how the reactive component of current at the output manifests itself at the input side.

The answer stems from an inspection of equation (5.83). According to this equation, the phase angle of the load at the output determines the amplitude of the steady component of power, which is matched by the real component of current at the input, and it determines the phase of the oscillatory component of power, but not its amplitude. The instantaneous power due to any reactive component of current at the output terminals is thus inherently contained within the oscillatory term of equation (5.83); as we have already seen, this component of instantaneous power at the output is supplied by the principal pulse-number-independent extrabasal components of current at the input, which generally have frequencies of $f_I \pm 2f_O$. Thus, a *reactive* component of current at the *output* terminals always manifests itself as an *extrabasal* component, or components, of current at the *input* terminals.

Consider, for example, the case of the above type of frequency changer, with theoretically infinite pulse number, supplying a single-phase purely reactive load at its output. None of the three input current waves, each of which consists of discrete segments of the output current wave, has a fundamental component, because the real power is zero, and by definition no reactive component of current flows at the input side. Thus, all constituents of the input current wave have extrabasal frequencies. The principal components, which may generally have frequencies of $f_I \pm 2f_O$, supply the reactive power at the output, and all other terms are merely "parasites" that make no contribution to the instantaneous power flow and are entirely the consequence of the method of waveform construction.

For a balanced three-phase output, the input current wave is sinusoidal because the extrabasal components cancel each other in the input—that is, they circulate between the input terminals of the frequency changer. In this way, it can be said that an instantaneous power exchange is established between the output phases via the switches and input terminals of the individual frequency changer circuits. Again, the interesting case of a purely reactive balanced three-phase load exemplifies this statement. The total fundamental current drawn from the source is zero, because no fundamental component flows at the input terminal of any of the individual frequency changer circuits. Moreover, no extrabasal component flows through the source, since, as has been shown, these circulate between the input terminals of the three frequency changer circuits. Consequently, the current in the input source is zero. The frequency changer thus serves to interconnect the output phases in such a way that the reactive load currents freely flow between them. Viewing this from the output terminals of the frequency changer, we could say that the frequency changer establishes a *reactive* power exchange between the load phases.

This explanation of how a reactive component of current at the output manifests itself in *extrabasal form* at the input is of course generally valid, and not only for the specific case considered of a purely reactive load with no real component of output current.

The general explanation can also be extended to other frequency changers producing different types of output voltage waveforms. In this case, however, the input current wave generally contains a fundamental quadrature component, and this means that a reactive power exchange takes place between the phases of the a-c source via the switches of the frequency changer.

This reactive power exchange is entirely separate from the manifestation of reactive output power at the input side. It can be exemplified by considering the case of a naturally commutated cycloconverter supplying a balanced three-phase load with unity power factor and hence with no reactive output power. Because the NCC has a lagging input displacement factor, each current wave drawn from the three-phase a-c source comprises a fundamental real component and a quadrature component. The net instantaneous power contribution of a balanced set of quadrature currents is always zero:

$$\begin{aligned} P_Q &= V_I \sin \omega_I t \, I_{IQ} \cos \omega_I t \\ &\quad + V_I \sin\left(\omega_I t - \frac{2\pi}{3}\right) I_{IQ} \cos\left(\omega_I t - \frac{2\pi}{3}\right) \\ &\quad + V_I \sin\left(\omega_I t - \frac{4\pi}{3}\right) I_{IQ} \cos\left(\omega_I t - \frac{4\pi}{3}\right) \\ &= 0 \end{aligned} \tag{5.91}$$

This means that in effect the NCC serves to interconnect the input terminals in such a way that a lagging reactive current flows between the phases of the a-c source. It could be said, therefore, that the NCC establishes a reactive power exchange between the phases of the input source.

This reactive power exchange between the phases of the input source is a general characteristic of all static frequency changers without unity input displacement factor. As has been seen, however, the magnitude and "polarity" of the reactive input power is dependent upon the method of output waveform construction and upon the phase angle of the load.

Finally, one further point requires brief explanation; this is the presence of the pulse-number-dependent extrabasal components of current at the input, which so far we have generally ignored, by the simple theoretical expedient of assuming an infinite pulse number.

The presence of these components is due to the presence of the unwanted components in the output voltage wave (which, of course, are not present for a hypothetical frequency changer of infinite pulse number). The product of each of these unwanted voltage components with the output current wave gives rise to families of oscillatory "beat" components of power at the output terminals, and these too must be matched by corresponding families of extrabasal components of current at the input. Since the frequencies and amplitudes of the unwanted terms in the output voltage, to which these extrabasal input current components owe their existence, are dependent on the pulse number, so the frequencies and amplitudes of these extrabasal input current components also depend upon the pulse number; as such, they are termed pulse-number-dependent components.

CHAPTER SIX

OPERATING CHARACTERISTICS AND PERFORMANCE DATA

In Chapters 3, 4, and 5 a comprehensive theoretical analysis of the operating waveforms and characteristics of a family of frequency changers is presented. The primary objective there is the establishment and application of fundamental analytical methods. This treatment produces a wealth of raw analytical data that describe the external performance characteristics of the various frequency changers. The results of this analysis are potentially of vital importance to the system designer.

The purpose of this chapter is to present these analytical results in easily understandable and readily usable graphical and tabular forms. A further objective is to provide basic physical explanations, and a general appreciation of the practical significance of, and differences between, the external operating characteristics of the various frequency changers.

The material presented is complete in itself and can be followed and understood by the reader who is not necessarily interested in the manner of its derivation.

6.1 THE OUTPUT VOLTAGE—GENERAL CONSIDERATIONS

The output voltage waveform of the frequency changer consists of the wanted sinusoidal component and a series of superimposed unwanted components.

The frequencies of the unwanted components as a rule are not integral multiples of the wanted output frequency; rather they are sums and/or differences of integral multiples of the input frequency and integral multiples of the output frequency. Thus, except at certain discrete ratios of output to input frequency, the unwanted components are not "locked" to the wanted component but are in a continual state of drift with respect to it. It is important to understand this basic point, since it is a quite different state of affairs from, for example, a conventional d-c to a-c inverter or a rotating a-c generator in which any distortion components that appear in the output voltage generally are integral multiples—that is, "true" harmonics—of the wanted output frequency.

The production of these *beat frequency* components in the output voltage of the frequency changer is a result of the basic waveform construction process. The basic "building pieces" for the output voltage waveform are selected segments of the input voltage waves. Since like points on successive input voltage waves occur only at discrete intervals of time, it is not possible for the waveform of output voltage during one cycle to be precisely the same as during the preceding one unless the output frequency happens to be an exact integral submultiple of the product of the input frequency and the pulse number of the frequency changer. This does not necessarily mean, however, that subfrequency components are present in the output voltage. The "shifting" appearance of the output voltage waveforms theoretically can be accounted for solely by nonintegral multiple superfrequencies. The exact mix, and presence or absence, of sub- and superfrequency components in the output voltage wave are uniquely determined by the *control method* employed, which, as has been shown in earlier chapters, defines the particular type of frequency changer.

As shown in Chapters 3 and 4 and confirmed by the data presented in this chapter, the unrestricted frequency changer (UFC) produces only superfrequency components. The slow-switching frequency changer (SSFC), the unity displacement factor frequency changer (UDFFC), the controllable displacement factor frequency changer (CDFFC), and the naturally commutated cycloconverter (NCC), on the other hand, generally produce both super- and subfrequency components.

It is a remarkable fact that for any given frequency changer, for a given level of output voltage (and—for the CDFFC and the NCC—for a given waveform switching angle) the same characteristic sum and difference unwanted components are present, with the same relative amplitudes, at all output to input frequency ratios. This does not mean, however, that the "quality" of the output waveform remains the same as the ratio between the output and input frequency changes; this is because the frequencies of the unwanted components relative to the wanted output frequency change with changing output to input frequency ratio.

6.2 THE WANTED COMPONENT OF OUTPUT VOLTAGE

6.2.1 The Maximum Value of the Wanted Component

It is usually desired to construct at an output voltage waveform the mean value of which varies sinusoidally. The maximum amplitude of the wanted component of such a wave depends only on the power circuit configuration and is independent of the control method employed; that is, it is independent of the type of frequency changer. This amplitude is equal to the maximum steady average value obtainable from the circuit:

$$V_{O\max} = S \cdot \frac{3\sqrt{3}}{2\pi} V_I = V_{d\max} \tag{6.1}$$

where V_I = amplitude of the input line-to-neutral voltage of each three-pulse group
S = number of three-pulse groups connected in series in each output phase.

For example, for a simple three-pulse group, such as in Figure 1.25, $S = 1$. For a six-pulse bridge circuit, such as in Figure 1.26*c*, which effectively consists of two three-pulse groups connected in series, $S = 2$. And for two six-pulse bridges connected in series, such as in Figure 1.29*a*, $S = 4$.

It may be required under some conditions to operate the NCC with a trapezoidal or square mean output voltage. The maximum amplitude $V'_{O\max}$ of the wanted component attainable with a full square waveform is simply the amplitude of the fundamental component of a square wave with amplitude $V_{O\max}$:

$$V'_{O\max} = \frac{4}{\pi} V_{O\max}$$

$$= S \cdot \frac{6\sqrt{3}}{\pi^2} V_I \tag{6.2}$$

The difference between $V_{O\max}$ (6.1) and $V'_{O\max}$ (6.2) should be carefully noted. $V_{O\max}$ is defined as the maximum possible amplitude of the wanted component, obtained with a mean *sinusoidal* output voltage. $V'_{O\max}$ is defined as the absolute maximum possible amplitude of the wanted component of output voltage obtained with a *square* mean output voltage.

Throughout this chapter, we refer to the *output voltage ratio*, denoted by r. This is defined as the level of the wanted component of output voltage, with respect to the maximum possible value obtainable with a *sinusoidal* mean output voltage, $V_{O\max}$. Thus, an output voltage ratio greater than unity invariably implies trapezoidal or square wave operation. An output voltage ratio less than unity generally implies operation with a sinusoidal mean output voltage. The only exception in this book is for the NCC, for which consideration is given to square and trapezoidal operation, as well as to sinusoidal operation, at output voltage ratios less than unity.

6.2.2 Relationships Between Control Parameters and the Amplitude of the Wanted Output Voltage

6.2.2.1 *The UFC and SSFC with Pulse-Width Modulation.* The basic waveform construction principle of the UFC is to turn on each switch in sequence for a fixed time frame, T, the duration of which determines the frequency of the wanted output component. This simple control process invariably produces a mean sinusoidal output voltage, and the amplitude of the wanted component is invariably $V_{O\max}$, independent of the output frequency.

The normally preferred method of controlling the amplitude of the output voltage is by pulse-width modulation. Each time frame T is subdivided into an *active* and a *passive* interval. During the active interval, the appropriate switch in each three-pulse group is turned on, as for full output voltage; during the passive interval, this switch is turned off, and either another switch* within the three-pulse group is turned on, or an additional "freewheeling" switch connected at the output terminal of the three-pulse group is turned on.

Assuming that an additional freewheeling switch is not used, one of the following switching strategies will generally be employed, depending on the configuration of the power circuit:

1. The passive interval occupies the first portion of the time frame T, and the switch of the same three-pulse group associated with the active interval of the *next* time frame is turned on during the passive interval. For a six-pulse frequency changer (comprised of two separate three-pulse groups), this so-called *stepping ahead* procedure results in zero net output voltage during the passive intervals, as is explained in Chapter 4 (see waveforms of Figure 4.2). This is the generally preferred voltage control approach for frequency changers with even pulse number.

Control of the output voltage from maximum to zero is brought about by a variation of the active interval, t_A, between the whole time frame, T, and half the time frame, $T/2$. In Chapter 4, the output voltage ratio is shown to be given by

$$r = 2\cos\left(\frac{\pi}{3} + \frac{\beta}{2}\right) \tag{6.3}$$

* For the control method illustrated in Figure 7.3, it happens that in *one* three-pulse group of the three-phase arrangement the same switch that conducts during the active interval actually also conducts during the passive interval.

where β is the angle of the passive interval, which varies between 0° at full output voltage and 60° at zero output voltage.

The above equation can be rewritten in terms of the ratio of the active interval, t_A, to the total time frame T, as follows:

$$r = 2\cos\left[\left(1 + \frac{t_A}{T}\right)\frac{\pi}{3}\right] \tag{6.4}$$

$$\frac{1}{2} \leq \frac{t_A}{T} \leq 1$$

This relationship is shown graphically in Figure 6.1.

2. For midpoint circuits with three-wire three-phase output, the three switches connected to a given input line are simultaneously turned on during the passive interval. It should be recognized that the basic time frames for all output phases are the same; only the allocation of these time frames to the various switches is different. Generally, the three switches selected for simultaneous conduction are rotated from one passive interval to the next in order to ensure balanced load sharing by all switches. This method produces zero voltage between the output terminals

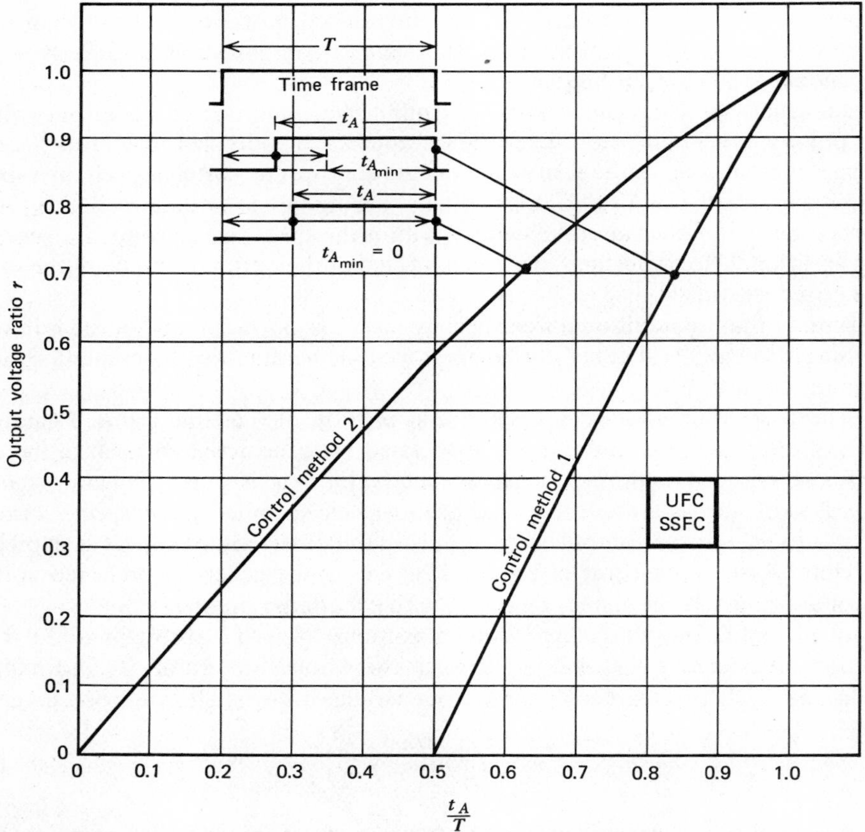

Figure 6.1 Variation with t_A/T of normalized output voltage of UFC and SSFC for pulse-width modulation methods 1 and 2 described in Section 6.2.2.1.

of three-pulse groups connected to a given set of input phases during the passive interval. Implementation of this method is described in detail in Chapter 7.

Control of the output voltage from maximum to zero is accomplished by varying the active interval t_A between the whole time frame, T, and zero. The output voltage ratio is given by:

$$r = \frac{2}{\sqrt{3}} \sin\left(\frac{t_A}{T}\frac{\pi}{3}\right) \tag{6.5}$$

This relationship is shown graphically in Figure 6.1.

It is to be noted that this relationship also applies to a three-pulse group with a separate "freewheeling" switch connected across its output terminals, which is turned on during each passive interval.

6.2.2.2 *The UFC and SSFC with Phase-Shift Control.* An alternative method of controlling the output voltage of the UFC and SSFC is by shifting the phase of the wanted components of two individual power circuit groups. In this event, the output voltage ratio is given simply by:

$$r = \cos \xi \tag{6.6}$$

where ξ is half the angular phase shift between the wanted components of the two groups.

6.2.2.3 *The UDFFC, CDFFC, and NCC with Sinusoidal Mean Output Voltage.* The normal method of voltage control of the UDFFC, CDFFC, and NCC is by periodic modulation of the switch conduction periods. In Chapters 3 and 4 it is seen that a periodic modulating function may take the general form $M(t) = \sin^{-1}\{\sum_{n=1}^{\infty} b_{1,n} \sin n(\omega_O t + \psi)\}$. It was also shown that in order to produce a sinusoidal mean output voltage, the coefficients of all but the first term in the above series must be zero.

As is shown in Chapter 7, in order to implement the theoretically "pure" modulating function $M(t) = \sin^{-1}\{r \sin(\omega_O t + \psi)\}$, the conduction periods of the switches within the frequency changer are determined from the intersection points of an analog sinusoidal reference voltage with a set of "cosine" timing waves synchronized to the input voltage waves. Two complementary sets of timing waves are used: one to produce a positive-type output voltage wave, the other to produce a negative-type output voltage wave, as illustrated in Figure 7.6. The constituent power circuits of the UDFFC produce both these waveform types simultaneously. The CDFFC and the NCC produce each in turn for selected intervals.

Normally the control circuitry is arranged so that the maximum amplitude of the reference voltage presented to the timing comparator effectively cannot exceed some level cV_T, where V_T is the amplitude of the timing wave, and the *clamp level* c is less than or equal to unity, even though the amplitude of the externally applied reference may exceed this value. This is illustrated by the waveforms of Figure 6.2.

In order to produce the above theoretically pure modulating function, and hence a sinusoidal mean output voltage, the normalized amplitude, κ, of the externally applied reference wave, defined as the amplitude of the applied reference relative to the amplitude of the timing waves, must be less than, or in the limiting case equal to the clamp level, c. Under this condition, the actual output voltage ratio r is equal to the normalized amplitude of the reference, κ, and the instantaneous value of the wanted component of output voltage is directly proportional to the instantaneous value of the reference wave.

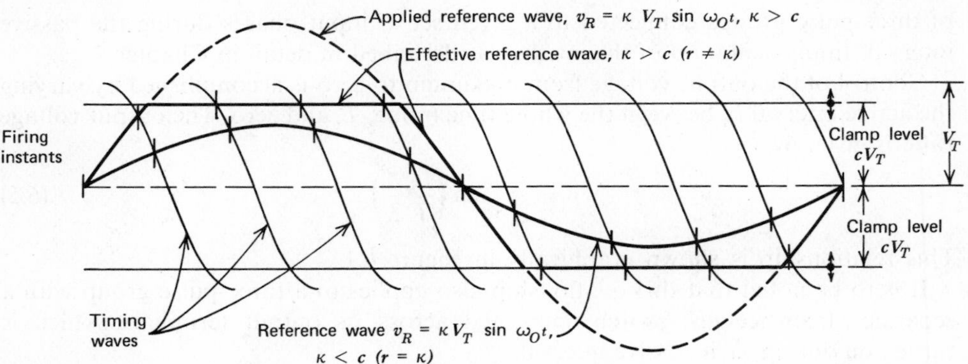

Figure 6.2 Reference and timing waves, showing firing instants for amplitude of reference less than and greater than clamp level.

Thus, for a given applied reference wave, $\kappa V_T \sin \omega_O t$, the corresponding wanted component of output voltage is:

$$v_O = rV_{O\max} \sin \omega_O t \tag{6.7}$$

where $r = \kappa$.

Thus, within this operating range, the frequency changer, taken in conjunction with its timing control circuits, in effect behaves as a *linear voltage amplifier*, with *no phase shift* between the input reference voltage and the wanted component of output voltage.

6.2.2.4 *The NCC with Trapezoidal and Square Mean Output Voltage.* The type of control arrangement illustrated in Figure 6.2 provides a natural transition from a sinusoidal to a trapezoidal mean output voltage as the amplitude of the externally applied reference is increased beyond the clamp level, cV_T. The UDFFC and the CDFFC would always be operated within the range $\kappa \leqq c$; (in which c would normally be 1). The NCC, on the other hand, may be operated outside this range, with κ assuming very large values, as the output wave is pushed towards the fully *square* waveshape. Of course, in this mode of operation, the theoretically pure modulating function $M(t) = \sin^{-1}\{b_{1,1} \sin(\omega_O t + \psi)\}$ is no longer produced. Now all the odd coefficients belonging to the general form of the modulating function $M(t) = \sin^{-1}\{\sum_{n=1}^{\infty} b_{1,n} \sin n(\omega_O t + \psi)\}$ take on finite values.

Obviously, the amplitude of the wanted component of output voltage is no longer directly proportional to the amplitude of the applied reference, although its phase remains the same as that of the reference.

The relationship between κ/c (proportional to the amplitude of the applied reference) and r/c (proportional to the amplitude of the wanted component of output voltage), for $\kappa \geq c$, is shown in Figure 6.3. As would be expected, for large values of κ/c:

$$\frac{r}{c} \to \frac{4}{\pi} \tag{6.8}$$

The data presented in this chapter for the NCC, for normalized voltages both higher and lower than the clamp level, c, are generally based on this particular waveform control method, unless stated otherwise.

The NCC can also be operated with a square reference voltage wave, with a corresponding square mean output voltage wave, at all levels of output voltage. However,

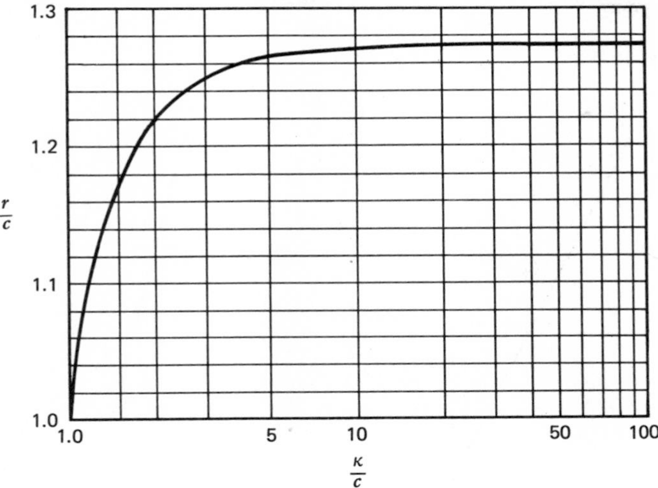

Figure 6.3 Universal relationship between r/c and κ/c, for $\kappa \geqq c$.

as is explained in Section 6.6.2.5, this generally would be advantageous only under abnormal conditions.

If a square reference voltage of amplitude, κV_T, is employed (where $\kappa \leq c$), the output voltage ratio is given by:

$$r = \frac{4}{\pi}\kappa \tag{6.9}$$

6.3 THE UNWANTED COMPONENTS OF OUTPUT VOLTAGE

6.3.1 The UFC

6.3.1.1 *Unwanted Frequencies.* The frequencies of the unwanted components present in the output voltage of the UFC are given by the following general expression:

$$f_U = Pkf_I + (Pk \pm 1)f_O \tag{6.10}$$

where P is the pulse number and k is any integer from 1 to ∞.

If the output voltage is controlled by phase shifting the wanted components of two individual power circuit groups, the value of P to be used is the pulse number of each of the individual groups and thus is half of the overall circuit pulse number (except for the special condition of full output voltage). If the voltage is controlled by pulse-width modulation, on the other hand, the appropriate value of P is the pulse number of the overall circuit.

From expression (6.10), the following linear relationship is evident:

$$\frac{f_U}{f_I} = Pk + (Pk \pm 1)\frac{f_O}{f_I} \tag{6.11}$$

The right-hand portion of the "frequency chart" of Figure 6.4 shows the ratios of unwanted frequency to input frequency, f_U/f_I, plotted against the output to input frequency ratio, f_O/f_I, for values of Pk up to 12.

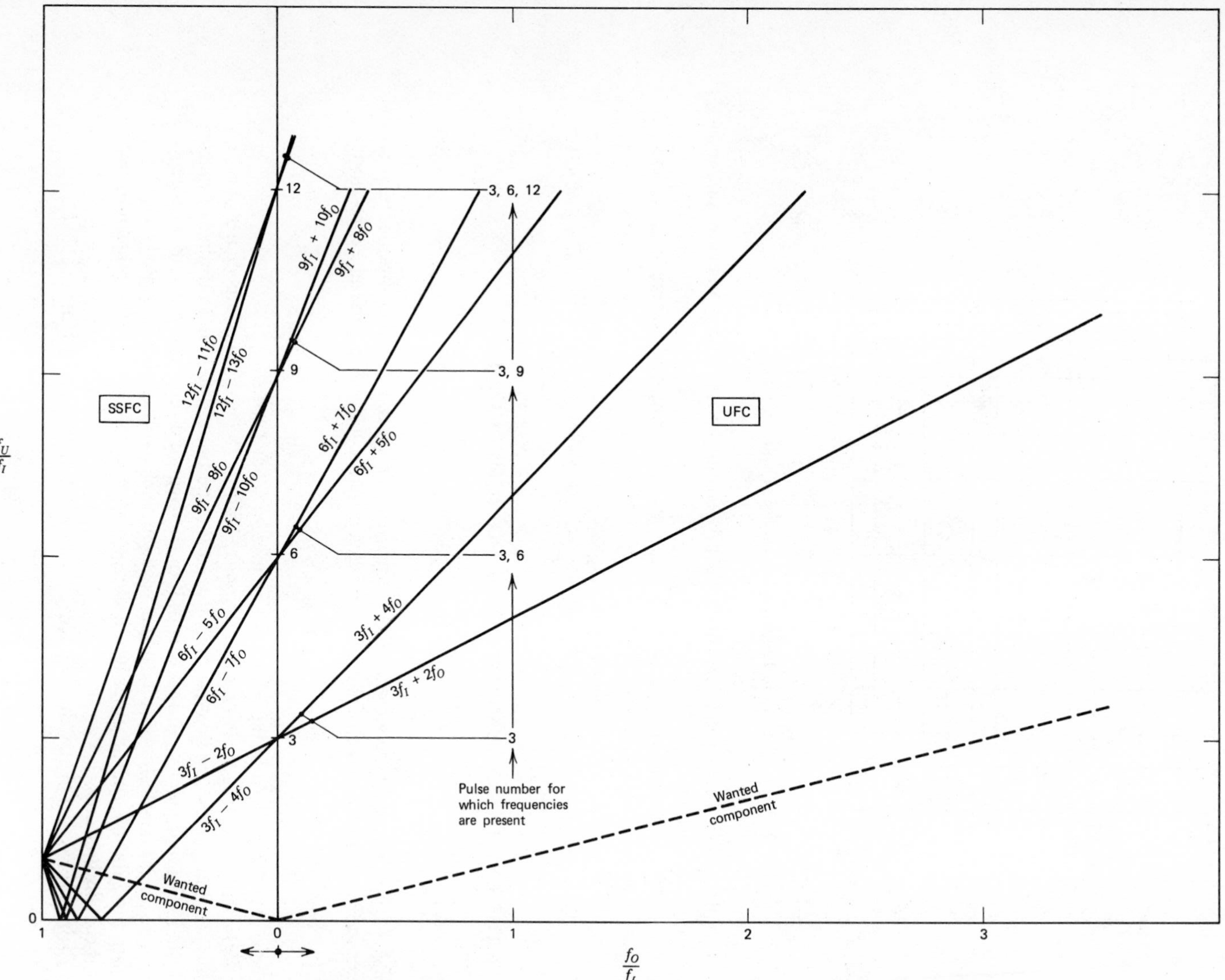

Figure 6.4 Frequencies of unwanted components in output voltage of the UFC and SSFC, expressed as ratio of input frequency, versus output to input frequency ratio.

This chart clearly illustrates that the frequencies of the unwanted components present in the output voltage of the UFC are always greater than the wanted frequency, irrespective of the output to input frequency ratio. For a UFC of pulse number P, the lowest ratio of unwanted frequency to input frequency occurs at zero output frequency and is P. The corresponding ratio of unwanted frequency to output frequency at this point is infinite. As the output to input frequency ratio increases, so the ratio of the lowest unwanted frequency to the *input* frequency increases; however, the ratio of the lowest unwanted frequency to the *output* frequency decreases and tends to a limiting value of $(P - 1)$ times the wanted output frequency.

Thus, for a six-pulse UFC, for example, the limiting minimum unwanted frequency is five times the output frequency.

6.3.1.2 *Amplitudes of Unwanted Components.* Figure 6.5 shows the amplitudes of the principal unwanted components present in the output voltage of the UFC, plotted against the output voltage ratio, for voltage control by pulse-width modulation. Figures 6.6 and 6.7 show similar curves for voltage control by phase shifting between individual groups.

6.3.2 The SSFC

6.3.2.1 *Unwanted Frequencies.* The frequencies of the unwanted components present in the output voltage of the SSFC are *complementary* to those present in the output voltage of the UFC. Thus, whereas the unwanted frequencies present in the output of the UFC are *sums* of given multiples of the input frequency f_I and the output frequency f_O, the unwanted frequencies present in the output of the SSFC are *differences* of these same multiples of f_I and f_O:

$$f_U = Pkf_I - (Pk \pm 1)f_O \tag{6.12}$$

Hence

$$\frac{f_U}{f_I} = Pk - (Pk \pm 1)\frac{f_O}{f_I} \tag{6.13}$$

The left-hand portion of the frequency chart of Figure 6.4 shows the ratios of unwanted frequency to input frequency, f_U/f_I, plotted against the output to input frequency ratio, f_O/f_I, for values of Pk up to 12.

This chart clearly illustrates how the distortion of the output voltage deteriorates with increasing ratio of output to input frequency because of the encroachment of the unwanted frequencies upon the wanted frequency.

6.3.2.2 *Amplitudes of Unwanted Components.* For given values of P and k, the amplitude of any given unwanted component with frequency $Pkf_I - (Pk \pm 1)f_O$ in the output voltage of the SSFC, at any given output voltage ratio, is the same as that of the complementary component in the output of the UFC, with frequency $Pkf_I + (Pk \pm 1)f_O$. Thus the curves of Figures 6.5–6.7 also apply to the SSFC.

6.3.3 The UDFFC

6.3.3.1 *Unwanted Frequencies.* The frequencies of the unwanted components present in the output voltage of the UDFFC are given by the following general expression:

$$f_U = Pkf_I \pm nf_O \tag{6.14}$$

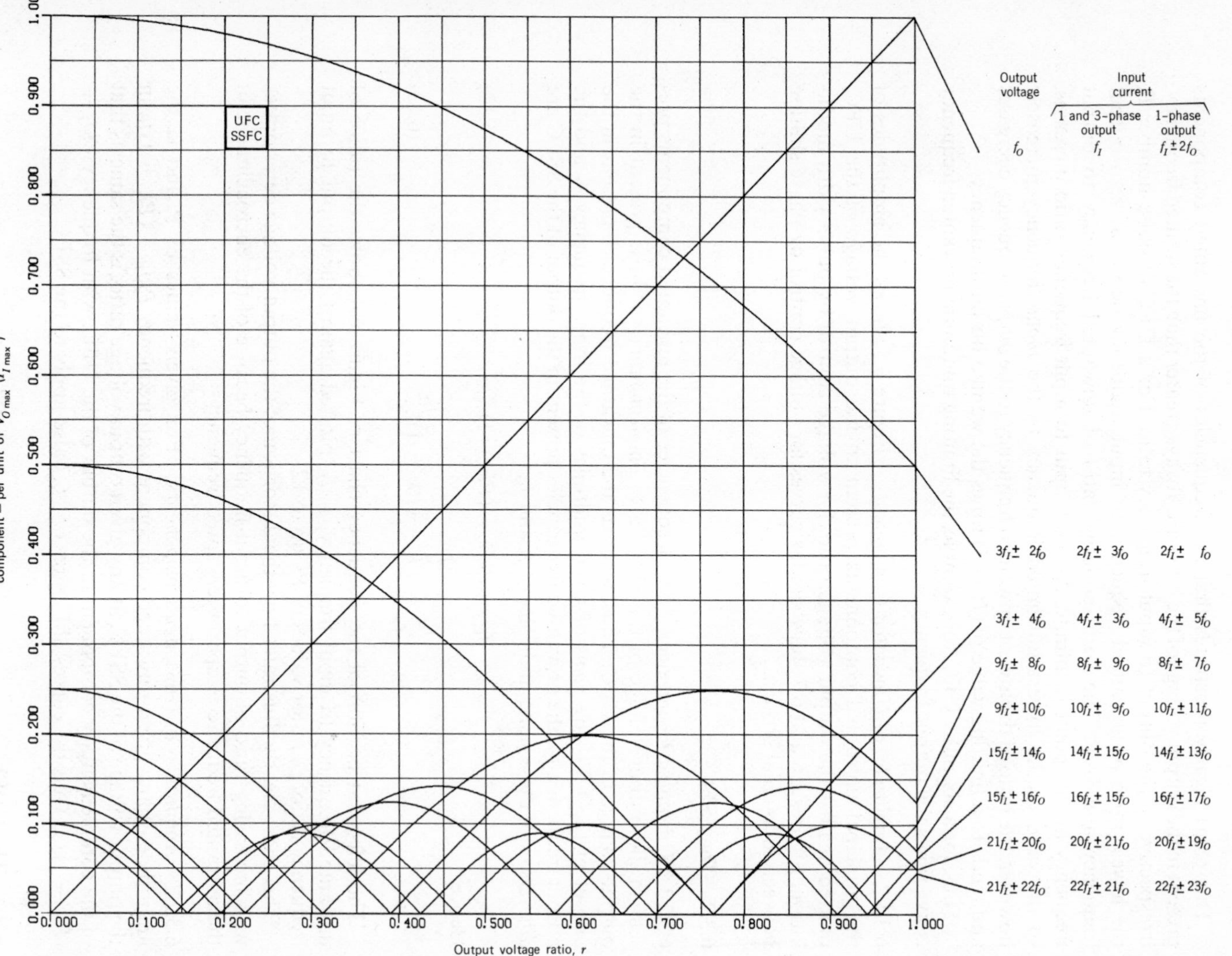

UFC
SSFC
Output voltage
Input current
1 and 3-phase output
1-phase output
f_O
f_I
$f_I \pm 2f_O$
$3f_I \pm 2f_O$ $2f_I \pm 3f_O$ $2f_I \pm f_O$
$3f_I \pm 4f_O$ $4f_I \pm 3f_O$ $4f_I \pm 5f_O$
$9f_I \pm 8f_O$ $8f_I \pm 9f_O$ $8f_I \pm 7f_O$
$9f_I \pm 10f_O$ $10f_I \pm 9f_O$ $10f_I \pm 11f_O$
$15f_I \pm 14f_O$ $14f_I \pm 15f_O$ $14f_I \pm 13f_O$
$15f_I \pm 16f_O$ $16f_I \pm 15f_O$ $16f_I \pm 17f_O$
$21f_I \pm 20f_O$ $20f_I \pm 21f_O$ $20f_I \pm 19f_O$
$21f_I \pm 22f_O$ $22f_I \pm 21f_O$ $22f_I \pm 23f_O$
Amplitude of the unwanted (extrabasal) component – per unit of $V_{O\,max}$ ($I_{I\,max}$)
1.000 0.900 0.800 0.700 0.600 0.500 0.400 0.300 0.200 0.100 0.000
0.000 0.100 0.200 0.300 0.400 0.500 0.600 0.700 0.800 0.900 1.000
Output voltage ratio, r

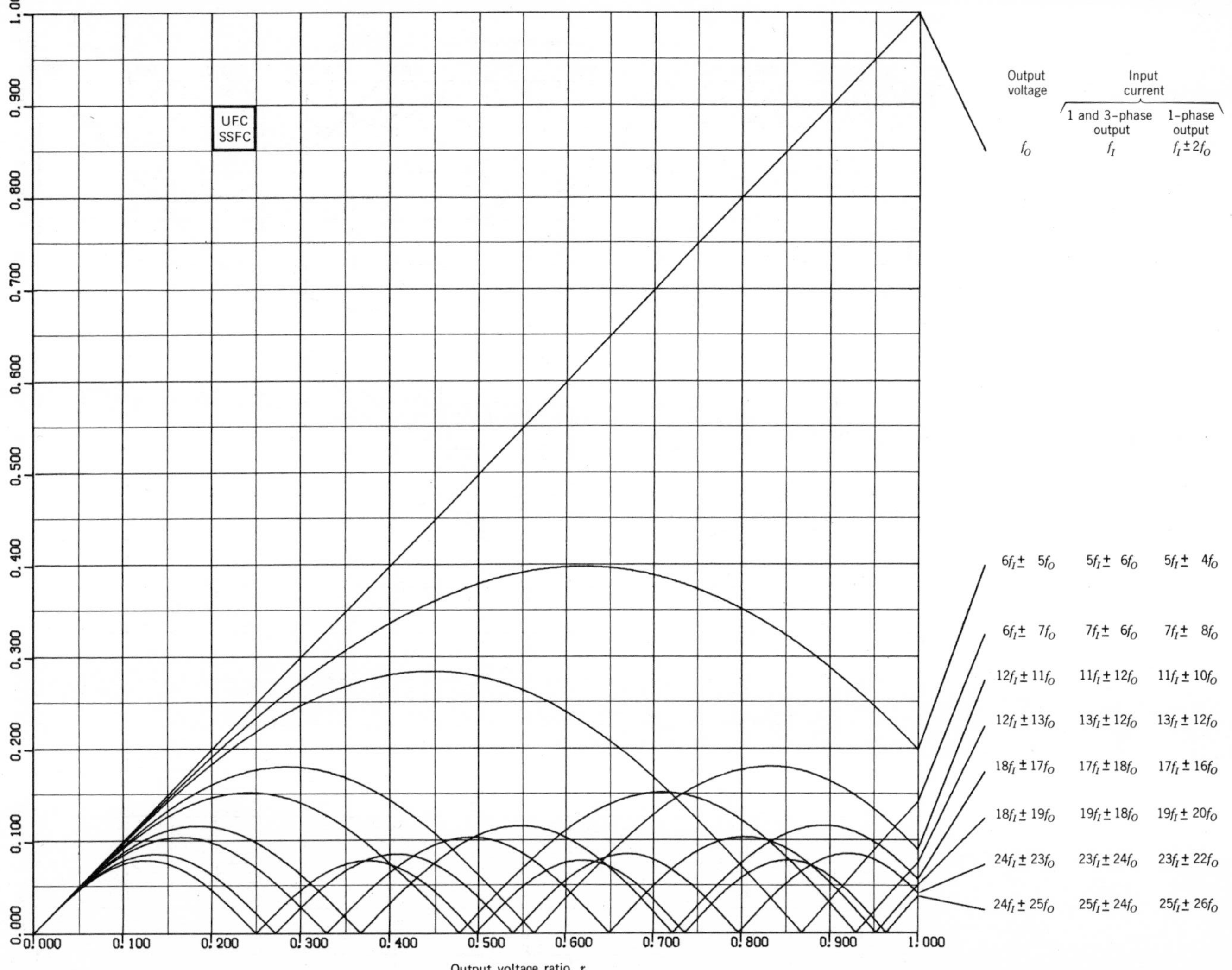

Figure 6.5 Normalized amplitudes of wanted and unwanted components in the output voltage, or of fundamental and extrabasal components in the input current, for the UFC and SSFC with pulse-width modulation of the output voltage, versus output voltage ratio. The UFC has only "sum" components. The SSFC has only "difference" components.

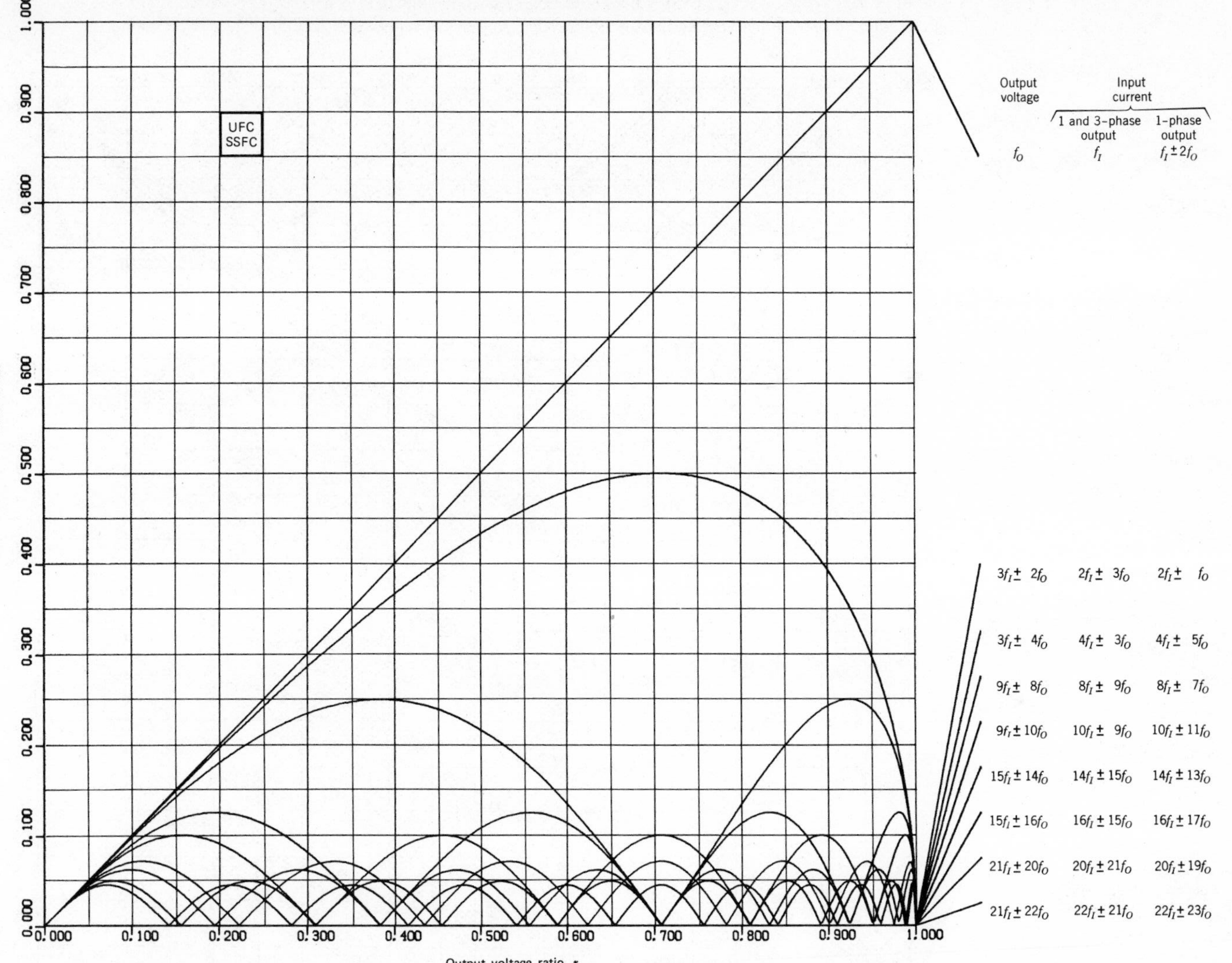
UFC
SSFC
Output voltage
Input current
1 and 3-phase output
1-phase output
f_O
f_I
$f_I \pm 2f_O$
$3f_I \pm 2f_O$ $2f_I \pm 3f_O$ $2f_I \pm f_O$
$3f_I \pm 4f_O$ $4f_I \pm 3f_O$ $4f_I \pm 5f_O$
$9f_I \pm 8f_O$ $8f_I \pm 9f_O$ $8f_I \pm 7f_O$
$9f_I \pm 10f_O$ $10f_I \pm 9f_O$ $10f_I \pm 11f_O$
$15f_I \pm 14f_O$ $14f_I \pm 15f_O$ $14f_I \pm 13f_O$
$15f_I \pm 16f_O$ $16f_I \pm 15f_O$ $16f_I \pm 17f_O$
$21f_I \pm 20f_O$ $20f_I \pm 21f_O$ $20f_I \pm 19f_O$
$21f_I \pm 22f_O$ $22f_I \pm 21f_O$ $22f_I \pm 23f_O$
0.000
0.100
0.200
0.300
0.400
0.500
0.600
0.700
0.800
0.900
1.000
Output voltage ratio, r
Amplitude of the unwanted (extrabasal) component — per unit of $V_{O\max}$ ($I_{I\max}$)

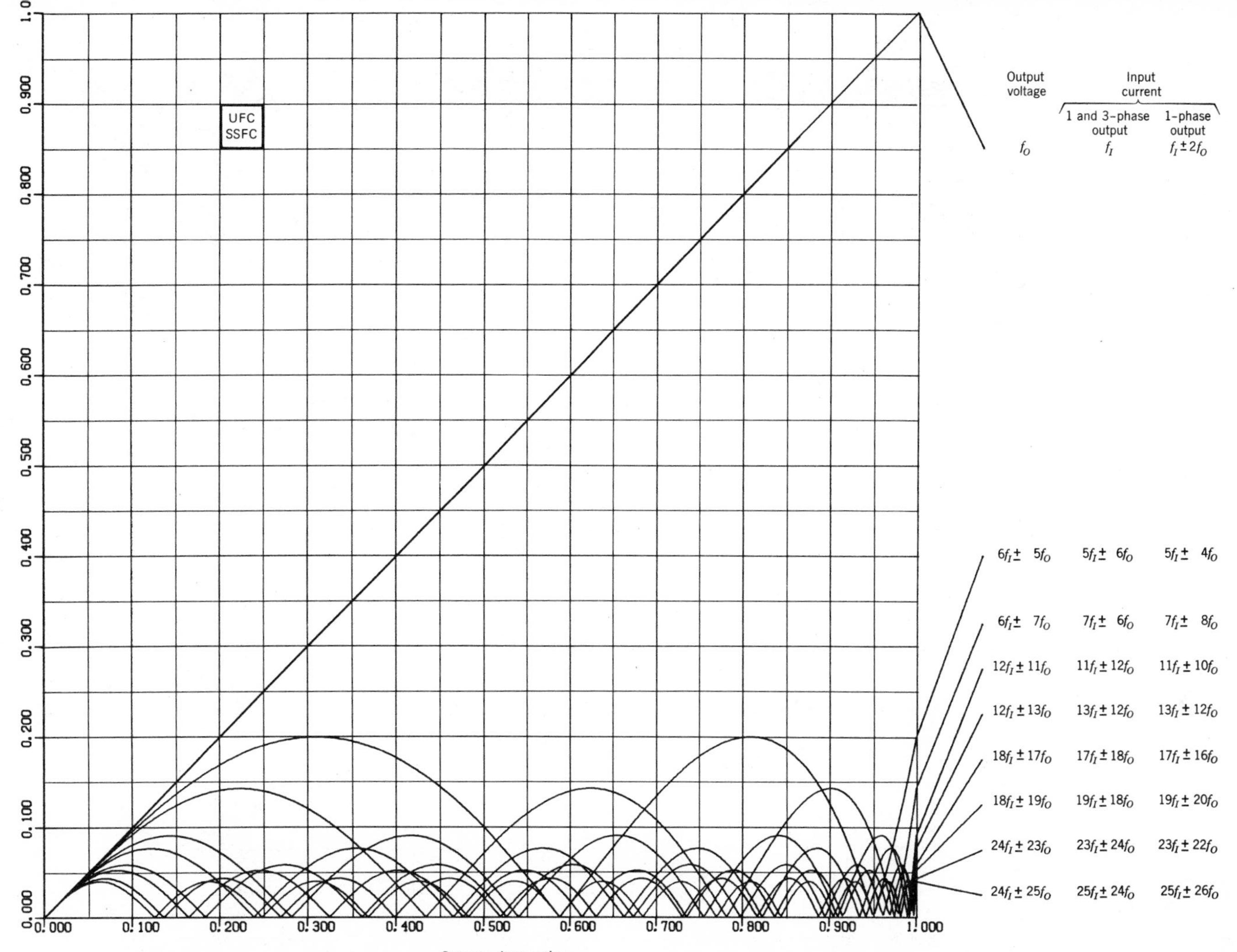

Figure 6.6 Normalized amplitudes of wanted and unwanted components in the output voltage, or of fundamental and extrabasal components in the input current, for a six-pulse UFC and SSFC with phase-shift control of the output voltage, versus output voltage ratio. The UFC has only "sum" components. The SSFC has only "difference" components.

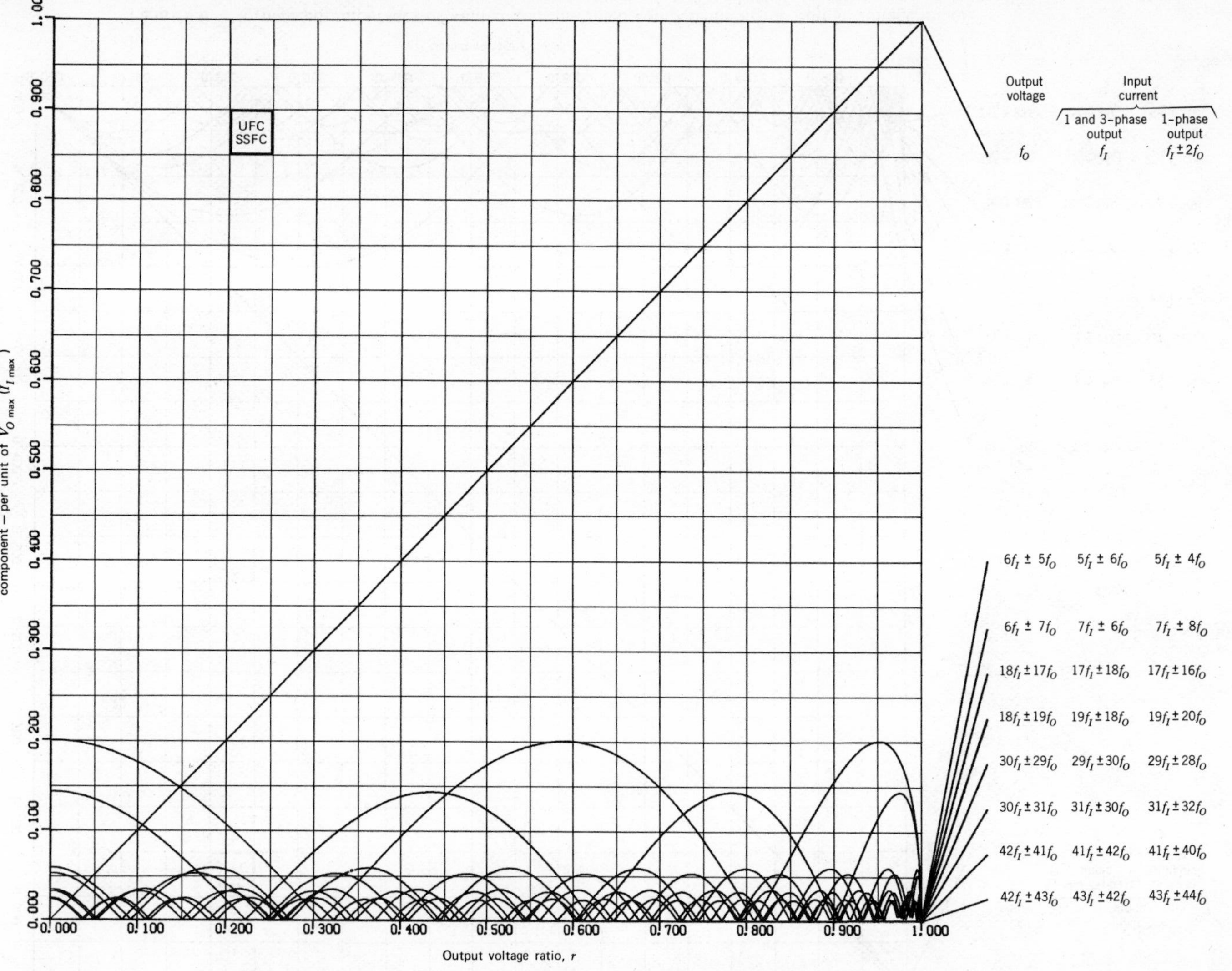

Output voltage
Input current
1 and 3-phase output
1-phase output
f_O
f_I
$f_I \pm 2f_O$
$6f_I \pm 5f_O$ $5f_I \pm 6f_O$ $5f_I \pm 4f_O$
$6f_I \pm 7f_O$ $7f_I \pm 6f_O$ $7f_I \pm 8f_O$
$18f_I \pm 17f_O$ $17f_I \pm 18f_O$ $17f_I \pm 16f_O$
$18f_I \pm 19f_O$ $19f_I \pm 18f_O$ $19f_I \pm 20f_O$
$30f_I \pm 29f_O$ $29f_I \pm 30f_O$ $29f_I \pm 28f_O$
$30f_I \pm 31f_O$ $31f_I \pm 30f_O$ $31f_I \pm 32f_O$
$42f_I \pm 41f_O$ $41f_I \pm 42f_O$ $41f_I \pm 40f_O$
$42f_I \pm 43f_O$ $43f_I \pm 42f_O$ $43f_I \pm 44f_O$
UFC
SSFC
0.000 0.100 0.200 0.300 0.400 0.500 0.600 0.700 0.800 0.900 1.000
Output voltage ratio, r
Amplitude of the unwanted (extrabasal) component – per unit of $V_{O\max}$ ($I_{I\max}$)
0.000 0.100 0.200 0.300 0.400 0.500 0.600 0.700 0.800 0.900 1.000

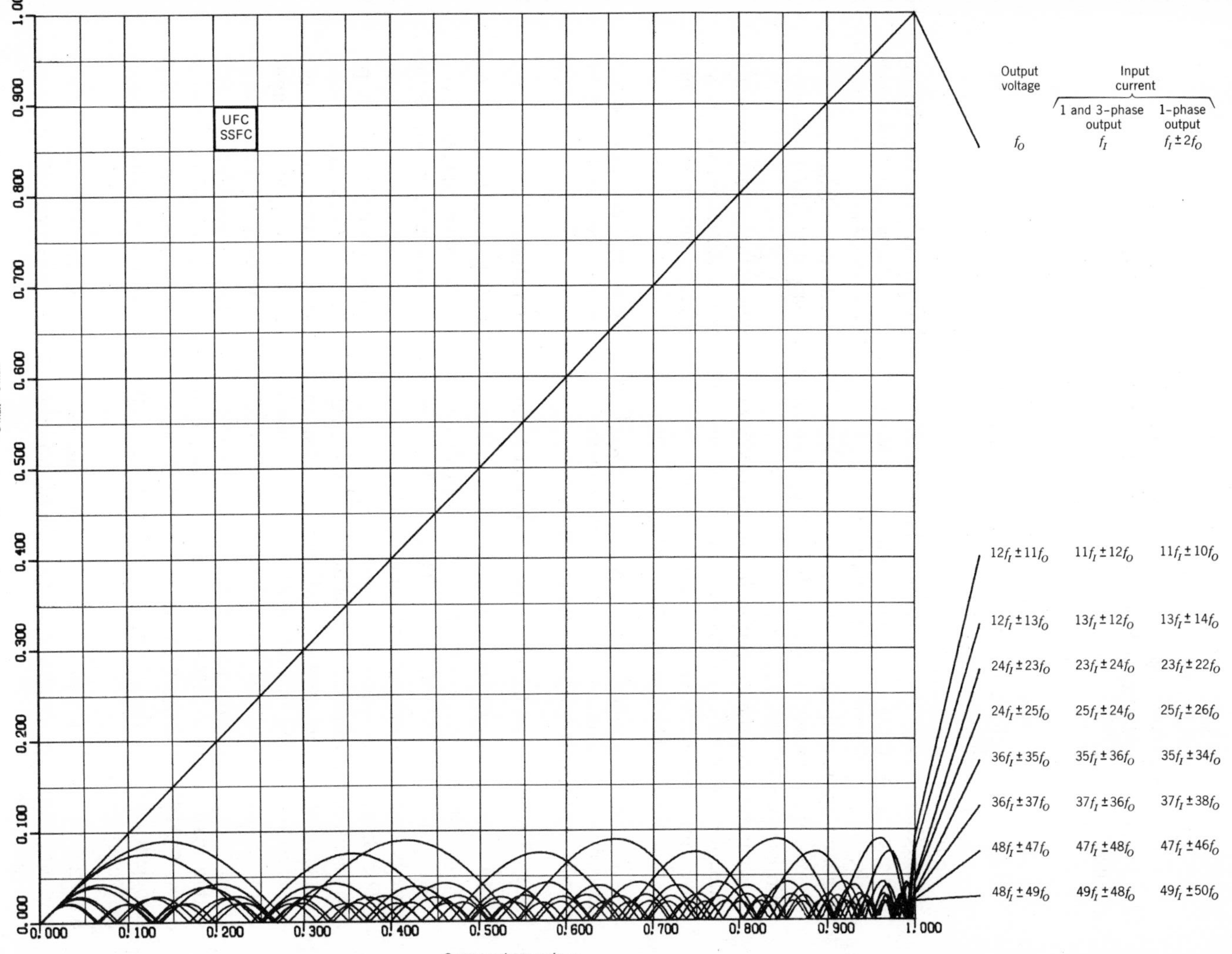

Figure 6.7 Normalized amplitudes of wanted and unwanted components in the output voltage, or of fundamental and extrabasal components in the input current, for a twelve-pulse UFC and SSFC with phase-shift control of the output voltage, versus output voltage ratio. The UFC has only "sum" components. The SSFC has only "difference" components.

where P is the pulse number,
k is any integer from 1 to ∞,
n is any even integer from 0 to $(Pk + 1)$ for Pk odd, and
n is any odd integer from 1 to $(Pk + 1)$ for Pk even.

Thus

$$\frac{f_U}{f_I} = Pk \pm n\frac{f_O}{f_I} \tag{6.15}$$

The frequency chart of Figure 6.8 shows the unwanted frequency to input frequency ratios, f_U/f_I, plotted against the output to input frequency ratio, f_O/f_I, for values of Pk up to 12.

This chart clearly illustrates how the distortion of the output voltage deteriorates with increasing ratio of output to input frequency. As the frequency ratio increases, so the frequencies of the difference unwanted components (the $Pkf_I - nf_O$ terms) encroach upon, and ultimately become less than, the wanted output frequency. For this reason, the useful range of continuous control of the output to input frequency ratio is generally less than unity.

As can be seen, the output to input frequency ratio at which the lowest unwanted frequency becomes equal to the wanted output frequency depends on the circuit pulse number. This frequency ratio increases with increasing circuit pulse number, but it is always less than unity for all pulse numbers.

6.3.3.2 *Amplitudes of Unwanted Components.* Figure 6.9 shows the amplitudes of the principal unwanted components present in the output voltage of the UDFFC plotted against the output voltage ratio.

6.3.4 The NCC and CDFFC with Sinusoidal Mean Output Voltage

6.3.4.1 *Similarity of Voltage Waveforms.* In both the CDFFC and the NCC, the output voltage wave is switched from a positive-type to a negative-type, and vice versa, at regular 180° intervals. Thus, both these frequency changers produce the same basic type of output voltage wave.

The difference resides in the fact that, whereas with the NCC the positive-type and negative-type segments of the output voltage wave of necessity always correspond to the positive and negative half-cycles of output current, with the CDFFC the waveform switching instants are determined in accordance with the desired input displacement factor and generally do not correspond to the output current zero crossings. At all events, for a given waveform switching angle, output voltage ratio, and ratio of output to input frequency, it is evident that the output voltage waveforms of the CDFFC and the NCC are identical. Thus a single set of quantitative data is sufficient to define the distortion of the output voltage waveforms of both types of frequency changer.

6.3.4.2 *Unwanted Frequencies.* The frequencies of the unwanted components present in the output voltage of the CDFFC and the NCC are given by the following general expression:

$$f_U = Pkf_I \pm (n - 1)f_O \tag{6.16}$$

where P is the pulse number,
k is any positive integer from 1 to ∞,
n is any odd integer from 1 to ∞ for Pk odd, and
n is any even integer from 2 to ∞ for Pk even.

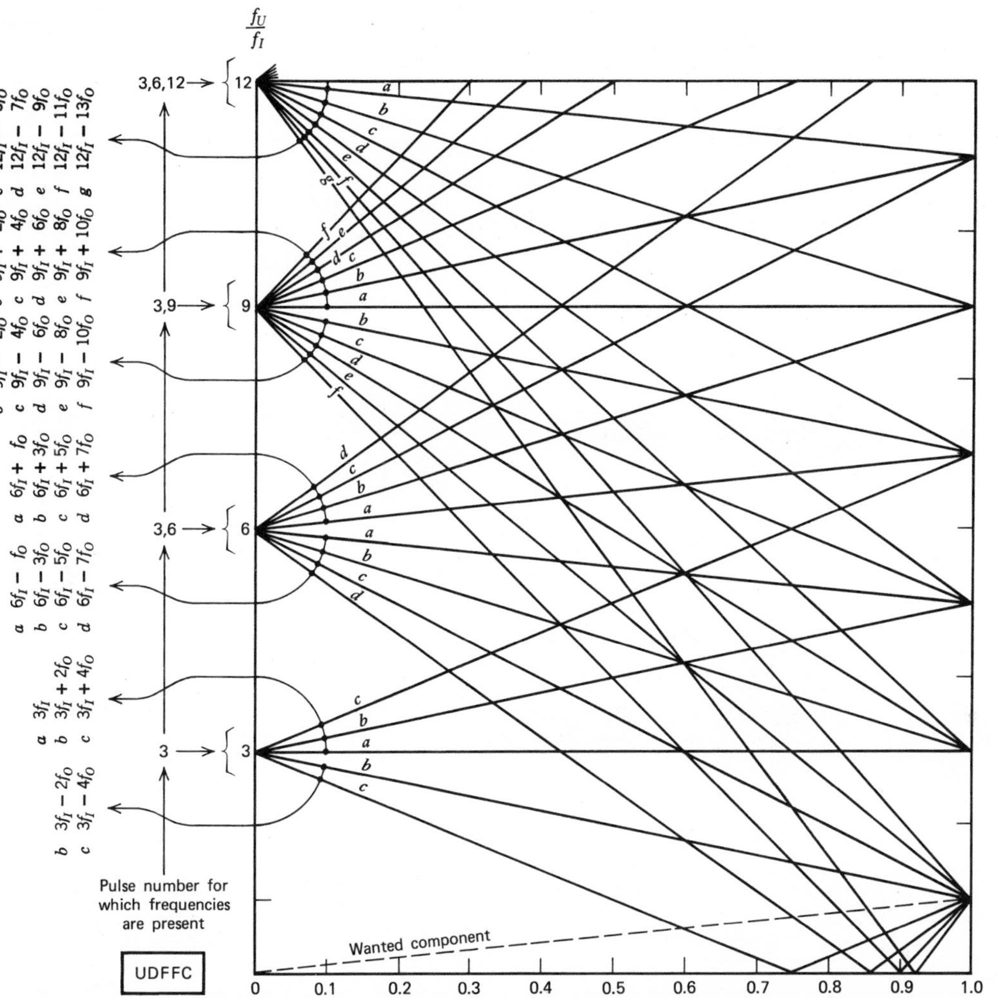

Figure 6.8 Frequencies of unwanted components in output voltage of UDFFC, expressed as ratio of input frequency, versus output to input frequency ratio.

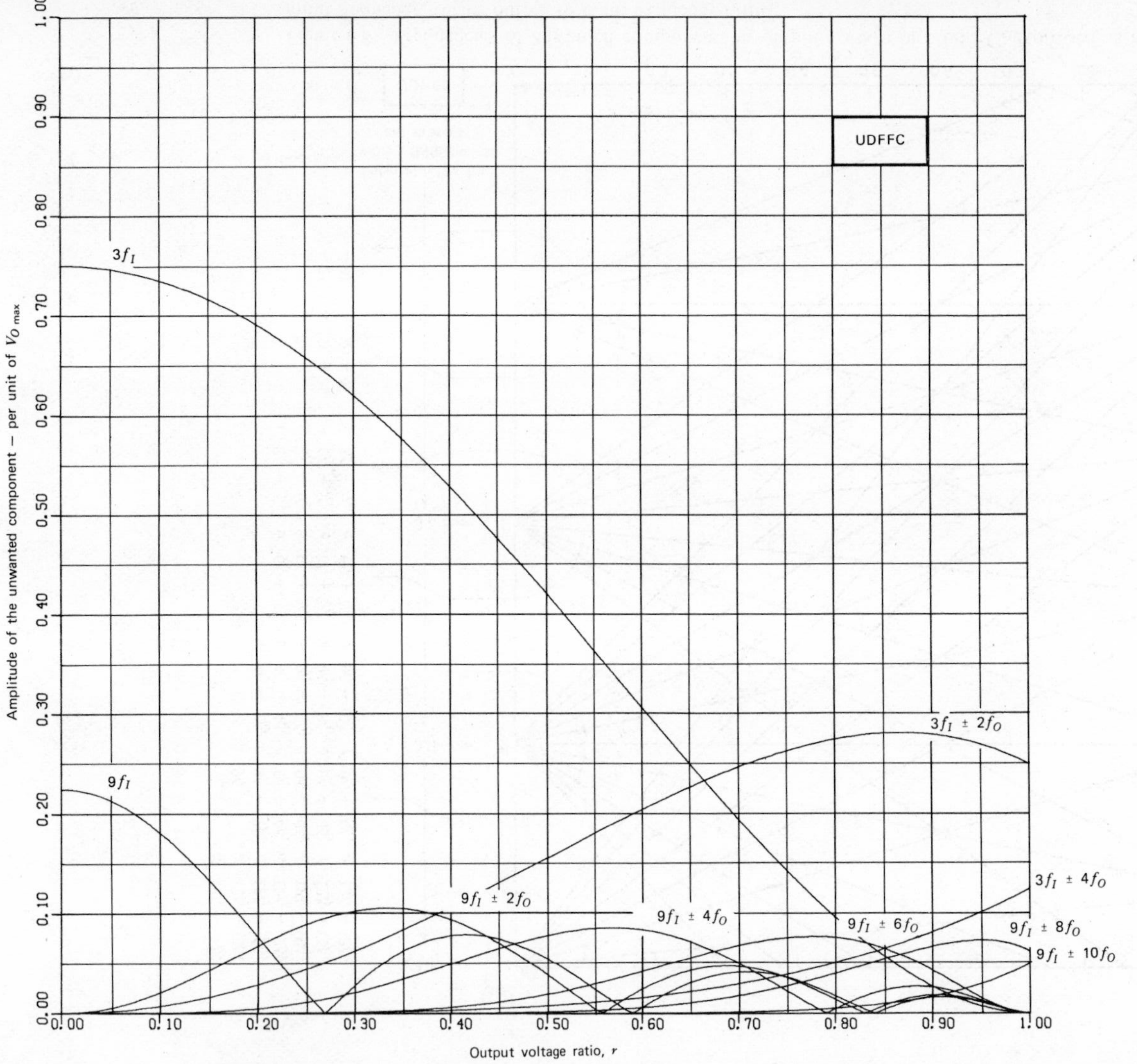

UDFFC
3f_I
9f_I
3f_I ± 2f_O
3f_I ± 4f_O
9f_I ± 2f_O
9f_I ± 4f_O
9f_I ± 6f_O
9f_I ± 8f_O
9f_I ± 10f_O
0.00 0.10 0.20 0.30 0.40 0.50 0.60 0.70 0.80 0.90 1.00
Amplitude of the unwanted component – per unit of V_O max
0.00 0.10 0.20 0.30 0.40 0.50 0.60 0.70 0.80 0.90 1.00
Output voltage ratio, r

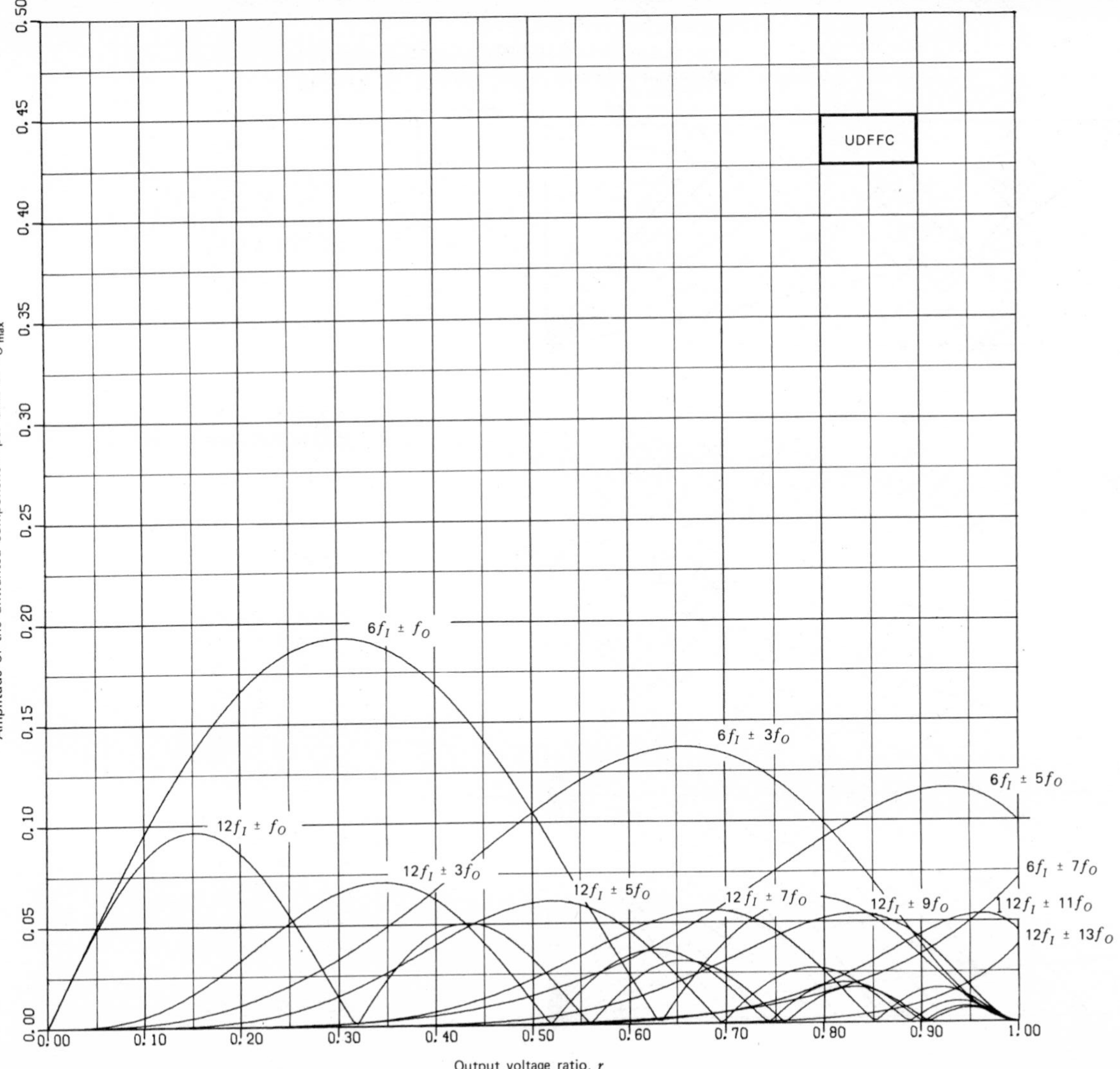

Figure 6.9 Normalized amplitudes of unwanted components in the output voltage of the UDFFC versus output voltage ratio.

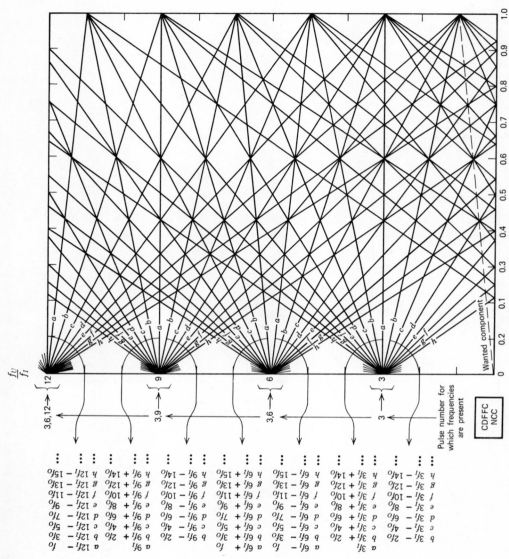

Figure 6.10 Frequencies of principal unwanted components in output voltage of CDFFC and NCC, expressed as ratio of input frequency, versus output to input frequency ratio.

Thus

$$\frac{f_U}{f_I} = Pk \pm (n - 1)\frac{f_O}{f_I} \tag{6.17}$$

The frequency chart of Figure 6.10 shows the ratios f_U/f_I for the principal unwanted components plotted against the output to input frequency ratio, f_O/f_I, for values of Pk up to 12.

This chart clearly illustrates how the preponderance of principal unwanted components with frequencies close to or less than the wanted output frequency tends to increase with increasing ratio of output to input frequency. Thus, the maximum usable output to input frequency ratio is always less than unity, regardless of the circuit pulse number; but this does increase as the pulse number increases.

6.3.4.3 *Amplitudes of Unwanted Components.* Tables 6.1–6.3 show the amplitudes of the principal unwanted components present in the output voltage of the CDFFC and the NCC, when producing a sinusoidal mean voltage envelope, for different waveform switching angles, for output voltage ratios from 1 to 0.1.

The waveform switching angle, ρ, is defined as zero when the switching from the negative to the positive type wave occurs at 0° on the output voltage wave; this angle is defined as being *positive* when the waveform switching occurs *ahead* of this point and negative when it occurs *after* the point.

Thus, for the NCC, the waveform switching angle is equal to the output displacement angle:

$$\rho = \phi_O \tag{6.18}$$

As is explained in Chapter 7, for practical reasons the angle at which the voltage wave of the CDFFC is switched from one type to the other would normally be controlled with respect to the output *current* wave, rather than with respect to the output *voltage* wave.

For this reason, we introduce for the CDFFC an angle, σ, which we call the *control angle.* This is the angle at which the voltage wave is switched with respect to the output *current* wave and is defined in Figure 6.11.

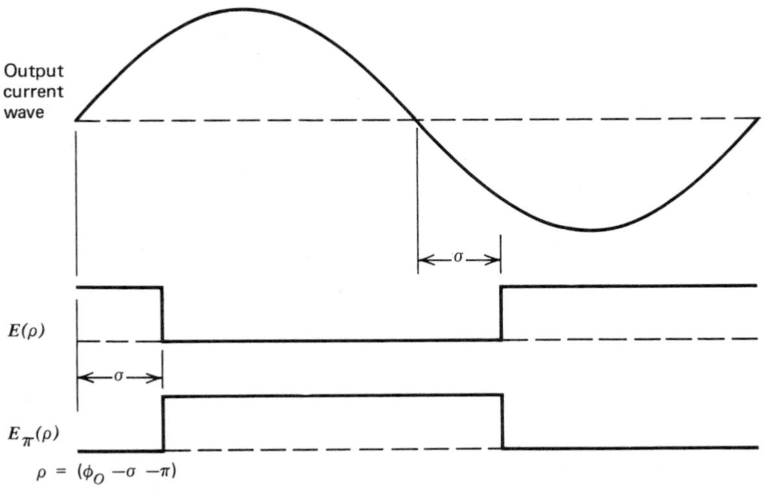

Figure 6.11 Waveforms defining the control angle σ of the CDFFC.

TABLE 6.1. Normalized Amplitudes of Unwanted Components with Frequencies of $3f_I \pm 2nf_O$, in the Output Voltage of the NCC and the CDFFC with Sinusoidal Mean Voltage

	$3f_i \pm 2nf_O$																	
	$\rho = 0°, 180°$								$\rho = \pm 30°, \pm 150°$									
$2n\rightarrow$	0	2	4	6	8	10	12	14	0	2 (black)	2 (white)	4 (black)	4 (white)	6	8	10	12	14
$r\downarrow$																		
1.0	0.318	0.272	0.164	0.064	0.021	0.015	0.009	0.007	0.179	0.333	0.167	0.279	0.134	0.095	0.062	0.044	0.037	0.031
0.9	0.394	0.283	0.137	0.048	0.020	0.013	0.008	0.006	0.264	0.362	0.207	0.237	0.138	0.086	0.058	0.044	0.036	0.030
0.8	0.470	0.276	0.112	0.038	0.018	0.011	0.007	0.005	0.354	0.364	0.229	0.197	0.133	0.079	0.054	0.042	0.034	0.029
0.7	0.538	0.257	0.090	0.031	0.015	0.009	0.006	0.005	0.438	0.348	0.235	0.162	0.122	0.071	0.050	0.038	0.032	0.027
0.6	0.596	0.230	0.071	0.025	0.013	0.008	0.005	0.004	0.516	0.317	0.229	0.131	0.108	0.063	0.044	0.035	0.028	0.024
0.5	0.644	0.199	0.055	0.020	0.011	0.007	0.004	0.003	0.584	0.028	0.212	0.103	0.092	0.054	0.038	0.030	0.025	0.021
0.4	0.632	0.163	0.040	0.015	0.008	0.005	0.004	0.003	0.642	0.227	0.184	0.079	0.074	0.044	0.031	0.025	0.020	0.017
0.3	0.712	0.125	0.028	0.011	0.006	0.004	0.003	0.002	0.689	0.173	0.148	0.057	0.056	0.033	0.024	0.019	0.016	0.013
0.2	0.734	0.084	0.018	0.007	0.004	0.003	0.002	0.001	0.722	0.116	0.104	0.037	0.037	0.023	0.016	0.013	0.011	0.009
0.1	0.746	0.042	0.009	0.004	0.002	0.001	0.001	0.001	0.743	0.057	0.054	0.019	0.019	0.011	0.008	0.007	0.005	0.005

	$3f_i \pm 2nf_O$																			
	$\rho = \pm 60°, \pm 120°$										$\rho = \pm 90°$									
$2n\rightarrow$	0	2 (black)	2 (white)	4 (black)	4 (white)	6	8	10	12	14	0	2 (black)	2 (white)	4 (black)	4 (white)	6	8	10	12	14
$r\downarrow$																				
1.0	0.020	0.486	0.020	0.269	0.019	0.017	0.016	0.014	0.012	0.010	0.000	0.500	0.000	0.250	0.000	0.000	0.000	0.000	0.000	0.000
0.9	0.081	0.540	0.063	0.210	0.049	0.038	0.030	0.024	0.020	0.017	0.027	0.579	0.020	0.149	0.015	0.012	0.010	0.008	0.007	0.006
0.8	0.167	0.554	0.110	0.167	0.075	0.054	0.041	0.033	0.028	0.024	0.097	0.613	0.062	0.059	0.043	0.032	0.026	0.021	0.018	0.015
0.7	0.267	0.536	0.151	0.141	0.094	0.065	0.049	0.039	0.033	0.028	0.195	0.604	0.109	0.011	0.071	0.051	0.039	0.032	0.027	0.023
0.6	0.372	0.491	0.180	0.126	0.104	0.070	0.052	0.042	0.035	0.030	0.307	0.561	0.150	0.059	0.091	0.063	0.048	0.039	0.032	0.028
0.5	0.474	0.426	0.193	0.113	0.104	0.069	0.051	0.041	0.034	0.029	0.422	0.490	0.177	0.085	0.101	0.068	0.052	0.041	0.034	0.030
0.4	0.566	0.347	0.189	0.099	0.096	0.062	0.046	0.037	0.031	0.026	0.529	0.399	0.185	0.092	0.099	0.066	0.049	0.039	0.033	0.029
0.3	0.642	0.260	0.167	0.080	0.079	0.051	0.038	0.030	0.025	0.021	0.621	0.298	0.171	0.084	0.086	0.056	0.042	0.033	0.028	0.024
0.2	0.701	0.169	0.127	0.057	0.056	0.036	0.027	0.021	0.018	0.015	0.691	0.193	0.135	0.063	0.063	0.041	0.030	0.024	0.020	0.017
0.1	0.738	0.081	0.071	0.029	0.029	0.019	0.014	0.011	0.009	0.008	0.735	0.092	0.077	0.033	0.033	0.021	0.016	0.013	0.011	0.009

Notes: 1. Tables show amplitude of component as per-unit value of $v_{O\max}$.
2. These components are present in the output voltage of three-pulse circuits.
3. Where there is only one column for a given value of $2n$, the values given apply to both the $3f_I + 2nf_O$ and $3f_I - 2nf_O$ components.
4. Where there are two columns for a given value of $2n$:
The values given in the "black" column apply to the $3f_I + 2nf_O$ components for positive ρ, and to the $3f_I - 2nf_O$ components for negative ρ.
The values given in the "white" column apply to the $3f_I + 2nf_O$ components for negative ρ, and to the $3f_I - 2nf_O$ components for positive ρ.

TABLE 6.2. Normalized Amplitudes of Unwanted Components with Frequencies of $6f_I \pm (2n+1)f_O$, in the Output Voltage of the NCC and the CDFFC with Sinusoidal Mean Voltage

$6f_I \pm (2n+1)f_O$

$\rho = 0°, 180°$

$(2n+1)\rightarrow$ / $r\downarrow$	1	3	5	7	9	11	13	15
1.0	0.006	0.055	0.105	0.100	0.055	0.026	0.022	0.017
0.9	0.036	0.097	0.117	0.081	0.041	0.026	0.020	0.017
0.8	0.069	0.123	0.111	0.065	0.035	0.023	0.021	0.017
0.7	0.101	0.136	0.098	0.053	0.032	0.023	0.019	0.016
0.6	0.130	0.138	0.084	0.045	0.029	0.022	0.018	0.015
0.5	0.156	0.132	0.071	0.040	0.027	0.021	0.018	0.015
0.4	0.178	0.120	0.060	0.036	0.026	0.021	0.017	0.015
0.3	0.196	0.105	0.052	0.034	0.025	0.020	0.017	0.015
0.2	0.208	0.090	0.047	0.032	0.025	0.020	0.017	0.015
0.1	0.216	0.078	0.044	0.031	0.024	0.020	0.017	0.015

$\rho = \pm 30°, \pm 150°$

$(2n+1)\rightarrow$ / $r\downarrow$	1 (black)	1 (white)	3 (black)	3 (white)	5 (black)	5 (white)	7 (black)	7 (white)	9	11	13	15
1.0	0.018	0.018	0.045	0.045	0.150	0.058	0.136	0.055	0.042	0.027	0.018	0.015
0.9	0.024	0.057	0.107	0.079	0.163	0.071	0.096	0.051	0.033	0.022	0.017	0.014
0.8	0.042	0.100	0.158	0.096	0.145	0.067	0.064	0.041	0.026	0.019	0.012	0.011
0.7	0.097	0.130	0.183	0.095	0.114	0.055	0.041	0.030	0.018	0.013	0.010	0.008
0.6	0.162	0.142	0.185	0.081	0.081	0.040	0.024	0.020	0.011	0.008	0.006	0.004
0.5	0.221	0.134	0.168	0.062	0.053	0.027	0.014	0.013	0.008	0.005	0.004	0.003
0.4	0.266	0.112	0.140	0.049	0.036	0.025	0.015	0.015	0.011	0.008	0.007	0.006
0.3	0.288	0.098	0.109	0.052	0.033	0.031	0.021	0.021	0.016	0.013	0.011	0.009
0.2	0.286	0.117	0.084	0.063	0.038	0.038	0.026	0.026	0.020	0.017	0.014	0.012
0.1	0.262	0.165	0.074	0.071	0.042	0.042	0.030	0.030	0.023	0.019	0.016	0.014

$6f_i \pm (2n+1)f_O$,

$\rho = \pm 60°, \pm 120°$

$(2n+1)\rightarrow$ / $r\downarrow$	1 (black)	1 (white)	3 (black)	3 (white)	5 (black)	5 (white)	7 (black)	7 (white)	9	11	13	15
1.0	0.023	0.023	0.022	0.022	0.181	0.021	0.151	0.019	0.016	0.014	0.011	0.009
0.9	0.072	0.052	0.097	0.037	0.209	0.025	0.085	0.017	0.012	0.009	0.007	0.005
0.8	0.087	0.045	0.183	0.026	0.188	0.016	0.036	0.011	0.008	0.006	0.004	0.003
0.7	0.065	0.045	0.238	0.036	0.147	0.027	0.017	0.021	0.016	0.013	0.011	0.010
0.6	0.088	0.083	0.247	0.058	0.103	0.039	0.025	0.028	0.022	0.018	0.015	0.013
0.5	0.174	0.112	0.213	0.063	0.066	0.038	0.025	0.026	0.020	0.016	0.013	0.012
0.4	0.260	0.109	0.152	0.047	0.032	0.025	0.016	0.016	0.012	0.009	0.008	0.007
0.3	0.316	0.071	0.084	0.020	0.007	0.008	0.004	0.004	0.002	0.002	0.001	0.001
0.2	0.327	0.047	0.046	0.032	0.021	0.022	0.016	0.016	0.012	0.010	0.009	0.008
0.1	0.291	0.126	0.062	0.061	0.038	0.038	0.027	0.027	0.021	0.017	0.015	0.013

$\rho = \pm 90°$

$(2n+1)\rightarrow$ / $r\downarrow$	1 (black)	1 (white)	3 (black)	3 (white)	5 (black)	5 (white)	7 (black)	7 (white)	9	11	13	15
1.0	0.000	0.000	0.000	0.000	0.200	0.000	0.143	0.000	0.000	0.000	0.000	0.000
0.9	0.039	0.027	0.059	0.020	0.246	0.016	0.056	0.012	0.010	0.009	0.007	0.006
0.8	0.081	0.043	0.174	0.026	0.200	0.017	0.018	0.012	0.009	0.006	0.008	0.006
0.7	0.067	0.015	0.266	0.002	0.117	0.002	0.015	0.003	0.003	0.003	0.002	0.002
0.6	0.010	0.039	0.298	0.032	0.041	0.025	0.023	0.019	0.015	0.012	0.010	0.010
0.5	0.123	0.088	0.265	0.054	0.007	0.036	0.028	0.027	0.021	0.017	0.015	0.013
0.4	0.235	0.104	0.186	0.051	0.020	0.031	0.022	0.022	0.016	0.014	0.011	0.010
0.3	0.313	0.072	0.090	0.023	0.008	0.011	0.007	0.007	0.005	0.004	0.003	0.003
0.2	0.337	0.005	0.003	0.019	0.015	0.015	0.011	0.011	0.009	0.007	0.006	0.005
0.1	0.301	0.110	0.054	0.057	0.036	0.036	0.026	0.026	0.020	0.016	0.014	0.012

Notes: 1. Tables show amplitude of component as per-unit value of $V_{O\max}$.
2. These components are present in the output voltage of three- and six-pulse circuits.
3. Where there is only one column for a given value of $(2n+1)$, the values given apply to both the $6f_I + (2n+1)f_O$ and $6f_I - (2n+1)f_O$ components.
4. Where there are two values for a given value of $(2n+1)$:
The values given in the "black" column apply to the $6f_I + (2n+1)f_O$ components for positive ρ, and to the $6f_I - (2n+1)f_O$ components for negative ρ.
The values given in the "white" column apply to the $6f_I + (2n+1)f_O$ components for negative ρ, and to the $6f_I - (2n+1)f_O$ components for positive ρ.

TABLE 6.3. Normalized Amplitudes of Unwanted Components with Frequencies of $12f_I \pm (2n+1)f_O$, in the Output Voltage of the NCC and the CDFFC with Sinusoidal Mean Voltage

	$12f_I \pm (2n+1)f_O$																								
	$\rho = 0°, 180°$									$\rho = \pm 30°, \pm 150°$															
$(2n+1)\rightarrow$	1	3	5	7	9	11	13	15	17	1		3		5		7		9		11		13		15	17
$r\downarrow$										■	□	■	□	■	□	■	□	■	□	■	□	■	□		
1.0	0.002	0.001	0.007	0.005	0.027	0.050	0.049	0.027	0.011	0.002	0.002	0.003	0.003	0.002	0.002	0.010	0.010	0.020	0.020	0.072	0.027	0.069	0.026	0.020	0.012
0.9	0.011	0.016	0.010	0.031	0.053	0.049	0.030	0.016	0.011	0.017	0.015	0.006	0.007	0.025	0.023	0.014	0.033	0.069	0.033	0.071	0.026	0.034	0.018	0.012	0.008
0.8	0.022	0.021	0.029	0.052	0.053	0.036	0.020	0.013	0.009	0.025	0.011	0.030	0.031	0.017	0.040	0.061	0.036	0.079	0.026	0.045	0.017	0.015	0.010	0.007	0.005
0.7	0.029	0.027	0.050	0.057	0.043	0.025	0.015	0.011	0.008	0.017	0.035	0.042	0.044	0.036	0.038	0.085	0.028	0.062	0.019	0.024	0.012	0.008	0.008	0.006	0.004
0.6	0.035	0.045	0.061	0.051	0.032	0.018	0.012	0.009	0.008	0.039	0.044	0.030	0.043	0.074	0.035	0.080	0.026	0.040	0.018	0.015	0.012	0.009	0.009	0.008	0.006
0.5	0.043	0.061	0.061	0.041	0.023	0.014	0.011	0.009	0.007	0.044	0.049	0.055	0.050	0.085	0.038	0.057	0.026	0.024	0.017	0.013	0.012	0.010	0.010	0.008	0.007
0.4	0.057	0.071	0.056	0.030	0.017	0.012	0.010	0.008	0.007	0.045	0.070	0.088	0.055	0.072	0.036	0.031	0.019	0.013	0.012	0.009	0.009	0.007	0.007	0.006	0.005
0.3	0.075	0.070	0.041	0.022	0.014	0.011	0.009	0.008	0.007	0.090	0.079	0.092	0.042	0.039	0.020	0.012	0.010	0.006	0.006	0.004	0.004	0.003	0.003	0.002	0.002
0.2	0.091	0.059	0.029	0.018	0.013	0.010	0.009	0.007	0.006	0.134	0.060	0.069	0.025	0.018	0.012	0.007	0.007	0.005	0.005	0.004	0.004	0.003	0.003	0.003	0.002
0.1	0.103	0.044	0.023	0.016	0.012	0.010	0.008	0.007	0.006	0.142	0.058	0.041	0.031	0.018	0.018	0.013	0.013	0.010	0.010	0.008	0.008	0.007	0.007	0.006	0.005

$12f_I \pm (2n+1)f_O$

	$\rho = \pm 60°, \pm 120°$															
$(2n+1)\rightarrow$	1		3		5		7		9		11		13		15	17
$r\downarrow$	black	white	black	white	black	white	black	white	black	white	black	white	black	white		
1.0	0.001	0.001	0.003	0.003	0.005	0.005	0.007	0.006	0.008	0.008	0.085	0.008	0.078	0.008	0.007	0.006
0.9	0.019	0.018	0.017	0.016	0.008	0.013	0.021	0.010	0.078	0.008	0.090	0.006	0.022	0.005	0.004	0.003
0.8	0.020	0.024	0.017	0.023	0.036	0.019	0.046	0.015	0.102	0.012	0.048	0.009	0.004	0.007	0.006	0.005
0.7	0.043	0.032	0.044	0.022	0.013	0.014	0.103	0.009	0.069	0.006	0.011	0.004	0.003	0.003	0.002	0.002
0.6	0.031	0.029	0.049	0.025	0.074	0.019	0.102	0.015	0.030	0.011	0.007	0.009	0.008	0.007	0.006	0.006
0.5	0.062	0.047	0.041	0.030	0.108	0.019	0.058	0.012	0.009	0.008	0.006	0.006	0.005	0.005	0.004	0.004
0.4	0.064	0.030	0.109	0.017	0.094	0.008	0.014	0.008	0.005	0.006	0.005	0.005	0.004	0.004	0.003	0.003
0.3	0.051	0.050	0.126	0.033	0.051	0.022	0.013	0.016	0.012	0.012	0.010	0.010	0.008	0.008	0.007	0.006
0.2	0.130	0.058	0.076	0.025	0.017	0.013	0.008	0.008	0.006	0.006	0.005	0.005	0.004	0.004	0.004	0.003
0.1	0.161	0.023	0.023	0.016	0.010	0.010	0.008	0.008	0.006	0.006	0.005	0.005	0.004	0.004	0.004	0.003

$12f_I \pm (2n+1)f_O$

	$\rho = \pm 90°$															
$(2n+1)\rightarrow$	1		3		5		7		9		11		13		15	17
$r\downarrow$	black	white	black	white	black	white	black	white	black	white	black	white	black	white		
1.0	0.000	0.000	0.000	0.000	0.000	0.000	0.000	0.000	0.000	0.000	0.091	0.000	0.077	0.000	0.000	0.000
0.9	0.002	0.003	0.002	0.004	0.012	0.004	0.035	0.003	0.087	0.003	0.086	0.003	0.022	0.002	0.002	0.002
0.8	0.018	0.010	0.032	0.005	0.051	0.003	0.050	0.002	0.106	0.001	0.038	0.001	0.005	0.001	0.000	0.000
0.7	0.027	0.022	0.023	0.017	0.017	0.013	0.122	0.010	0.055	0.008	0.019	0.007	0.005	0.006	0.005	0.004
0.6	0.029	0.011	0.066	0.003	0.093	0.000	0.092	0.001	0.026	0.001	0.002	0.001	0.001	0.001	0.001	0.001
0.5	0.035	0.031	0.000	0.023	0.139	0.017	0.033	0.013	0.017	0.010	0.008	0.008	0.007	0.007	0.006	0.005
0.4	0.066	0.028	0.114	0.012	0.091	0.002	0.011	0.004	0.004	0.003	0.002	0.002	0.002	0.002	0.001	0.001
0.3	0.003	0.003	0.155	0.022	0.015	0.016	0.015	0.012	0.010	0.010	0.008	0.008	0.007	0.007	0.006	0.005
0.2	0.117	0.056	0.093	0.027	0.011	0.016	0.012	0.011	0.009	0.009	0.007	0.007	0.006	0.006	0.005	0.005
0.1	0.166	0.000	0.002	0.009	0.007	0.007	0.005	0.005	0.004	0.004	0.003	0.003	0.003	0.003	0.003	0.002

Notes: 1. Tables show amplitude of component as per-unit value of $V_{O\max}$.

2. These components are present in the output voltage of three-, six-, and twelve-pulse circuits.

3. Where there is only one column for a given value of $(2n+1)$, the values given apply to both the $12f_I + (2n+1)f_O$ and $12f_I - (2n+1)f_O$ components.

4. Where there are two columns for a given value of $(2n+1)$:
The values given in the "black" column apply to the $12f_I + (2n+1)f_O$ components for positive ρ, and to the $12f_I - (2n+1)f_O$ components for negative ρ.
The values given in the "white" column apply to the $12f_I + (2n+1)f_O$ components for negative ρ, and to the $12f_I - (2n+1)f_O$ components for positive ρ.

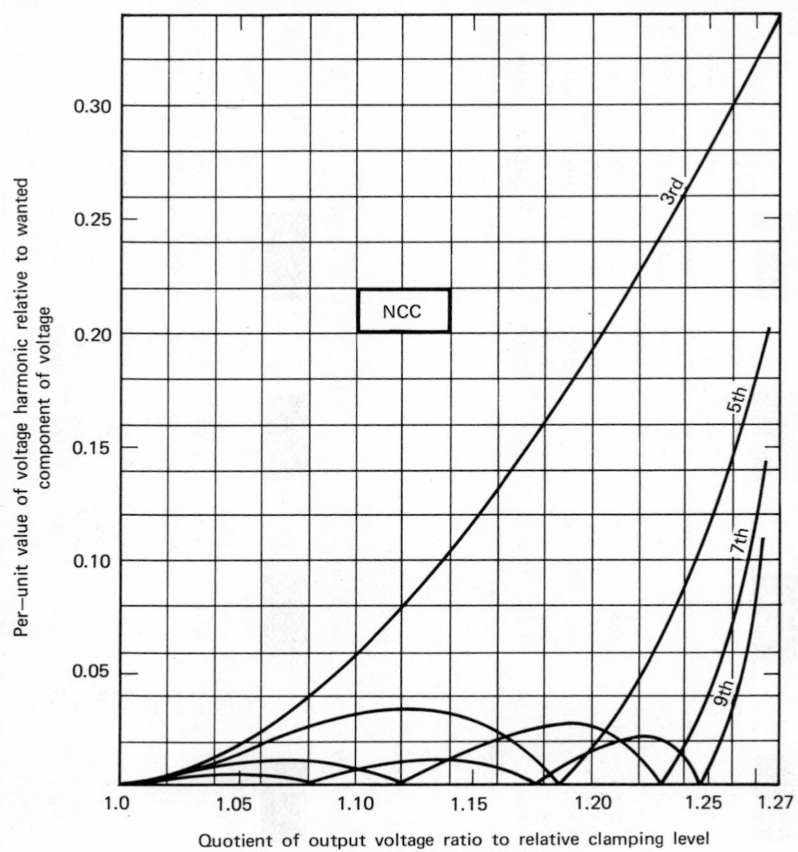

Figure 6.12 Relationships between harmonics in the output voltage and r/c for the NCC with pseudotrapesoidal mean output voltage.

The relationship between the waveform switching angle, ρ, the control angle, σ, and the displacement angle, ϕ_O, of the output current of the CDFFC, is as follows:

$$\rho = (\phi_O - \sigma - \pi) \tag{6.19}$$

6.3.5 The NCC with Trapezoidal Mean Output Voltage

With reference to Figure 6.2, if κ is greater than c, the frequency changer produces a pseudotrapezoidal mean output voltage waveshape.

In this mode, unwanted components whose frequencies are direct integral harmonics of the output frequency are produced, in addition to the beat frequency components already discussed. The relationships between the per unit amplitudes of the principal harmonic components produced in this operating mode and the output voltage ratio are shown in Figure 6.12.

6.4 THE INPUT CURRENT—GENERAL CONSIDERATIONS

The frequency changer in its basic form consists of an array of switches that link the a-c source directly to the output terminals. The basic operating principle is to construct an output waveform with the wanted frequency by closing and opening the switches according to some specified program. Thus, unlike other types of frequency converter—for example, a motor-generator set, or a rectifier-inverter with an intermediate d-c filter—there are basically no energy storage elements within the system. Thus the process of energy transfer through the frequency changer is direct, and it is inherent that *the net instantaneous power at the input terminals must always be equal to the net instantaneous power at the output terminals* (assuming that the losses in the switches themselves can be neglected).

The input current wave of the frequency changer has the following basic properties:

1. The amplitude of the fundamental real component of current is strictly a function of the average power delivered at the output, independent of the type of frequency changer. The amplitude of the real component of current of a group of frequency changers supplying three- (or multi-) phase outputs is the sum of the in-phase components of the individual circuits.

2. A fundamental quadrature component of input current may or may not exist, depending upon the type of frequency changer.

The UDFFC does not have a quadrature input current under any circumstances. The amplitude and sign of the quadrature input current of the CDFFC is controllable within certain limits. The UFC, SSFC, and NCC have quadrature components of input current, the amplitudes of which are a function of the output load and the relative output voltage.

The input displacement angle of the UFC is always equal, but of opposite sign, to that of the output load; that of the SSFC is the same as that of the load, and the input displacement angle of the NCC is invariably lagging.

The net quadrature component of current of a group of frequency changers supplying three- or multiphase output is the sum of the quadrature components of the individual circuits.

3. Any frequency changer supplying a single-phase output has extrabasal components of input current *of substantial amplitude* with frequencies of $f_I \pm 2f_O$, except the UFC and SSFC, which have only the $f_I + 2f_O$ and $f_I - 2f_O$ components, respectively. A component with frequency $|f_I - 2f_O|$ is potentially objectionable, since within the normal operating range of the frequency changer this frequency is less than the input frequency. Indeed, at $f_O = \frac{1}{2}f_I$, this frequency is zero—which indicates that a substantial direct component of current is obtained at this operating point.

With a balanced three-phase output, these pulse-number-independent extrabasal components are absent from the net input current wave. Thus a frequency changer with a balanced three-phase output constitutes a much more "normal" load on the input source, inasmuch as its input current is free of the most objectionable extrabasal components.

4. Additional pulse-number-dependent families of generally nonsynchronous extrabasal components of input current are obtained. The presence or absence of specific components depends on the type of frequency changer, the circuit pulse number, and the number of output phases. In general, the higher the circuit pulse number and the number of output phases, the fewer of these components are present.

6.5 DEFINITION OF BASIC INPUT PARAMETERS

6.5.1 Input Displacement Angle

The input displacement angle ϕ_I is the angle between the input voltage and the corresponding *fundamental* component of input current.

6.5.2 Input Displacement Factor

The input displacement factor is the cosine of the input displacement angle:

$$\cos\phi_I = \frac{I_{IR}}{\sqrt{I_{IR}^2 + I_{IQ}^2}} \tag{6.20}$$

where I_{IR} is the real component of input current and I_{IQ} is the quadrature component of input current.

6.5.3 Input Distortion Factor

The input distortion factor μ is the ratio of the r.m.s. value of the fundamental component of input current $I_{IF,RMS}$ to r.m.s. value of the total input current wave, $I_{I,RMS}$:

$$\mu = \frac{I_{IF,RMS}}{I_{I,RMS}} \tag{6.21}$$

6.5.4 Input Power Factor

The input power factor λ is the ratio of the input power to the total r.m.s. input volt amperes. Thus:

$$\lambda = \frac{V_{I,RMS}I_{IF,RMS}\cos\phi_I}{V_{I,RMS}I_{I,RMS}}$$

$$= \mu\cos\phi_I \tag{6.22}$$

6.6 THE FUNDAMENTAL COMPONENT OF INPUT CURRENT

6.6.1 The Real Component of Input Current

As stated in section 6.4, the real component of current at the input of the frequency changer is strictly proportional to the average power output and is independent of the type of frequency changer. Thus, for all frequency changers a universal relationship exists between the amplitude of the real component of input current, the amplitude and displacement angle of the output current, and the output voltage ratio:

$$I_{IR} = p\cdot S\cdot r\frac{\sqrt{3}}{2\pi}I_O\cos\phi_O \tag{6.23}$$

where p = number of output phases, and S = number of three-pulse groups connected in series in each output phase, as in expression (6.1).

This relationship assumes that all output phases are balanced.

If we define the real component of input current obtained at $r = 1.0$, $\phi_O = 0$ with a given output current, I_O, as having 1 per-unit value, then the per-unit real component of input current, $I_{IR,PU}$, with any other values of r and ϕ_O, with the same output current I_O, is given by:

$$I_{IR,PU} = r\cos\phi_O \tag{6.24}$$

The universal relationships between $I_{IR,PU}$, ϕ_O, and r for all frequency changers are shown graphically in Figure 6.13.

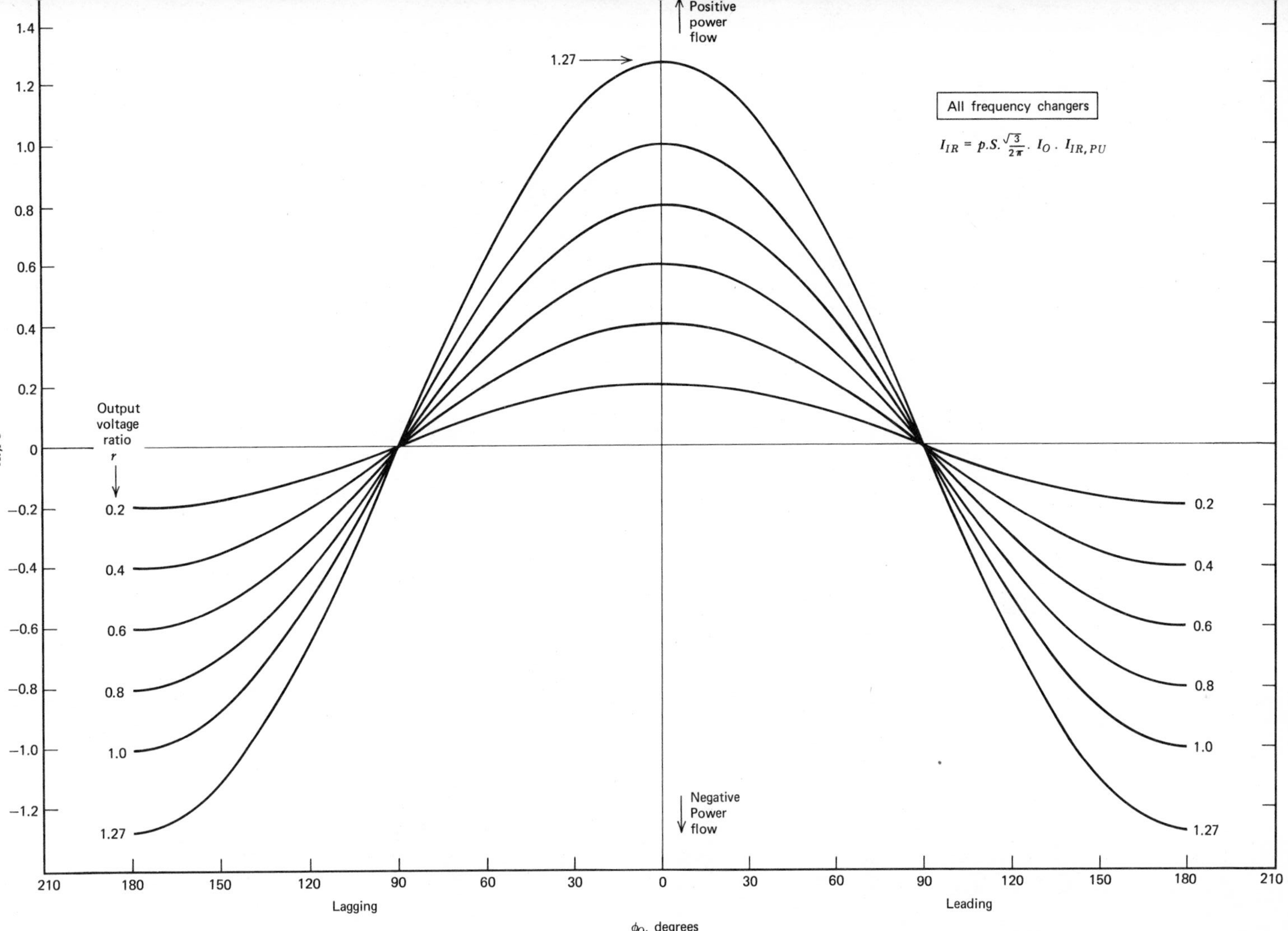

Figure 6.13 Universal relationships between per-unit real component of input current $I_{IR,PU}$, output displacement angle ϕ_O, and output voltage ratio r, for all frequency changers.

From equations (6.23) and (6.24), the relationship between the absolute value of the real component of input current, I_{IR} and the per-unit value, $I_{IR,PU}$, is thus:

$$I_{IR} = p \cdot S \cdot \frac{\sqrt{3}}{2\pi} \cdot I_O \cdot I_{IR,PU} \tag{6.25}$$

6.6.2 The Quadrature Component of Input Current

As stated in Section 6.4, all types of frequency changers except the UDFFC generally draw a fundamental quadrature component of input current.

In the following sections, the relationships between the quadrature component of input current and the operating parameters on which it depends are presented for each type of frequency changer.

The *per unit quadrature input current*, $I_{IQ,PU}$ is defined as the ratio of the amplitude of the quadrature input current for given values of r, ϕ_O, and I_O to the amplitude of *the real component of current for* $r = 1.0$ *and* $\phi_O = 0°$, for the same given value of I_O.

The relationship between the absolute value of the quadrature component of input current, I_{IQ} and the per unit value, $I_{IQ,PU}$ is thus:

$$I_{IQ} = p \cdot S \cdot \frac{\sqrt{3}}{2\pi} \cdot I_O \cdot I_{IQ,PU} \tag{6.26}$$

where p is the number of output phases, and S is the number of three-pulse groups connected in series in each output phase.

6.6.2.1 *The UFC and SSFC.* The quadrature component of input current of the UFC and SSFC is directly proportional to the quadrature component of output current and to the output voltage ratio. For the UFC, however, a lagging displacement angle at the output is reflected as a leading displacement angle at the input, and vice versa, whereas for the SSFC the input displacement angle has the same sign as the output load angle.

The relationships between the per-unit quadrature input current and the output displacement angle for various values of output voltage ratio are shown graphically in Figure 6.14 for both the UFC and SSFC. These relationships apply to control of the output voltage both by pulse-width modulation and by phase shift between two individual circuit groups.

The corresponding relationship between the input displacement angle, ϕ_I, and the output displacement angle, ϕ_O, is shown in Figure 6.15.

6.6.2.2 *The UDFFC.* As explained previously, the UDFFC has no component of quadrature current at the input under any operating conditions.

6.6.2.3 *The CDFFC.* The CDFFC has the unique property that the amplitude of the quadrature component of input current can be controlled, within certain limits, by adjustment of the control angle, σ, defined in Figure 6.11. The limits of variation of the amplitude of the per-unit quadrature component of input current as a function of the output displacement angle and the output voltage ratio are illustrated graphically in Figure 6.16.

For any given output displacement angle, the amplitude of the quadrature component of input current can be adjusted between equal limits in the lagging and leading directions. These limits actually are between the lagging quadrature component obtained with the NCC and an equal leading component; for example, if

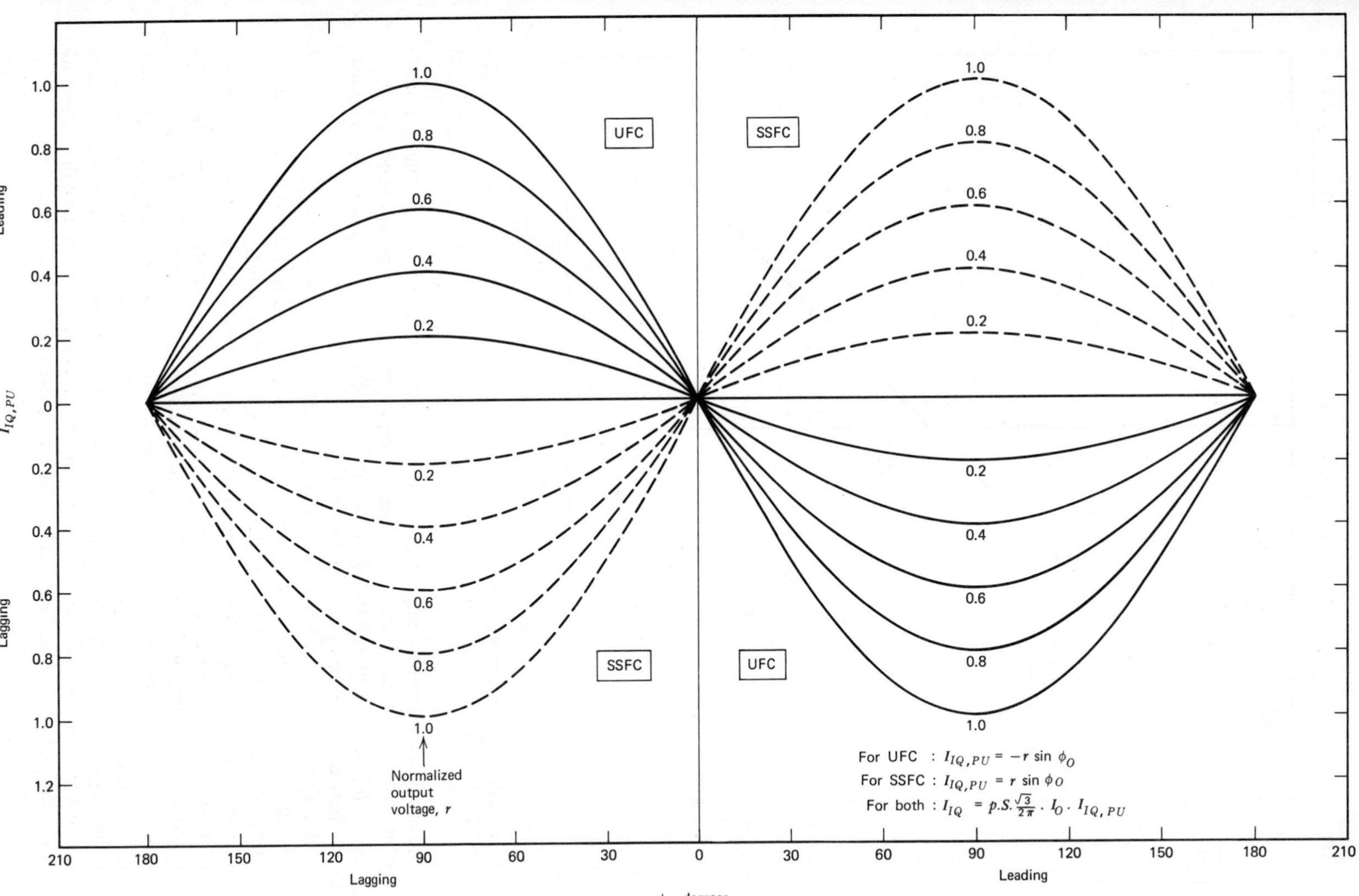

Figure 6.14 Relationships between per-unit quadrature component of input current $I_{IQ,PU}$, output displacement angle ϕ_O, and output voltage ratio r, for the UFC and SSFC. Applicable to both pulse-width modulation and phase-shift control of the output voltage.

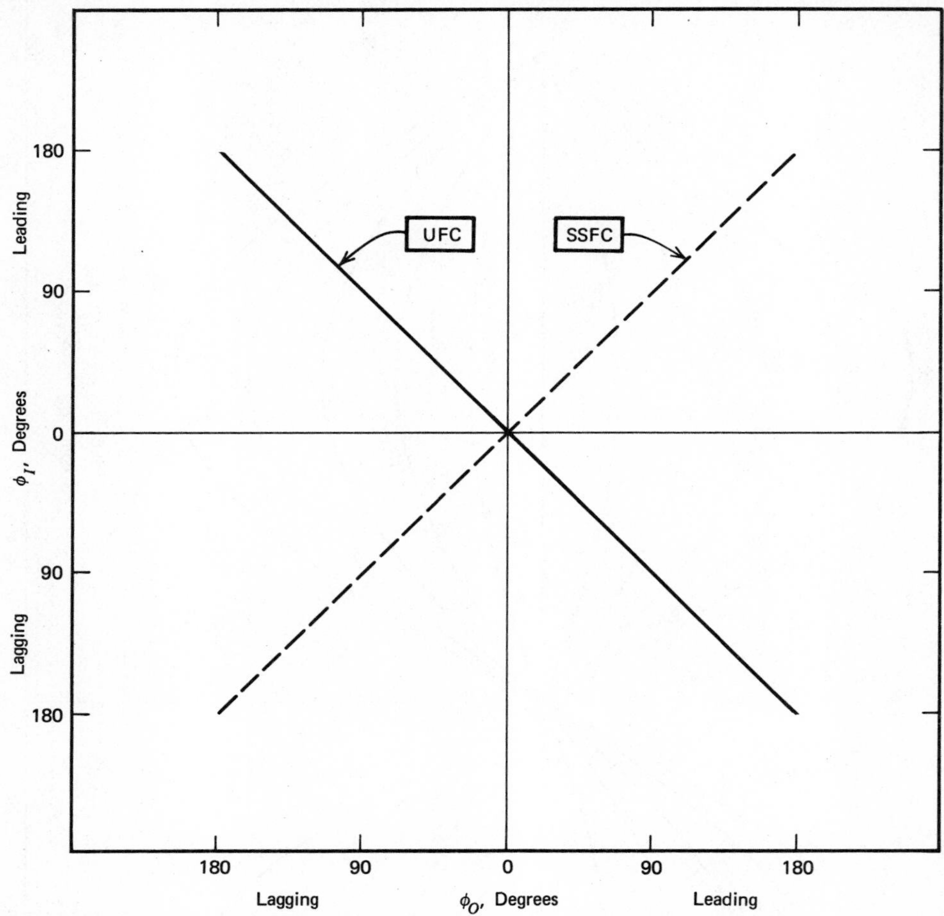

Figure 6.15 Relationships between input displacement angle ϕ_I and output displacement angle ϕ_O for the UFC and SSFC. Applicable to all values of *r*.

the output displacement angle is 0°, and the output voltage ratio is 0.9, the amplitude of the per-unit quadrature component of input current can be adjusted anywhere between 0.83 lagging and 0.83 leading, and with $\phi_O = 90°$, $r = 1.0$, $I_{IQ,PU}$ is adjustable between 1.0 lagging and 1.0 leading.

Relationships between the control angle σ, the input displacement angle ϕ_I, and the output voltage ratio, *r*, are shown in Figures 6.17 and 6.18 for output displacement angles ϕ_O of 0° and 180° and ±45° and ±135°, respectively.

A special case arises when the control is arranged rigidly to produce the positive-type and negative-type output voltage waves, v_O and $v_{O\pi}$, during the positive and negative half-cycles of the wanted output *voltage* wave, respectively (or vice versa), regardless of the output displacement angle. In this case, for a given level of output voltage, the input displacement angle remains fixed regardless of the output displacement angle, as shown graphically in Figure 6.19. The corresponding relationships between the per-unit quadrature component of input current, the output displacement angle, and the output voltage ratio are shown in Figure 6.20.

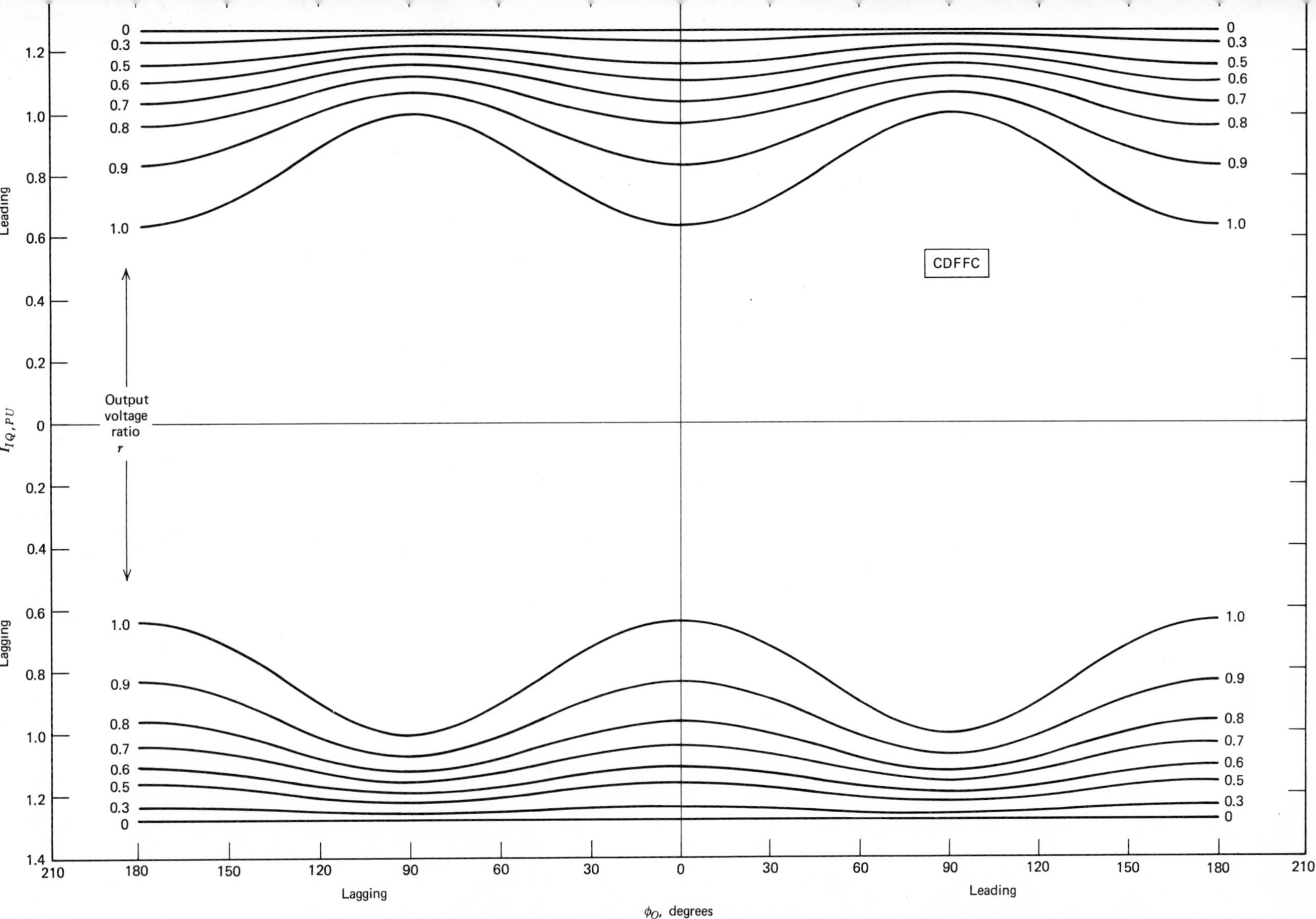

Figure 6.16 Limits of variation of per-unit quadrature component of input current of the CDFFC, as a function of the output displacement angle ϕ_O and the output voltage ratio r. $I_{IQ,PU}$ may lie anywhere between upper and lower curves for that value of r, depending on the control angle σ.

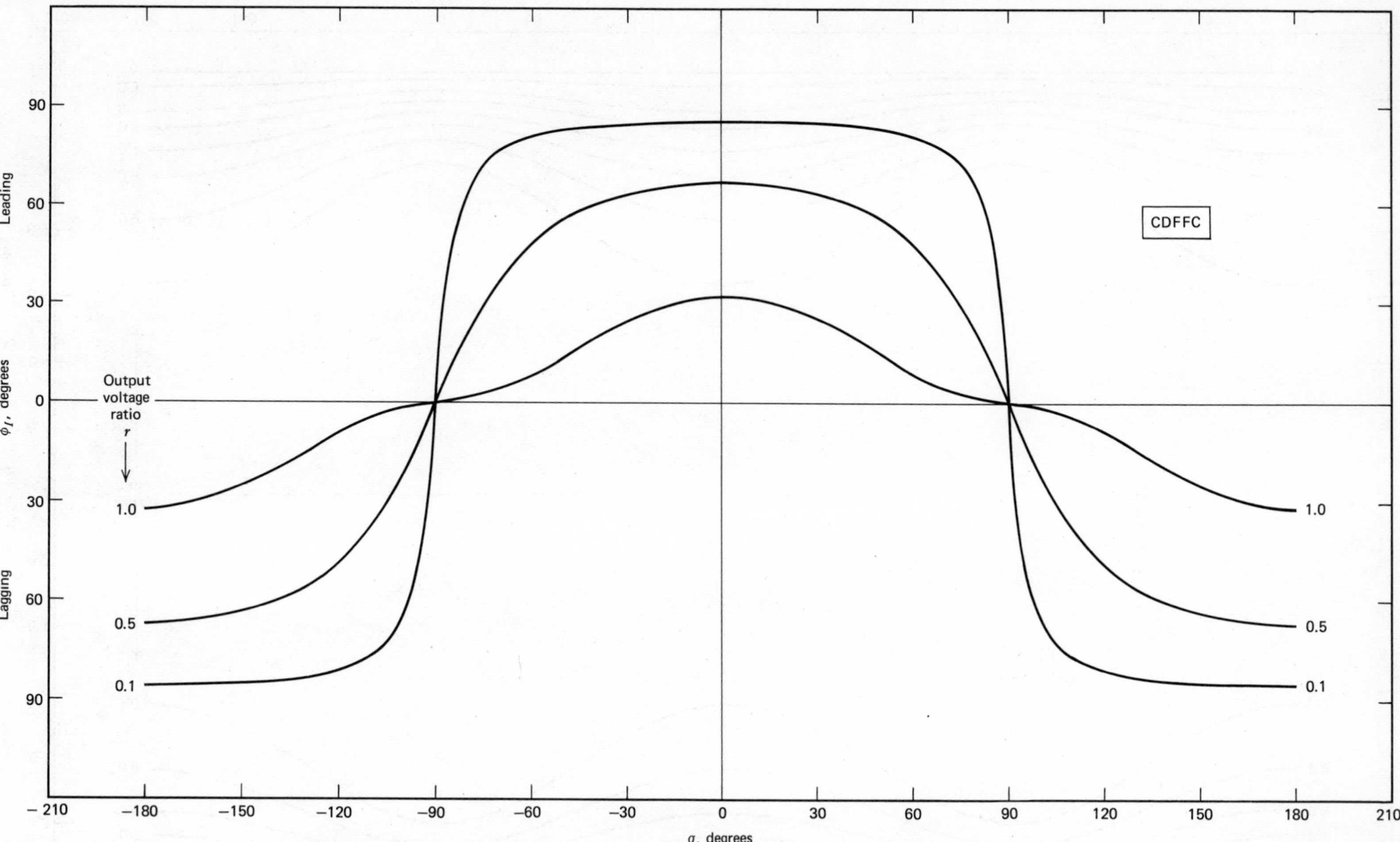

Figure 6.17 Relationships between input displacement angle ϕ_I, control angle σ, and output voltage ratio r, for CDFFC with $\phi_O = 0°$. For $\phi_O = 180°$, ϕ_I is leading/lagging by 180° minus leading/lagging angle given above.

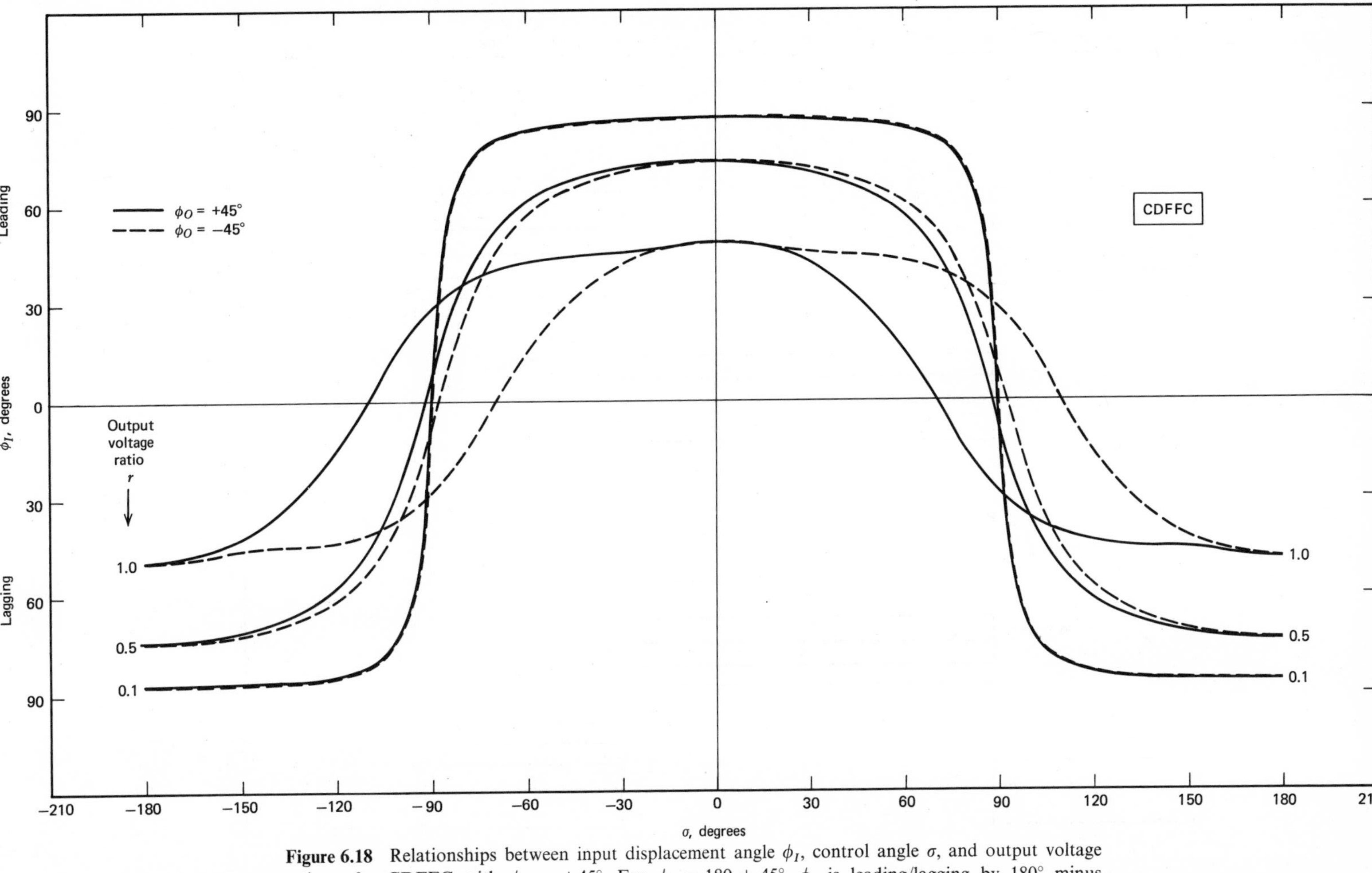

Figure 6.18 Relationships between input displacement angle ϕ_I, control angle σ, and output voltage ratio r, for CDFFC with $\phi_O = \pm 45°$. For $\phi_O = 180 \pm 45°$, ϕ_I is leading/lagging by 180° minus leading/lagging angle given above.

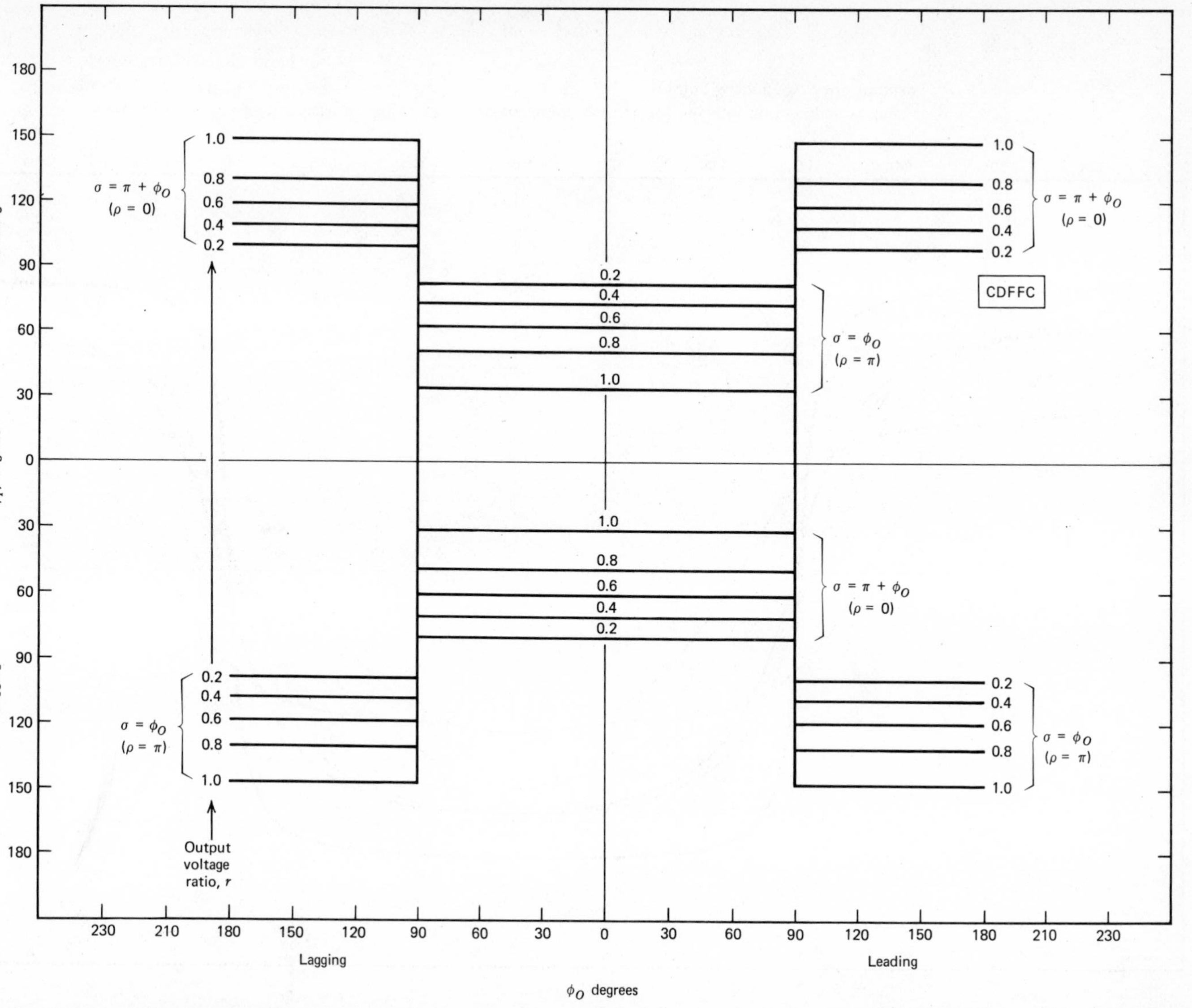
CDFFC
$\sigma = \pi + \phi_O$
$(\rho = 0)$
$\sigma = \phi_O$
$(\rho = \pi)$
Output voltage ratio, r
ϕ_I, degrees
Leading
Lagging
ϕ_O degrees

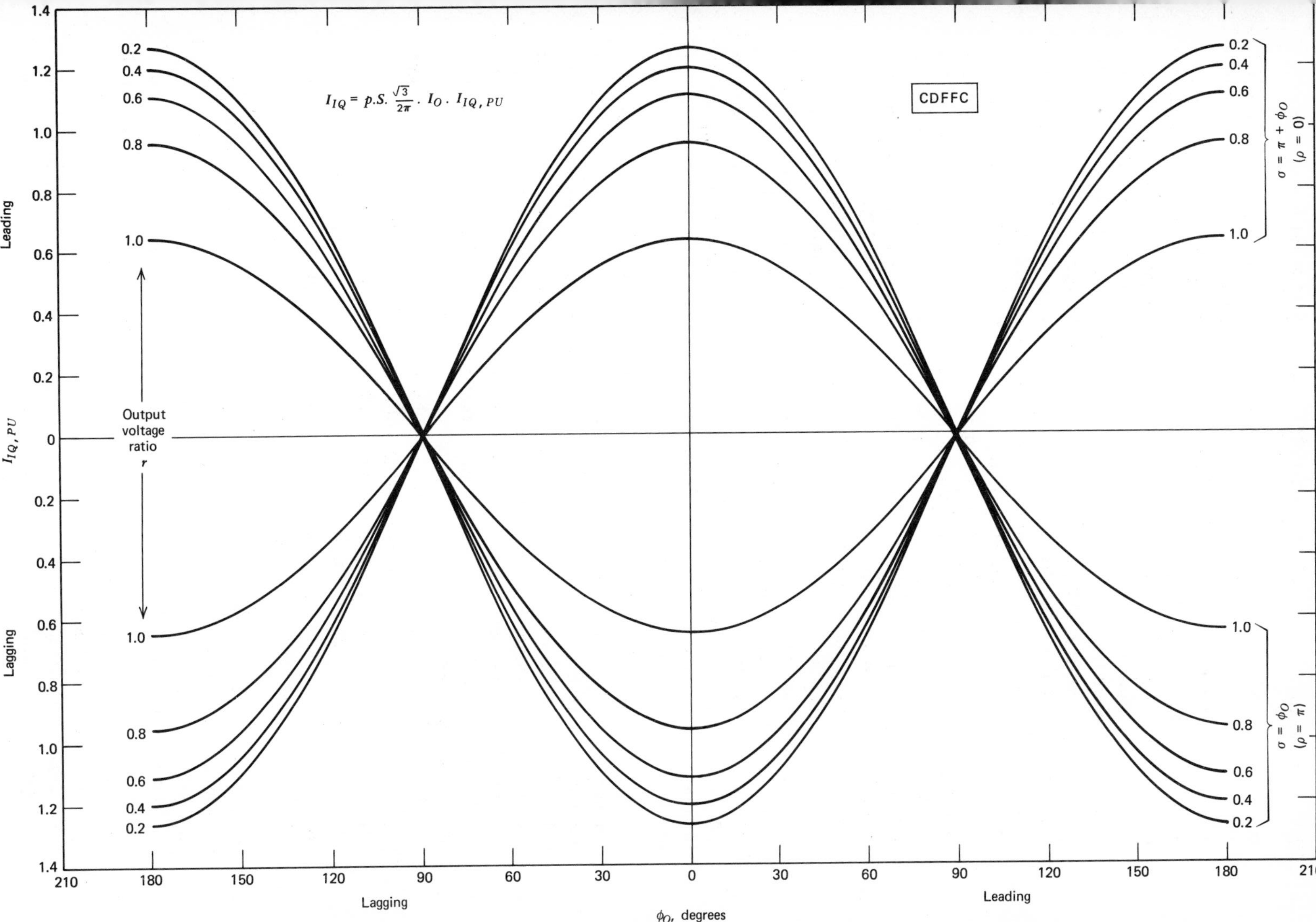

Figure 6.20 Relationships between per-unit quadrature component of input current $I_{IQ,PU}$ output displacement angle ϕ_O, and output voltage ratio r, for CDFFC with $\sigma = \phi_O$ and $\sigma = \pi + \phi_O$.

6.6.2.4 *The NCC with Sinusoidal/Trapezoidal Mean Output Voltage.* The NCC generally draws a lagging quadrature component of current at its input terminals regardless of the output phase angle. Relationships between the per-unit quadrature input current, the output displacement angle, and the output voltage ratio are shown in Figures 6.21–6.23 for values of c of 1.0, 0.95, and 0.9, respectively. (c is the "clamp level" of the reference voltage, as illustrated in Figure 6.2.) The corresponding relationships between the input displacement angle, the output displacement angle, and the normalized output voltage are shown in Figures 6.24–6.26.

It is evident that for any given value of r, the quadrature input current decreases as the output phase angle decreases; but even with no reactive current at the output—that is, with $\phi_O = 0°$—a reactive component of input current still remains. It is also evident that for any given output displacement angle, the quadrature component of input current decreases as the output voltage ratio increases. This is one of the benefits of operating the NCC in the trapezoidal region of operation, that is, with output voltage ratios greater than c. It is of interest to note that for the special condition of maximum square output voltage (Figure 6.21, $r = 1.273$), no quadrature input current is obtained, regardless of the output displacement angle. This, of course, is a theoretical condition that cannot be attained in practice due to the finite commutation margins required, as well to the practical presence of source impedance. Moreover, this condition generally cannot be approximated with any closeness in practice, because the amplitude of the quadrature input current theoretically increases quite steeply as r decreases below the maximum theoretical value. For example, with the maximum value of r (1.21) corresponding to a *clamp level* c of 0.95, the per-unit quadrature input current is already 0.4 for all values of ϕ_O, as shown in Figure 6.22.

6.6.2.5 *The NCC with Square Mean Output Voltage.* Relationships between the per-unit quadrature input current, the output displacement angle, and the output voltage ratio, for the NCC operating with a fully square mean output voltage at all output voltage levels are shown in Figure 6.27. Corresponding curves for sinusoidal and trapezoidal voltage operation, for selected values of the output voltage ratio, are shown superimposed over the curves. Corresponding relationships between the input displacement angle, the output displacement angle, and the output voltage ratio are shown in Figure 6.28.

It is seen that at any given level of output voltage, the amplitude of the quadrature input current with a square mean output voltage is *fixed, regardless of the output displacement angle.* This is a situation different from that with a sinusoidal or trapezoidal voltage, in which the amplitude of the quadrature input current changes with the output displacement angle. As the output voltage ratio increases, the quadrature input current decreases.

It is of interest to note that for any given level of output voltage, the amplitude of the quadrature input current with a square mean output voltage is *higher* than with a sinusoidal/trapezoidal mean output voltage for relatively *small* output displacement angles and *lower* for relatively *large* output displacement angles.

From the viewpoint of minimizing the quadrature component of input current, therefore, operation with a sinusoidal/trapezoidal voltage wave is to be preferred for relatively small output displacement angles, whereas operation with a square voltage is to be preferred for relatively large output displacement angles.

To consider a *practical example*, operation with a sinusoidal/trapezoidal voltage envelope would generally be preferred for a variable speed induction motor drive,

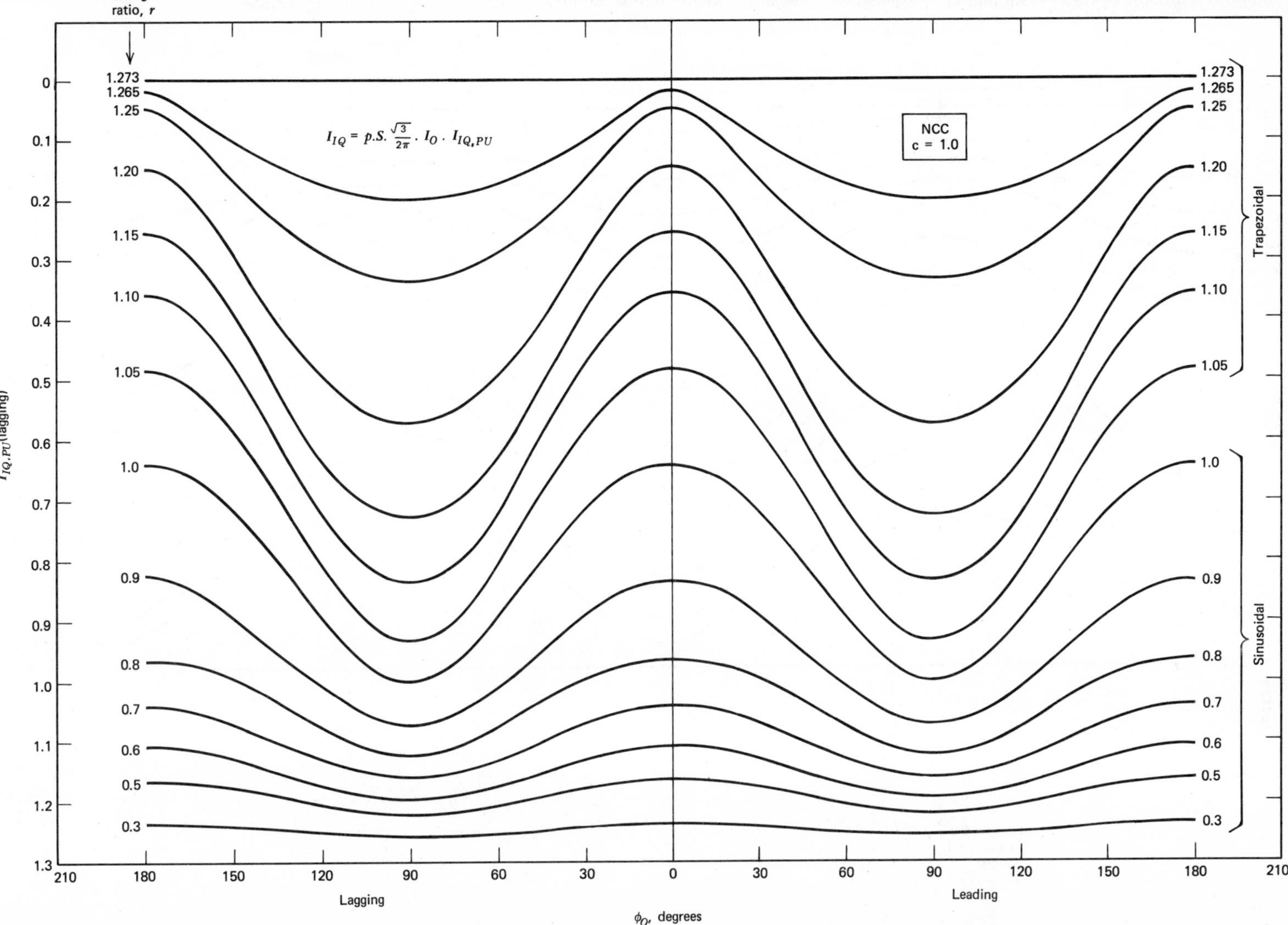

Figure 6.21 Relationships between per-unit quadrature component of input current $I_{IQ,PU}$, output displacement angle ϕ_O, and output voltage ratio r, for the NCC with sinusoidal/trapezoidal mean voltage. $c = 1.0$.

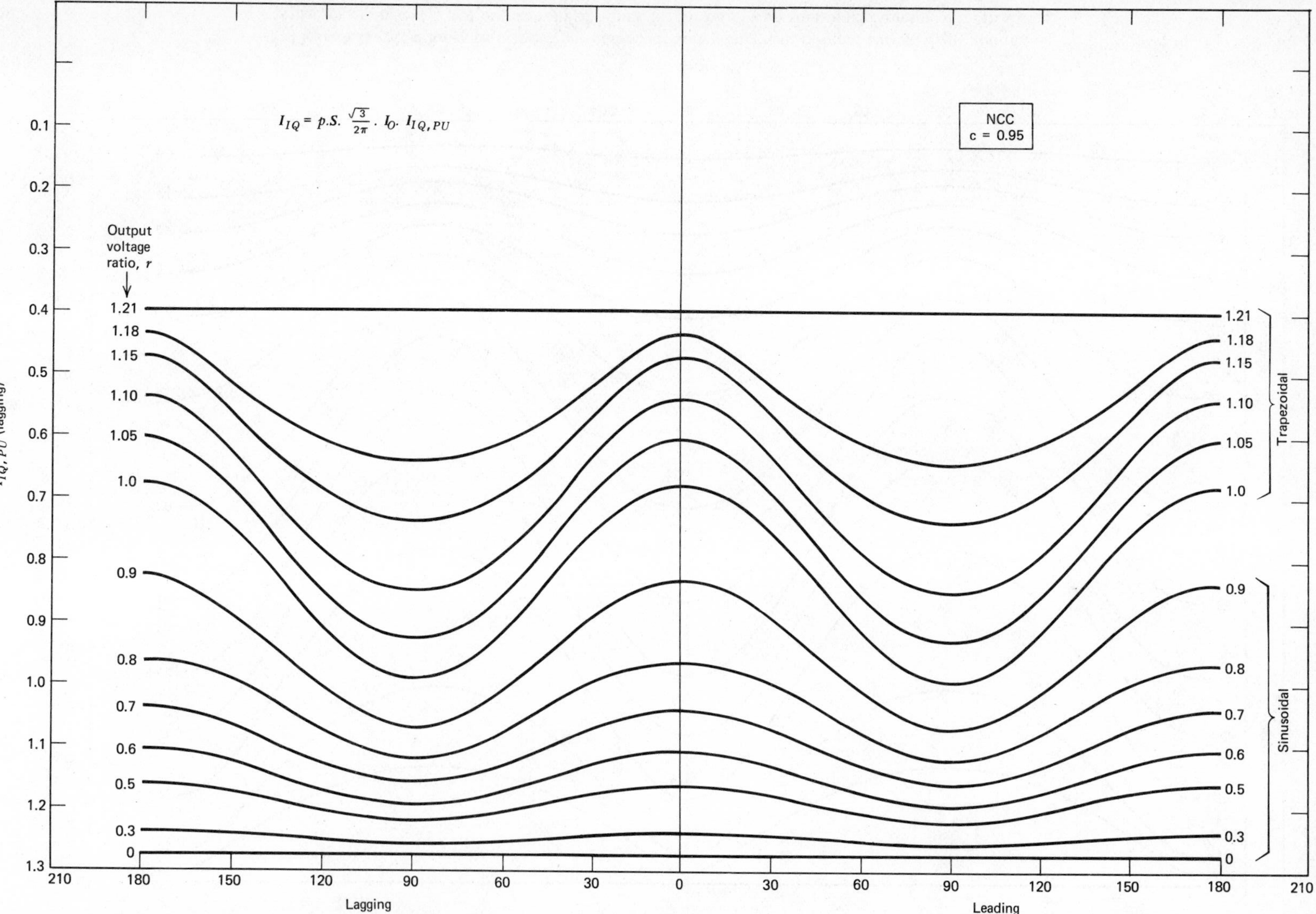

Figure 6.22 Relationships between per-unit quadrature component of input current $I_{IQ,PU}$, output dis-

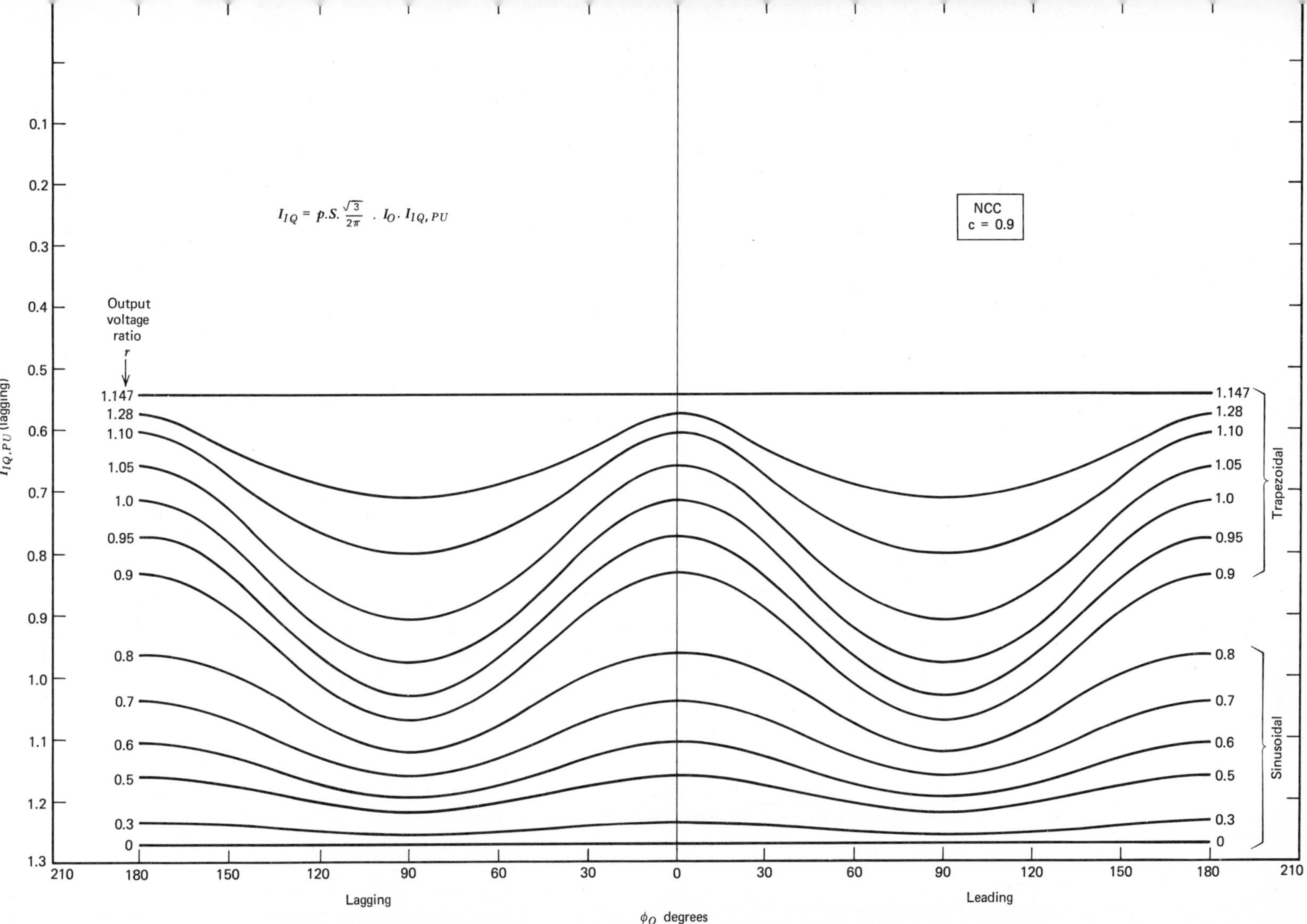

Figure 6.23 Relationships between per-unit quadrature component of input current $I_{IQ,PU}$, output displacement angle ϕ_O, and output voltage ratio r, for the NCC with sinusoidal/trapezoidal mean voltage. $c = 0.9$.

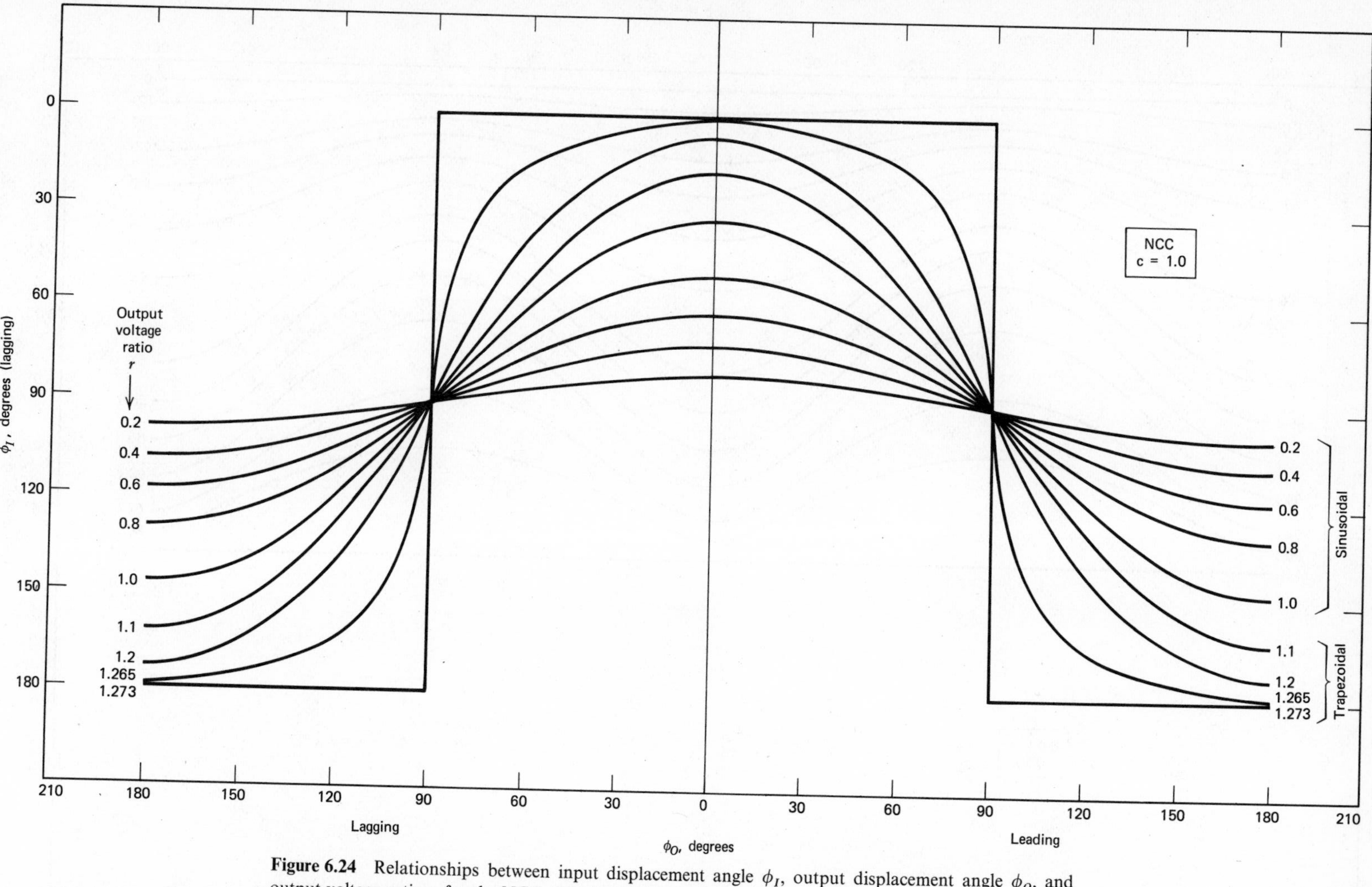

Figure 6.24 Relationships between input displacement angle ϕ_I, output displacement angle ϕ_O, and output voltage ratio r, for the NCC with sinusoidal/trapezoidal mean voltage. $c = 1.0$.

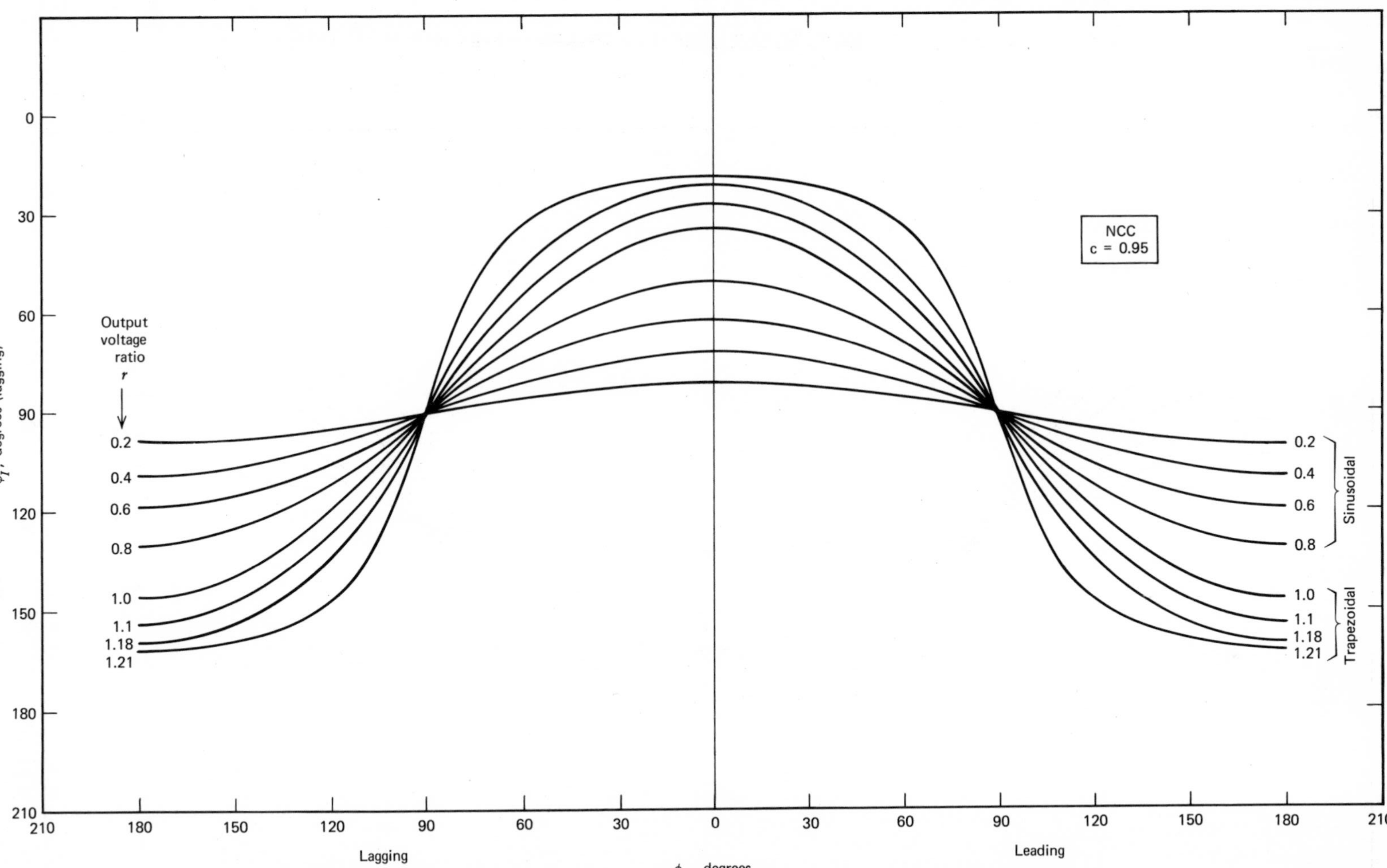

Figure 6.25 Relationships between input displacement angle ϕ_I, output displacement angle ϕ_O, and output voltage ratio r, for the NCC with sinusoidal/trapezoidal mean voltage. $c = 0.95$.

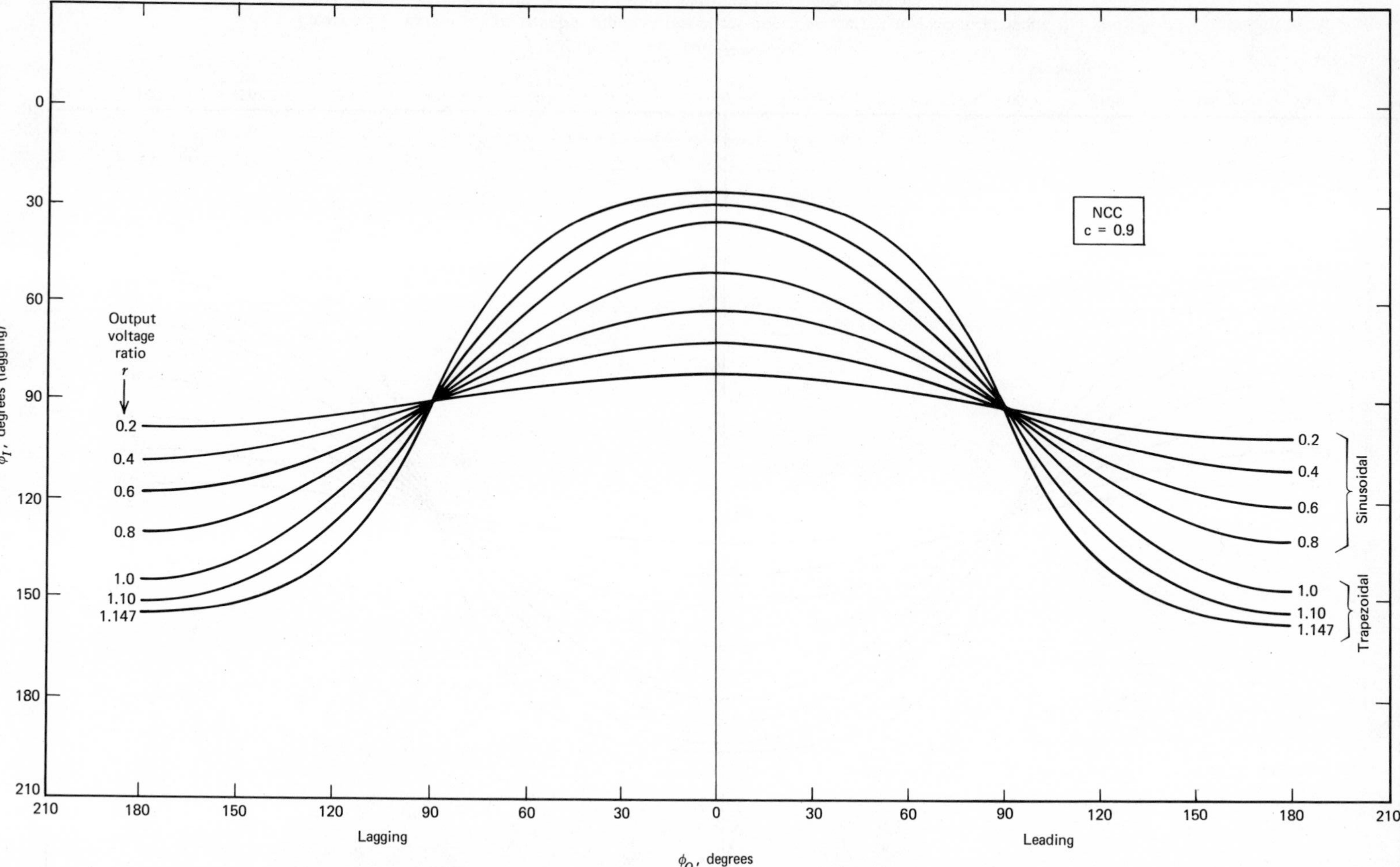

Figure 6.26 Relationships between input displacement angle ϕ_I, output displacement angle ϕ_O, and output voltage ratio r, for the NCC with sinusoidal/trapezoidal mean voltage. $c = 0.9$.

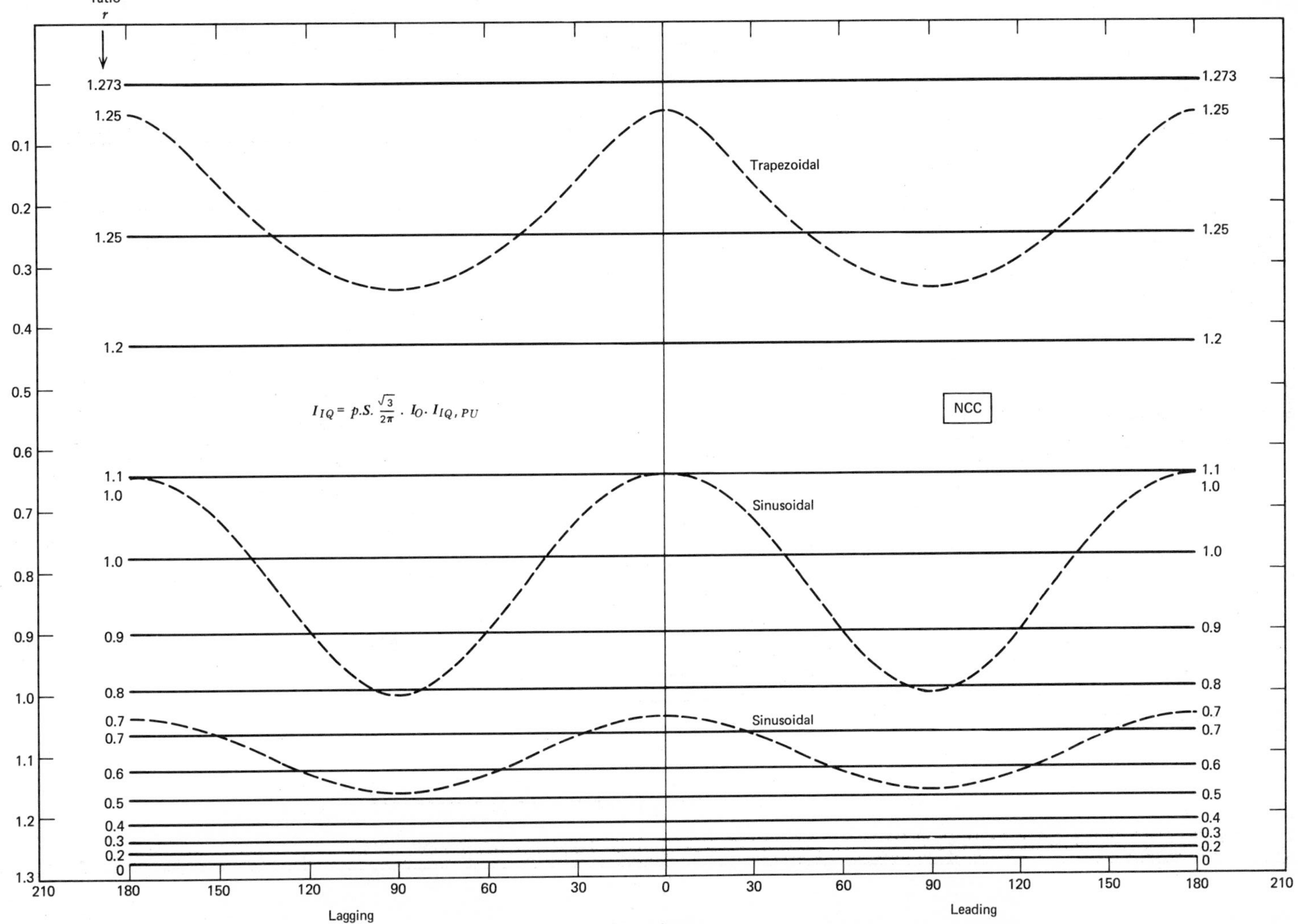

Figure 6.27 Relationships between per-unit quadrature component of input current, output displacement angle ϕ_O, and output voltage ratio r, for the NCC with square mean voltage. Dashed curves are for sinusoidal or trapezoidal mean voltage. $c = 1.0$.

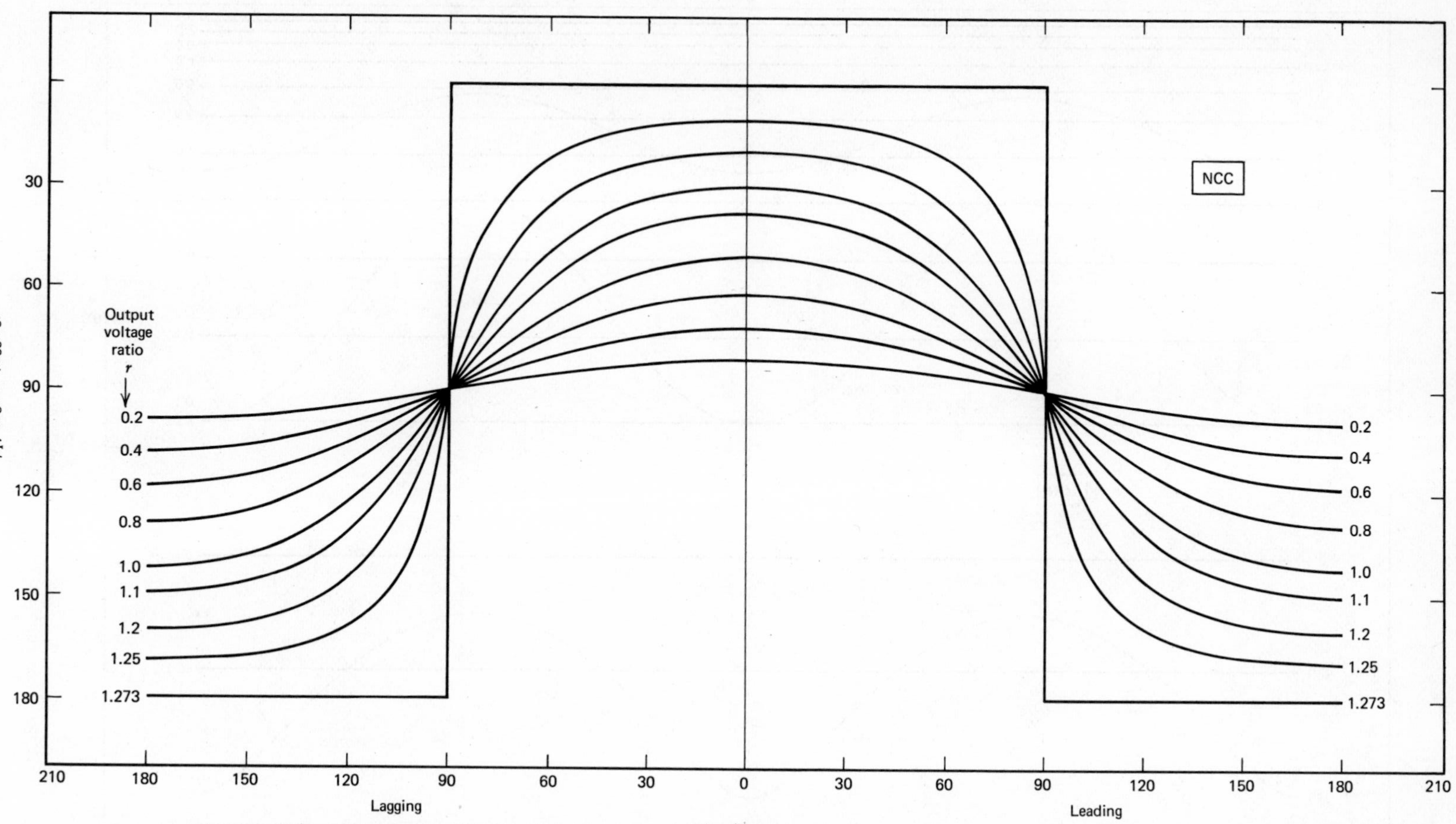

Figure 6.28 Relationships between input displacement angle ϕ_I, output displacement angle ϕ_O, and output voltage ratio r, for the NCC with square mean voltage.

in which the full load power factor of the motor is, for example, 0.9. On the other hand, operation of a VSCF system with a square output voltage under external short-circuit conditions, in which the effective load on the NCC is just the output filter reactor, would be advantageous; this would minimize the load on the input generator, while delivering a given specified short-circuit current at the output.

6.6.3 The Total Fundamental Component of Input Current

The amplitude of the total fundamental component of input current of the frequency changer is the vector addition of the real and quadrature components:

$$I_I = \sqrt{I_{IR}^2 + I_{IQ}^2} \tag{6.27}$$

Thus the amplitude of the net fundamental component of input current of a given frequency changer under a given set of operating conditions can be obtained from the data already presented in Section 6.6.1 and 6.6.2 relating to the constituent real and quadrature components.

6.7 THE EXTRABASAL COMPONENTS OF INPUT CURRENT

6.7.1 The UFC

6.7.1.1 *Extrabasal Frequencies.* The extrabasal frequencies present in the input current wave of the UFC supplying a single-phase output are given by the following general expressions:

$$f_E = f_I + 2f_O \tag{6.28}$$

$$f_E = (Pk - 1)f_I + (Pk - 1 \pm 1)f_O \tag{6.29}$$

and

$$f_E = (Pk + 1)f_I + (Pk + 1 \pm 1)f_O \tag{6.30}$$

where P is the pulse number, and k is any integer from 1 to ∞.

Thus

$$\frac{f_E}{f_I} = 1 + \frac{2f_O}{f_I} \tag{6.31}$$

$$\frac{f_E}{f_I} = (Pk - 1) + (Pk - 1 \pm 1)\frac{f_O}{f_I} \tag{6.32}$$

and

$$\frac{f_E}{f_I} = (Pk + 1) + (Pk + 1 \pm 1)\frac{f_O}{f_I} \tag{6.33}$$

For a balanced three-phase output the extrabasal frequencies present in the input current wave are given by:

$$f_E = (Pk \pm 1)f_I + Pkf_O \tag{6.34}$$

Thus

$$\frac{f_E}{f_I} = (Pk \pm 1) + Pk\frac{f_O}{f_I} \tag{6.35}$$

where P is the pulse number, and k is any integer from 1 to ∞.

If the output voltage is controlled by phase shifting the wanted components of two constituent power circuit groups, the value of P to be used in the above relationships is the pulse number of each of the individual groups and thus is half of the overall circuit pulse number (except for the special condition of full output voltage). If the voltage is controlled by pulse-width modulation, on the other hand, the appropriate value of P is that of the overall circuit.

The right-hand portion of the frequency chart of Figure 6.29 shows the ratios of the extrabasal frequency to input frequency, f_E/f_I, plotted against the output to input frequency ratio, f_O/f_I, for values of Pk up to 12, for both single-phase and balanced three-phase outputs.

This chart clearly illustrates that the frequencies of the extrabasal components present in the input current of the UFC are always greater than the input frequency, irrespective of the output to input frequency ratio. The lowest ratio of extrabasal frequency to input frequency occurs at zero output frequency and is $(P - 1)$.

6.7.1.2 *Amplitudes of Extrabasal Components.* The normalized amplitude of the extrabasal component of current with frequency $(Pk \pm 1)f_I + Pkf_O$ in the input current of the UFC is the same as the normalized amplitude of the unwanted component in the output voltage with frequency $Pkf_I + (Pk \pm 1)f_O$, for the same values of P and k, at the same output voltage ratio. Moreover, the amplitude of the $(Pk \pm 1)f_I + (Pk \pm 2)f_O$ component of current (obtained just with a single-phase output) is equal to that of the $(Pk \pm 1)f_I + Pkf_O$ component, for the same values of P and k, at the same output voltage ratio. This is true for voltage control both by pulse-width modulation and by phase shifting the voltages of two individual circuit groups. Thus the curves of Figures 6.5–6.7, which show the amplitudes of the unwanted components in the output voltage of UFCs of various pulse numbers, plotted against the output voltage ratio, are also applicable to the amplitudes of the extrabasal components of input current, so long as the frequency attached to each curve is appropriately relabelled as indicated.

6.7.1.3 *Distortion Factor of Input Current.* Figure 6.30 shows the distortion factor of the input current plotted against the output voltage ratio for three-, six-, nine-, and twelve-pulse UFCs, with pulse-width modulation of the output voltage.

Figure 6.31 shows similar curves for UFCs of overall circuit pulse numbers six and twelve, with voltage control by phase shifting two individual groups (the overall circuit pulse number being that of the output voltage at $r = 1.0$).

6.7.2 The SSFC

6.7.2.1 *Extrabasal Frequencies.* The frequencies of the extrabasal components present in the input current of the SSFC are *complementary* to those present in the input current of the UFC. Thus, whereas the extrabasal frequencies present in the input current of the UFC are *sums* of given multiples of the input frequency f_I and the output frequency f_O, the extrabasal frequencies present in the input current of the SSFC are *differences* of these same multiples of f_I and f_O.

Thus, for a SSFC supplying a single-phase output:

$$\frac{f_E}{f_I} = 1 - 2\frac{f_O}{f_I} \tag{6.36}$$

$$\frac{f_E}{f_I} = (Pk - 1) - (Pk - 1 \pm 1)\frac{f_O}{f_I} \tag{6.37}$$

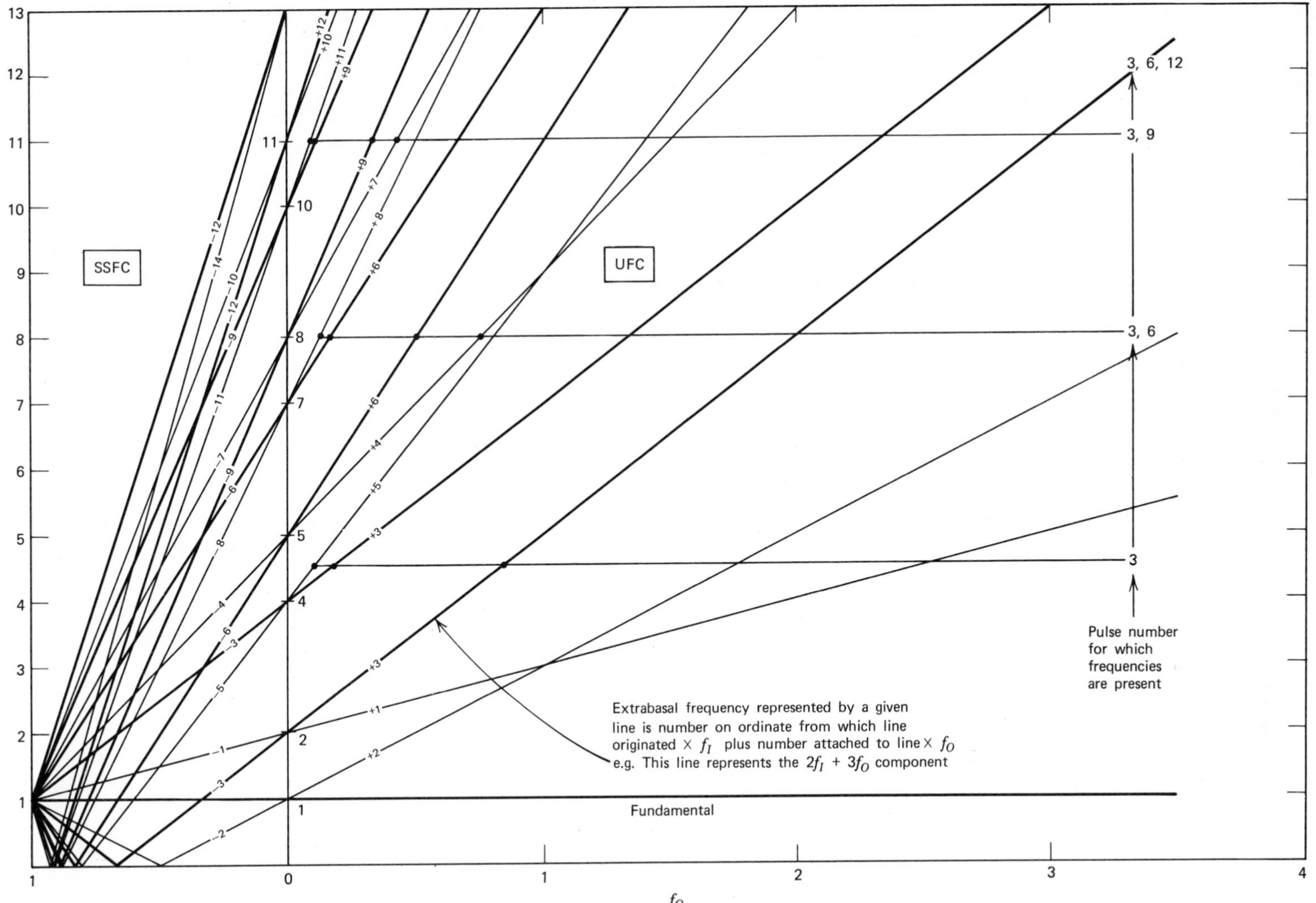

Figure 6.29 Frequencies of extrabasal components in input current of UFC and SSFC, expressed as ratio of input frequency, versus output to input frequency ratio. For single-phase output, all frequencies shown are present. For balanced three-phase output, only frequencies shown by heavy lines are present.

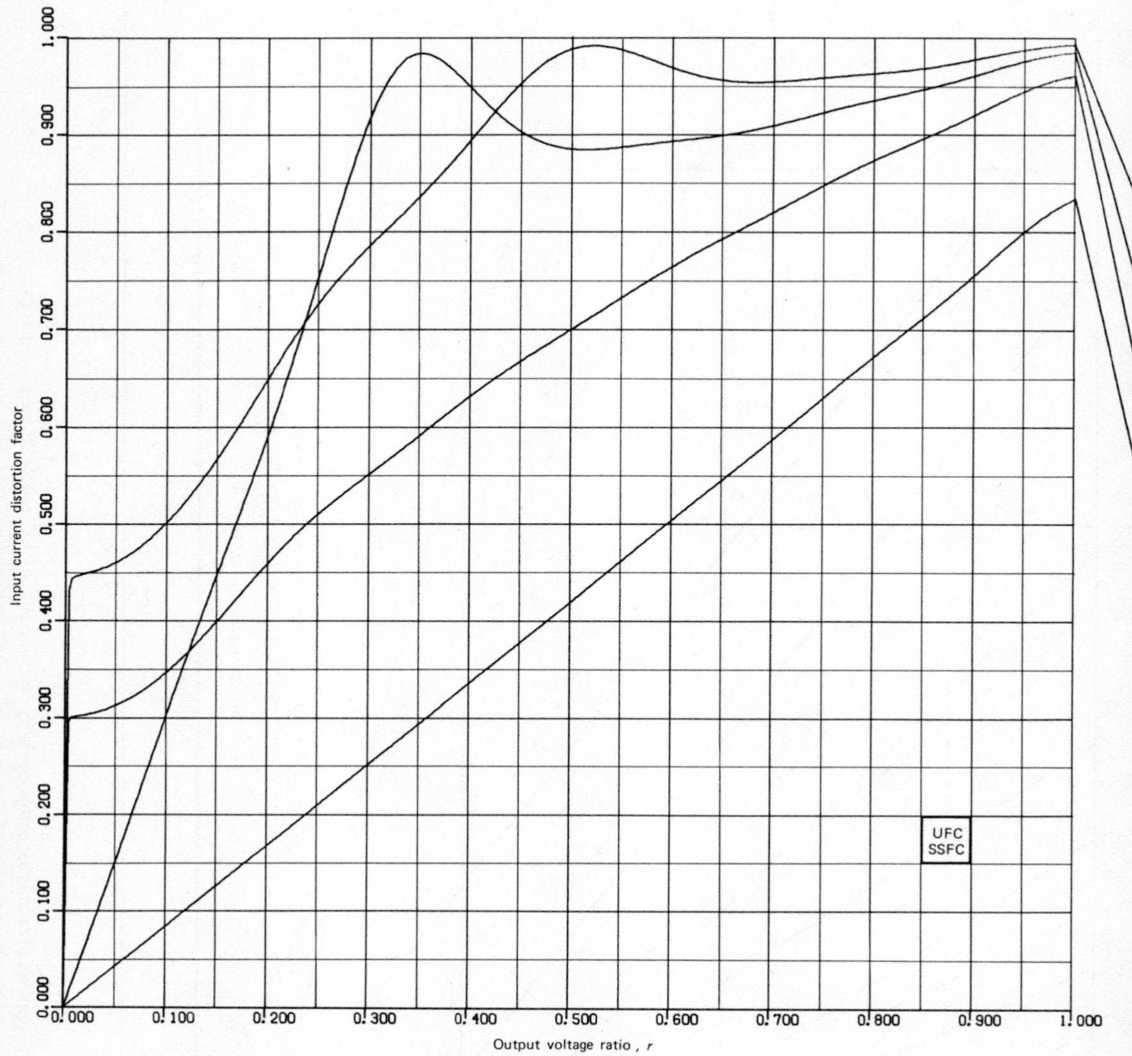

Figure 6.30 Variation of the input current distortion factor with the output voltage ratio, for the UFC and SSFC, of pulse numbers three, six, nine, and twelve. Output voltage is controlled by pulse-width modulation. Curves are for balanced three-phase output. For single-phase output, multiply distortion factor given by 0.707.

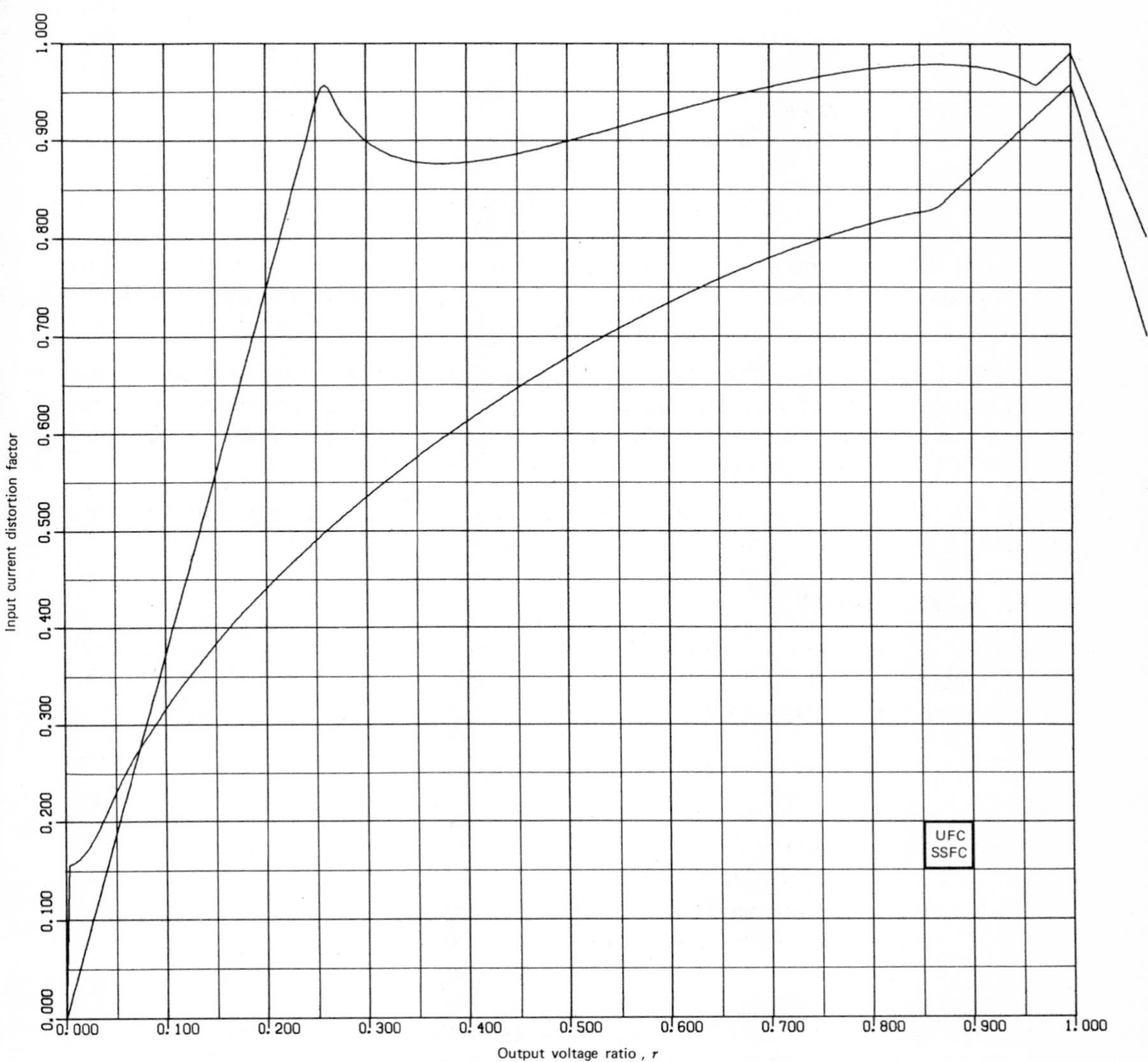

Figure 6.31 Variation of the input current distortion factor with the output voltage ratio, for the UFC and SSFC, of overall circuit pulse numbers six and twelve. Output voltage is controlled by phase shift. Curves are for balanced three-phase output. For single-phase output, multiply distortion factor given by 0.707.

and

$$\frac{f_E}{f_I} = (Pk + 1) - (Pk + 1 \pm 1)\frac{f_O}{f_I} \tag{6.38}$$

For a balanced three-phase output:

$$\frac{f_E}{f_I} = (Pk \pm 1) - Pk\frac{f_O}{f_I} \tag{6.39}$$

The left-hand portion of the frequency chart of Figure 6.29 shows the ratios of extrabasal frequency to input frequency, f_E/f_I, plotted against the output to input frequency ratio, f_O/f_I, for values of Pk up to 12.

6.7.2.2 *Amplitudes of Extrabasal Components.* For given values of P and k, the amplitude of any given extrabasal component in the input current of the SSFC at any given output voltage ratio is the same as that of the complementary component for the UFC. Thus, Figures 6.5–6.7 also apply to the SSFC.

6.7.2.3 *Distortion Factor of Input Current.* The curves of Figure 6.30 and 6.31 are also applicable to the SSFC.

6.7.3 The UDFFC

6.7.3.1 *Extrabasal Frequencies.* The extrabasal frequencies present in the input current wave of the UDFFC supplying a single-phase output are given by the following general expressions:

$$f_E = f_I \pm 2f_O \tag{6.40}$$

$$f_E = (Pk - 1)f_I \pm nf_O \tag{6.41}$$

where P is the pulse number,
k is any integer from 1 to ∞,
n is any odd integer from 1 to Pk for Pk odd,
n is any even integer from 0 to Pk for Pk even, and

$$f_E = (Pk + 1)f_I \pm nf_O \tag{6.42}$$

where n is any odd integer from 1 to $(Pk + 2)$ for Pk odd, and
n is any even integer from 0 to $(Pk + 2)$ for Pk even.

Thus

$$\frac{f_E}{f_I} = 1 \pm 2\frac{f_O}{f_I} \tag{6.43}$$

$$\frac{f_E}{f_I} = (Pk - 1) \pm n\frac{f_O}{f_I} \tag{6.44}$$

and

$$\frac{f_E}{f_I} = (Pk + 1) \pm n\frac{f_O}{f_I} \tag{6.45}$$

For a balanced three-phase output:

$$f_E = (Pk - 1)f_I \pm 3nf_O \tag{6.46}$$

and

$$f_E = (Pk + 1)f_I \pm 3nf_O \tag{6.47}$$

where n is any odd integer from 1 to $Pk/3$ for Pk odd, and
n is any even integer from 0 to $Pk/3$ for Pk even.

Thus

$$\frac{f_E}{f_I} = (Pk - 1) \pm 3n\frac{f_O}{f_I} \tag{6.48}$$

and

$$\frac{f_E}{f_I} = (Pk + 1) \pm 3n\frac{f_O}{f_I} \tag{6.49}$$

The frequency chart of Figure 6.32 shows the ratios of extrabasal frequency to input frequency, f_E/f_I, plotted against the output to input frequency ratio, f_O/f_I, for values of Pk up to 12, for both single-phase and balanced three-phase outputs.

With a single-phase output, the $f_I - 2f_O$ term, ever present in the input current regardless of the circuit pulse number, is always less than the input frequency f_I; indeed, at the particular frequency ratio of 0.5, this component has zero frequency.

For a balanced three-phase output, the $f_I \pm 2f_O$ term is absent, and the distortion of the input current wave is generally much reduced. As the output to input frequency ratio increases, so the frequencies of certain of the pulse-number-dependent components encroach upon, and ultimately become less than, the input frequency. As can be seen, the output to input frequency ratio at which the lowest extrabasal frequency becomes equal to the input frequency depends on the circuit pulse number. This frequency ratio increases with increasing circuit pulse number, but it is always less than unity for all pulse numbers.

6.7.3.2 *Amplitudes of Extrabasal Components.* Tables 6.4–6.6 show the normalized amplitudes of the principal extrabasal components present in the input current of the UDFFC with single- and balanced three-phase outputs for various output displacement angles. Figures 6.33 and 6.34 show the amplitudes of the principal extrabasal components obtained with a balanced three-phase output, plotted against the output voltage ratio, for the same output displacement angles.

6.7.3.3 *Distortion Factor of Input Current.* Figure 6.35 shows the distortion factor of the input current of the UDFFC, plotted against the output voltage ratio, for three-, six-, nine-, and twelve-pulse circuits, with single- and balanced three-phase outputs, for output displacement angles of 0 and 180°, ±30° and ±150°, and ±60° and ±120°.

6.7.4 The NCC

6.7.4.1 *Extrabasal Frequencies.* The extrabasal frequencies present in the input current wave of the NCC with a sinusoidal, trapezoidal, or square mean output voltage supplying a single-phase output are given by the following general expressions:

$$f_E = f_I \pm 2nf_O \tag{6.50}$$

$$f_E = (Pk - 1)f_I \pm nf_O \tag{6.51}$$

and

$$f_E = (Pk + 1)f_I \pm nf_O \tag{6.52}$$

where P is the pulse number,
k is any integer from 1 to ∞,
n is any odd integer from 1 to ∞ for Pk odd, and
n is any even integer from 0 to ∞ for Pk even.

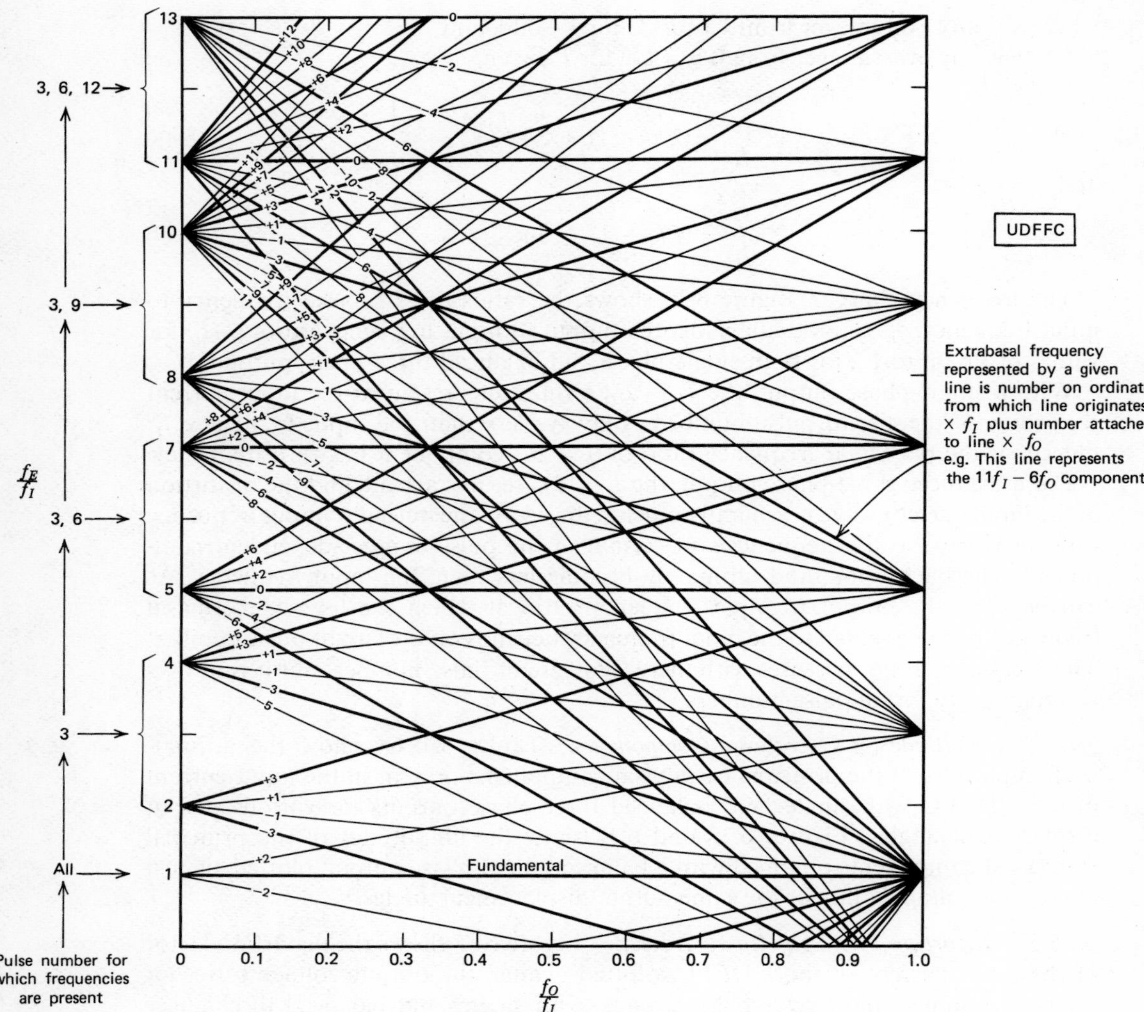

Figure 6.32 Frequencies of extrabasal components in input current of UDFFC, expressed as ratio of input frequency, versus output to input frequency ratio. For single-phase output, all frequencies shown are present. For balanced three-phase output, only frequencies shown by heavy lines are present.

TABLE 6.4. Normalized Amplitudes of the Extrabasal Components of Input Current of the UDFFC. For a Balanced Three-Phase Output, Only Those Components Whose Numbers are Boxed Thus □ are Present.

Normalized Amplitude

$$= \frac{\text{Amplitude of component with given } r,\ \phi_O, \text{ and output current } I_O}{\text{Amplitude of fundamental component with } r = 1.0,\ \phi_O = 0, \text{ and output current } I_O}$$

$\phi_O = 0°, 180°$

Extrabasal Frequency: Multiple of f_I	± Multiple of f_O	r = 1.0	0.9	0.8	0.7	0.6	0.5	0.4	0.3	0.2	0.1
1	2	0.50	0.45	0.40	0.35	0.30	0.25	0.20	0.15	0.10	0.05
2	1	0.13	0.05	0.01	0.07	0.12	0.16	0.19	0.22	0.24	0.25
2	**3**	0.25	0.20	0.16	0.12	0.09	0.06	0.04	0.02	0.01	0.00
4	1	0.00	0.07	0.10	0.09	0.06	0.02	0.02	0.06	0.10	0.12
4	**3**	0.13	0.01	0.06	0.10	0.10	0.09	0.06	0.04	0.02	0.01
4	5	0.13	0.08	0.05	0.03	0.02	0.01	0.00	0.00	0.00	0.00
5	**0**	0.00	0.11	0.08	0.01	0.11	0.19	0.23	0.22	0.18	0.10
5	2	0.00	0.12	0.13	0.08	0.02	0.05	0.09	0.10	0.08	0.05
5	4	0.10	0.01	0.06	0.07	0.06	0.04	0.03	0.01	0.00	0.00
5	**6**	0.10	0.06	0.03	0.02	0.01	0.00	0.00	0.00	0.00	0.00
7	**0**	0.00	0.04	0.04	0.09	0.06	0.02	0.11	0.16	0.16	0.09
7	2	0.00	0.05	0.03	0.09	0.09	0.05	0.01	0.06	0.07	0.05
7	4	0.00	0.09	0.05	0.00	0.04	0.05	0.04	0.02	0.01	0.00
7	**6**	0.07	0.02	0.04	0.04	0.02	0.01	0.00	0.00	0.00	0.00
7	8	0.07	0.03	0.02	0.01	0.00	0.00	0.00	0.00	0.00	0.00
8	1	0.00	0.01	0.03	0.03	0.01	0.04	0.05	0.03	0.01	0.05
8	**3**	0.00	0.03	0.05	0.08	0.05	0.00	0.04	0.05	0.03	0.01
8	5	0.00	0.07	0.03	0.02	0.04	0.03	0.02	0.01	0.00	0.00
8	7	0.06	0.02	0.04	0.03	0.01	0.01	0.00	0.00	0.00	0.00
8	**9**	0.06	0.03	0.01	0.00	0.00	0.00	0.00	0.00	0.00	0.00
10	1	0.00	0.01	0.01	0.02	0.03	0.00	0.04	0.04	0.01	0.03
10	**3**	0.00	0.02	0.04	0.02	0.06	0.04	0.00	0.04	0.03	0.01
10	5	0.00	0.00	0.05	0.04	0.00	0.03	0.02	0.01	0.00	0.00
10	7	0.00	0.05	0.00	0.02	0.02	0.01	0.00	0.00	0.00	0.00
10	**9**	0.05	0.02	0.02	0.01	0.01	0.00	0.00	0.00	0.00	0.00
10	11	0.05	0.02	0.01	0.00	0.00	0.00	0.00	0.00	0.00	0.00
11	**0**	0.00	0.03	0.00	0.04	0.00	0.06	0.04	0.04	0.10	0.09
11	2	0.00	0.03	0.00	0.05	0.01	0.05	0.06	0.01	0.04	0.04
11	4	0.00	0.02	0.02	0.04	0.05	0.01	0.02	0.03	0.01	0.00
11	**6**	0.00	0.01	0.05	0.02	0.01	0.02	0.02	0.01	0.00	0.00
11	8	0.00	0.04	0.01	0.02	0.02	0.01	0.00	0.00	0.00	0.00
11	10	0.04	0.02	0.02	0.01	0.00	0.00	0.00	0.00	0.00	0.00
11	**12**	0.04	0.01	0.00	0.00	0.00	0.00	0.00	0.00	0.00	0.00
13	**0**	0.00	0.02	0.03	0.00	0.04	0.01	0.05	0.01	0.07	0.08
13	2	0.00	0.02	0.03	0.00	0.04	0.00	0.05	0.04	0.02	0.04
13	4	0.00	0.03	0.02	0.02	0.03	0.04	0.00	0.02	0.02	0.00
13	**6**	0.00	0.03	0.01	0.04	0.01	0.01	0.02	0.01	0.00	0.00
13	8	0.00	0.02	0.03	0.00	0.02	0.01	0.00	0.00	0.00	0.00
13	10	0.00	0.02	0.01	0.02	0.01	0.00	0.00	0.00	0.00	0.00
13	**12**	0.04	0.02	0.01	0.00	0.00	0.00	0.00	0.00	0.00	0.00
13	14	0.04	0.01	0.00	0.00	0.00	0.00	0.00	0.00	0.00	0.00

TABLE 6.5. Normalized Amplitudes of the Extrabasal Components of Input Current of the UDFFC. For Balanced Three-Phase Output, Only Those Components Whose Numbers are Boxed Thus □ are Present.

Normalized Amplitude

$$= \frac{\text{Amplitude of component with given } r,\ \phi_O, \text{ and output current } I_O}{\text{Amplitude of fundamental component with } r = 1.0,\ \phi_O = 0, \text{ and output current } I_O}$$

$\phi_O = \pm 30°, \pm 150°$

Extrabasal frequency: Multiple of f_I	± Multiple of f_O	r = 1.0	0.9	0.8	0.7	0.6	0.5	0.4	0.3	0.2	0.1
1	2	0.50	0.45	0.40	0.35	0.30	0.25	0.20	0.15	0.10	0.05
2	1	0.13	0.09	0.09	0.11	0.14	0.17	0.20	0.22	0.24	0.25
[2]	[3]	0.25	0.20	0.16	0.12	0.09	0.06	0.04	0.02	0.01	0.00
4	1	0.00	0.06	0.09	0.08	0.06	0.04	0.05	0.07	0.10	0.12
[4]	[3]	0.13	0.08	0.10	0.11	0.11	0.09	0.07	0.04	0.02	0.01
4	5	0.13	0.08	0.05	0.03	0.02	0.01	0.00	0.00	0.00	0.00
[5]	[0]	0.00	0.09	0.07	0.01	0.09	0.16	0.20	0.19	0.15	0.08
5	2	0.00	0.11	0.12	0.09	0.06	0.08	0.10	0.11	0.09	0.05
5	4	0.10	0.06	0.08	0.08	0.07	0.05	0.03	0.01	0.00	0.00
[5]	[6]	0.10	0.06	0.03	0.02	0.01	0.00	0.00	0.00	0.00	0.00
[7]	[0]	0.00	0.03	0.04	0.08	0.05	0.02	0.10	0.14	0.13	0.08
7	2	0.00	0.04	0.03	0.08	0.08	0.05	0.05	0.07	0.07	0.05
7	4	0.00	0.08	0.06	0.04	0.05	0.05	0.04	0.02	0.01	0.00
[7]	[6]	0.07	0.05	0.05	0.04	0.02	0.01	0.00	0.00	0.00	0.00
7	8	0.07	0.03	0.02	0.01	0.00	0.00	0.00	0.00	0.00	0.00
8	1	0.00	0.01	0.03	0.02	0.01	0.04	0.04	0.03	0.02	0.05
[8]	[3]	0.00	0.03	0.04	0.07	0.05	0.04	0.05	0.05	0.03	0.01
8	5	0.00	0.06	0.04	0.04	0.05	0.04	0.02	0.01	0.00	0.00
8	7	0.06	0.04	0.04	0.03	0.01	0.01	0.00	0.00	0.00	0.00
[8]	[9]	0.06	0.03	0.01	0.00	0.00	0.00	0.00	0.00	0.00	0.00
10	1	0.00	0.01	0.01	0.02	0.02	0.00	0.03	0.03	0.02	0.04
[10]	[3]	0.00	0.01	0.03	0.02	0.05	0.04	0.03	0.04	0.03	0.01
10	5	0.00	0.01	0.05	0.04	0.03	0.04	0.03	0.01	0.00	0.00
10	7	0.00	0.04	0.03	0.03	0.03	0.01	0.00	0.00	0.00	0.00
[10]	[9]	0.05	0.04	0.03	0.01	0.01	0.00	0.00	0.00	0.00	0.00
10	11	0.05	0.02	0.01	0.00	0.00	0.00	0.00	0.00	0.00	0.00
[11]	[0]	0.00	0.02	0.00	0.04	0.00	0.05	0.04	0.03	0.09	0.07
11	2	0.00	0.02	0.00	0.04	0.01	0.04	0.05	0.03	0.04	0.04
11	4	0.00	0.02	0.02	0.03	0.04	0.03	0.03	0.03	0.01	0.00
[11]	[6]	0.00	0.01	0.04	0.03	0.03	0.03	0.02	0.01	0.00	0.00
11	8	0.00	0.04	0.03	0.03	0.02	0.01	0.00	0.00	0.00	0.00
11	10	0.05	0.03	0.02	0.01	0.00	0.00	0.00	0.00	0.00	0.00
[11]	[12]	0.05	0.01	0.00	0.00	0.00	0.00	0.00	0.00	0.00	0.00
[13]	[0]	0.00	0.02	0.02	0.00	0.03	0.01	0.04	0.01	0.06	0.07
13	2	0.00	0.02	0.02	0.00	0.03	0.01	0.04	0.04	0.03	0.04
13	4	0.00	0.02	0.02	0.02	0.03	0.03	0.02	0.03	0.02	0.00
[13]	[6]	0.00	0.02	0.01	0.03	0.02	0.03	0.02	0.01	0.00	0.00
13	8	0.00	0.02	0.03	0.02	0.02	0.01	0.00	0.00	0.00	0.00
13	10	0.00	0.03	0.02	0.02	0.01	0.00	0.00	0.00	0.00	0.00
[13]	[12]	0.04	0.03	0.01	0.00	0.00	0.00	0.00	0.00	0.00	0.00
13	14	0.04	0.01	0.00	0.00	0.00	0.00	0.00	0.00	0.00	0.00

TABLE 6.6. Normalized Amplitudes of the Extrabasal Components of Input Current of the UDFFC. For Balanced Three-Phase Output, Only Those Components Whose Numbers are Boxed Thus □ are Present.

Normalized Amplitude

$$= \frac{\textbf{Amplitude of component with given } r,\ \phi_O, \textbf{ and output current } I_O}{\textbf{Amplitude of fundamental component with } r = 1.0,\ \phi_O = 0, \textbf{ and output current } I_O}$$

$\phi_O = \pm 60°, \pm 120°$

Extrabasal frequency: Multiple of f_I	± Multiple of f_O	r = 1.0	0.9	0.8	0.7	0.6	0.5	0.4	0.3	0.2	0.1
1	2	0.50	0.45	0.40	0.35	0.30	0.25	0.20	0.15	0.10	0.05
2	1	0.13	0.13	0.15	0.17	0.19	0.20	0.22	0.23	0.24	0.25
$\boxed{2}$	$\boxed{3}$	0.25	0.20	0.16	0.12	0.09	0.06	0.04	0.02	0.01	0.00
4	1	0.00	0.04	0.05	0.05	0.05	0.06	0.08	0.09	0.11	0.12
$\boxed{4}$	$\boxed{3}$	0.13	0.14	0.15	0.14	0.12	0.10	0.07	0.04	0.02	0.01
4	5	0.13	0.08	0.05	0.03	0.02	0.01	0.00	0.00	0.00	0.00
$\boxed{5}$	$\boxed{0}$	0.00	0.05	0.04	0.00	0.05	0.09	0.11	0.11	0.09	0.05
5	2	0.00	0.06	0.08	0.09	0.11	0.12	0.13	0.12	0.09	0.05
5	4	0.10	0.11	0.11	0.10	0.07	0.05	0.03	0.01	0.00	0.00
$\boxed{5}$	$\boxed{6}$	0.10	0.06	0.03	0.02	0.01	0.00	0.00	0.00	0.00	0.00
$\boxed{7}$	$\boxed{0}$	0.00	0.02	0.02	0.04	0.03	0.01	0.06	0.08	0.08	0.05
7	2	0.00	0.03	0.02	0.05	0.06	0.07	0.08	0.09	0.08	0.05
7	4	0.00	0.05	0.06	0.08	0.08	0.07	0.04	0.02	0.01	0.00
$\boxed{7}$	$\boxed{6}$	0.07	0.08	0.07	0.05	0.03	0.01	0.00	0.00	0.00	0.00
7	8	0.07	0.03	0.02	0.01	0.00	0.00	0.00	0.00	0.00	0.00
8	1	0.00	0.00	0.01	0.01	0.01	0.02	0.03	0.03	0.04	0.06
$\boxed{8}$	$\boxed{3}$	0.00	0.02	0.03	0.04	0.05	0.07	0.07	0.06	0.03	0.01
8	5	0.00	0.04	0.06	0.07	0.06	0.04	0.02	0.01	0.00	0.00
8	7	0.06	0.07	0.05	0.03	0.02	0.01	0.00	0.00	0.00	0.00
$\boxed{8}$	$\boxed{9}$	0.06	0.03	0.01	0.00	0.00	0.00	0.00	0.00	0.00	0.00
10	1	0.00	0.01	0.01	0.01	0.01	0.01	0.02	0.02	0.03	0.04
$\boxed{10}$	$\boxed{3}$	0.00	0.01	0.02	0.02	0.03	0.04	0.05	0.06	0.04	0.01
10	5	0.00	0.01	0.03	0.04	0.05	0.05	0.03	0.01	0.00	0.00
10	7	0.00	0.04	0.05	0.05	0.03	0.01	0.00	0.00	0.00	0.00
$\boxed{10}$	$\boxed{9}$	0.05	0.05	0.03	0.02	0.01	0.00	0.00	0.00	0.00	0.00
10	11	0.05	0.02	0.01	0.00	0.00	0.00	0.00	0.00	0.00	0.00
$\boxed{11}$	$\boxed{0}$	0.00	0.01	0.00	0.02	0.00	0.03	0.02	0.02	0.05	0.04
11	2	0.00	0.01	0.01	0.02	0.01	0.02	0.03	0.04	0.06	0.04
11	4	0.00	0.01	0.02	0.02	0.03	0.04	0.05	0.04	0.02	0.00
$\boxed{11}$	$\boxed{6}$	0.00	0.01	0.03	0.04	0.05	0.04	0.02	0.01	0.00	0.00
11	8	0.00	0.04	0.05	0.04	0.02	0.01	0.00	0.00	0.00	0.00
11	10	0.05	0.05	0.03	0.01	0.00	0.00	0.00	0.00	0.00	0.00
$\boxed{11}$	$\boxed{12}$	0.05	0.01	0.00	0.00	0.00	0.00	0.00	0.00	0.00	0.00
$\boxed{13}$	$\boxed{0}$	0.00	0.01	0.01	0.00	0.02	0.01	0.03	0.00	0.04	0.04
13	2	0.00	0.01	0.01	0.00	0.02	0.01	0.02	0.03	0.05	0.04
13	4	0.00	0.01	0.01	0.01	0.02	0.03	0.04	0.04	0.02	0.00
$\boxed{13}$	$\boxed{6}$	0.00	0.01	0.01	0.02	0.03	0.04	0.03	0.01	0.00	0.00
13	8	0.00	0.01	0.03	0.04	0.03	0.02	0.01	0.00	0.00	0.00
13	10	0.00	0.03	0.04	0.02	0.01	0.00	0.00	0.00	0.00	0.00
$\boxed{13}$	$\boxed{12}$	0.04	0.04	0.02	0.00	0.00	0.00	0.00	0.00	0.00	0.00
13	14	0.04	0.01	0.00	0.00	0.00	0.00	0.00	0.00	0.00	0.00

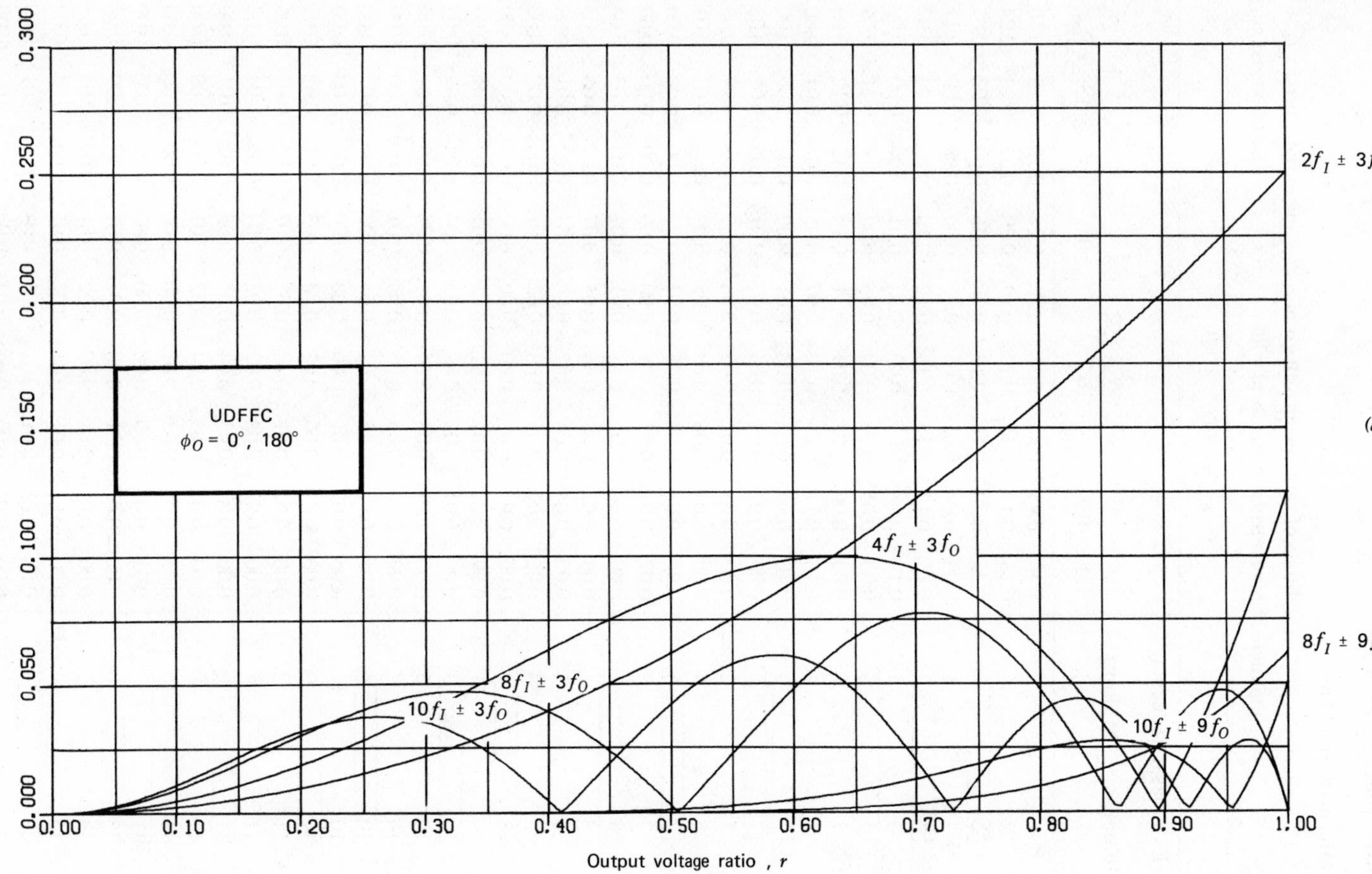
UDFFC
$\phi_O = 0°, 180°$
$2f_I \pm 3f_O$
$4f_I \pm 3f_O$
$8f_I \pm 3f_O$
$10f_I \pm 3f_O$
$8f_I \pm 9f_O$
$10f_I \pm 9f_O$
Normalized amplitude of the extrabasal component
0.000
0.050
0.100
0.150
0.200
0.250
0.300
0.00
0.10
0.20
0.30
0.40
0.50
0.60
0.70
0.80
0.90
1.00
Output voltage ratio , r
(a)

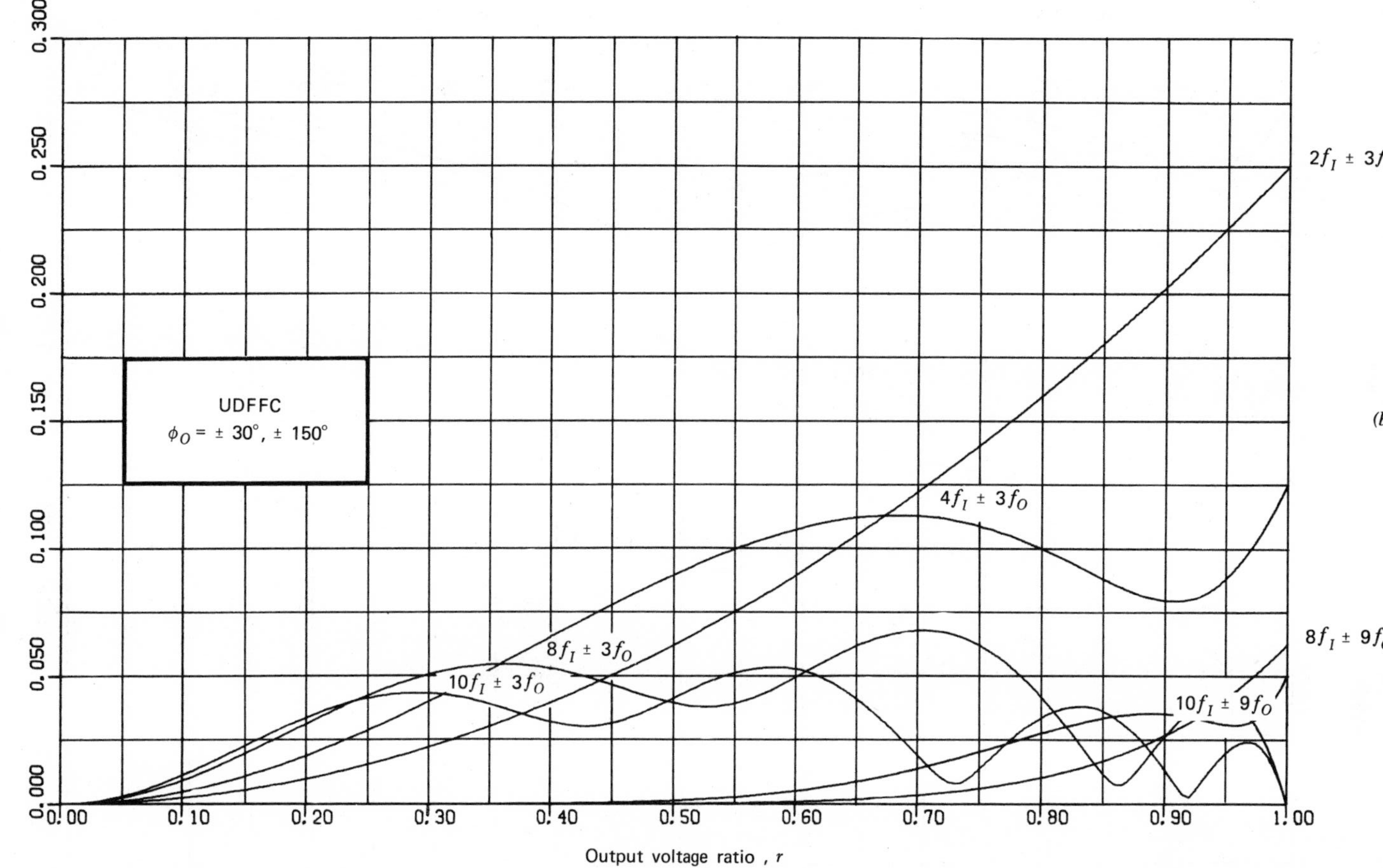

UDFFC
$\phi_O = \pm 30°, \pm 150°$
$2f_I \pm 3f_O$
$4f_I \pm 3f_O$
$8f_I \pm 3f_O$
$10f_I \pm 3f_O$
$8f_I \pm 9f_O$
$10f_I \pm 9f_O$
(b)
Normalized amplitude of the extrabasal component
0.000
0.050
0.100
0.150
0.200
0.250
0.300
Output voltage ratio , r
0.00
0.10
0.20
0.30
0.40
0.50
0.60
0.70
0.80
0.90
1.00

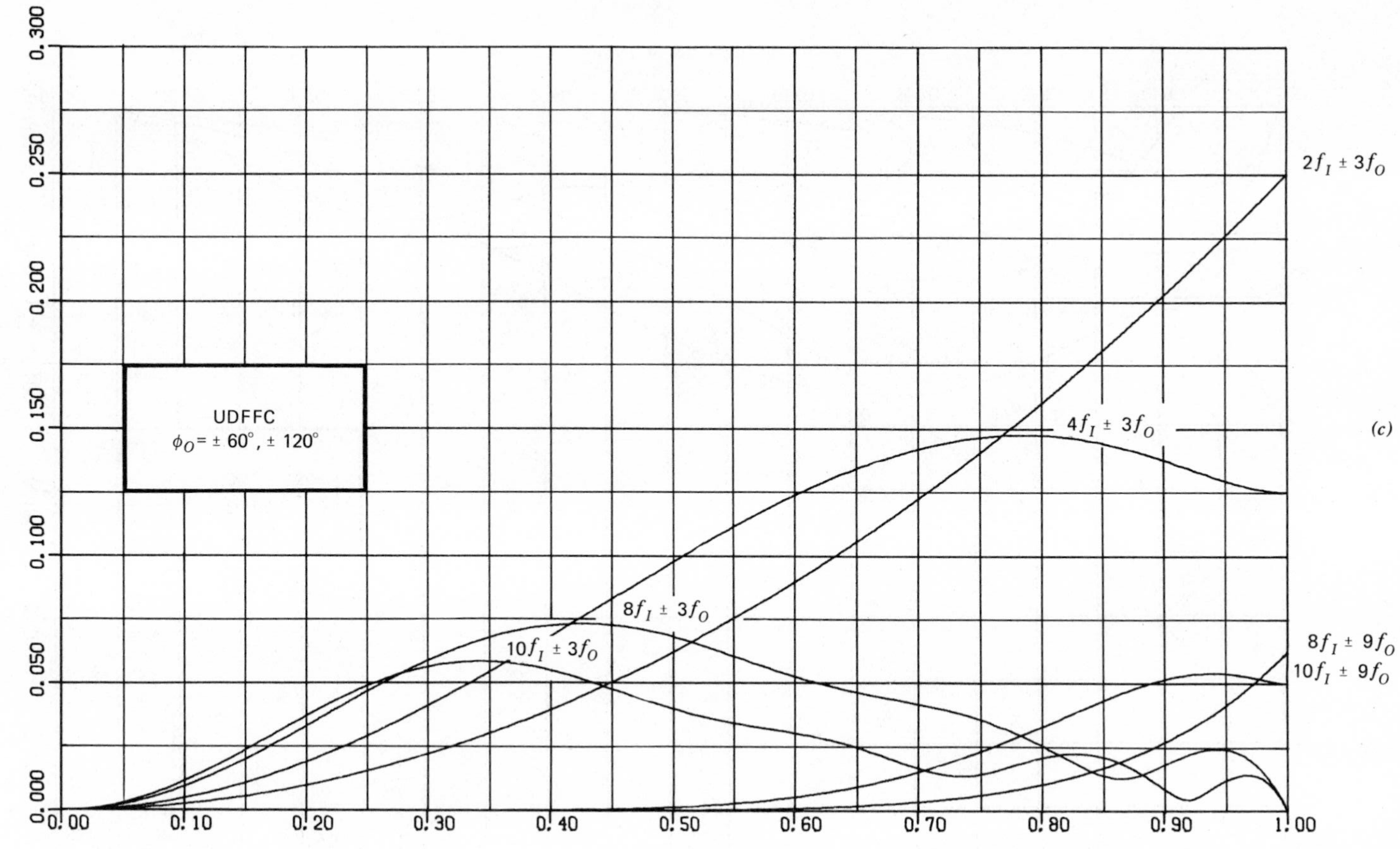

Figure 6.33 Normalized amplitudes of the extrabasal components in the input current of the UDFFC with balanced three-phase output versus the output voltage ratio. *a* $\phi_O = 0°$ and $180°$; *b* $\phi_O = \pm 30°$ and $\pm 150°$; *c* $\phi_O = \pm 60°$ and $\pm 120°$.

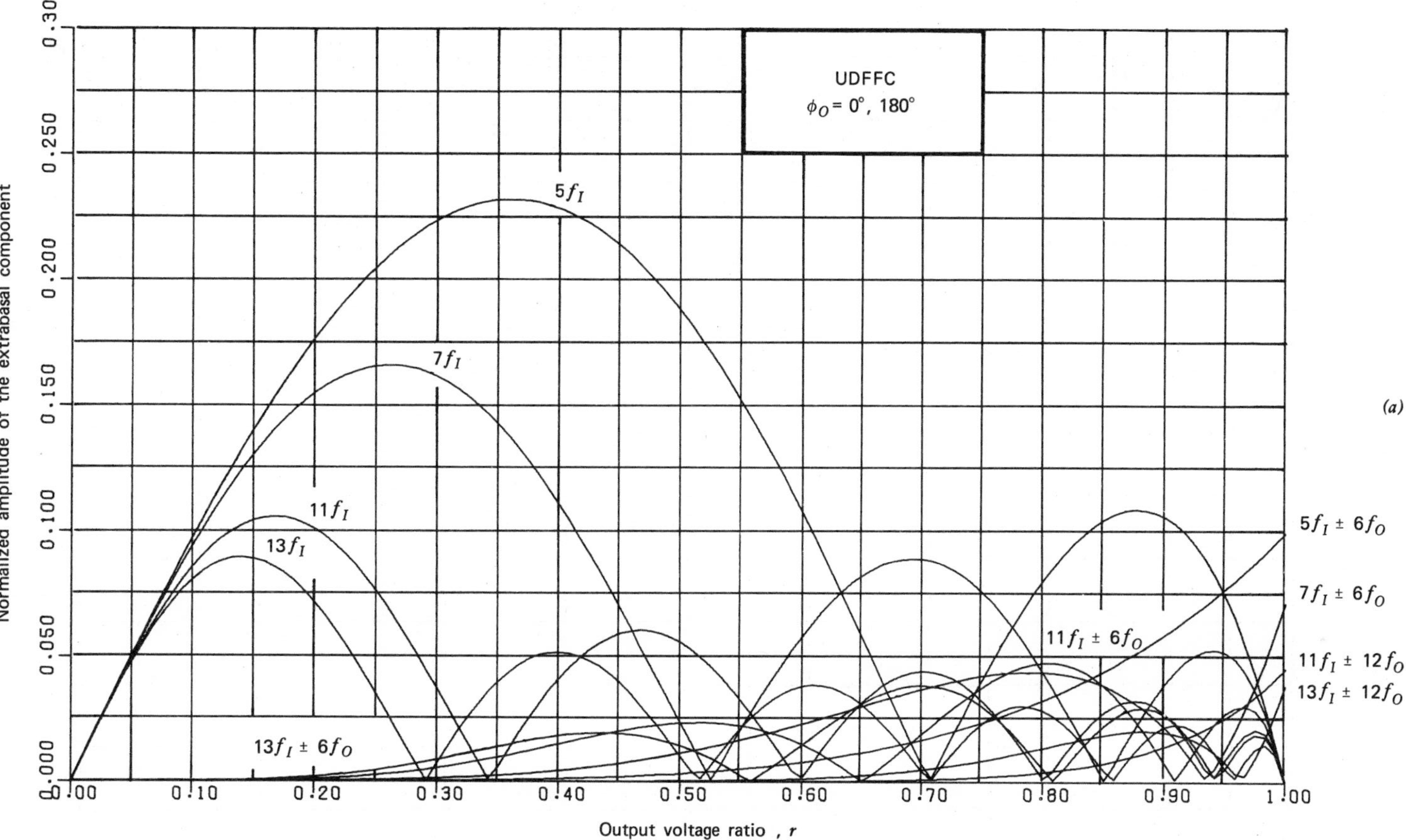
UDFFC
$\phi_O = 0°, 180°$
$5f_I$
$7f_I$
$11f_I$
$13f_I$
$13f_I \pm 6f_O$
$11f_I \pm 6f_O$
$5f_I \pm 6f_O$
$7f_I \pm 6f_O$
$11f_I \pm 12f_O$
$13f_I \pm 12f_O$
0.000
0.050
0.100
0.150
0.200
0.250
0.300
Normalized amplitude of the extrabasal component
0.00
0.10
0.20
0.30
0.40
0.50
0.60
0.70
0.80
0.90
1.00
Output voltage ratio , r

(a)

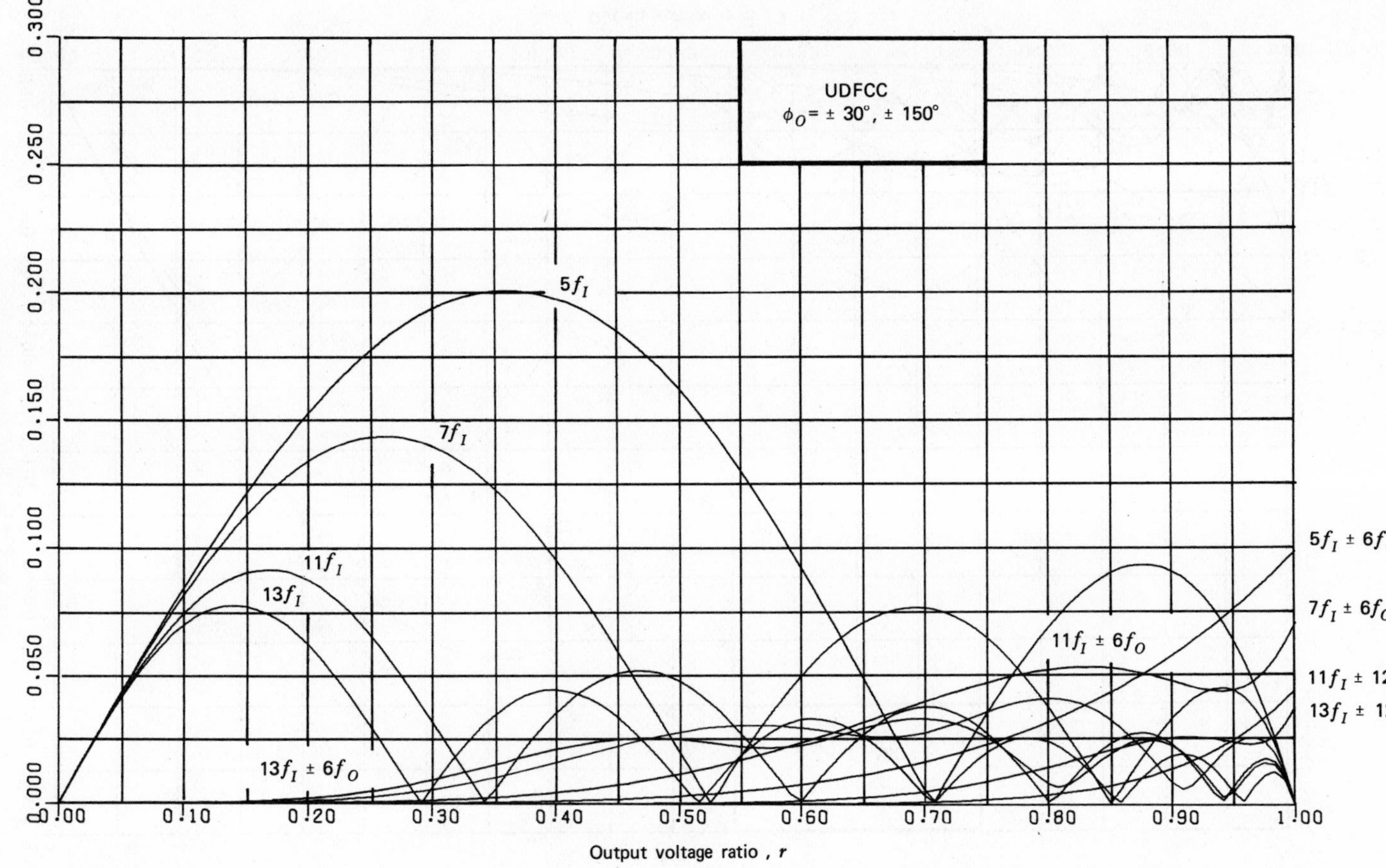
UDFCC
$\phi_O = \pm 30°, \pm 150°$
$5f_I$
$7f_I$
$11f_I$
$13f_I$
$13f_I \pm 6f_O$
$11f_I \pm 6f_O$
$5f_I \pm 6f_O$
$7f_I \pm 6f_O$
$11f_I \pm 12f_O$
$13f_I \pm 12f_O$
Normalized amplitude of the extrabasal component
0.000
0.050
0.100
0.150
0.200
0.250
0.300
Output voltage ratio, r
0.00
0.10
0.20
0.30
0.40
0.50
0.60
0.70
0.80
0.90
1.00
(b)

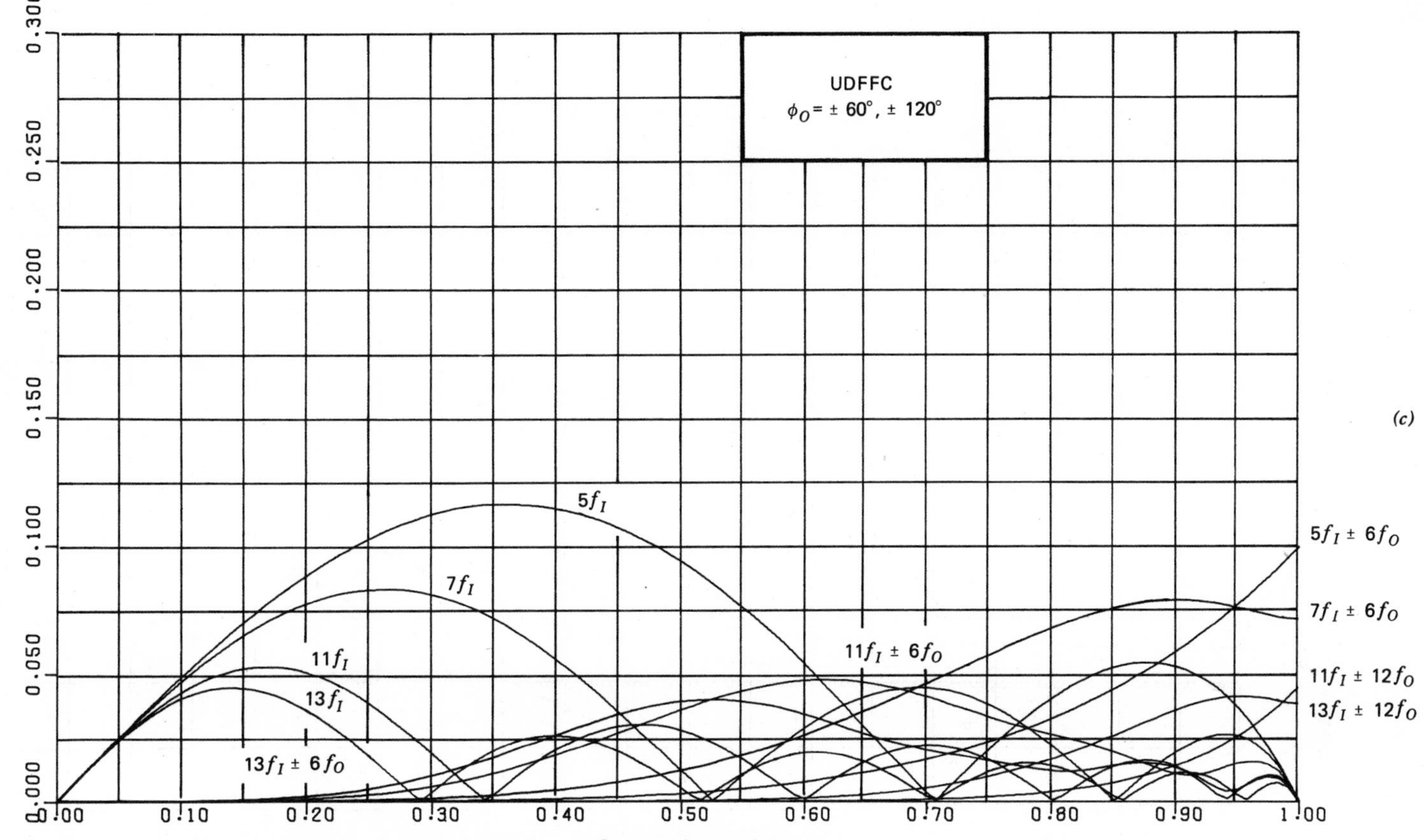

Figure 6.34 Normalized amplitudes of the extrabasal components in the input current of the UDFFC with balanced three-phase output versus the output voltage ratio. *a* $\phi_O = 0°$ and $180°$; *b* $\phi_O = \pm 30°$ and $\pm 150°$; *c* $\phi_O = \pm 60°$ and $\pm 120°$.

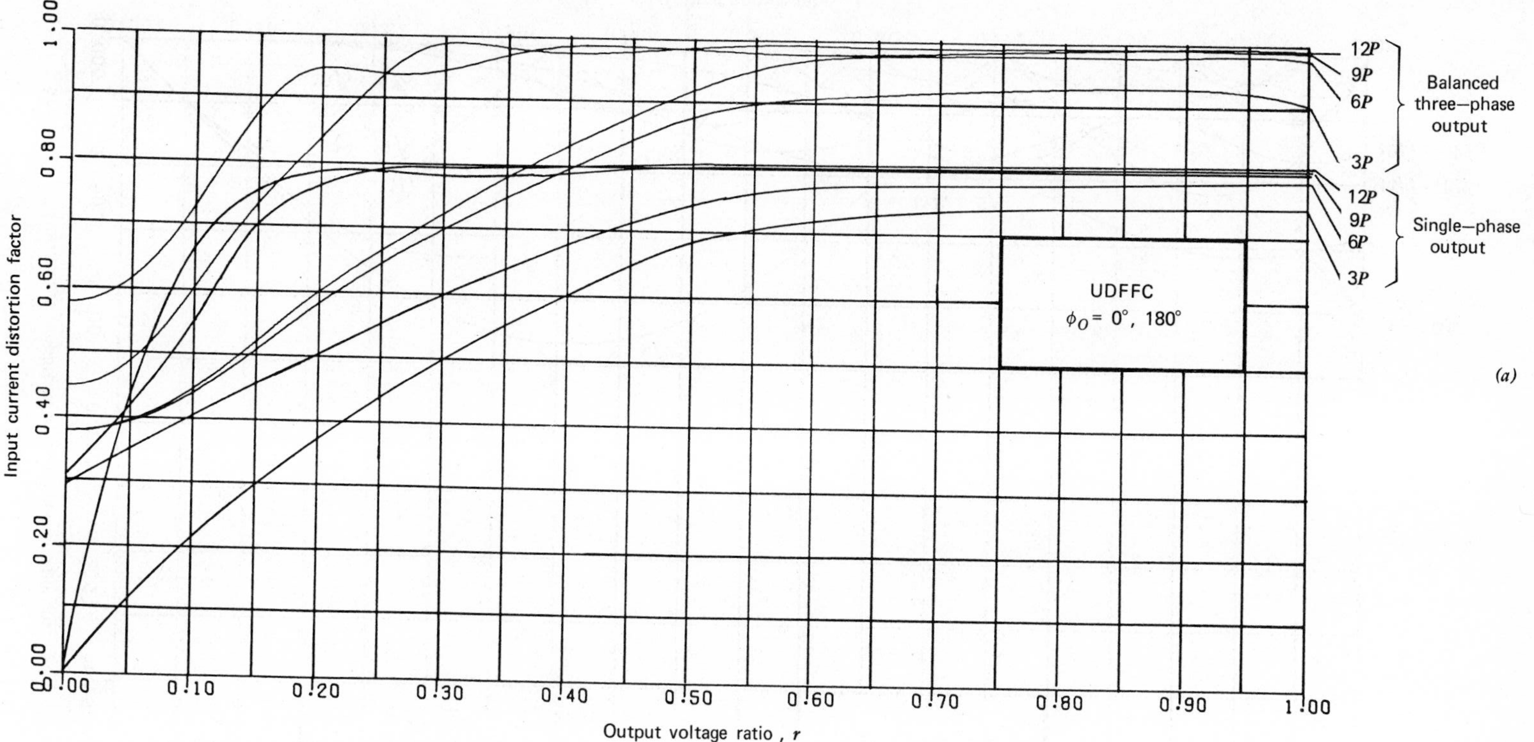

12P
9P
6P
3P
Balanced three–phase output
12P
9P
6P
3P
Single–phase output
UDFFC
$\phi_O = 0°, 180°$
Input current distortion factor
0.00
0.20
0.40
0.60
0.80
1.00
Output voltage ratio , r
0.00
0.10
0.20
0.30
0.40
0.50
0.60
0.70
0.80
0.90
1.00

(a)

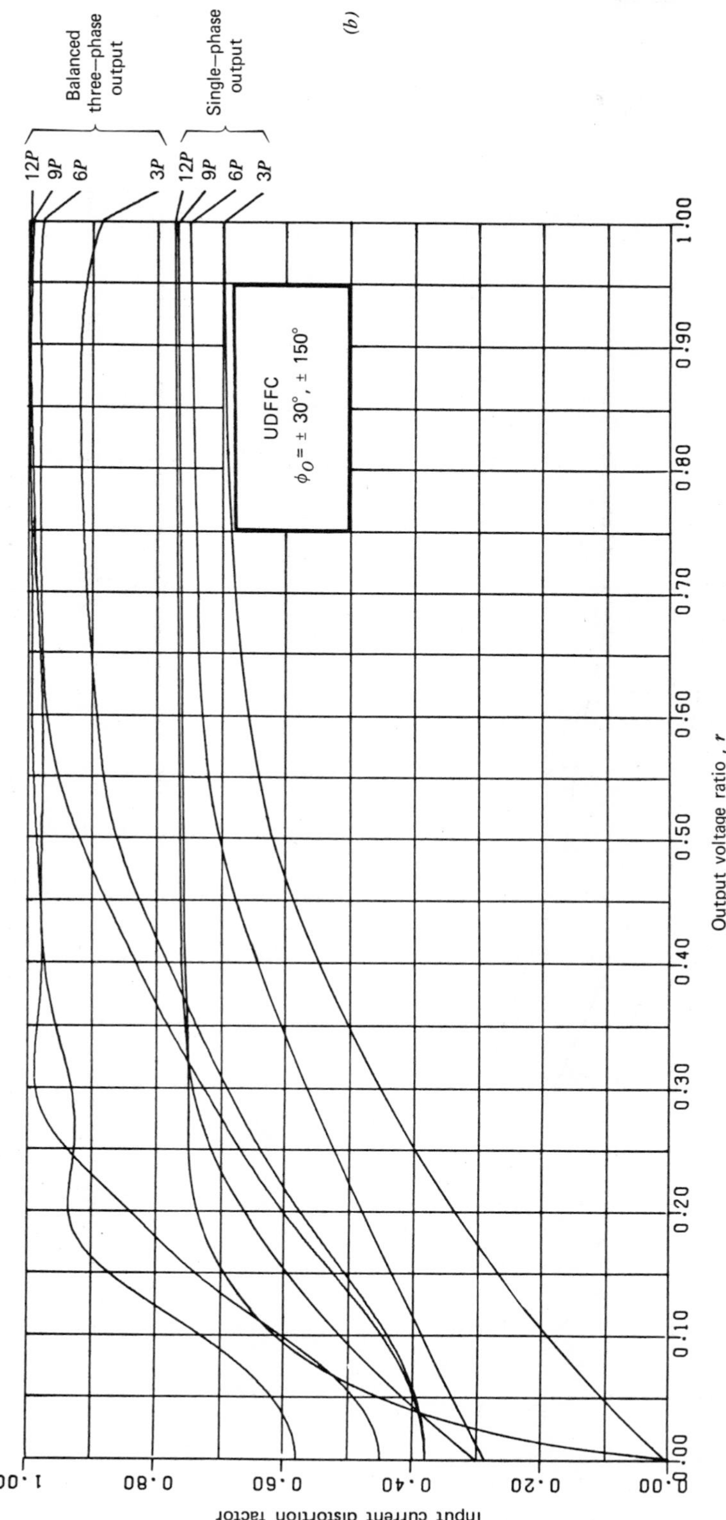

Balanced three-phase output
12P
9P
6P
3P
Single-phase output
12P
9P
6P
3P
UDFFC
$\phi_O = \pm 30°, \pm 150°$
Input current distortion factor
0.00
0.20
0.40
0.60
0.80
1.00
Output voltage ratio, r
0.00
0.10
0.20
0.30
0.40
0.50
0.60
0.70
0.80
0.90
1.00

(b)

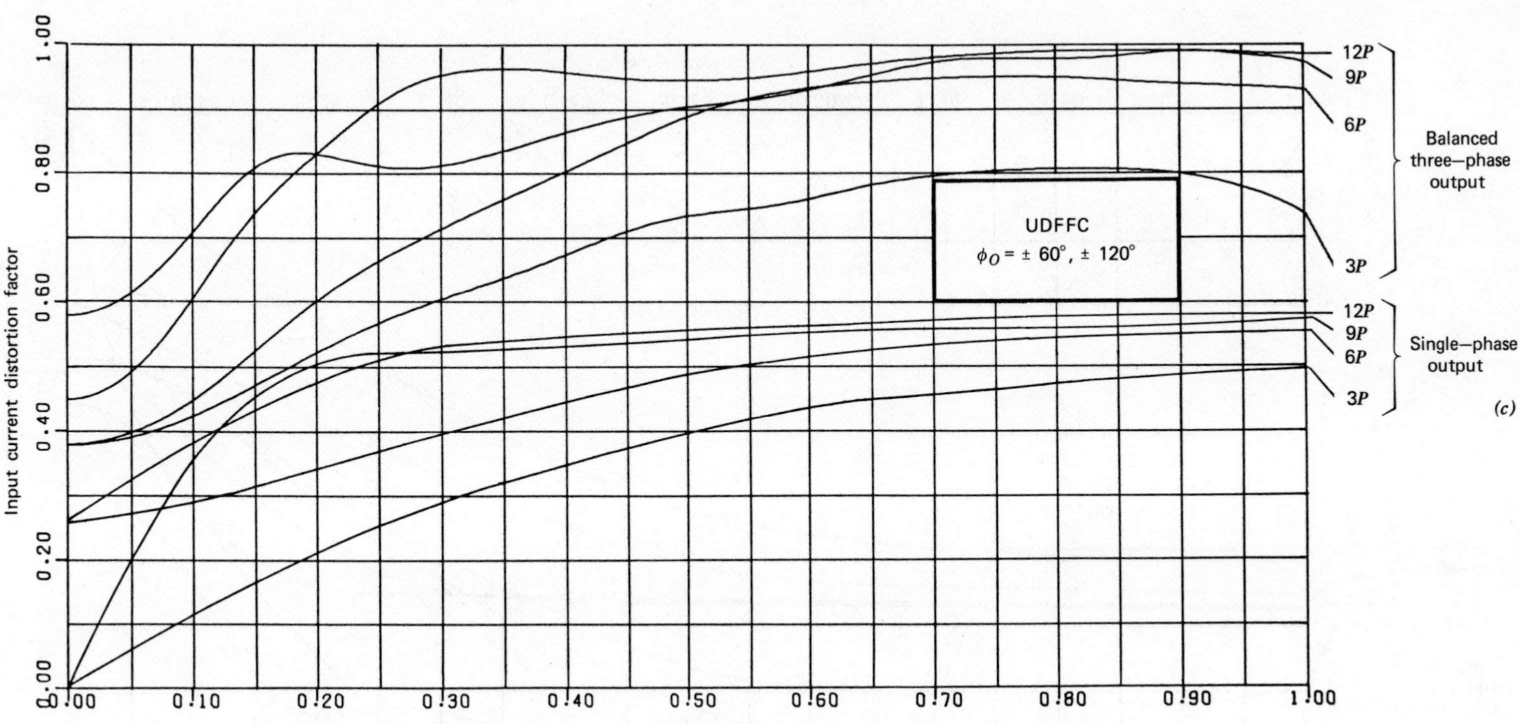

Figure 6.35 Variation of the input current distortion factor of the UDFFC, with the output voltage ratio, for pulse numbers three, six, nine, and twelve. *a* $\phi_O = 0°$ and 180°; *b* $\phi_O = \pm 30°$ and $\pm 150°$; *c* $\phi_O = \pm 60°$ and $\pm 120°$.

Thus

$$\frac{f_E}{f_I} = 1 \pm 2n\frac{f_O}{f_I} \tag{6.53}$$

$$\frac{f_E}{f_I} = (Pk - 1) \pm n\frac{f_O}{f_I} \tag{6.54}$$

and

$$\frac{f_E}{f_I} = (Pk + 1) \pm n\frac{f_O}{f_I} \tag{6.55}$$

For a balanced three-phase output:

$$f_E = f_I \pm 6nf_O \tag{6.56}$$

$$f_E = (Pk - 1)f_I \pm 3nf_O \tag{6.57}$$

and

$$f_E = (Pk + 1)f_I \pm 3nf_O \tag{6.58}$$

where P, k, and n are as defined above.

Thus

$$\frac{f_E}{f_I} = 1 \pm 6n\frac{f_O}{f_I} \tag{6.59}$$

$$\frac{f_E}{f_I} = (Pk - 1) \pm 3n\frac{f_O}{f_I} \tag{6.60}$$

and

$$\frac{f_E}{f_I} = (Pk + 1) \pm 3n\frac{f_O}{f_I} \tag{6.61}$$

The frequency chart of Figure 6.36 shows the ratios of extrabasal frequency to input frequency, f_E/f_I, plotted against the output to input frequency ratio, f_O/f_I, for values of Pk up to 12, for both single-phase and balanced three-phase outputs.

The frequency chart is similar to that of the UDFFC, except that each family of extrabasal components now contains an infinite number of members (of diminishing amplitude).

With a single-phase output, as for the UDFFC, the $f_I - 2f_O$ component, ever present regardless of the circuit pulse number, is the most objectionable. For a balanced three-phase output, this component is absent, and the distortion of the input current wave is generally much improved.

6.7.4.2 *Amplitudes of Extrabasal Components with Sinusoidal Mean Output Voltage.* Tables 6.7–6.11 show the amplitudes of the principal extrabasal components present in the input current of the NCC with sinusoidal mean output voltage, with single- and balanced three-phase outputs, for various output displacement angles.

6.7.4.3 *Distortion Factor of the Input Current with Sinusoidal Mean Output Voltage.* Figure 6.37 shows the distortion factor of the input current of the NCC with sinusoidal mean output voltage, plotted against the output voltage ratio, for three-, six-, and twelve-pulse circuits, with single- and balanced three-phase outputs, for various output displacement angles.

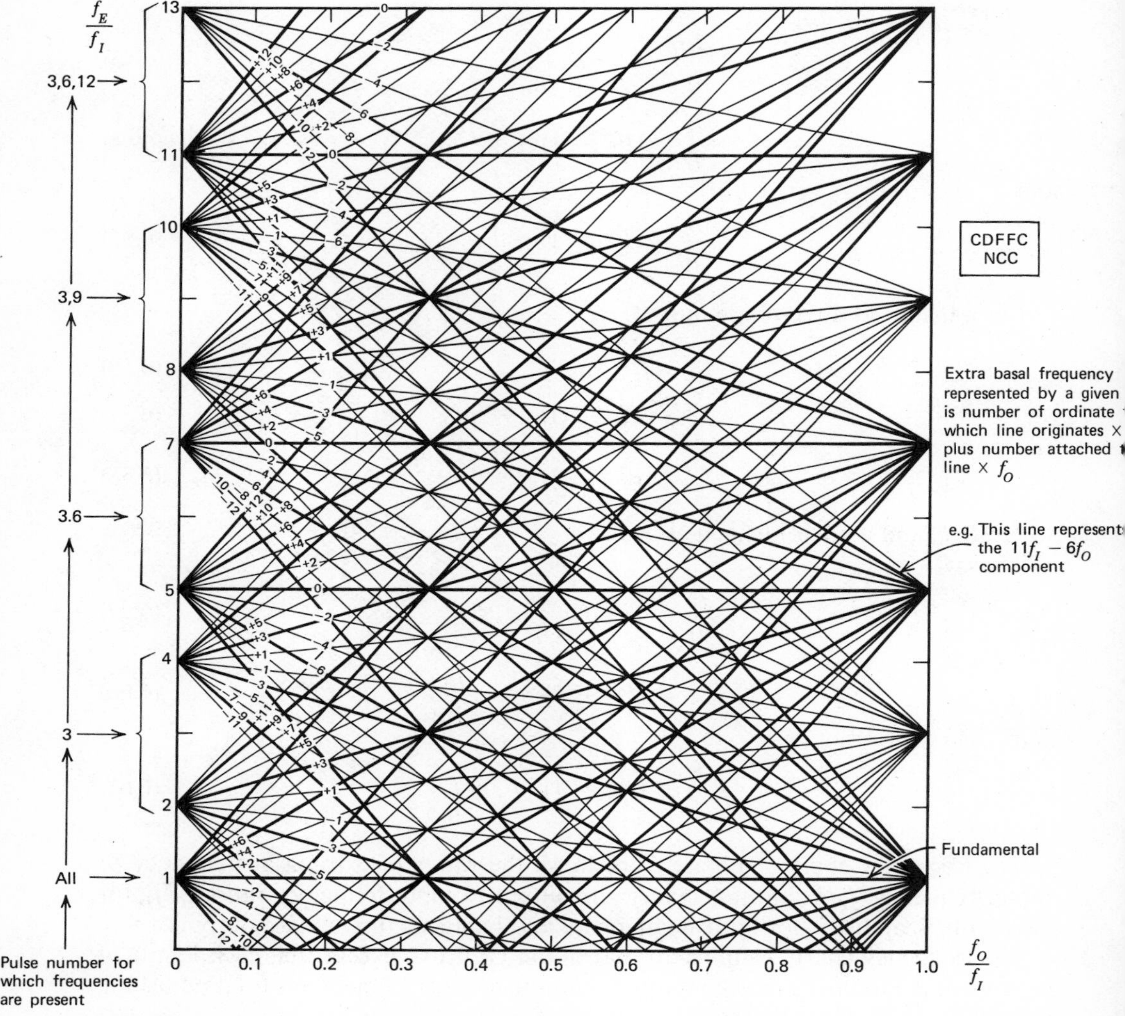

Figure 6.36 Frequencies of principal extrabasal components in input current of NCC and CDFFC, expressed as ratio of input frequency, versus output to input frequency ratio. For single-phase output, all frequencies shown are present. For balanced three-phase output, only frequencies shown by heavy lines are present.

TABLE 6.7. Amplitudes of Extrabasal Components with Frequencies of $f_I \pm 2nf_O$, in the Input Current of the NCC with Sinusoidal Mean Output Voltage

	$f_I \pm 2nf_O$																										
	$\phi_O = 0°, 180°$						$\phi_O = \pm 30°, \pm 150°$							$\phi_O = \pm 60°, \pm 120°$							$\phi_O = \pm 90°$						
$2n \rightarrow$	2	4	[6]	8	10	[12]	2		4	[6]	8	10	[12]	2		4	[6]	8	10	[12]	2		4	[6]	8	10	[12]
$r\downarrow$							(black)	(white)						(black)	(white)						(black)	(white)					
1.0	0.42	0.18	0.00	0.04	0.00	0.02	0.72	0.17	0.12	0.06	0.01	0.01	0.01	0.95	0.03	0.03	0.02	0.02	0.01	0.01	1.00	0.00	0.00	0.00	0.00	0.00	0.00
0.9	0.39	0.12	0.03	0.02	0.01	0.01	0.61	0.19	0.09	0.03	0.01	0.01	0.01	0.80	0.06	0.04	0.02	0.01	0.01	0.01	0.86	0.02	0.01	0.01	0.01	0.00	0.00
0.8	0.37	0.10	0.03	0.02	0.01	0.01	0.56	0.20	0.08	0.03	0.02	0.01	0.01	0.71	0.09	0.04	0.02	0.01	0.01	0.01	0.77	0.05	0.03	0.02	0.01	0.01	0.00
0.7	0.36	0.09	0.03	0.02	0.01	0.01	0.52	0.22	0.08	0.03	0.02	0.01	0.01	0.64	0.12	0.05	0.02	0.01	0.01	0.01	0.69	0.09	0.04	0.02	0.01	0.01	0.01
0.6	0.35	0.08	0.03	0.02	0.01	0.01	0.48	0.23	0.07	0.03	0.02	0.01	0.01	0.58	0.15	0.06	0.03	0.01	0.01	0.01	0.62	0.12	0.05	0.02	0.01	0.01	0.01
0.5	0.34	0.08	0.03	0.02	0.01	0.01	0.45	0.25	0.07	0.03	0.02	0.01	0.01	0.53	0.18	0.06	0.03	0.01	0.01	0.01	0.56	0.15	0.05	0.02	0.01	0.01	0.01
0.4	0.34	0.07	0.03	0.02	0.01	0.01	0.42	0.26	0.07	0.03	0.02	0.01	0.01	0.49	0.21	0.06	0.03	0.02	0.01	0.01	0.51	0.19	0.06	0.03	0.01	0.01	0.01
0.3	0.34	0.07	0.03	0.02	0.01	0.01	0.40	0.28	0.07	0.03	0.02	0.01	0.01	0.44	0.24	0.06	0.03	0.02	0.01	0.01	0.46	0.22	0.06	0.03	0.02	0.01	0.01
0.2	0.34	0.07	0.03	0.02	0.01	0.01	0.38	0.30	0.07	0.03	0.02	0.01	0.01	0.41	0.27	0.07	0.03	0.02	0.01	0.01	0.42	0.26	0.06	0.03	0.02	0.01	0.01
0.1	0.33	0.07	0.03	0.02	0.01	0.01	0.35	0.31	0.07	0.03	0.02	0.01	0.01	0.37	0.30	0.07	0.03	0.02	0.01	0.01	0.37	0.30	0.07	0.03	0.02	0.01	0.01

Notes: 1. Tables show amplitude of component as per-unit value of the total fundamental component.

2. These components are present in the input current of all NCCs regardless of pulse number. For a balanced 3-phase output, only those components whose numbers are boxed thus □ are present.

3. For all values of $2n$ except $2n = 2$, the values given apply to both the $f_I + 2nf_O$ and $f_I - 2nf_O$ components.
For $\phi_O = 0°, 180°$, and $2n = 2$, the values given apply to both the $f_I + 2f_O$ and $f_I - 2f_O$ components.
For other values of ϕ_O, and $2n = 2$:
The values given in the "black" column apply to the $f_I + 2f_O$ component for positive ϕ_O, and to the $f_I - 2f_O$ component for negative ϕ_O.
The values given in the "white" column apply to the $f_I + 2f_O$ component for negative ϕ_O, and to the $f_I - 2f_O$ component for positive ϕ_O.

TABLE 6.8. Amplitudes of the Extrabasal Components Having Frequencies of $2f_I \pm (2n+1)f_O$ and $4f_I \pm (2n+1)f_O$, in the Input Current of the NCC with Sinusoidal Mean Output Voltage

$2f_I \pm (2n+1)f_O$

$\phi_O = 0°, 180°$

r↓ \ $(2n+1)$→	1	[3]	5	7	[9]	11
1.0	0.35	0.23	0.09	0.02	0.02	0.01
0.9	0.37	0.17	0.04	0.00	0.00	0.00
0.8	0.38	0.13	0.03	0.00	0.00	0.00
0.7	0.38	0.11	0.02	0.00	0.00	0.00
0.6	0.39	0.09	0.02	0.00	0.00	0.00
0.5	0.39	0.07	0.01	0.00	0.00	0.00
0.4	0.39	0.06	0.01	0.00	0.00	0.00
0.3	0.39	0.04	0.01	0.00	0.00	0.00
0.2	0.39	0.03	0.00	0.00	0.00	0.00
0.1	0.39	0.01	0.00	0.00	0.00	0.00

$\phi_O = \pm 30°, \pm 150°$

r↓ \ $(2n+1)$→	1 (black)	1 (white)	[3] (black)	[3] (white)	5	7	[9]	11
1.0	0.48	0.16	0.33	0.13	0.08	0.03	0.01	0.01
0.9	0.49	0.21	0.24	0.11	0.04	0.01	0.01	0.00
0.8	0.49	0.23	0.19	0.09	0.03	0.01	0.01	0.00
0.7	0.48	0.26	0.15	0.08	0.03	0.01	0.00	0.00
0.6	0.48	0.28	0.12	0.07	0.02	0.01	0.00	0.00
0.5	0.46	0.30	0.10	0.06	0.02	0.01	0.00	0.00
0.4	0.45	0.32	0.07	0.05	0.01	0.00	0.00	0.00
0.3	0.44	0.34	0.05	0.04	0.01	0.00	0.00	0.00
0.2	0.43	0.36	0.03	0.03	0.01	0.00	0.00	0.00
0.1	0.41	0.38	0.02	0.02	0.00	0.00	0.00	0.00

$\phi_O = \pm 60°, \pm 120°$

r↓ \ $(2n+1)$→	1 (black)	1 (white)	[3] (black)	[3] (white)	5	7	[9]	11
1.0	0.51	0.03	0.46	0.03	0.02	0.02	0.02	0.01
0.9	0.53	0.07	0.35	0.04	0.02	0.01	0.01	0.01
0.8	0.54	0.11	0.28	0.05	0.02	0.01	0.01	0.01
0.7	0.53	0.15	0.22	0.06	0.02	0.01	0.01	0.00
0.6	0.52	0.19	0.18	0.06	0.02	0.01	0.01	0.00
0.5	0.51	0.23	0.14	0.06	0.02	0.01	0.01	0.00
0.4	0.49	0.26	0.10	0.05	0.02	0.01	0.00	0.00
0.3	0.47	0.30	0.07	0.04	0.01	0.01	0.00	0.00
0.2	0.45	0.33	0.04	0.03	0.01	0.00	0.00	0.00
0.1	0.42	0.36	0.02	0.02	0.00	0.00	0.00	0.00

$\phi_O = \pm 90°$

r↓ \ $(2n+1)$→	1 (black)	1 (white)	[3] (black)	[3] (white)	5	7	[9]	11
1.0	0.50	0.00	0.50	0.00	0.00	0.00	0.00	0.00
0.9	0.53	0.03	0.40	0.02	0.01	0.01	0.01	0.00
0.8	0.54	0.07	0.32	0.03	0.02	0.01	0.01	0.00
0.7	0.54	0.11	0.26	0.04	0.02	0.01	0.01	0.00
0.6	0.54	0.16	0.20	0.05	0.02	0.01	0.01	0.00
0.5	0.52	0.20	0.15	0.05	0.02	0.01	0.01	0.00
0.4	0.50	0.24	0.11	0.05	0.02	0.01	0.00	0.00
0.3	0.48	0.28	0.08	0.04	0.01	0.01	0.00	0.00
0.2	0.45	0.32	0.05	0.03	0.01	0.00	0.00	0.00
0.1	0.43	0.36	0.02	0.02	0.00	0.00	0.00	0.00

$4f_I \pm (2n+1)f_O$

$\phi_O = 0°, 180°$

r↓ \ $(2n+1)$→	1	[3]	5	7	[9]	11
1.0	0.09	0.14	0.12	0.05	0.01	0.01
0.9	0.14	0.13	0.07	0.02	0.00	0.00
0.8	0.16	0.11	0.05	0.01	0.00	0.00
0.7	0.17	0.10	0.03	0.01	0.00	0.00
0.6	0.18	0.08	0.02	0.01	0.00	0.00
0.5	0.18	0.07	0.02	0.00	0.00	0.00
0.4	0.19	0.05	0.01	0.00	0.00	0.00
0.3	0.19	0.04	0.01	0.00	0.00	0.00
0.2	0.19	0.03	0.00	0.00	0.00	0.00
0.1	0.20	0.01	0.00	0.00	0.00	0.00

$\phi_O = \pm 30°, \pm 150°$

r↓ \ $(2n+1)$→	1 (black)	1 (white)	[3] (black)	[3] (white)	5 (black)	5 (white)	7	[9]	11
1.0	0.08	0.08	0.20	0.08	0.18	0.06	0.04	0.02	0.01
0.9	0.16	0.10	0.20	0.06	0.11	0.04	0.02	0.01	0.00
0.8	0.19	0.10	0.18	0.05	0.07	0.03	0.01	0.01	0.00
0.7	0.21	0.09	0.15	0.05	0.05	0.02	0.01	0.00	0.00
0.6	0.23	0.10	0.13	0.05	0.04	0.02	0.01	0.00	0.00
0.5	0.23	0.11	0.10	0.04	0.02	0.02	0.01	0.00	0.00
0.4	0.24	0.12	0.08	0.04	0.02	0.01	0.00	0.00	0.00
0.3	0.23	0.14	0.06	0.03	0.01	0.01	0.00	0.00	0.00
0.2	0.22	0.16	0.04	0.03	0.01	0.01	0.00	0.00	0.00
0.1	0.21	0.18	0.02	0.01	0.00	0.00	0.00	0.00	0.00

$\phi_O = \pm 60°, \pm 120°$

r↓ \ $(2n+1)$→	1 (black)	1 (white)	[3] (black)	[3] (white)	5 (black)	5 (white)	7	[9]	11
1.0	0.02	0.02	0.25	0.02	0.23	0.02	0.02	0.01	0.01
0.9	0.09	0.05	0.27	0.03	0.14	0.01	0.01	0.00	0.00
0.8	0.14	0.05	0.25	0.02	0.09	0.01	0.00	0.00	0.00
0.7	0.18	0.05	0.23	0.02	0.06	0.01	0.00	0.00	0.00
0.6	0.21	0.04	0.19	0.02	0.04	0.01	0.00	0.00	0.00
0.5	0.24	0.04	0.15	0.02	0.02	0.01	0.01	0.00	0.00
0.4	0.25	0.06	0.12	0.03	0.01	0.01	0.01	0.00	0.00
0.3	0.25	0.10	0.08	0.03	0.01	0.01	0.00	0.00	0.00
0.2	0.24	0.13	0.05	0.02	0.01	0.01	0.00	0.00	0.00
0.1	0.22	0.17	0.02	0.02	0.00	0.00	0.00	0.00	0.00

$\phi_O = \pm 90°$

r↓ \ $(2n+1)$→	1 (black)	1 (white)	[3] (black)	[3] (white)	5 (black)	5 (white)	7	[9]	11
1.0	0.00	0.00	0.25	0.00	0.25	0.00	0.00	0.00	0.00
0.9	0.04	0.02	0.29	0.01	0.16	0.01	0.00	0.00	0.00
0.8	0.09	0.04	0.28	0.02	0.10	0.01	0.00	0.00	0.00
0.7	0.15	0.04	0.26	0.01	0.05	0.00	0.00	0.00	0.00
0.6	0.20	0.02	0.22	0.00	0.02	0.00	0.00	0.00	0.00
0.5	0.23	0.00	0.18	0.01	0.01	0.01	0.00	0.00	0.00
0.4	0.25	0.04	0.13	0.02	0.00	0.01	0.01	0.00	0.00
0.3	0.25	0.08	0.09	0.03	0.01	0.01	0.01	0.00	0.00
0.2	0.25	0.12	0.06	0.02	0.01	0.01	0.00	0.00	0.00
0.1	0.23	0.16	0.02	0.02	0.00	0.00	0.00	0.00	0.00

Notes: 1. Tables show amplitude of harmonic, as per-unit value of the total fundamental component.

2. These components are present in the input current of the 3-pulse NCC. For a balanced 3-phase output, only those components whose numbers are boxed thus □ are present.

3. Where there is only one column for a given value of $(2n+1)$, the values given apply to both the "plus" and "minus" $(2n+1)f_O$ components.

Where there are two columns for a given value of $(2n+1)$:

The values given in the "black" column apply to the "plus" $(2n+1)f_O$ components for positive ϕ_O, and to the "minus" $(2n+1)f_O$ components for negative ϕ_O.

The values given in the "white" column apply to the "plus" $(2n+1)f_O$ components for negative ϕ_O, and to the "minus" $(2n+1)f_O$ components for positive ϕ_O.

TABLE 6.9. Amplitudes of the Extrabasal Components Having Frequencies of $5f_I \pm 2nf_O$ and $7f_I \pm 2nf_O$, in the Input Current of the NCC with Sinusoidal Mean Output Voltage

$5f_I \pm 2nf_O$

	$\phi_O = 0°, 180°$						$\phi_O = \pm 30°, \pm 150°$									$\phi_O = \pm 60°, \pm 120°$									$\phi_O = \pm 90°$								
$2n \rightarrow$ / $r \downarrow$	[0]	2	4	[6]	8	10	[0]	2		4		[6]		8	10	[0]	2		4		[6]		8	10	[0]	2		4		[6]		8	10
1.0	0.04	0.07	0.11	0.09	0.05	0.01	0.05	0.05	0.05	0.16	0.06	0.14	0.05	0.04	0.02	0.02	0.02	0.02	0.20	0.02	0.18	0.02	0.01	0.01	0.00	0.00	0.00	0.20	0.00	0.20	0.00	0.00	0.00
0.9	0.09	0.11	0.09	0.05	0.02	0.00	0.08	0.12	0.06	0.15	0.05	0.08	0.03	0.01	0.00	0.05	0.09	0.03	0.21	0.01	0.10	0.01	0.00	0.00	0.02	0.04	0.01	0.23	0.01	0.12	0.00	0.00	0.00
0.8	0.11	0.11	0.07	0.03	0.01	0.00	0.09	0.15	0.07	0.13	0.04	0.05	0.02	0.01	0.00	0.05	0.14	0.02	0.19	0.01	0.06	0.01	0.00	0.00	0.03	0.11	0.01	0.21	0.00	0.06	0.00	0.00	0.00
0.7	0.14	0.11	0.06	0.02	0.01	0.00	0.10	0.16	0.06	0.10	0.03	0.03	0.01	0.00	0.00	0.04	0.17	0.02	0.15	0.01	0.04	0.01	0.00	0.00	0.02	0.16	0.00	0.18	0.00	0.03	0.00	0.00	0.00
0.6	0.15	0.10	0.05	0.02	0.01	0.00	0.12	0.16	0.06	0.08	0.02	0.02	0.01	0.00	0.00	0.05	0.19	0.03	0.12	0.01	0.02	0.01	0.00	0.00	0.00	0.19	0.01	0.14	0.01	0.01	0.01	0.00	0.00
0.5	0.17	0.10	0.04	0.01	0.00	0.00	0.14	0.16	0.06	0.06	0.02	0.01	0.01	0.00	0.00	0.08	0.20	0.03	0.08	0.01	0.01	0.01	0.00	0.00	0.05	0.21	0.02	0.09	0.01	0.00	0.01	0.00	0.00
0.4	0.18	0.09	0.03	0.01	0.00	0.00	0.16	0.15	0.05	0.04	0.01	0.01	0.01	0.00	0.00	0.11	0.19	0.03	0.05	0.01	0.00	0.00	0.00	0.00	0.09	0.20	0.03	0.05	0.01	0.00	0.00	0.00	0.00
0.3	0.19	0.08	0.02	0.01	0.00	0.00	0.18	0.13	0.04	0.03	0.01	0.01	0.01	0.00	0.00	0.15	0.17	0.02	0.02	0.00	0.00	0.00	0.00	0.00	0.13	0.18	0.02	0.02	0.00	0.00	0.00	0.00	0.00
0.2	0.20	0.07	0.02	0.01	0.00	0.00	0.19	0.11	0.04	0.02	0.01	0.01	0.01	0.00	0.00	0.18	0.14	0.02	0.01	0.01	0.00	0.00	0.00	0.00	0.17	0.15	0.00	0.00	0.00	0.00	0.00	0.00	0.00
0.1	0.20	0.07	0.01	0.01	0.00	0.00	0.20	0.09	0.05	0.01	0.01	0.01	0.01	0.00	0.00	0.19	0.10	0.04	0.01	0.01	0.01	0.01	0.00	0.00	0.19	0.11	0.03	0.01	0.01	0.00	0.00	0.00	0.00

$7f_I \pm 2nf_O$

$\phi_O = 0°, 180°$

$2n \rightarrow$ / $r\downarrow$	[0]	2	4	[6]	8	10
1.0	0.03	0.02	0.05	0.07	0.07	0.03
0.9	0.05	0.06	0.07	0.06	0.03	0.01
0.8	0.06	0.07	0.07	0.04	0.02	0.01
0.7	0.07	0.08	0.06	0.03	0.01	0.00
0.6	0.09	0.08	0.05	0.02	0.01	0.00
0.5	0.10	0.08	0.04	0.01	0.00	0.00
0.4	0.12	0.07	0.03	0.01	0.00	0.00
0.3	0.13	0.06	0.02	0.01	0.00	0.00
0.2	0.14	0.06	0.02	0.01	0.00	0.00
0.1	0.14	0.05	0.01	0.00	0.00	0.00

$\phi_O = \pm 30°, \pm 150°$

$2n \rightarrow$ / $r\downarrow$	[0]	2 (black)	2 (white)	4 (black)	4 (white)	[6] (black)	[6] (white)	8 (black)	8 (white)	10
1.0	0.02	0.03	0.03	0.04	0.04	0.11	0.04	0.10	0.04	0.03
0.9	0.05	0.05	0.05	0.09	0.04	0.10	0.03	0.05	0.02	0.01
0.8	0.06	0.07	0.05	0.10	0.03	0.07	0.02	0.03	0.01	0.00
0.7	0.06	0.09	0.04	0.10	0.03	0.05	0.01	0.01	0.01	0.00
0.6	0.07	0.10	0.05	0.09	0.02	0.03	0.01	0.01	0.00	0.00
0.5	0.08	0.11	0.04	0.07	0.02	0.02	0.01	0.00	0.00	0.00
0.4	0.09	0.11	0.04	0.05	0.01	0.01	0.00	0.00	0.00	0.00
0.3	0.11	0.10	0.03	0.03	0.01	0.01	0.00	0.00	0.00	0.00
0.2	0.13	0.09	0.03	0.02	0.01	0.00	0.00	0.00	0.00	0.00
0.1	0.14	0.07	0.03	0.01	0.01	0.00	0.00	0.00	0.00	0.00

$7f_I \pm 2nf_O$

$\phi_O = \pm 60°, \pm 120°$

$2n \rightarrow$ / $r\downarrow$	[0]	2 (black)	2 (white)	4 (black)	4 (white)	[6] (black)	[6] (white)	8 (black)	8 (white)	10
1.0	0.01	0.01	0.01	0.01	0.01	0.14	0.01	0.13	0.01	0.01
0.9	0.02	0.04	0.02	0.08	0.01	0.14	0.01	0.06	0.01	0.00
0.8	0.03	0.04	0.02	0.12	0.01	0.11	0.01	0.03	0.00	0.00
0.7	0.04	0.06	0.02	0.13	0.01	0.08	0.00	0.01	0.00	0.00
0.6	0.04	0.09	0.02	0.12	0.01	0.05	0.00	0.00	0.00	0.00
0.5	0.03	0.12	0.02	0.10	0.01	0.02	0.00	0.00	0.00	0.00
0.4	0.04	0.14	0.02	0.07	0.01	0.01	0.00	0.00	0.00	0.00
0.3	0.07	0.13	0.02	0.04	0.01	0.00	0.00	0.00	0.00	0.00
0.2	0.11	0.11	0.01	0.01	0.00	0.00	0.00	0.00	0.00	0.00
0.1	0.13	0.08	0.02	0.01	0.01	0.00	0.00	0.00	0.00	0.00

$\phi_O = \pm 90°$

$2n \rightarrow$ / $r\downarrow$	[0]	2 (black)	2 (white)	4 (black)	4 (white)	[6] (black)	[6] (white)	8 (black)	8 (white)	10
1.0	0.00	0.00	0.00	0.00	0.00	0.14	0.00	0.14	0.00	0.00
0.9	0.01	0.02	0.01	0.05	0.00	0.17	0.00	0.06	0.00	0.00
0.8	0.00	0.02	0.00	0.12	0.00	0.14	0.00	0.03	0.00	0.00
0.7	0.02	0.01	0.01	0.15	0.01	0.09	0.00	0.01	0.00	0.00
0.6	0.03	0.07	0.01	0.15	0.00	0.05	0.00	0.00	0.00	0.00
0.5	0.02	0.11	0.00	0.12	0.00	0.02	0.00	0.00	0.00	0.00
0.4	0.02	0.14	0.02	0.08	0.01	0.00	0.00	0.00	0.00	0.00
0.3	0.06	0.14	0.02	0.04	0.01	0.00	0.00	0.00	0.00	0.00
0.2	0.10	0.12	0.01	0.01	0.00	0.00	0.00	0.00	0.00	0.00
0.1	0.13	0.09	0.01	0.00	0.00	0.00	0.00	0.00	0.00	0.00

Notes: 1. Tables show amplitude of harmonic, as per-unit value of the total fundamental component.

2. These components are present in the input current of 3- and 6-pulse NCCs. For a balanced 3-phase output, only those components whose numbers are boxed thus □ are present.

3. Where there is only one column for a given value of $2n$, the values given apply to both the "plus" and "minus" $2nf_O$ components.
Where there are two columns for a given value of $2n$:
The values given in the "black" column apply to the "plus" $2nf_O$ components for positive ϕ_O, and to the "minus" $2nf_O$ components for negative ϕ_O.
The values given in the "white" column apply to the "plus" $2nf_O$ components for negative ϕ_O, and to the "minus" $2nf_O$ components for positive ϕ_O.

TABLE 6.10. Amplitudes of the Extrabasal Components with Frequencies of $11f_I \pm 2nf_O$ in the Input Current of the NCC with Sinusoidal Mean Output Voltage

	$11f_I \pm 2nf_O$																							
	$\phi_O = 0°, 180°$									$\phi_O = \pm 30°, \pm 150°$														
$2n \rightarrow$	[0]	2	4	[6]	8	10	[12]	14	16	[0]	2		4		[6]		8		10		[12]		14	16
$r \downarrow$											black	white	black	white	black	white	black	white	black	white	black	white		
1.0	0.01	0.01	0.01	0.01	0.03	0.05	0.04	0.02	0.01	0.01	0.01	0.01	0.01	0.01	0.01	0.01	0.02	0.02	0.07	0.03	0.07	0.02	0.02	0.01
0.9	0.02	0.03	0.03	0.04	0.04	0.03	0.01	0.00	0.00	0.02	0.02	0.02	0.03	0.02	0.03	0.02	0.06	0.02	0.05	0.01	0.02	0.01	0.00	0.00
0.8	0.03	0.03	0.04	0.04	0.03	0.02	0.01	0.00	0.00	0.03	0.03	0.03	0.03	0.02	0.05	0.02	0.06	0.01	0.03	0.01	0.01	0.00	0.00	0.00
0.7	0.04	0.04	0.04	0.03	0.02	0.01	0.00	0.00	0.00	0.03	0.04	0.03	0.04	0.02	0.06	0.01	0.04	0.01	0.02	0.00	0.00	0.00	0.00	0.00
0.6	0.04	0.04	0.04	0.03	0.01	0.01	0.00	0.00	0.00	0.04	0.04	0.03	0.06	0.02	0.05	0.01	0.03	0.01	0.01	0.00	0.00	0.00	0.00	0.00
0.5	0.05	0.05	0.04	0.02	0.01	0.00	0.00	0.00	0.00	0.04	0.05	0.03	0.06	0.02	0.04	0.01	0.01	0.00	0.00	0.00	0.00	0.00	0.00	0.00
0.4	0.06	0.05	0.03	0.01	0.00	0.00	0.00	0.00	0.00	0.04	0.06	0.03	0.05	0.01	0.02	0.01	0.01	0.00	0.00	0.00	0.00	0.00	0.00	0.00
0.3	0.07	0.05	0.02	0.01	0.00	0.00	0.00	0.00	0.00	0.05	0.07	0.03	0.04	0.01	0.01	0.00	0.00	0.00	0.00	0.00	0.00	0.00	0.00	0.00
0.2	0.08	0.04	0.01	0.00	0.00	0.00	0.00	0.00	0.00	0.07	0.07	0.02	0.02	0.01	0.00	0.00	0.00	0.00	0.00	0.00	0.00	0.00	0.00	0.00
0.1	0.09	0.03	0.01	0.00	0.00	0.00	0.00	0.00	0.00	0.08	0.05	0.02	0.01	0.01	0.00	0.00	0.00	0.00	0.00	0.00	0.00	0.00	0.00	0.00

	$11f_I \pm 2nf_O$																													
	$\phi_O = \pm 60°, \pm 120°$															$\phi_O = \pm 90°$														
$2n \rightarrow$	[0]	2		4		[6]		8		10		[12]		14	16	[0]	2		4		[6]		8		10		[12]		14	16
$r \downarrow$		black	white	black	white	black	white	black	white	black	white	black	white				black	white	black	white	black	white	black	white	black	white	black	white		
1.0	0.01	0.01	0.01	0.01	0.01	0.01	0.01	0.01	0.01	0.09	0.01	0.09	0.01	0.01	0.01	0.00	0.00	0.00	0.00	0.00	0.00	0.00	0.00	0.00	0.09	0.00	0.09	0.00	0.00	0.00
0.9	0.01	0.02	0.01	0.02	0.01	0.02	0.01	0.07	0.00	0.08	0.00	0.03	0.00	0.00	0.00	0.00	0.00	0.00	0.00	0.00	0.02	0.00	0.06	0.00	0.10	0.00	0.03	0.00	0.00	0.00
0.8	0.01	0.02	0.01	0.03	0.01	0.04	0.01	0.08	0.00	0.05	0.00	0.01	0.00	0.00	0.00	0.00	0.01	0.00	0.02	0.00	0.02	0.00	0.10	0.00	0.05	0.00	0.01	0.00	0.00	0.00
0.7	0.02	0.03	0.01	0.03	0.01	0.07	0.00	0.06	0.00	0.02	0.00	0.00	0.00	0.00	0.00	0.01	0.01	0.01	0.01	0.00	0.08	0.00	0.08	0.00	0.02	0.00	0.00	0.00	0.00	0.00
0.6	0.02	0.03	0.01	0.05	0.01	0.08	0.00	0.04	0.00	0.01	0.00	0.00	0.00	0.00	0.00	0.01	0.02	0.00	0.03	0.00	0.09	0.00	0.04	0.00	0.01	0.00	0.00	0.00	0.00	0.00
0.5	0.02	0.03	0.01	0.08	0.01	0.06	0.00	0.02	0.00	0.00	0.00	0.00	0.00	0.00	0.00	0.01	0.01	0.01	0.08	0.00	0.07	0.00	0.01	0.00	0.00	0.00	0.00	0.00	0.00	0.00
0.4	0.03	0.05	0.01	0.08	0.00	0.03	0.00	0.00	0.00	0.00	0.00	0.00	0.00	0.00	0.00	0.02	0.04	0.01	0.09	0.00	0.03	0.00	0.00	0.00	0.00	0.00	0.00	0.00	0.00	0.00
0.3	0.02	0.08	0.01	0.06	0.01	0.01	0.00	0.00	0.00	0.00	0.00	0.00	0.00	0.00	0.00	0.00	0.08	0.01	0.07	0.00	0.01	0.00	0.00	0.00	0.00	0.00	0.00	0.00	0.00	0.00
0.2	0.05	0.09	0.02	0.03	0.00	0.00	0.00	0.00	0.00	0.00	0.00	0.00	0.00	0.00	0.00	0.03	0.09	0.01	0.03	0.00	0.00	0.00	0.00	0.00	0.00	0.00	0.00	0.00	0.00	0.00
0.1	0.08	0.06	0.01	0.01	0.00	0.00	0.00	0.00	0.00	0.00	0.00	0.00	0.00	0.00	0.00	0.07	0.07	0.00	0.00	0.00	0.00	0.00	0.00	0.00	0.00	0.00	0.00	0.00	0.00	0.00

Notes: 1. Tables show amplitude of harmonic, as per-unit value of the total fundamental component.
2. These components are present in the input current of 3-, 6-, and 12-pulse NCCs. For a balanced 3-phase output, only those components whose numbers are boxed thus □ are present.
3. Where there is only one column for a given value of $2n$, the values given apply to both the "plus" and "minus" $2nf_O$ components.
Where there are two columns for a given value of $2n$:
The values given in the "black" column apply to the "plus" $2nf_O$ components for positive ϕ_O, and to the "minus" $2nf_O$ components for negative ϕ_O.
The values given in the "white" column apply to the "plus" $2nf_O$ components for negative ϕ_O, and to the "minus" $2nf_O$ components for positive ϕ_O.

TABLE 6.11. Amplitudes of the Extrabasal Components with Frequencies of $13f_I \pm 2nf_O$ in the Input Current of the NCC with Sinusoidal Mean Output Voltage

$13f_I \pm 2nf_O$

$\phi_O = 0°, 180°$

$2n \rightarrow$ / $r\downarrow$	[0]	2	4	[6]	8	10	[12]	14	16
1.0	0.01	0.01	0.01	0.01	0.01	0.02	0.04	0.04	0.02
0.9	0.02	0.02	0.02	0.02	0.03	0.03	0.02	0.01	0.00
0.8	0.02	0.02	0.02	0.03	0.03	0.02	0.01	0.00	0.00
0.7	0.03	0.03	0.03	0.03	0.02	0.01	0.01	0.00	0.00
0.6	0.03	0.03	0.03	0.03	0.02	0.01	0.00	0.00	0.00
0.5	0.03	0.04	0.03	0.02	0.01	0.00	0.00	0.00	0.00
0.4	0.04	0.04	0.03	0.01	0.01	0.00	0.00	0.00	0.00
0.3	0.05	0.04	0.02	0.01	0.00	0.00	0.00	0.00	0.00
0.2	0.07	0.04	0.01	0.00	0.00	0.00	0.00	0.00	0.00
0.1	0.07	0.03	0.01	0.00	0.00	0.00	0.00	0.00	0.00

$\phi_O = \pm 30°, \pm 150°$

$2n \rightarrow$ / $r\downarrow$	[0]	2 (black)	2 (white)	4 (black)	4 (white)	[6] (black)	[6] (white)	8 (black)	8 (white)	10 (black)	10 (white)	[12] (black)	[12] (white)	14 (black)	14 (white)	16
1.0	0.01	0.01	0.01	0.01	0.01	0.01	0.01	0.01	0.01	0.02	0.02	0.06	0.02	0.06	0.02	0.02
0.9	0.02	0.02	0.02	0.02	0.02	0.02	0.02	0.03	0.02	0.05	0.01	0.04	0.01	0.02	0.00	0.00
0.8	0.02	0.02	0.02	0.03	0.02	0.03	0.02	0.05	0.01	0.04	0.01	0.02	0.00	0.01	0.00	0.00
0.7	0.02	0.03	0.02	0.03	0.02	0.04	0.01	0.04	0.01	0.03	0.00	0.01	0.00	0.00	0.00	0.00
0.6	0.03	0.03	0.02	0.04	0.02	0.05	0.01	0.03	0.01	0.01	0.00	0.00	0.00	0.00	0.00	0.00
0.5	0.03	0.03	0.02	0.05	0.02	0.04	0.01	0.02	0.00	0.01	0.00	0.00	0.00	0.00	0.00	0.00
0.4	0.04	0.05	0.02	0.05	0.01	0.03	0.01	0.01	0.00	0.00	0.00	0.00	0.00	0.00	0.00	0.00
0.3	0.04	0.06	0.02	0.04	0.01	0.01	0.00	0.00	0.00	0.00	0.00	0.00	0.00	0.00	0.00	0.00
0.2	0.06	0.06	0.02	0.02	0.01	0.00	0.00	0.00	0.00	0.00	0.00	0.00	0.00	0.00	0.00	0.00
0.1	0.07	0.05	0.02	0.01	0.00	0.00	0.00	0.00	0.00	0.00	0.00	0.00	0.00	0.00	0.00	0.00

$13f_I \pm 2nf_O$

$\phi_O = \pm 60°, \pm 120°$

$2n \rightarrow$ / $r\downarrow$	[0]	2 (black)	2 (white)	4 (black)	4 (white)	[6] (black)	[6] (white)	8 (black)	8 (white)	10 (black)	10 (white)	[12] (black)	[12] (white)	14 (black)	14 (white)	16
1.0	0.00	0.01	0.01	0.01	0.01	0.01	0.01	0.01	0.01	0.01	0.01	0.07	0.01	0.07	0.01	0.01
0.9	0.01	0.01	0.01	0.02	0.01	0.02	0.01	0.02	0.00	0.06	0.00	0.06	0.00	0.02	0.01	0.00
0.8	0.01	0.02	0.01	0.02	0.01	0.02	0.00	0.05	0.00	0.06	0.00	0.03	0.00	0.00	0.00	0.00
0.7	0.01	0.02	0.01	0.03	0.01	0.03	0.00	0.06	0.00	0.04	0.00	0.01	0.00	0.00	0.00	0.00
0.6	0.02	0.02	0.01	0.03	0.01	0.06	0.00	0.05	0.00	0.02	0.00	0.00	0.00	0.00	0.00	0.00
0.5	0.01	0.03	0.01	0.05	0.01	0.06	0.00	0.03	0.00	0.00	0.00	0.00	0.00	0.00	0.00	0.00
0.4	0.02	0.03	0.01	0.07	0.00	0.04	0.00	0.01	0.00	0.00	0.00	0.00	0.00	0.00	0.00	0.00
0.3	0.02	0.06	0.01	0.06	0.00	0.02	0.00	0.00	0.00	0.00	0.00	0.00	0.00	0.00	0.00	0.00
0.2	0.03	0.07	0.01	0.03	0.00	0.00	0.00	0.00	0.00	0.00	0.00	0.00	0.00	0.00	0.00	0.00
0.1	0.06	0.06	0.01	0.01	0.00	0.00	0.00	0.00	0.00	0.00	0.00	0.00	0.00	0.00	0.00	0.00

$\phi_O = \pm 90°$

$2n \rightarrow$ / $r\downarrow$	[0]	2 (black)	2 (white)	4 (black)	4 (white)	[6] (black)	[6] (white)	8 (black)	8 (white)	10 (black)	10 (white)	[12] (black)	[12] (white)	14 (black)	14 (white)	16
1.0	0.00	0.00	0.00	0.00	0.00	0.00	0.00	0.00	0.00	0.00	0.00	0.08	0.00	0.08	0.00	0.00
0.9	0.00	0.00	0.00	0.00	0.00	0.00	0.00	0.01	0.00	0.07	0.00	0.07	0.00	0.02	0.00	0.00
0.8	0.00	0.00	0.00	0.01	0.00	0.02	0.00	0.04	0.00	0.08	0.00	0.03	0.00	0.00	0.00	0.00
0.7	0.00	0.01	0.00	0.02	0.00	0.01	0.00	0.08	0.00	0.05	0.00	0.01	0.00	0.00	0.00	0.00
0.6	0.01	0.01	0.00	0.01	0.00	0.06	0.00	0.06	0.00	0.02	0.00	0.00	0.00	0.00	0.00	0.00
0.5	0.00	0.02	0.00	0.04	0.00	0.07	0.00	0.03	0.00	0.01	0.00	0.00	0.00	0.00	0.00	0.00
0.4	0.01	0.00	0.01	0.07	0.00	0.05	0.00	0.01	0.00	0.00	0.00	0.00	0.00	0.00	0.00	0.00
0.3	0.01	0.05	0.00	0.07	0.00	0.02	0.00	0.00	0.00	0.00	0.00	0.00	0.00	0.00	0.00	0.00
0.2	0.02	0.08	0.01	0.04	0.00	0.00	0.00	0.00	0.00	0.00	0.00	0.00	0.00	0.00	0.00	0.00
0.1	0.06	0.06	0.00	0.01	0.00	0.00	0.00	0.00	0.00	0.00	0.00	0.00	0.00	0.00	0.00	0.00

Notes: 1. Tables show amplitude of harmonic, as per-unit value of the total fundamental component.

2. These components are present in the input current of 3-, 6-, and 12-pulse NCCs. For a balanced 3-phase output, only those components whose numbers are boxed thus □ are present.

3. Where there is only one column for a given of $2n$, the values given apply to both the "plus" and "minus" $2nf_O$ components.

Where there are two columns for a given value of $2n$:

The values given in the "black" column apply to the "plus" $2nf_O$ components for positive ϕ_O, and to the "minus" $2nf_O$ components for negative ϕ_O.

The values given in the "white" column apply to the "plus" $2nf_O$ components for negative ϕ_O, and to the "minus" $2nf_O$ components for positive ϕ_O.

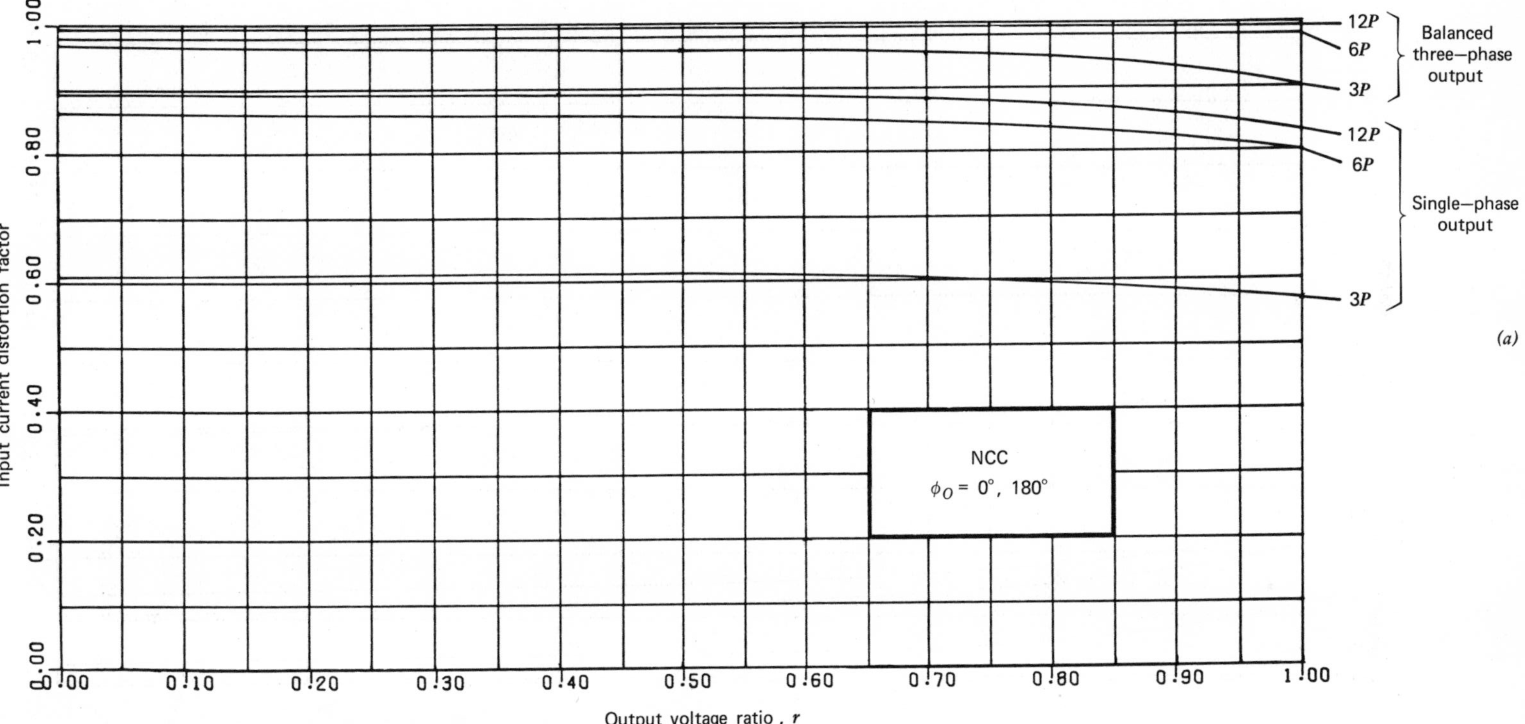

Input current distortion factor
1.00
0.80
0.60
0.40
0.20
0.00
0.00
0.10
0.20
0.30
0.40
0.50
0.60
0.70
0.80
0.90
1.00
Output voltage ratio , r
12P
6P
3P
Balanced three–phase output
12P
6P
3P
Single–phase output
NCC
$\phi_O = 0°, 180°$

(a)

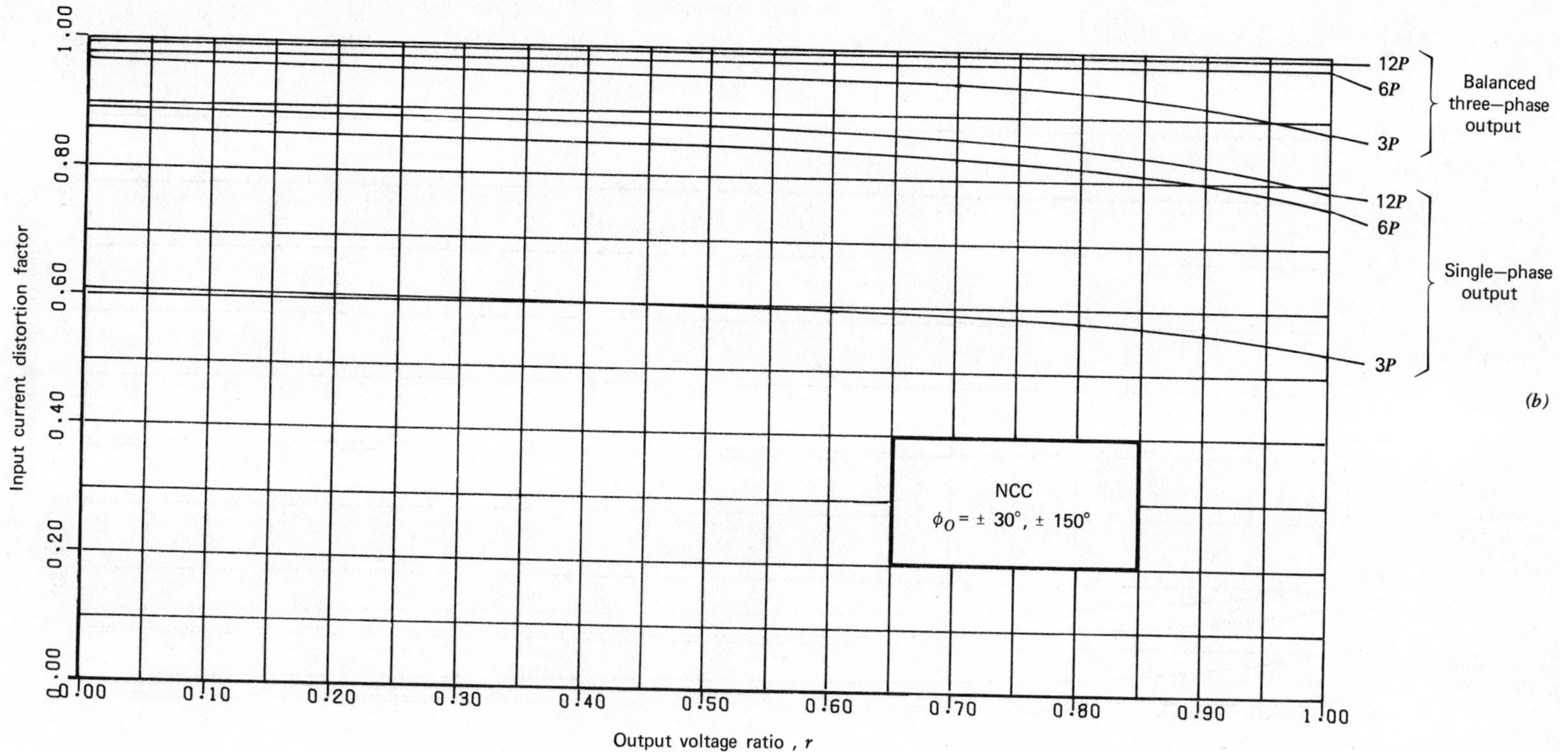

12P
6P
3P
Balanced three-phase output
12P
6P
3P
Single-phase output
NCC
$\phi_O = \pm 30°, \pm 150°$
Input current distortion factor
0.00
0.20
0.40
0.60
0.80
1.00
Output voltage ratio, r
0.00
0.10
0.20
0.30
0.40
0.50
0.60
0.70
0.80
0.90
1.00

(b)

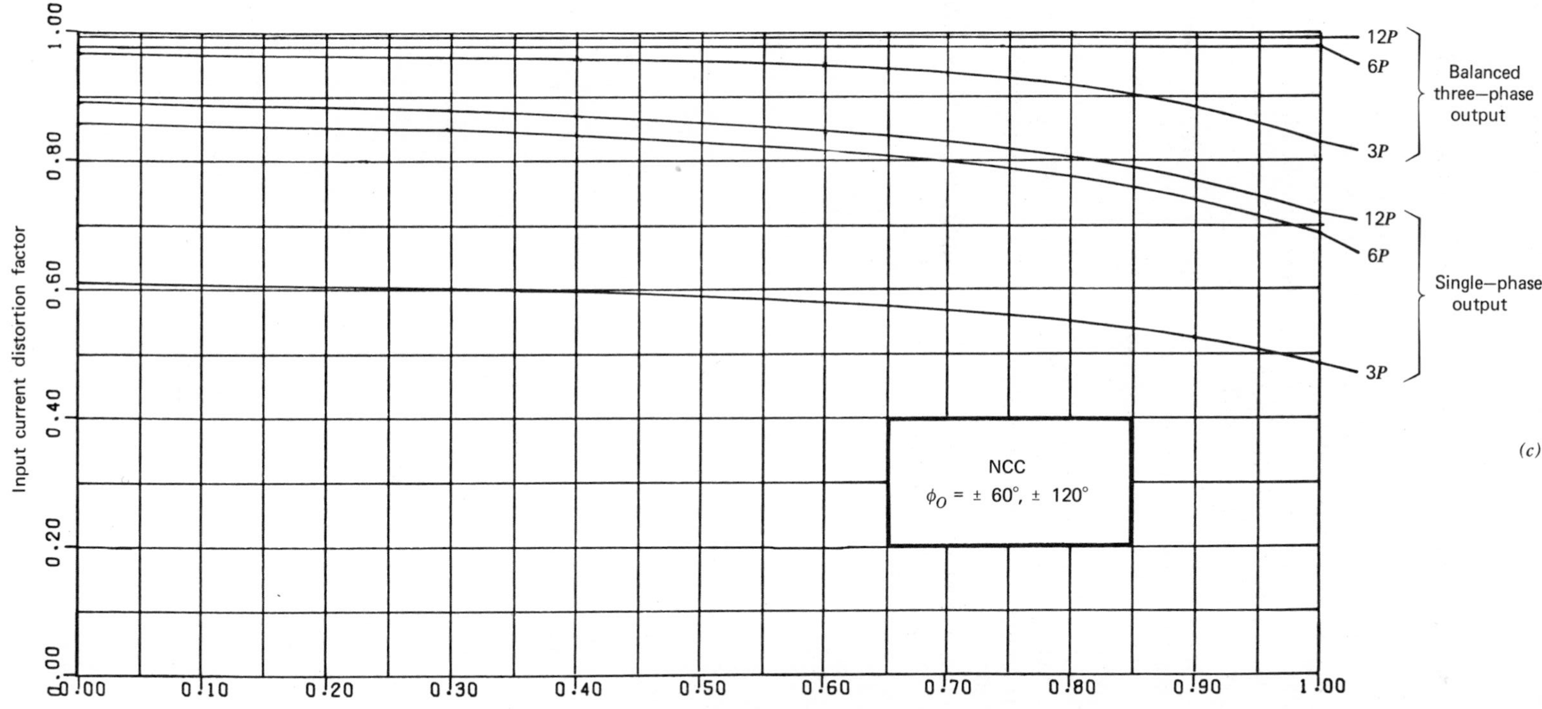

Figure 6.37 Variation of the input current distortion factor of the NCC with the output voltage ratio for pulse numbers three, six, and twelve, with sinusoidal mean output voltage. *a* $\phi_O = 0^\circ$ and 180°; *b* $\phi_O = \pm 30^\circ$ and $\pm 150^\circ$; *c* $\phi_O = \pm 60^\circ$ and $\pm 120^\circ$.

6.7.5 The CDFFC

The extrabasal frequencies present in the input current wave of the CDFFC are the same as those of the NCC and are shown in Figure 6.36.

The amplitudes of the extrabasal components are a function not only of the output voltage ratio and output displacement angle, as for the NCC, but also of the control angle σ (defined in Figure 6.11). A generalized presentation of the amplitudes of these components for different permutations of ϕ_O, σ, and r is not justified here.

Tables 6.7–6.11, for the NCC, are also applicable to the CDFFC for the special cases of $\sigma = 180°$, in which the CDFFC in fact operates as an NCC, and $\sigma = 0°$, in which the CDFFC operates as an "inverted NCC," that is, the positive-type and negative-type voltage waves correspond to the negative and positive half-cycles of output current, respectively. For this latter case, the amplitude of a given extrabasal component for a given value of ϕ_O shown in the table actually applies to an output displacement angle of $\pi + \phi_O$. For example, the per-unit amplitude of the $5f_I + 2f_O$ component for $r = 0.8$, $\phi_O = +30°$, given in Table 6.9, is 0.15. For the CDFFC with $\sigma = 0°$, this is actually the amplitude of the $5f_I + 2f_O$ component with $\phi_O = 30° + 180° = -150°$.

In general, for other values of control angle σ, the amplitudes of the extrabasal components can be computed from expression (5.61) in Chapter 5.

CHAPTER SEVEN
CONTROL CIRCUIT PRINCIPLES

It has been seen that the external performance characteristics of the frequency changer are uniquely determined by the manner in which the conduction periods of the switches are controlled. Various different types of frequency changers have been identified, according to the particular performance characteristics they provide. In this chapter, we examine the functional control circuit techniques that may be used to determine the conduction periods of the switches of the frequency changer, so as to produce the various different prescribed waveform types.

Generally, the basic circuit principles are exemplified by reference to simple three-pulse schemes. The approaches presented, however, are quite general and are naturally extendable to frequency changers of higher pulse number.

7.1 BASIC FUNCTIONAL REQUIREMENTS OF THE TIMING CONTROL CIRCUITS

In order to define the basic functional requirements of the timing control circuits, it is useful to review some ideas that are introduced in Chapters 3 and 4.

It will be remembered that the basic mathematical tool for describing the operation of the frequency changer is the *existence function.* A separate existence function is associated with each switch of the frequency changer. The existence function has unit amplitude whenever the associated switch is closed and zero amplitude whenever it is open. In effect, then, the *existence function* is a facsimile of the digital electrical *timing signal*, representing the desired conduction period, that must be derived for each switch of the frequency changer in order to synthesize the desired output voltage wave.

The basic objective with which we are concerned in this chapter is that of devising practically functional control circuitry that produces digital timing signals for the switches of the frequency changer, which are in exact correspondence with the mathematically desired existence functions. For convenience, the term *existence function* is often used to denote not only the pure mathematical function but also the corresponding digital electrical timing signal.

It is helpful to review the general mathematical principles upon which the timing of the existence functions is based. Once we have reviewed these principles, we can then proceed to a derivation of appropriate functional control circuitry that will produce these functions.

The concept of two complementary sets of quiescent existence functions, h_{11}, h_{12}, and h_{13}, and $h_{\pi 11}$, $h_{\pi 12}$, and $h_{\pi 13}$ [equations (3.4) and (3.5)] will be recalled. These sets of quiescent existence functions, illustrated in Figure 3.1, both have fundamental frequency equal to the input frequency of the frequency changer, but they are displaced by 180° from one another. Both sets of quiescent existence functions produce zero mean output voltage, but the ripple waveforms produced are phase-shifted images of one another.

Starting from either set of these quiescent waveforms, an output voltage wave with a given wanted component can be generated by appropriately modulating the periods of the existence functions with respect to the quiescent condition. In order to produce the same given wanted component of voltage with the same phase, starting from either set of quiescent waveforms, the angular deviation with respect to the quiescent condition of the two sets of existence functions at any given time must be equal, but of opposite sign. This angular deviation of the existence function, expressed as a function of time, is called the *modulating function.*

It was seen that the modulating function may either be a simple linear function, as illustrated in Figure 3.4, or it may be a periodic function with fundamental frequency equal to the wanted output frequency, as exemplified by the waveforms of Figures 3.2, 3.7, and 3.12.

If the modulating function is linear, this means simply that the angular deviation of the existence functions from the quiescent condition steadily increases with time. In other words, as in the quiescent condition, the conduction periods of all switches of the frequency changer remain equal to one another, but the duration of these periods is altered with respect to the quiescent condition. In order to produce the *same* wanted component of output voltage, with the *same phase*, from the two complementary sets of quiescent existence functions, the frequency of the h set must be *increased* by the desired output frequency, as illustrated in Figure 3.4*a*, whereas the frequency of the h_π set must be *decreased* by the desired output frequency, as illustrated in Figure 3.4*b*. The first waveform type characterizes the unrestricted frequency changer, whereas the second type characterizes the slow-switching frequency changer.

If the modulating function is periodic, this means that the angular deviation of the existence functions oscillates symmetrically to and fro with respect to the quiescent condition. In this case, each conduction period generally is not the same as the preceding one; sometimes the conduction period is longer than the quiescent period, and sometimes it is shorter. Over the course of a complete output cycle, however, the average conduction period is equal to the quiescent period. In order to produce the *same* wanted component of output voltage with the *same phase* from the two complementary sets of quiescent existence functions, these two sets of functions must be modulated with equal, but opposite polarity, modulating functions. This is illustrated for example, by the waveforms of Figure 3.7*a* and *b*, which are appropriate to the practically important modulating function $M(t) = \sin^{-1}(\sin \omega_O t)$. The two complementary positive-type and negative-type output voltage waves, v_O and $v_{O\pi}$, have the same wanted component with the same phase; however, as for the quiescent condition, the waveforms of the ripple voltage are phase-shifted images of one another.

A frequency changer that produces either one of the complementary waveforms of Figure 3.7*a* and *b* by itself may have limited practical use. However, frequency changers that produce combinations of these complementary waveforms in some prescribed manner constitute the bulk of types considered in this book. Thus, the unity displacement factor frequency changer uses two constituent groups of power circuit switches to produce the sum of these two complementary waveforms. The controllable displacement factor frequency changer and the naturally commutated cycloconverter produce selected portions of the two complementary waveforms in sequence, one after the other, in accordance with some prescribed *waveform existence function.*

7.2 IMPLEMENTATION OF LINEAR MODULATING FUNCTIONS

7.2.1 Full Ouput Voltage

In order to modulate the argument of the quiescent existence function with a linear function of time, $M(t) = \omega_O t$, or $-M(t) = -\omega_O t$, this requires simply that the *frequency* of the existence function be altered from the quiescent frequency by the desired wanted output frequency. Thus, as has already been stated, the conduction periods of all switches of the frequency changer invariably remain equal to one another, but their duration is either shortened (for the UFC) or lengthened (for the SSFC) by an amount determined by the wanted output frequency.

In practice, then, the linear modulating function is extremely simple to realize; all that is required is to produce the timing signals for the switches of the frequency changer at a constant rate, either higher or lower than the quiescent rate, depending on the waveform type required. Moreover, as seen in Chapters 3 and 4, a balanced three- (or multi-) phase output can be generated from one "master" set of timing signals that are distributed appropriately to the individual switches in the various output phases of the frequency changer.

The basic elements of a practical control scheme of this type for a three-pulse frequency changer are shown in Figure 7.1, and typical associated waveforms are illustrated in Figure 7.2.

The *voltage-controlled oscillator* produces a train of evenly spaced clock pulses whose frequency is controlled by the level of the analogue d-c input voltage, e_{IN}. These clock pulses are fed as the input to the *shift register*, which produces three distributed timing signals at its output, corresponding to the desired three existence functions. The *firing circuits* transform these timing signals into isolated firing signals for the power switches of the frequency changer.

With $e_{IN} = 0$, the frequency of the clock pulses is three times the input frequency, and the output frequency of the frequency changer is zero. With e_{IN} positive, the clock frequency is greater than $3f_I$, and the frequency changer operates as a UFC, producing a balanced set of output voltages with positive phase sequence. With e_{IN} negative, the clock frequency is less than $3f_I$, and the frequency changer operates as an SSFC, producing a balanced set of output voltages with negative phase sequence.

7.2.2 Output Voltage Control by Pulse-Width Modulation

As seen in Chapter 4, the amplitude of the output voltage of the UFC (or SSFC) can be controlled by a process of pulse-width modulation. The basic principle is very simple: With full output voltage, each input voltage is connected in turn for a given time frame T to a given output terminal. With reduced output voltage, on the other hand, each time frame T is subdivided into an active and passive interval; only during the active interval is the appropriate input voltage connected to the output terminal. During the passive interval, several courses of action can be followed. Theoretically, the most straightforward is to turn off all the "main" switches and to close a separate "freewheeling" switch across each output phase. In practice, however, it may be uneconomical to use separate "freewheeling" switches, and it may be preferable to provide a path for the load current through the "main" switches of the frequency changer, in some fashion, during the passive interval.

In bridge circuits, a freewheeling path can be provided across the output terminals by closing the two switches in *one leg* of the bridge. As seen in Chapter 4, the desired

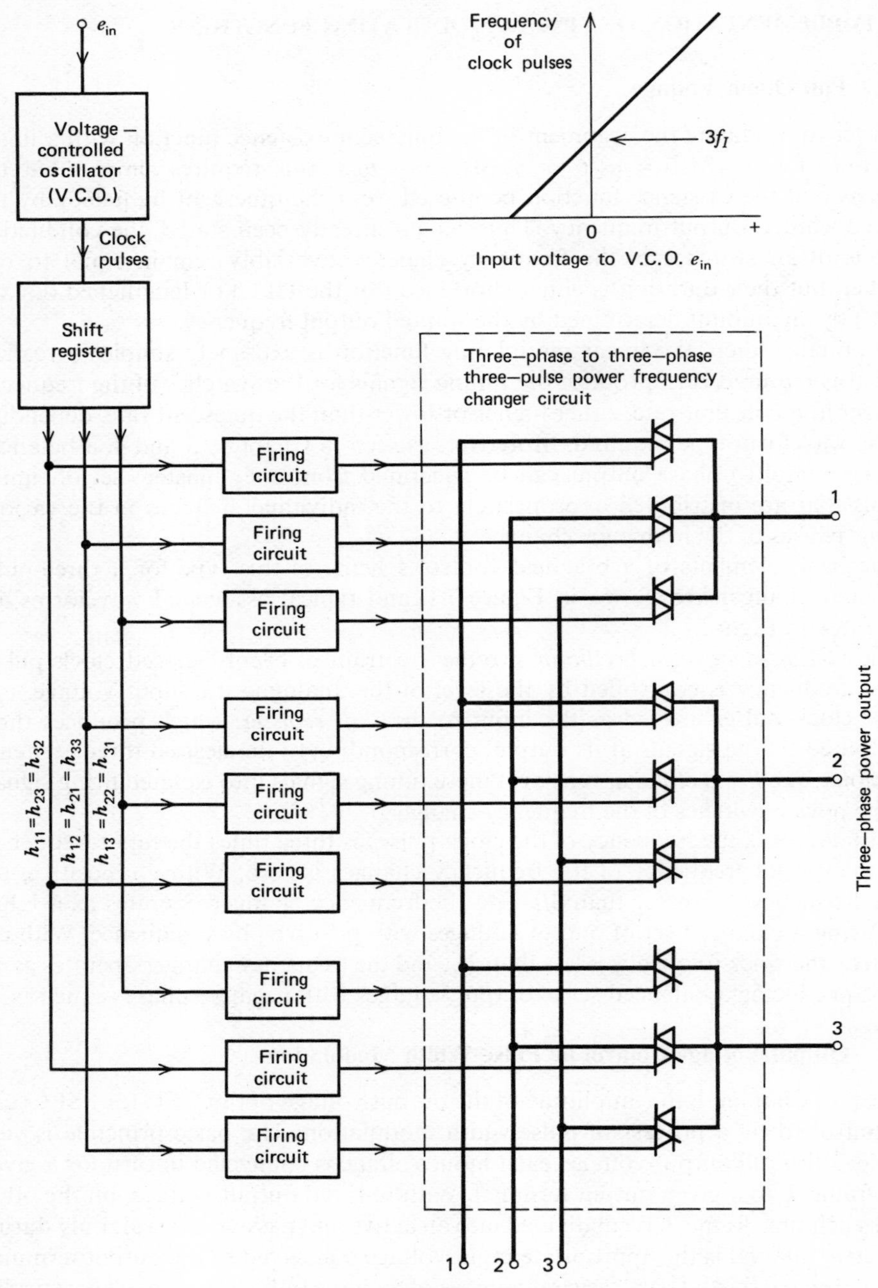

Figure 7.1 Simplified functional control scheme for a three-pulse UFC or SSFC, operating with full output voltage.

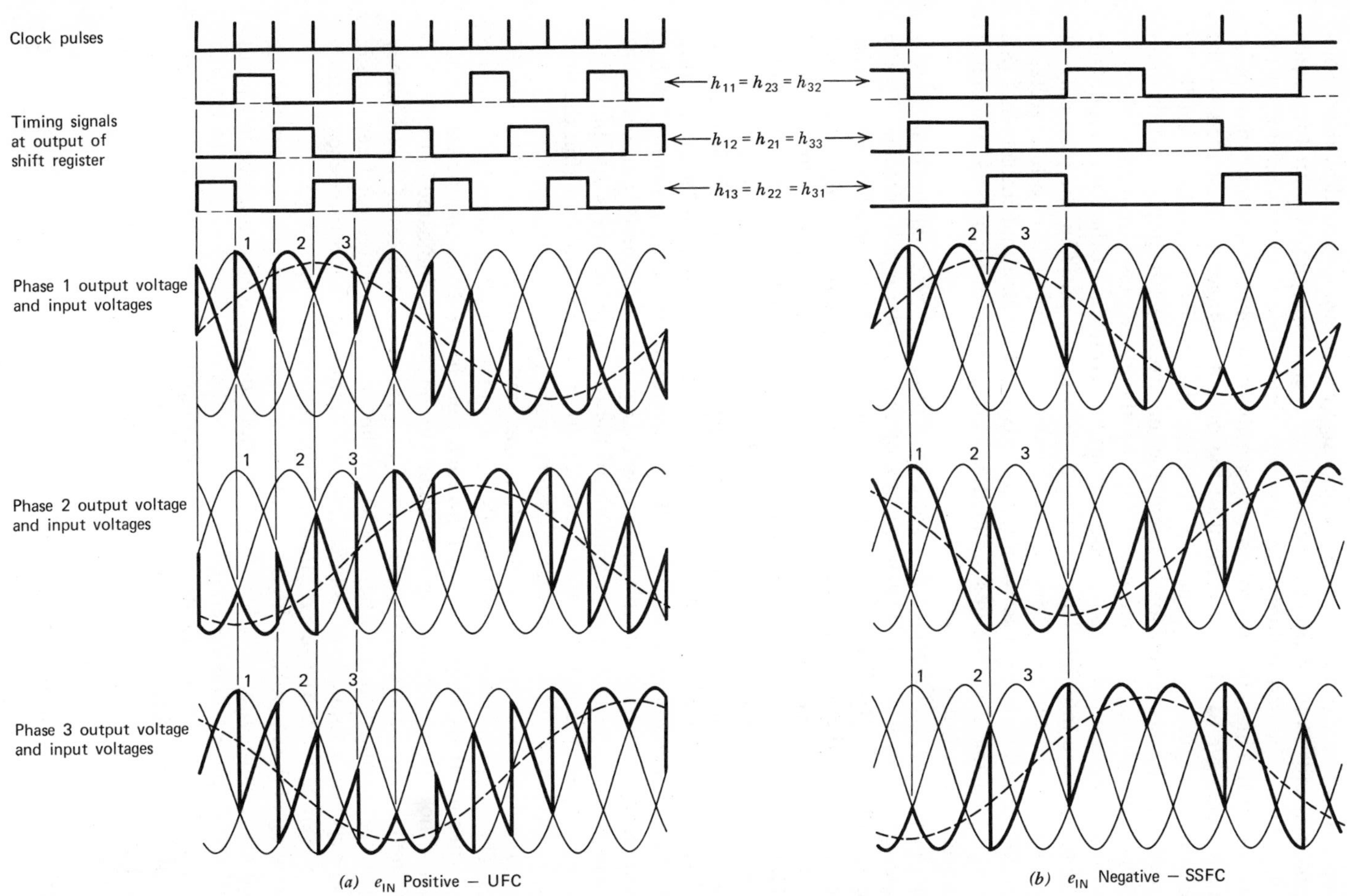

Figure 7.2 Waveforms associated with the control scheme of Figure 7.1.

sequence of switch closures for a six-pulse bridge can be implemented by means of a "stepping ahead" control process, whereby in each three-pulse group the switch associated with the active interval of the *next* time frame is turned on during the passive interval. This same control process can also be applied to a simple three-pulse frequency changer to provide control of the output voltage, as illustrated by the waveforms of Figure 4.3. In this case, however, the passive interval can hardly be regarded as such, because the load current does not freewheel, it simply flows through another input phase. Another possibility for the three-pulse frequency changer with three-phase output is to connect all output terminals to the same input line during the passive interval. This provides a freewheeling path for the load current between the three output terminals and renders the output line-to-line voltages essentially zero during the passive interval. A control scheme that implements this particular principle is shown in simplified functional form in Figure 7.3; associated waveforms are shown in Figure 7.4.

The *integrator*, *level detector* and *pulse generator*, and *reset circuit* constitute a *voltage-controlled oscillator*. The frequency of this oscillator is controlled by the *frequency reference*, V_f. The output pulses P_0 of this oscillator are fed to the *pulse delay circuit*, and the output pulses P_1 of the delay circuit clock the three-stage *shift register*. The three output signals of the shift register represent the time frames T for the switches of the frequency changer. This much is similar to the simple full-voltage control scheme of Figure 7.1.

Each period T is subdivided into active and passive intervals of variable duration by the variable pulse, P_2. The phase of this pulse is determined from the intersection point of the *amplitude reference*, V_a, with the "sawtooth" wave, e_s, generated within the voltage controlled oscillator. Clearly, increasing V_a retards the P_2 pulse, whereas decreasing V_a advances it. The amplitude of the sawtooth, e_s, stays constant with changing frequency, and hence the angular position of the P_2 pulse, within the time frame T, stays constant with changing frequency for any given value of V_a.

The *flip-flop* circuit is *set* by the P_1 pulses and normally is *reset* by the P_2 pulses. The complementary output signals A and $\bar{A}$ of the flip-flop represent the active and passive intervals, respectively, within each time frame T. By mixing the output signals of the shift register and flip-flop circuits in the manner indicated in Figure 7.3, the desired timing signals for the switches of all three output phases of the frequency changer are obtained. It is to be noted that the switches selected for freewheeling duty are cyclically rotated with succeeding time frames, so that all switches operate with an average 1:3 duty cycle regardless of the level of output voltage.

Summing of the P_0 pulse, (whose width must span the P_1 pulse) at the input of the *comparator* ensures that if V_a becomes too small to produce an intersection point with e_s, the P_2 pulse still is generated shortly after the P_1 pulse (that is, at the trailing edge of the P_0 pulse). Likewise, feeding the differentiated P_0 pulse, P_0', to the "reset" terminal of the flip-flop ensures that a finite passive interval is maintained in the event that V_a becomes too large to produce an intersection point with the sawtooth wave.

7.3 IMPLEMENTATION OF PERIODIC MODULATING FUNCTIONS

7.3.1 General Considerations

In Chapters 3 and 4 it was seen that a periodic modulating function may take the general form $M(t) = \sin^{-1}\{\sum_{n=1}^{\infty} b_{1,n} \sin n(\omega_O t + \psi)\}$. Usually, (but not always) it is

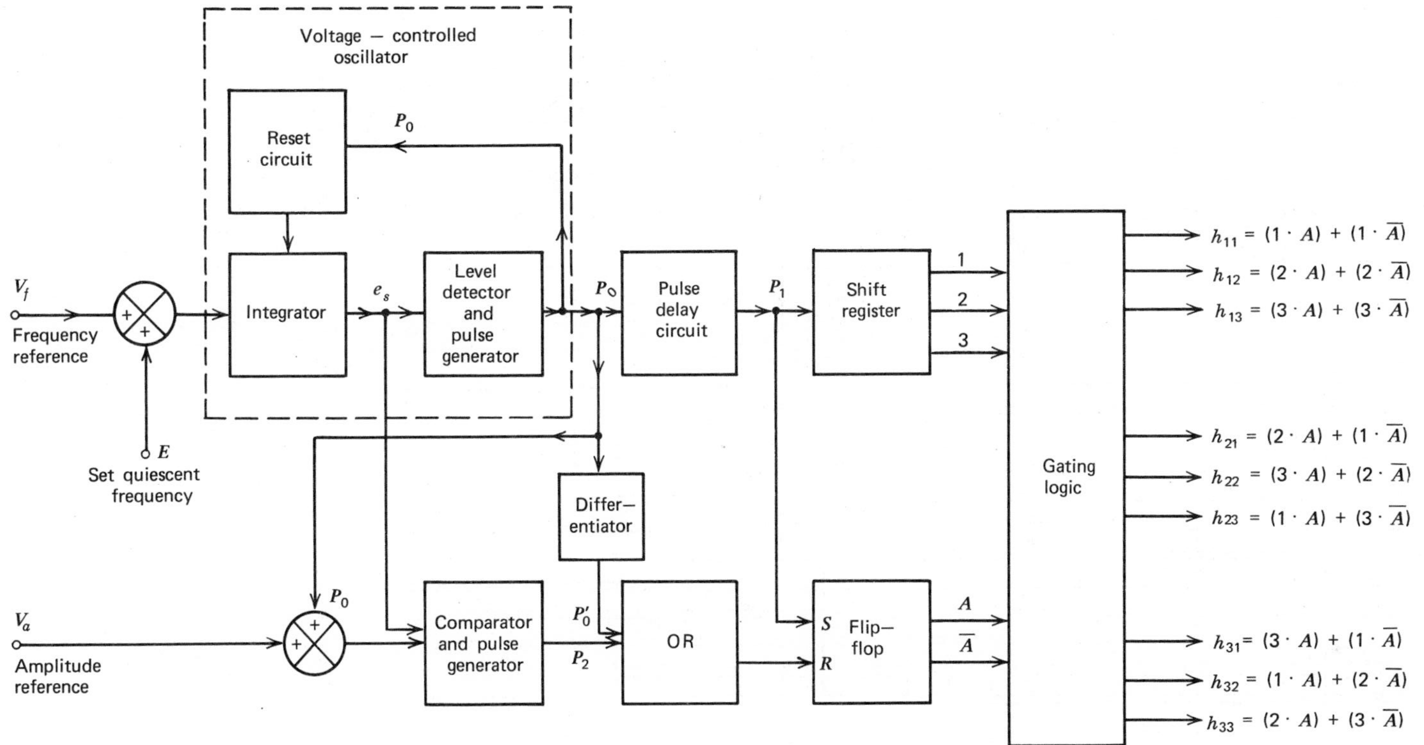

Figure 7.3 Simplified functional pulse-width modulation voltage control scheme for a three-pulse UFC or SSFC.

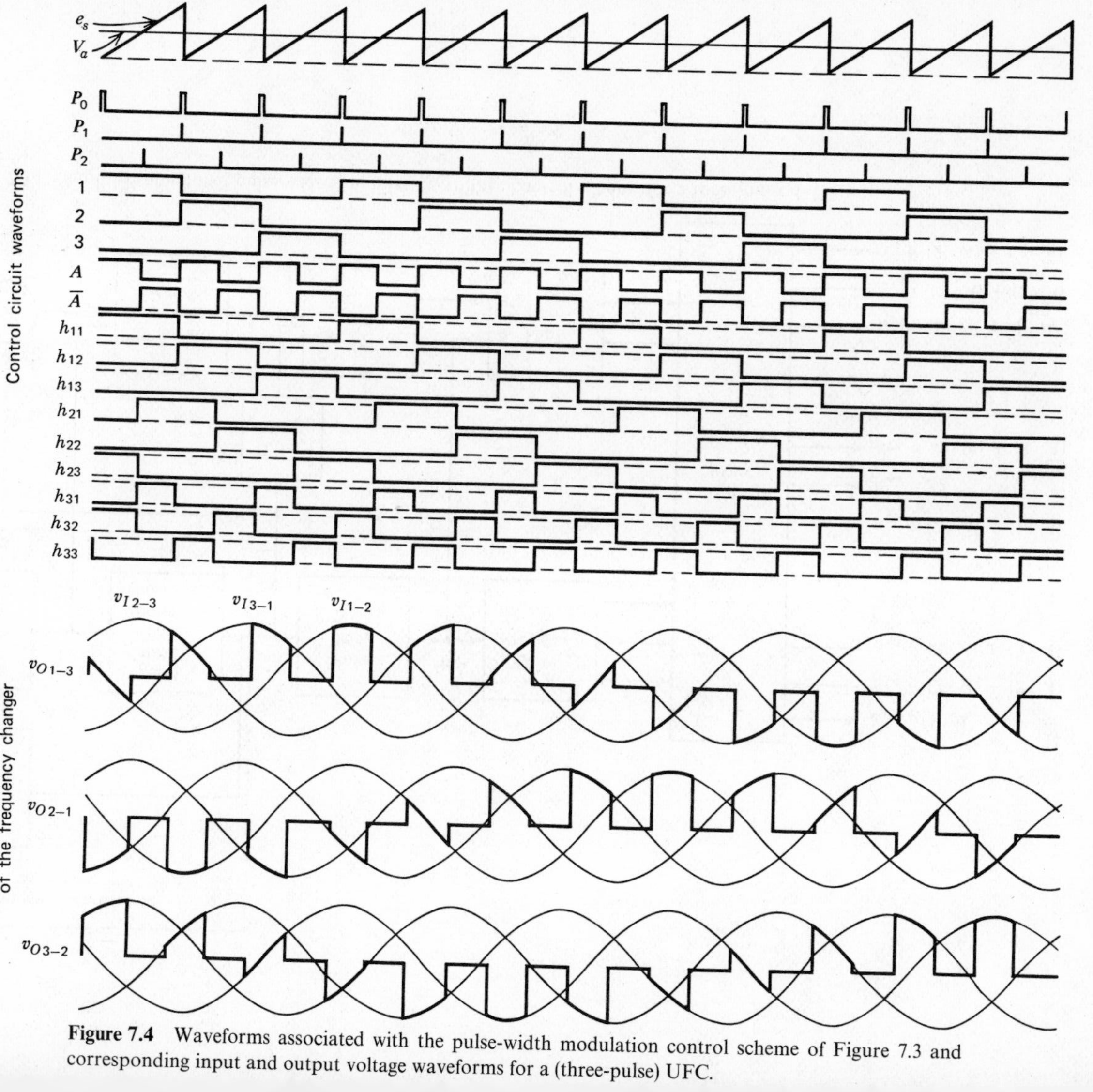

Figure 7.4 Waveforms associated with the pulse-width modulation control scheme of Figure 7.3 and corresponding input and output voltage waveforms for a (three-pulse) UFC.

required to produce an output voltage waveform that contains no direct harmonics of the wanted output frequency (although at certain discrete frequency ratios this to some extent cannot be avoided), and in this case all the coefficients of the above series must be zero, except for the first one, $b_{1,1}$. Thus, in theory the "purest" periodic modulating function takes the simple form $M(t) = \sin^{-1}\{r \sin(\omega_O t + \psi)\}$, where $r = b_{1,1} \leq 1$.

Although this "theoretically pure" modulating function produces no direct harmonics of the wanted output frequency (except at certain discrete frequency ratios), it does produce relatively low-amplitude unwanted components with frequencies that are less than the wanted output frequency. The presence of these unwanted components may be quite objectionable; thus in practice they must be eliminated.

Since the amplitudes of the low-frequency unwanted components are relatively low in comparison with the maximum possible wanted component of output voltage, it would be reasonable to suppose that a small but appropriate modification of the theoretically pure modulating function would be sufficient to eliminate them. This suggests the concept of constituting the control scheme from a timing circuit that produces the theoretically pure modulating function, in conjunction with a closed-loop feedback that automatically modifies this theoretically pure modulating function, sufficiently to eliminate the practically objectionable subfrequency terms. (An additional feature of such a feedback would be that it would automatically compensate for any small timing inaccuracies produced by practical circuit imperfections.)

This certainly is one approach. Another might be to devise a "composite" timing control scheme, an integral part of which is a feedback loop that inherently produces the practically desired modulating function. This also is feasible. In the following sections each of these types of control schemes is discussed.

First, an open-loop timing control scheme that produces the theoretically pure modulating function is considered; then various feedback control methods that can be used to complement this basic open-loop timing scheme are discussed. Finally, a composite timing control method with a self-contained corrective feedback is presented.

7.3.2 Production of the "Theoretically Pure" Modulating Function

7.3.2.1 *Basic Principles.* Figure 7.5*b* shows the modulating function $M(t) = \sin^{-1}(r \sin \omega_O t)$ expressed in radians (related to the *input* frequency, since the modulating function represents the required angular deviation of the quiescent existence functions, which of course are at *input* frequency), plotted against time t, over the course of one output cycle, for the particular conditions of $r = 1.0$ and $r = 0.5$. The output to input frequency ratio has been arbitrarily chosen as 1 : 3. Figure 7.5*a* shows the quiescent positive existence functions, h_{11}, h_{12}, and h_{13}, to be modulated by $M(t)$. The family of sloped parallel straight lines, f_{11}, f_{12}, and f_{13}, superimposed over the modulating functions are associated with the h_{11}, h_{12}, and h_{13} existence functions in sequence and show the angular displacement at any given time t from the point at which the quiescent existence function switches from zero to unit value. For example, time t_1 corresponds to $\pi/3$ ahead of the 0 to 1 switching instant of the h_{11} quiescent existence function; time t_2 corresponds to an angle $\pi/6$ after the 0 to 1 switching instant of the h_{12} quiescent existence function.

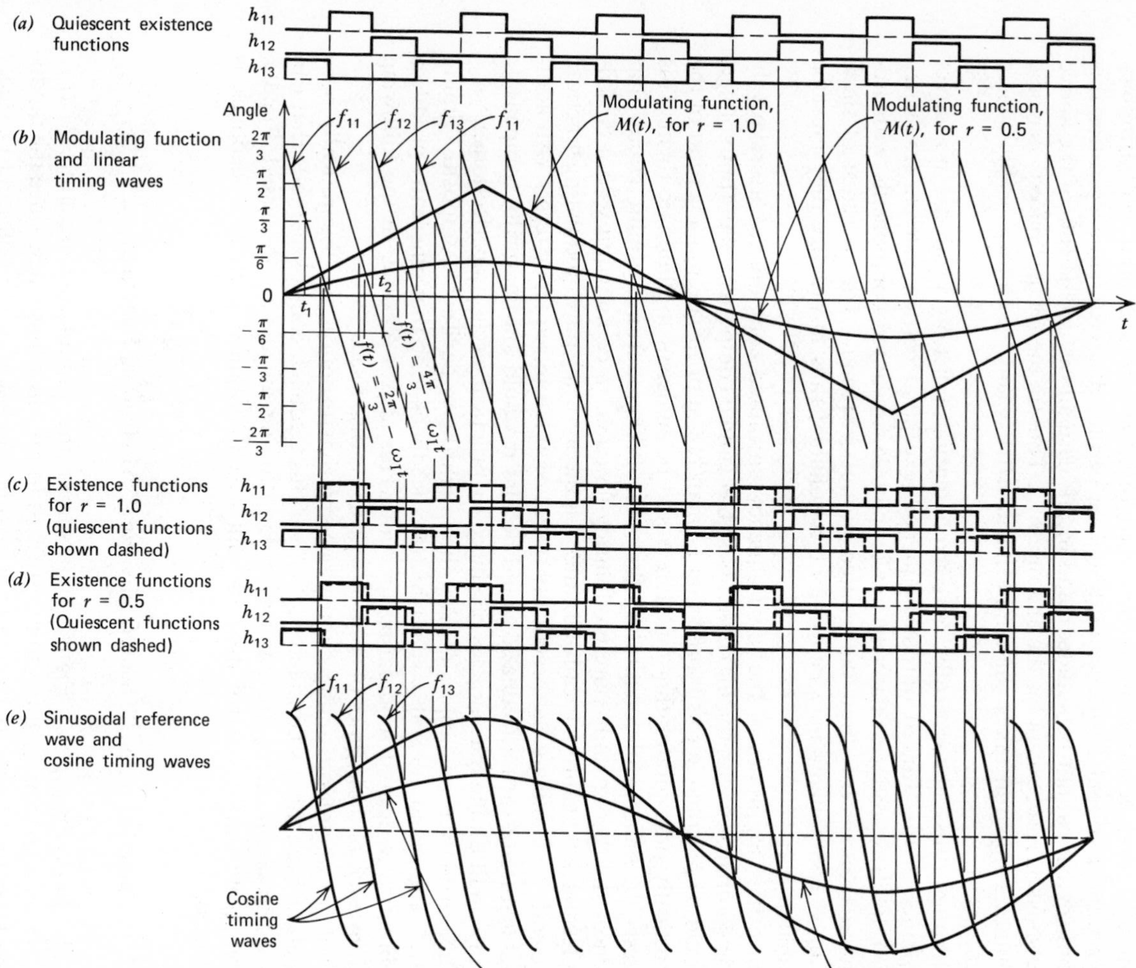

Figure 7.5 Realization of the modulating function $M(t) = \sin^{-1}(r \sin \omega_O)$ by the principle of intersecting a sinusoidal reference wave with cosine timing waves.

Since the modulating function represents the required angular deviation of the quiescent existence functions at any given time t, whereas the sloped parallel straight lines represent the angular distance from the switching point of the associated quiescent existence function at time t, it is clear that the intersection points of these straight lines, or *timing waves*, with the modulating function represent the required switching points of the associated existence functions. The required existence functions are therefore as shown at c and d for $r = 1.0$ and $r = 0.5$, respectively.

Consideration of Figure 7.5*b* suggests that a possible method for determining the positions of the existence functions would be to use the intersection points of a wave representing the desired modulating function, with a series of triangular timing waves, periodic at the input frequency, representing the angular deviation from the switching points of the quiescent existence functions. For $r = 1.0$, this could be implemented without difficulty, because the modulating function is a simple triangular wave. For lower values of r, however, the modulating function loses this simple form and is no longer readily producible in practice; hence this exact approach would be practically cumbersome.

A much more practical approach results from a realization of the fact that the intersection points of the modulating function and linear timing waves of Figure 7.5*b* are identical to those of a sinusoidal reference and cosinusoidal timing waves, as illustrated at *e*. This can be shown very simply as follows:

Consider, for example, the first f_{11} timing wave of Figure 7.5*b*. This is given by:

$$f_{11}(t) = \frac{2\pi}{3} - \omega_I t$$

Hence, an intersection of this wave with the modulating function is obtained at time t given by:

$$\sin^{-1}(r \sin \omega_O t) = \frac{2\pi}{3} - \omega_I t$$

that is, when

$$r \sin \omega_O t = \sin\left(\frac{2\pi}{3} - \omega_I t\right)$$

Thus it is clear that the intersection points of a sinusoidal reference voltage, $r \sin \omega_O t$, with a series of properly phased cosine timing waves synchronized to the input frequency are the required switching points of the existence functions representing the modulating function $M(t) = \sin^{-1}(r \sin \omega_O t)$. In practice, it is a simple matter to produce the desired sinusoidal reference voltage and cosine timing waves; thus this so-called *cosine wave crossing* timing principle can be readily implemented.

Since the actual wanted component of the output voltage wave of the frequency changer produced by the modulating function $M(t) = \sin^{-1}(r \sin \omega_O t)$ has the form $V_{O\max}\, r \sin \omega_O t$, it is evident that the sinusoidal reference wave $r \sin \omega_O t$ exactly represents the wanted component of output voltage, both in magnitude and phase. Thus the cosine wave timing control principle in effect reduces the frequency changer, in conjunction with its timing control circuits, to a linear voltage amplifier with no phase shift between the input reference signal and the final wanted component of output voltage.

So far we have considered only the production of the positive-type output voltage wave, v_O. In order to generate the complementary negative-type output voltage wave, $v_{O\pi}$, which has the *same* wanted component, with the *same* phase as v_O, the *same*

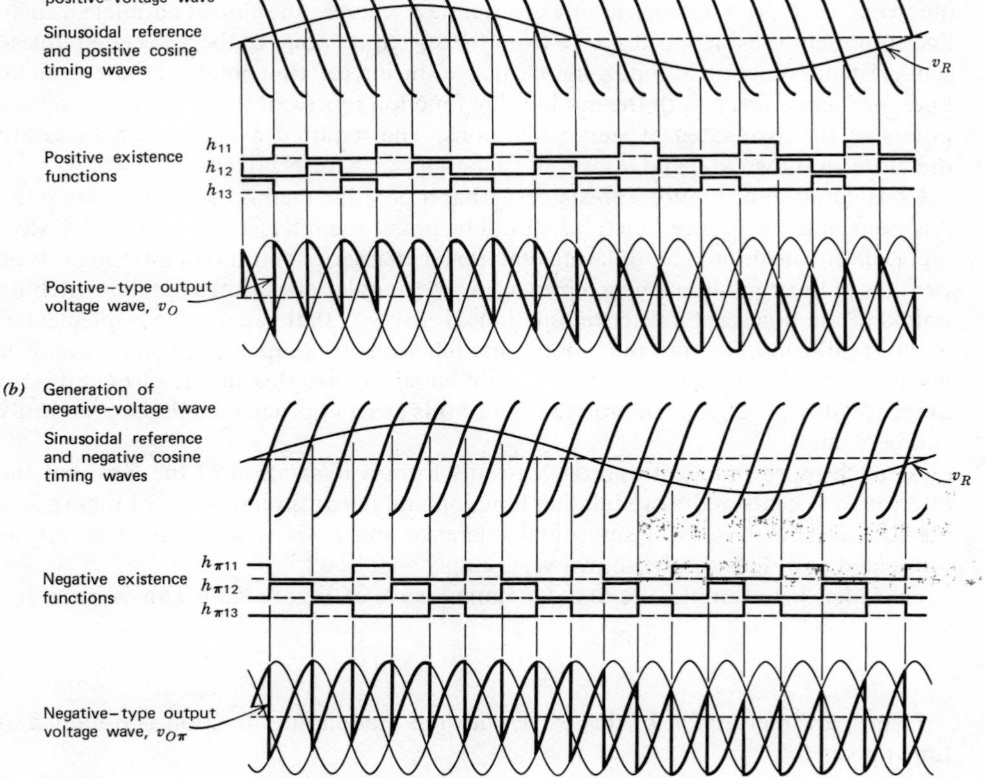

Figure 7.6 Generation of positive-type and negative-type output voltage waves v_O and $v_{O\pi}$, using the cosine wave crossing timing principle.

modulating function must be applied, but with *opposite* sign, to the negative set of quiescent existence functions. This can be accomplished simply by timing the negative existence functions from the intersection points of the reference voltage, $r \sin \omega_O t$, with a set of negative cosine timing waves.

Simultaneous production of the complementary output voltage waves, v_O and $v_{O\pi}$, using the intersection points of a common reference voltage $r \sin \omega_O t$ with positive and negative cosine timing waves is illustrated by the waveforms of Figure 7.6.

7.3.2.2 *Functional Cosine Wave Crossing Control Schemes.* A functional three-pulse timing scheme using the cosine wave crossing control principle is illustrated in Figure 7.7. This scheme basically consists of three identical channels, one for each existence function. In each channel, the reference voltage is subtracted from a cosine timing wave, derived from and synchronized to the appropriate input voltage wave of the frequency changer, and the resulting signal is applied to the input of a *zero detector*.

To produce the positive-type output voltage waveform of Figure 7.6*a*, the output of the zero detector is arranged to switch from a 0 to 1 value whenever its input signal changes polarity from positive to negative; that is, at the intersection point of the positive cosine timing wave with the reference voltage. This produces a corresponding *clock pulse* at the output of the associated *clock pulse generator*. The clock

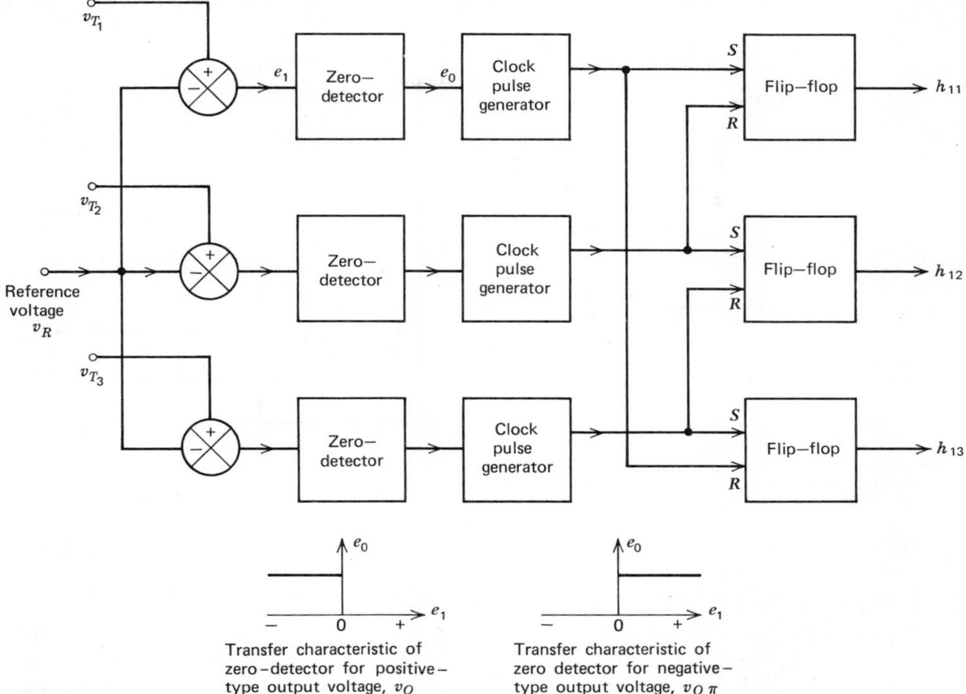

Figure 7.7 Functional three-pulse cosine wave crossing control scheme using individual timing circuits.

pulse sets the associated flip-flop circuit, which initiates the 1 period of that existence function. Each flip-flop is reset by the clock pulse from the following channel; thus the 0 period of each existence function automatically commences when the 1 period of the following existence function is initiated.

In order to produce the corresponding negative-type output voltage waveform, as shown in Figure 7.6*b*, it is necessary only to invert the function of the zero detector so that its output switches from a 0 to a 1 value whenever its input signal changes from negative to positive polarity.

A simplification of the above scheme results from a realization of the fact that it is not necessary to compare each timing voltage with the reference voltage on a continuous basis. In fact, there is no need to commence the sampling of any given timing wave until the point at which the preceding timing wave intersects the reference voltage. By the same token, there is no further need, for the time being, to sample a given timing wave once its "crossing point" has been reached and the 1 period of its associated existence function initiated. Thus, considering a three-pulse circuit, once the 1 period of the h_{11} existence function (for example) has been initiated, further sampling of the timing waveform associated with that existence function during the intervening period up to the point when the 1 period of the h_{13} existence function has been initiated is quite unnecessary. Thus, at any given time, only that timing waveform that will initiate the 1 period of the next existence function need be sampled.

A functional three-pulse control scheme that implements this principle is shown in Figure 7.8. The outputs of the three-stage *shift register* time the three existence

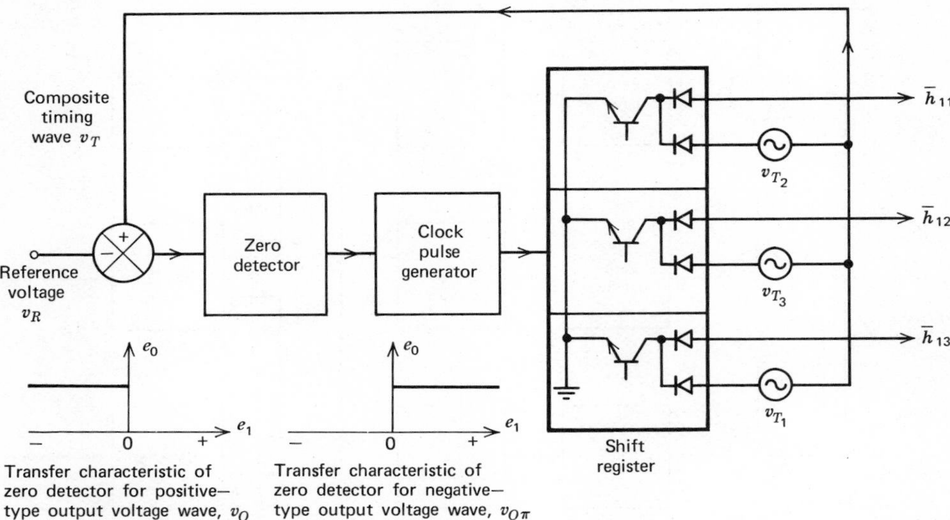

Figure 7.8 Functional three-pulse cosine wave crossing control scheme using common timing circuit.

functions, and this shift register serves also to connect each timing wave in turn to the input of the zero detector. At each crossing point of the reference wave with the "existing" timing wave, a *clock pulse* is produced that initiates the 1 period of the corresponding existence function and simultaneously connects the next timing wave in sequence to the input of the zero detector.

In order to produce the corresponding negative-type output voltage waveform, all that is required is a simple inversion of the transfer characteristic of the zero detector, as indicated in Figure 7.8.

7.3.3 Voltage Feedback Control Schemes

7.3.3.1 *Conventional Approaches.* As stated previously, the output voltage wave of the frequency changer generated by the modulating function $M(t) = \sin^{-1}(r \sin \omega_O t)$ generally contains small amounts of relatively low- and zero-frequency unwanted components. These components are objectionable in practice, even though they have relatively low amplitude, and thus they must be suppressed.

A simple expedient appears to be to separate out the objectionable low-frequency components in a low-pass filter and to send these back to the input of the cosine wave timing circuit, in a negative feedback loop. The functional control scheme of Figure 7.9*a* illustrates such an approach. This scheme is quite feasible provided that the required range of variation of the wanted output frequency lies sufficiently above the cut-off frequency of the low-pass filter. Thus, for example, this scheme would be quite satisfactory for a frequency changer producing a fixed output frequency of, for example, 20 Hz from an input frequency of 60 Hz, the cut-off frequency of the feedback filter being set at, for example, 5 Hz. With such an arrangement, all unwanted components with frequencies lower than this cut-off frequency could be virtually eliminated from the output.

If, on the other hand, it is required to control the wanted output frequency down to very low or zero value—as, for example, would usually be the case in a variable-speed motor drive—this approach is unsatisfactory. This is because the low-pass

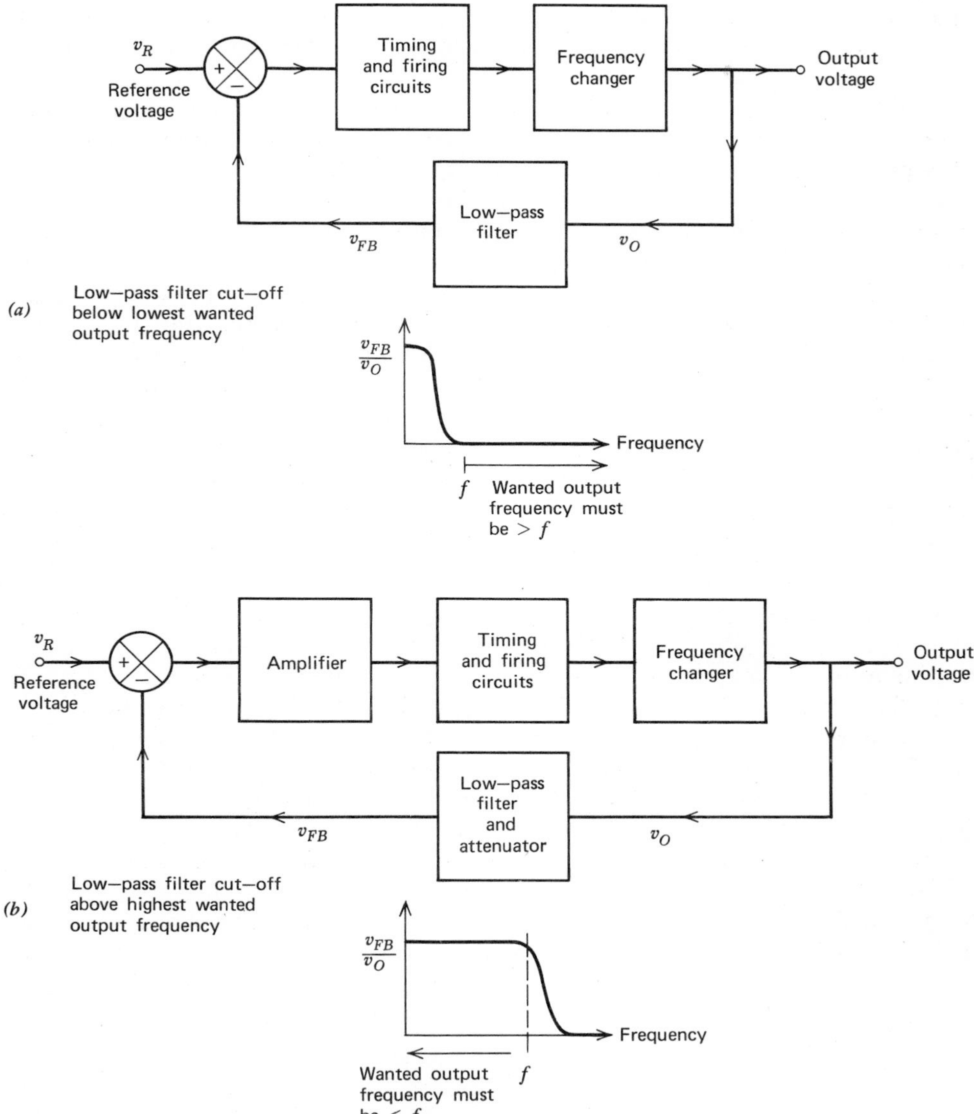

Figure 7.9 Conventional feedback methods for suppressing objectionable distortion components at the frequency changer output.

filter cannot distinguish between the wanted output frequency and the "objectionable" frequencies within the low-frequency range of operation, and thus the wanted component of output voltage within this frequency range would be suppressed by the feedback loop, along with the "objectionable" components.

A possible solution to the difficulty is shown in functional form in Figure 7.9*b*. In this scheme, the low-pass filter embraces the whole range of wanted output frequency, so that the wanted output voltage component is fed back to the input, as well as the objectionable low-frequency components, at all operating frequencies. In order to provide a constant closed-loop gain between the wanted component of output voltage and the input reference voltage with changing output frequency, it is essential, of course, that the transfer characteristic of the filter should be essentially flat over the whole output frequency range.

This approach is workable as long as the maximum desired output frequency is considerably less than the input frequency; however, it is not practical where relatively high output to input frequency ratios are required. The reason is that the cut-off frequency of the low-pass filter must be placed so that the predominant unwanted components at the output of the frequency changer are not fed back in appreciable measure to the input of the timing circuits; if this occurs a so-called *ripple instability* results. This ripple instability is characterized by a "ragged" and totally unacceptable mode of operation, with the timing of the firing instants becoming erratic.

As the maximum output to input frequency ratio increases, so the frequencies of certain of the predominant unwanted components decrease; thus the required cut-off frequency of the low-pass filter decreases with increasing output frequency, and a point is soon reached beyond which stable operation is impossible to achieve. Typically, for a six-pulse frequency changer, the maximum ratio of output to input frequency for stable operation is about 1 : 6.

7.3.3.2 *Ripple Voltage Integral Feedback.* The two voltage feedback control schemes just considered are each restricted in the range of output frequency over which they can operate. The scheme of Figure 7.9*a* is satisfactory above a certain minimum output frequency, whereas that of Figure 7.9*b* is satisfactory below a certain maximum output frequency. Many applications require a relatively wide range of control of the output frequency, from zero upwards. In this case, neither of the foregoing voltage feedback approaches is satisfactory, and it is necessary to find a "wide-band" feedback control approach that is compatible with the required wide range of output frequency. A control scheme that meets these general functional requirements is shown in simplified functional form in Figure 7.10.

The raw output voltage wave v_O of the frequency changer is divided down so that the wanted component of the resulting wave at the output of the *attenuator*, with the loop opened at the point F, has the same amplitude as the input sinusoidal reference wave v_R. Since the cosine wave crossing timing method generates a wanted component

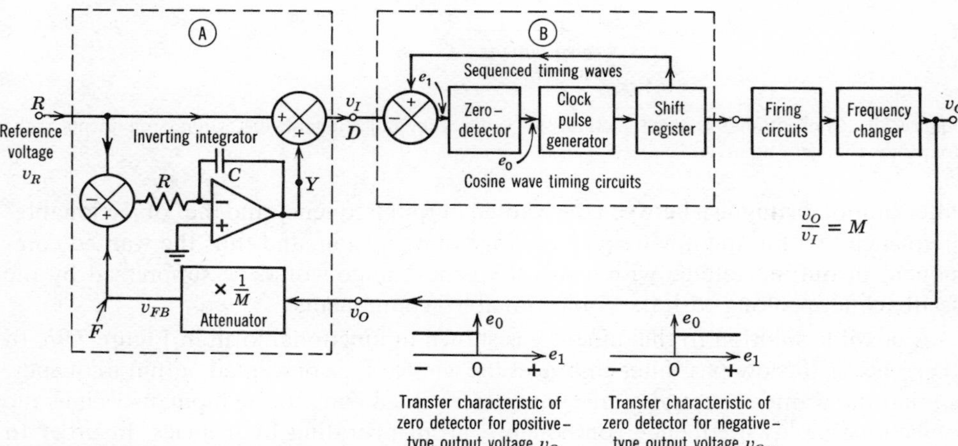

Figure 7.10 Functional diagram of cosine timing scheme with ripple voltage integral feedback.

of voltage at the output of the frequency changer that is proportional to, and in-phase with, the input sinusoidal reference, the difference between the output voltage wave of the attenuator, $v_{FB}(= v_O/M)$, and the reference wave, v_R, is a replica of the net ripple or distortion voltage wave at the output of the frequency changer. This ripple wave is applied as the input to an *integrator*, and the output of the integrator is fed, along with the sinusoidal reference, v_R, as a correcting input to the *cosine wave timing circuits*.

Assume that the integrator acts simply as a low-pass filter for any objectionable low-frequency distortion components applied at its input, and it does not pass any substantial amounts of the predominant higher-frequency ripple components back to the input of the timing circuit. In this case it is evident that when the operating conditions are such that there are no objectionable low-frequency unwanted components generated at the output of the frequency changer, the output signal of the integrator is essentially zero, and the feedback loop has no effect on the operation of the timing circuits. On the other hand, if the operating conditions of the frequency changer are such that a tendency does exist for objectionable low-frequency unwanted components to be generated at the output, these components will be amplified by the integrator, and the resulting correcting signal will be applied at the input of the timing circuits with the proper polarity to tend to suppress the net low-frequency distortion at the output.

Since the gain of the integrator is inversely proportional to the frequency of its input signal, it would be expected that this type of feedback control scheme should provide an effective suppression of very low- or zero-frequency unwanted components. At the same time, since the integrator acts only upon the *unwanted* components and not upon the *wanted* component, this approach presents no impediment to the production of a low- or zero-frequency *wanted* component of voltage at the output of the frequency changer.

It can be shown quite simply that this control scheme will attenuate (i.e., divide) any distortion component with frequency f by a factor of $\sqrt{1 + f_1^2/f^2}$, as compared with its open-loop amplitude, in which f_1 is the frequency at which the integrator has unit gain (i.e., $f_1 = 1/2\pi RC$). For low values of f, the above attenuation factor becomes approximately f_1/f. Thus, for example, if the unit gain frequency of the integrator is set at 10 Hz, unwanted components with a frequency of 1 Hz would be attenuated by a factor of 10, and unwanted components with a frequency of 0.1 Hz would be attenuated by a factor of 100.

A permissible unit gain frequency, f_1, of the integrator can be estimated on the basis that is should not pass any appreciable amounts of the predominant higher-frequency ripple components appearing at the output of the frequency changer back to the input of the timing circuit. For example, if the maximum required output frequency is relatively low in relation to the input frequency, so that the lowest predominant ripple frequency is essentially $3f_I$ (for a three-pulse frequency changer), the gain of the integrator at $3f_I$ should not be greater than, for example, 0.05. We leave it to the reader to verify for himself that with this gain, the peak amplitude of the $3f_I$ ripple component fed back to the timing circuit would be approximately 0.03 × the amplitude of the cosine timing wave. This means that the unit gain frequency f_1 is $0.05 \times 3f_I = 0.15f_I$. Thus, if f_I is for example, 60 Hz, f_1 would be 9 Hz.

This simple example is based on a fairly arbitrary assumption of the level of ripple that can be tolerated at the output of the integrator. It is pertinent to inquire into the correctness of this presumption, since if the integrator gain can be made higher than this presumption allows, the attenuation of the undesirable subfrequency components will be greater.

To obtain an answer to this question, it is useful to consider the operation of the system when the feedback loop is broken at point Y in Figure 7.10, so that the integral of the output ripple voltage is not fed back to the input of the timing circuit. Considering that interest now lies in the effect of the high-frequency ripple wave, appearing at the output of the integrator, upon the firing instants, in the event that the loop is reclosed, it is revealing to examine the operation under specific conditions when the basic open-loop timing control does not produce any low-frequency unwanted terms at the output of the frequency changer. For these specific operating conditions, the signal that appears at the output of the integrator as a result of the high-frequency ripple components applied to its input must not have any appreciable modifying effect upon the already "correct" open-loop firing instants. It would be reasonable to suppose that in order to satisfy this condition all that is necessary is that the output wave of the integrator should have near-zero values at each and every firing instant. As long as this is so, the modifying effect upon the firing instants when the loop is closed should be relatively slight. *Between* successive firing instants, on the other hand, relatively large excursions of the output signal of the integrator should be quite permissible, because such excursions in themselves will not effect the actual firing instants.

Consider first the operation in which the reference is a steady d-c voltage. Waveforms for this operating condition are illustrated in Figure 7.11; it is evident that the

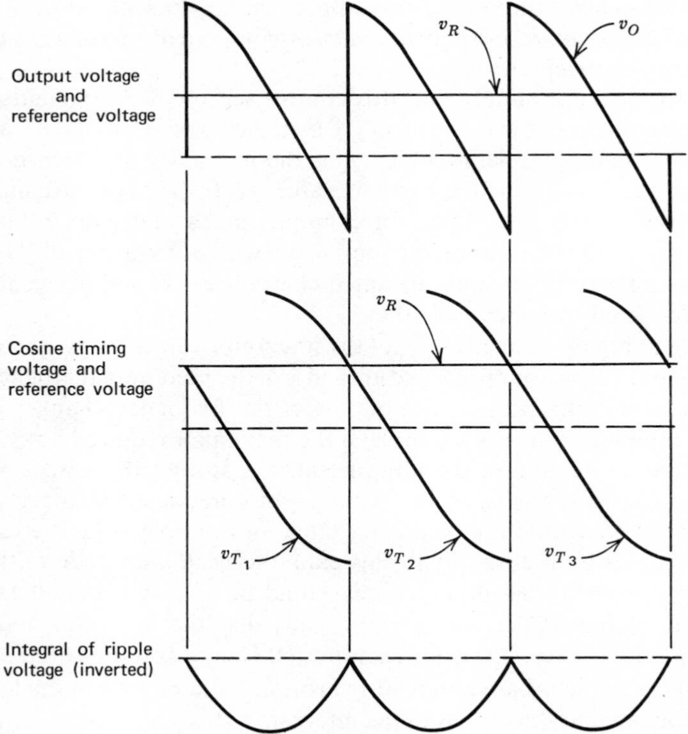

Figure 7.11 Three-pulse waveforms obtained with steady d-c reference voltage.

output signal of the integrator is *zero* at each firing instant. Thus the gain of the integrator (i.e., the unit gain frequency, f_1) could, in theory, be made infinite without producing any ripple instability for this extreme operating condition of zero output frequency. This is an interesting deduction because it is contrary to the original presumption that the gain of the integrator must be relatively low at the lowest predominant ripple frequency.

It can be expected, then, that for relatively low output to input frequency ratios, the output signal of the integrator will still return to the proximity of zero at each firing instant, and thus the gain of the integrator can be made considerably higher than was originally presumed. It is not yet evident, however, what the situation will be as the output frequency is raised beyond the point at which it can be said to be very low in relation to the input frequency.

Figure 7.12 shows the output waveform of a three-pulse frequency changer and the corresponding integral of the ripple voltage with an open-loop timing control for an output to input frequency ratio of 1:6, at which operating point no low-frequency components are produced in the output. The maximum deviation between the values of the integrator output signal at the firing instants is now about one-half of the total peak-to-peak output signal of the integrator. Hence, a twofold increase in the permissible gain of the integrator can now be expected, compared to what would be estimated on the simple assumption that the peak-to-peak ripple at the output of the integrator (rather than the peak deviation of this ripple *at the firing instants*) should not exceed a given fraction of the peak value of the timing waves.

As the output-to-input frequency ratio is further increased, the maximum deviation between the values of the integrator output signal at the firing instants stays at about one-half the total peak-to-peak ripple at the integrator output. However, since the absolute amplitude of the integral of the ripple voltage increases with increasing frequency ratio (because the frequencies of certain of the predominant ripple components decrease), so the maximum permissible gain of the integrator for stable operation decreases.

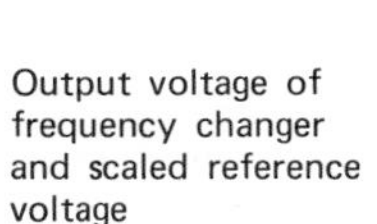

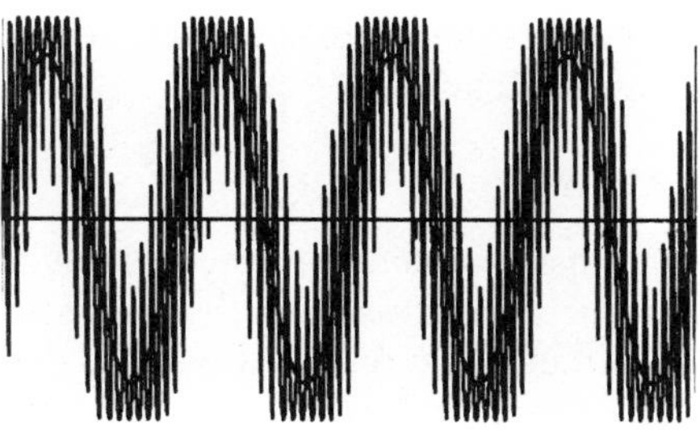

Figure 7.12 Positive-type output voltage of a three-pulse frequency changer and corresponding integral of ripple voltage with open-loop control (point Y in Figure 7.10 open). $f_O/f_I = 1/6$. Output voltage is 98.5% of maximum.

TABLE 7.1. Approximate Maximum Permissible Unit-Gain Frequency of Ripple Voltage Integrator at Various Output to Input Frequency Ratios for a Three-Pulse Frequency Changer.

f_O/f_I	Unit-Gain Frequency of Integrator-Multiple of f_I
$\frac{1}{9}$	0.19
$\frac{1}{6}$	0.14
$\frac{1}{3}$	0.11
$\frac{1}{2}$	0.09
$\frac{2}{3}$	0.07

For six-pulse circuit, multiply unit-gain frequency by 4.
For twelve-pulse circuit, multiply unit-gain frequency by 16.

Table 7.1 is a guide to the maximum permissible unit-gain frequency of the integrator, related to the input frequency, for a three-pulse frequency changer, at various frequency ratios. It should be noted that these values can be multiplied by approximately 4 and 16 for six- and twelve-pulse frequency changers, respectively, for which the integral of the ripple voltage has correspondingly lower peak values.

The output voltage waveform of a three-pulse frequency changer employing ripple voltage integral feedback, at an output to input frequency ratio of 0.37, is shown in Figure 7.13. With an open-loop control, subfrequency unwanted components would be produced in the output voltage at this frequency ratio. Since no appreciable subfrequency components are discernible in the integral of the ripple voltage, it is evident that these components are effectively suppressed by the action of the closed-loop ripple voltage feedback.

7.3.4 Integral Control

7.3.4.1 *General Considerations.* A practical difficulty with the cosine wave crossing control method sometimes arises from the presence of distortion on the input voltage waves from which the cosine timing waves are derived. This distortion, which may originate from the supply system or may be a direct result of the commutations of the frequency changer itself, may necessitate the use of quite heavy filtering for the cosine timing waves in order to present the control circuits with smooth timing waves and thereby prevent the production of spurious timing signals.

Typically, for applications in which the input frequency is fixed, the timing wave filters may comprise resistor-capacitor networks, giving a phase shift to the fundamental component of 60°. By designing the filters for this precise amount of phase shift, the timing waves can be given the correct phase position with respect to the frequency changer input voltages. For applications in which the input frequency is variable, however, it may be difficult to provide adequate filtering and, at the same time, to maintain the desired phase shift of the timing waves with respect to the

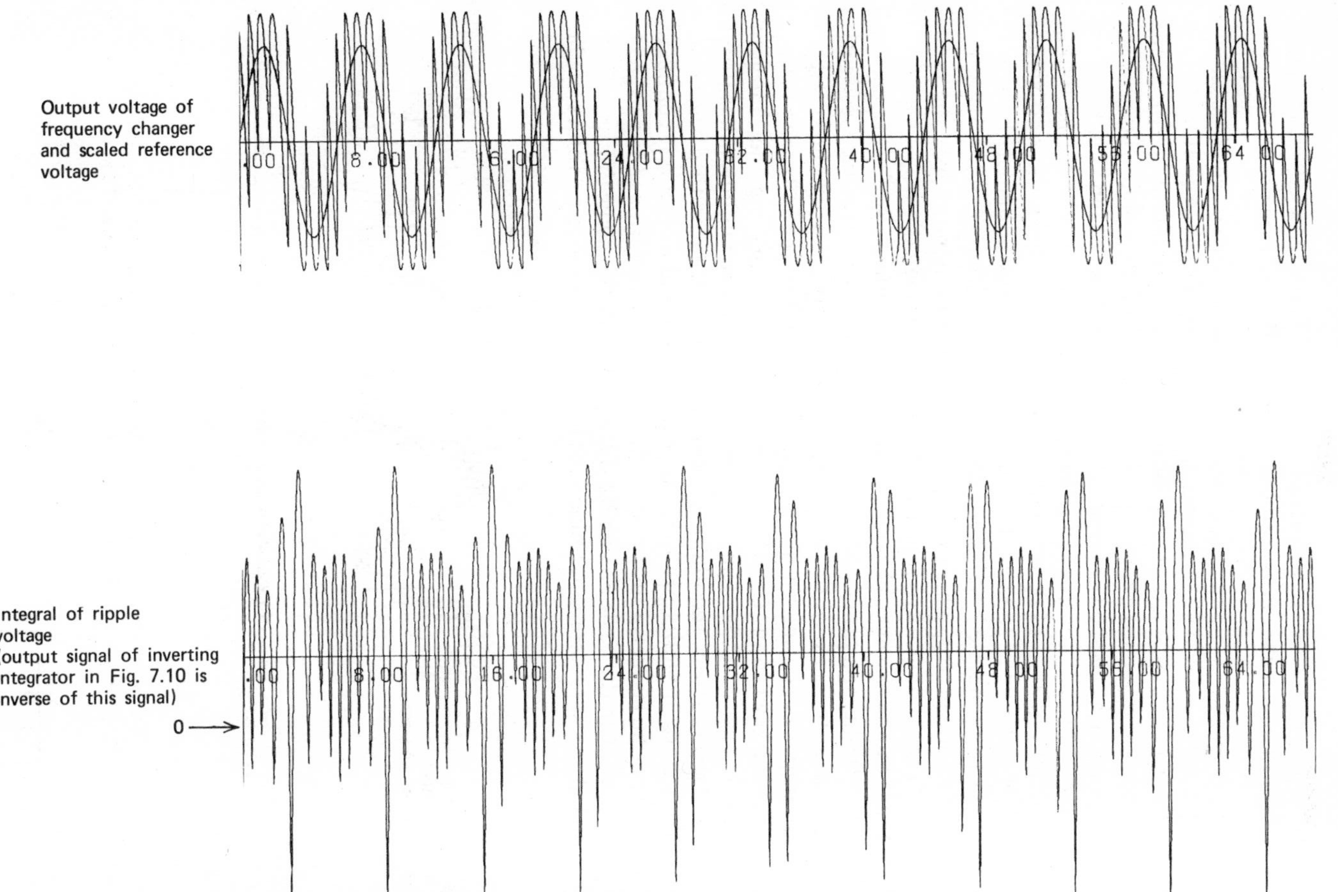

Figure 7.13 Positive-type output voltage of a three-pulse frequency changer and corresponding integral of ripple voltage with closed-loop ripple voltage integral feedback. $f_O/f_I = 0.37$. Output voltage is 90% of maximum. Unit-gain frequency of integrator is 0.1 f_I.

input voltage waves as the input frequency varies. In this case, a different timing approach, called the *integral control* method, can be used to advantage.

7.3.4.2 *Basic Approach.* The integral control method can be regarded as an extension of the ripple voltage feedback principle described in the previous section. In that scheme, the firing points are determined from the intersections of a set of cosine timing waves with the reference voltage, with the integral of the ripple voltage wave being added, in a certain specified amount, as a "correction" signal. The fundamental thought behind the integral control principle is the elimination of the cosine timing waves and the determination of the switching instants entirely from the zero values of the integral of the ripple voltage. The motivation for this is that if the cosine timing waves can be eliminated and the timing instants determined solely from the output signal of an integrator, which by its nature is inherently noise free, the practical difficulties of the timing wave scheme will also be eliminated.

In effect, then, the basic integral control concept in its unadorned state can be regarded as an extreme operating condition of the ripple voltage integral feedback scheme, under which the gain of the integrator is set so high that its output signal completely "swamps" the cosine timing waves, which could therefore be eliminated, without altering the operation. Clearly, this is equivalent to making the unit-gain frequency of the integrator of the ripple voltage feedback scheme infinite; thus (from the discussion of the previous section) it is clear that this concept in this basic state is unworkable, because it would produce extreme ripple instability, if not complete loss of control. That this is so is illustrated by the six-pulse waveforms of Figure 7.14, which are appropriate to the basic unstabilized integral control scheme of Figure 7.15. Here the switching instants are determined exclusively from the zero values of the

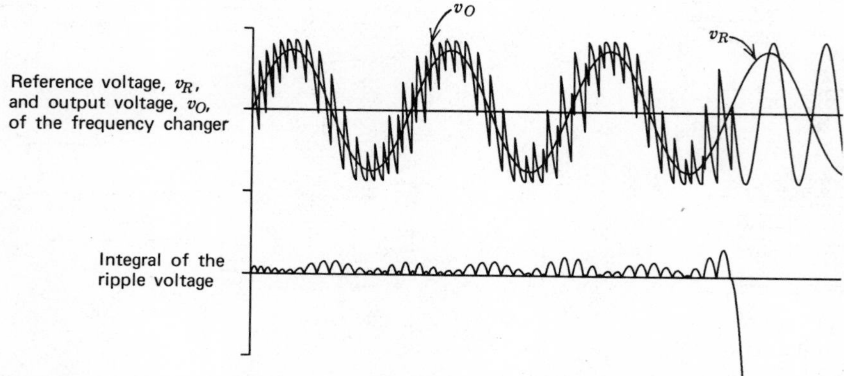

Figure 7.14 Waveforms for a six-pulse frequency changer, demonstrating ripple instability and complete loss of control produced by the basic unstabilized integral control scheme of Figure 7.15.

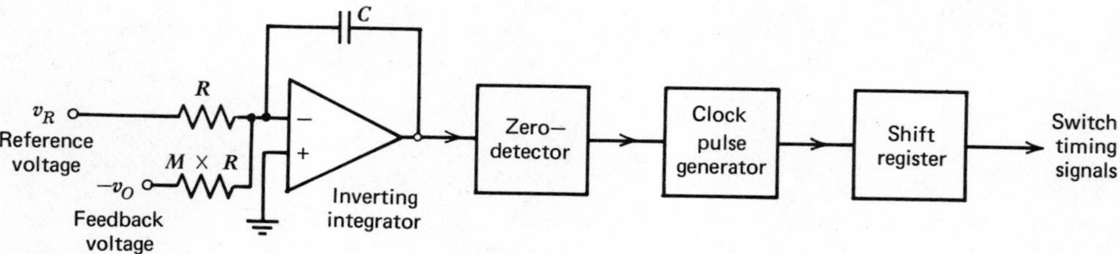

Figure 7.15 Basic unstabilized integral control scheme.

integral of the ripple voltage. Although the waveform construction process starts out apparently successfully, ripple instability soon sets in, and eventually the timing of the switching instants is completely lost.

Clearly, if this basic integral control concept is to be made to work properly, it must be complemented by some corrective means that counteracts the tendency to generate firing instants at grossly unevenly spaced time intervals.

By a reversal of thought processes, we could regard one such stabilizing means as being a set of line-synchronized cosine timing waves; this of course leads us straight back to the control scheme of the previous section and would defeat the objective of finding an inherently noise-free timing method. Obviously, we are now looking for a different stabilizing approach that rids us of the need for line-derived and "spike-prone" synchronizing waves.

7.3.4.3 *Practical Stabilization Method.* A simple stabilization method that transforms the raw integral control concept into a workable scheme is now described. It is introduced by considering the operation of a six-pulse frequency changer with zero reference voltage. Under this condition, the basic unstabilized integral control scheme, shown in Figure 7.15, that determines the firing instants strictly from the zero values of the integral of the ripple voltage, could produce the type of ripple instability shown by the waveforms of Figure 7.16, in which successive firing instants regularly occur early, then late.

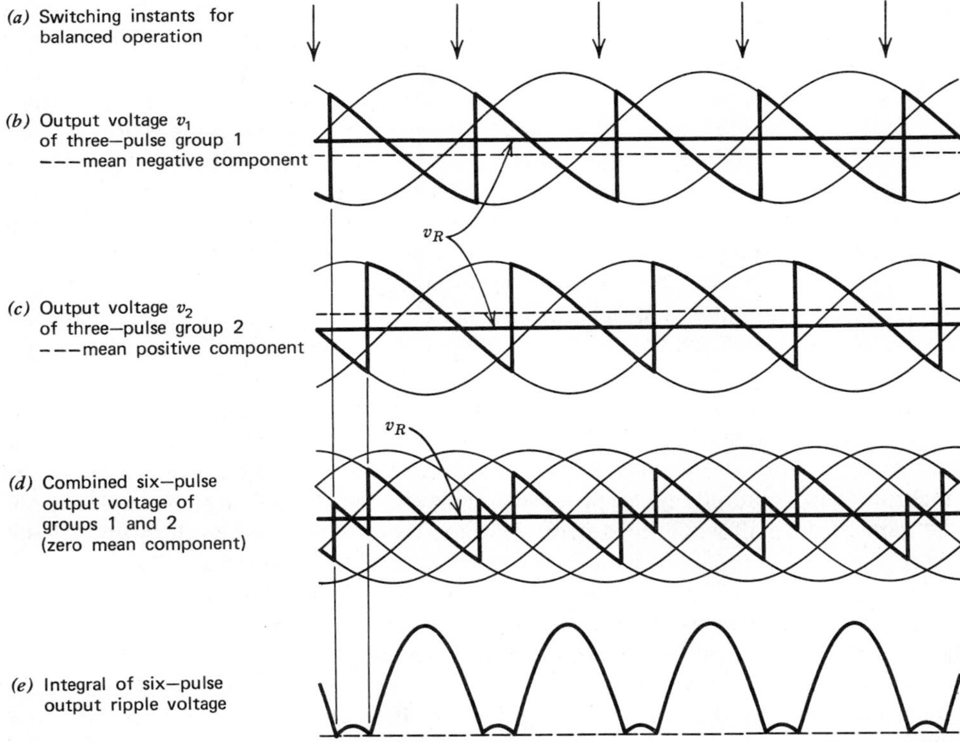

Figure 7.16 Theoretical waveforms for a six-pulse frequency changer, controlled by the simple unstabilized scheme of Figure 7.15, with zero reference voltage, demonstrating that ripple instability is accompanied by a permanent advance in the switching instants of one three-pulse group and a permanent retardation in those of the other.

The key to the stabilization method resides in the recognition of the simple fact that this six-pulse waveform is comprised of two three-pulse waveforms, as shown at *b* and *c*. It is evident that the firing instants for both these constituent waveforms occur at regular intervals, but the interlacing of these two waveforms is not balanced. One wave has a net positive value, whereas the other has an equal net negative value. This suggests that a simple indication of ripple instability in the final output waveform would be the fact that the average values of the constituent three-pulse waveforms deviate in opposite directions from the reference value; the constituent three-pulse waveform that is "too positive" has firing instants that are too early, whereas the constituent three-pulse waveform that is "too negative" has firing instants that are too late. Thus it can be surmised that the ripple instability could be eliminated by using the average positive and negative errors of the constituent waveforms to correct the firing instants produced by the basic integral control scheme. These errors could be measured quite simply by integrating the difference between the reference voltage and the output voltage of each of the individual three-pulse groups. A functional circuit implementation of the postulated approach is shown in Figure 7.17.

The *main integrator* integrates the difference between the reference voltage v_R and the output voltage v_O of the frequency changer, whereas the "*half-wave*" *integrators* 1 and 2 integrate the difference between the reference voltage and the output voltages v_1 and v_2, respectively, of the constituent three-pulse groups of the six-pulse frequency changer. The output of half-wave integrator 1 is summed with the output of the main integrator and fed to the input of *zero detector 1*, and the output of half-wave integrator 2 is summed with the output of the main integrator and fed to the input of *zero-detector 2*. Each zero detector produces a *clock pulse* at its output whenever the voltage applied to its input falls to zero. Thus the clock pulses P_1 and P_2 represent the desired firing instants for the switches within the respective three-pulse groups 1 and 2 of the frequency changer; these pulses are fed as inputs to the *shift register*, which delivers six separate timing signals in sequence, one for each switch of the frequency changer. The shift register is made up of two interlocked three-pulse units, which, in the event of simultaneous clock pulses appearing at both inputs, rejects the pulse in whichever channel last produced a pulse. The P_1 and P_2 clock pulses are also used to reset the outputs of their respective half-wave integrators to zero, at each firing instant of the associated three-pulse group.

Since the integral values of the ripple voltage of each of the constituent three-pulse groups are considerably larger than those of the combined ripple voltage appearing at the output of the frequency changer, and since the output signals of the half-wave integrators are required only to provide a relatively small stabilizing corrective action, the gain of the half-wave integrators is made considerably lower than that of the main integrator—typically by a factor that lies somewhere between 5 and 20.

The waveforms of Figure 7.18 illustrate the operation of this control scheme for the previously assumed simple condition of zero reference voltage. It is assumed that before time t the output signals of the half-wave integrators are not summed to the output of the main integrator and that the resulting output wave contains the same ripple instability as that shown in Figure 7.16. From time t onward, however, the output signals of the half-wave integrators are summed to the output signal of the main integrator. The corrective action of the half-wave integrators in eliminating the ripple instability is evident.

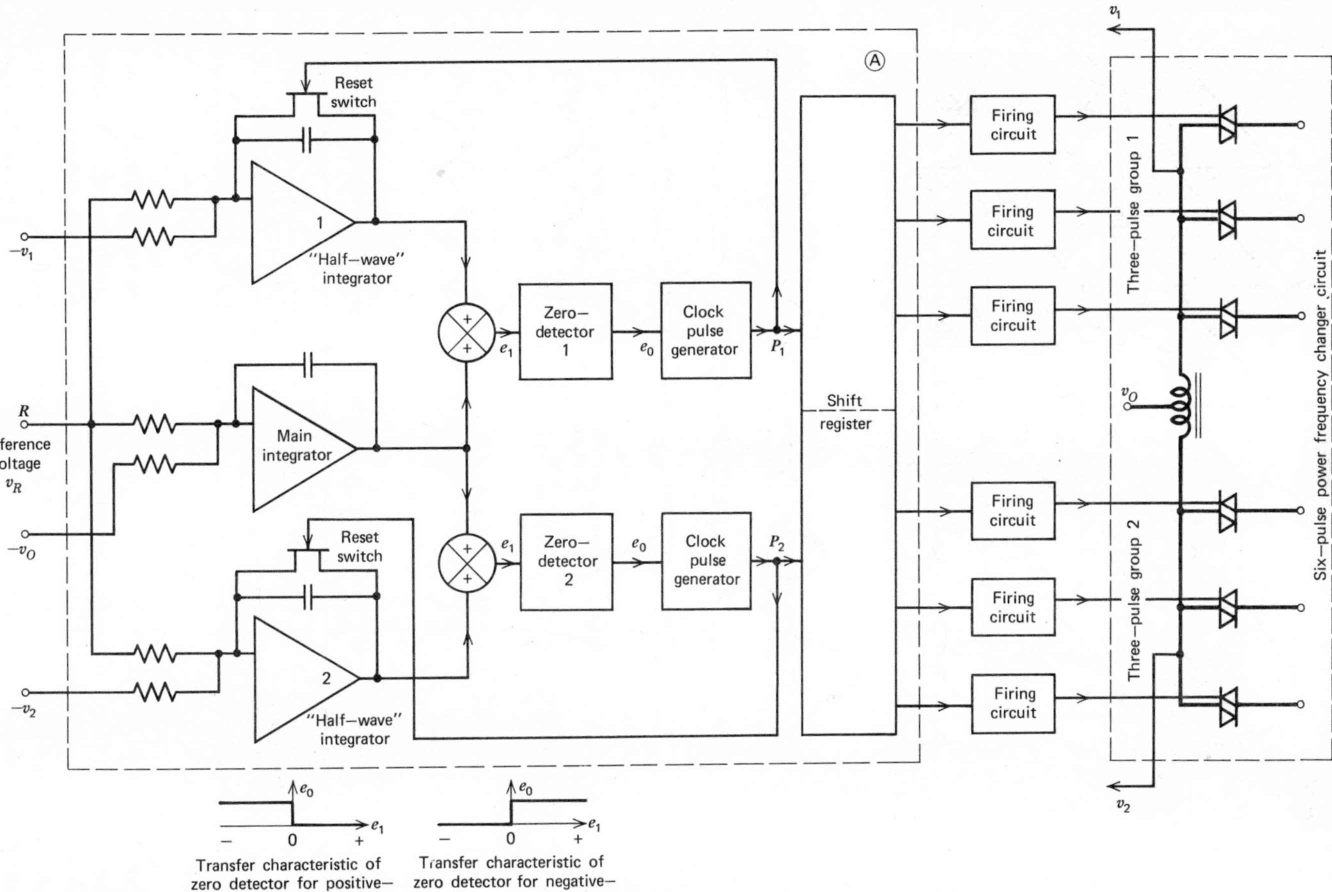

Figure 7.17 Functional integral control scheme for a six-pulse frequency changer, with stabilizing feedback from the constituent three-pulse groups.

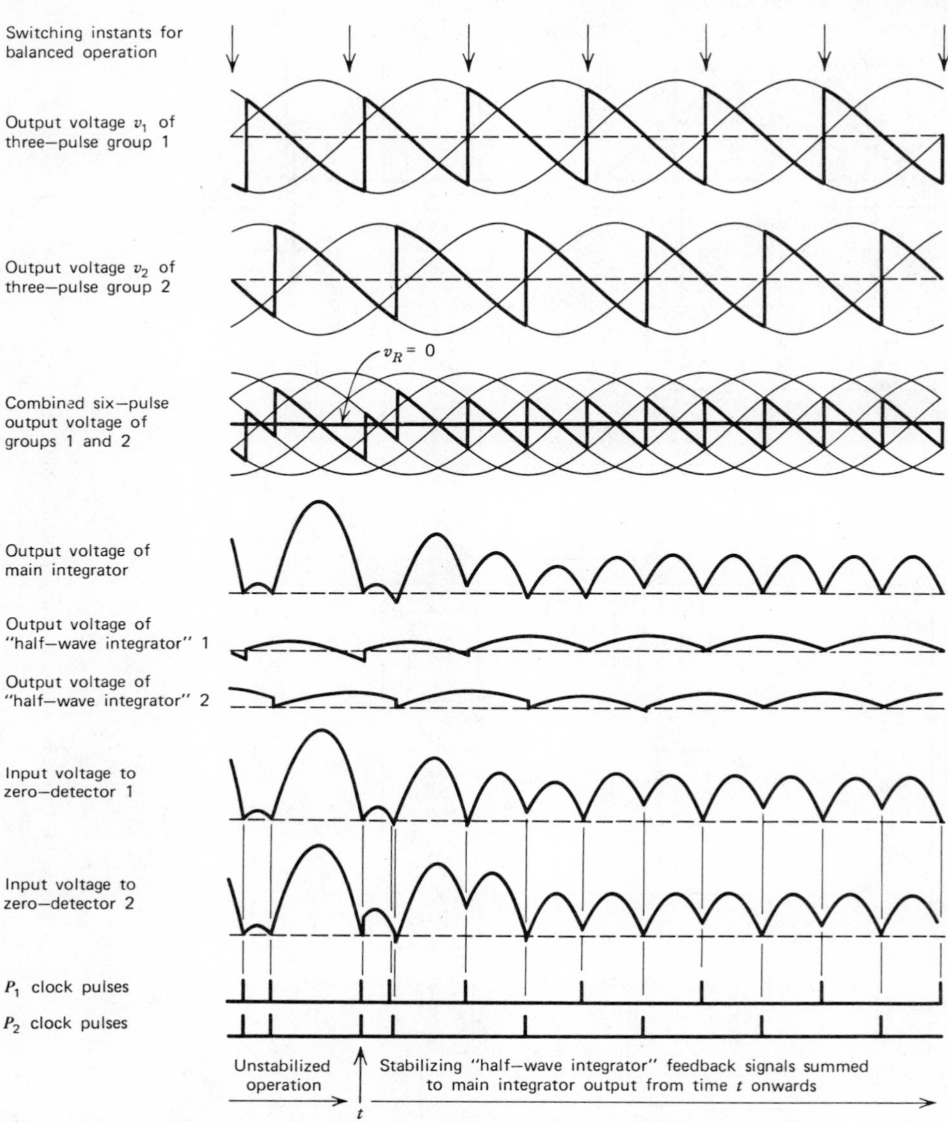

Figure 7.18 Waveforms illustrating the corrective action of the stabilizing feedback for the integral control scheme of Figure 7.17. Reference voltage v_R is zero.

These waveforms demonstrate the effectiveness of the stabilizing feedback for the simple condition of zero reference voltage. In practice, of course, the frequency changer is required to generate a wanted alternating component of output voltage. It has been seen that the basic integral control without any stabilizing means cannot accomplish this; it produces an ever-increasing ripple instability with possible eventual complete loss of control. Since the stabilizing feedback under consideration does work very effectively for a steady d-c output, it would be expected that it would also work properly when the frequency changer produces a wanted a-c output. This is indeed so.

The waveforms of Figure 7.19 illustrate the operation of the stabilizing feedback

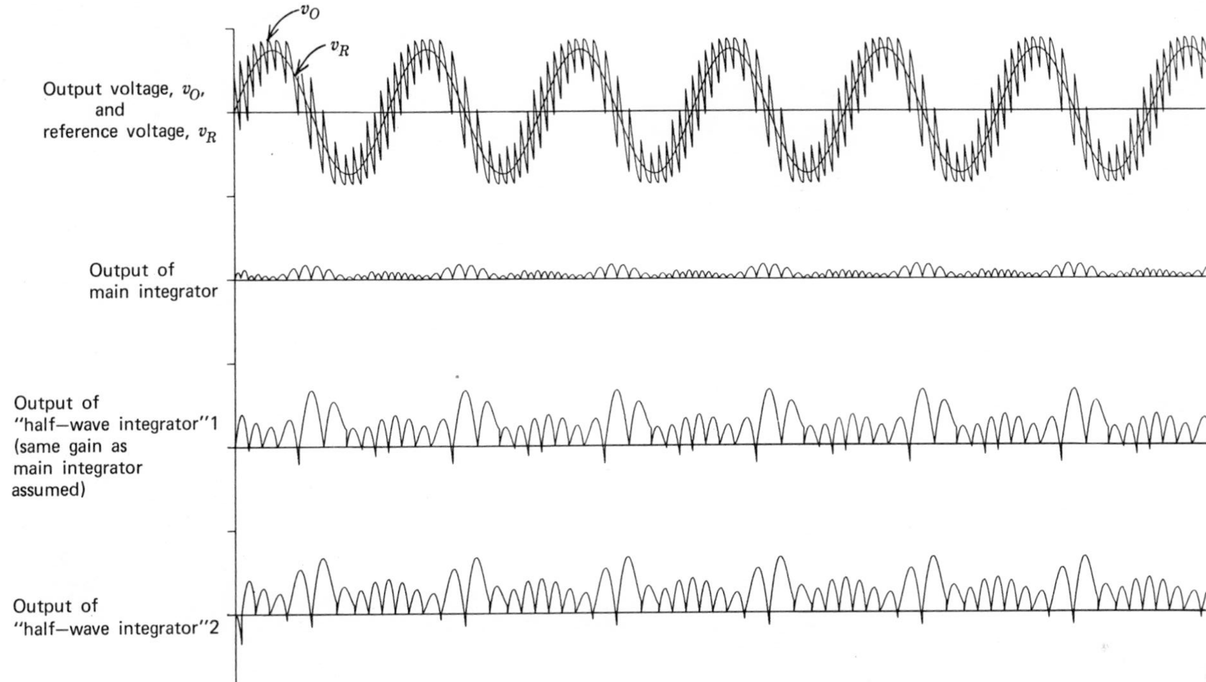

Figure 7.19 Waveforms illustrating the steady-state operation of the integral control scheme of Figure 7.17. $f_O/f_I = 1/3$. Reference voltage is 90% of maximum. 0.05 × "half-wave integrals" shown are used as stabilizing signals.

when the frequency changer is producing a substantial wanted component of output voltage. These waveforms correspond to the same level of reference voltage and output to input frequency ratio as those of Figure 7.14, for which there is no stabilizing feedback. It is quite evident that the stabilizing feedback does prevent ripple instability and maintains the waveform construction process under "tight" control. The waveforms of Figure 7.20 further illustrate the performance of this type of control scheme. Here a relatively large step reduction in the amplitude of the reference voltage, followed by a step increase of similar magnitude, is made. The waveform construction process is kept well under control, with only a short-lived ripple instability at the actual perturbation points.

7.3.4.4 *Quality of Voltage Wave Produced by the Integral Control Method.* It should be remembered that the original objective was to find practical methods of implementing the periodic modulating function $M(t) = \sin^{-1}(r \sin \omega_0 t)$ with some minor correction that would eliminate the small amounts of practically objectionable low-frequency distortion components produced by this theoretically pure modulating function. It was seen that one approach is the cosine wave crossing control method, which produces the theoretically pure modulating function, operating in conjunction with a negative voltage feedback loop, which suppresses the objectionable low-frequency distortion terms.

Consideration of the difficulties that can sometimes arise in implementing the cosine wave crossing control method then led to the integral control method. The basic motivation for the integral control method was a purely practical one, and no conscious attention was paid to its theoretical propriety as far as producing the desired modulating function is concerned. It is pertinent, then, to examine briefly the question of how the *quality* of the output voltage wave produced by the integral control method compares to that produced by the cosine wave crossing control method.

One point can be stated immediately. Since the integral control is a self-contained closed-loop control scheme in which the integral of the output ripple voltage is fed back to the timing detectors, it is inherent that unwanted low-frequency and d-c distortion components at the output of the frequency changer must be effectively suppressed.

There remains the question of how the predominant higher-frequency unwanted terms compare to those produced by the cosine wave crossing control method. Intuitively, one might expect that the integral control method would produce a near-optimum output voltage waveform; its basic mechanism tends to force equality between the average value of each segment of the output voltage wave and the average value of the reference wave over the same period. Thus, the output voltage wave "clings" tightly to the reference wave, and the possibility for producing integral multiple harmonics of the reference seems to be slight (except, of course, at certain discrete output to input frequency ratios at which this is theoretically unavoidable). An inspection of the waveforms of Figure 7.19 certainly gives the impression that the output voltage wave generated by the integral control scheme is generally similar in appearance to that which would be produced by the cosine wave crossing method.

It would be reasonable to predict, then, that the predominant unwanted components produced by both control methods must be substantially the same as one another. This in fact is so, as a detailed examination of these unwanted terms shows. To exemplify this, the amplitudes of the predominant unwanted components produced by both control methods for the particular output to input frequency ratio

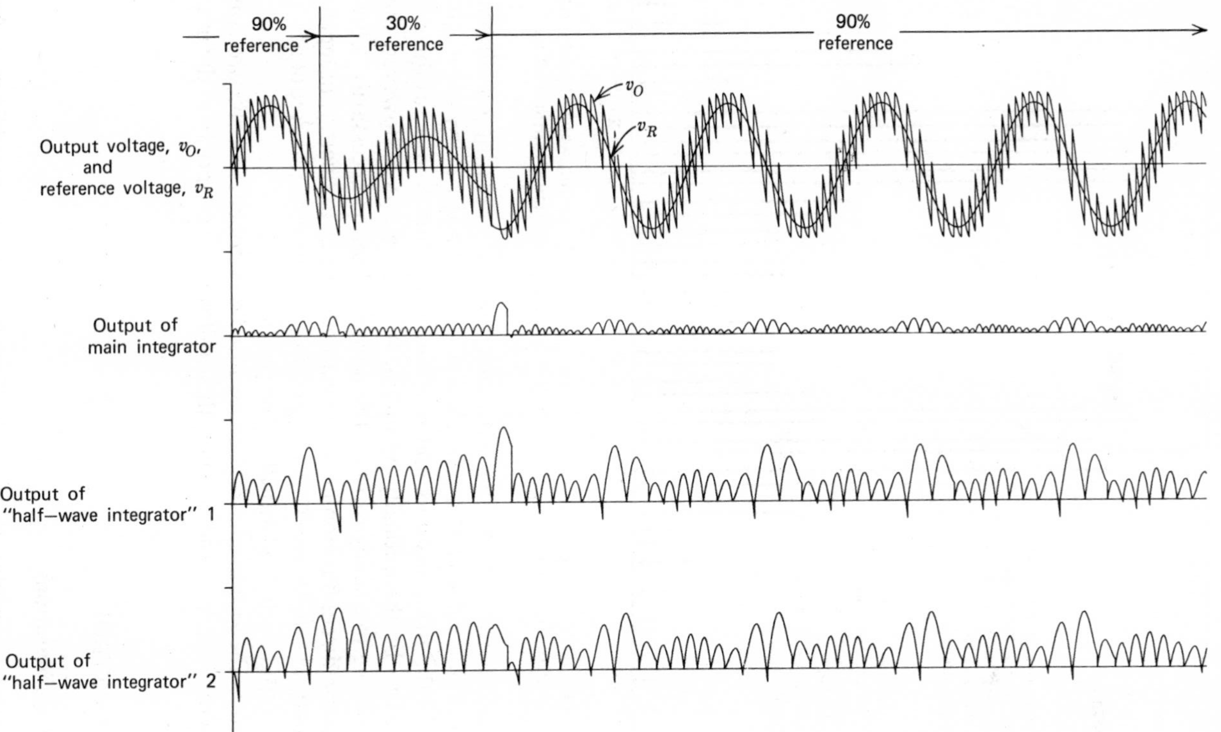

Figure 7.20 Waveforms illustrating the operation of the integral control scheme of Figure 7.17, when step changes are made in the amplitude of the reference voltage. $f_O/f_I = 1/3$. $0.05 \times$ "half-wave integrals" shown are used as stabilizing signals.

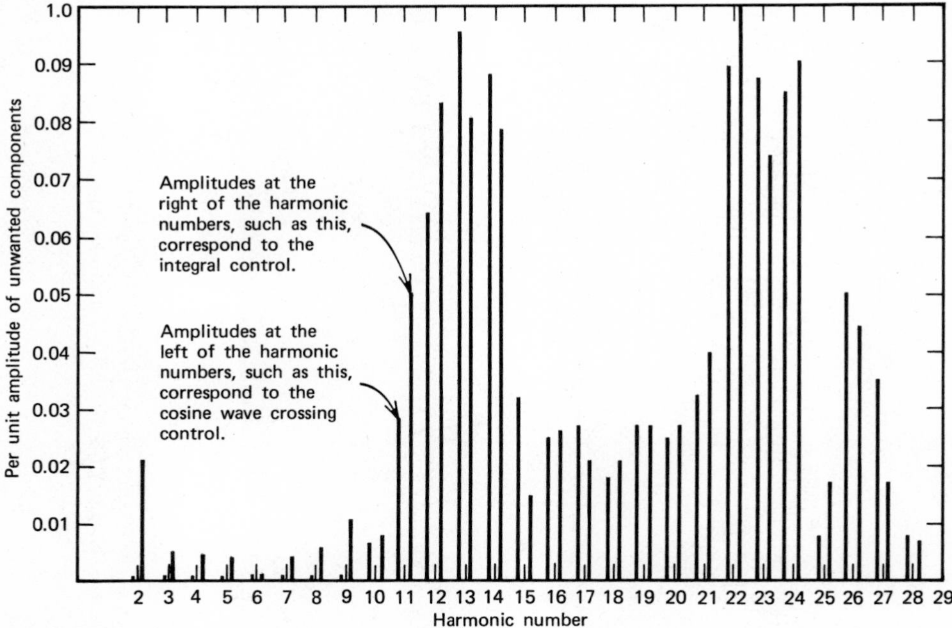

Figure 7.21 Amplitudes of unwanted terms in the output voltage, with cosine wave crossing control (left bar) and integral control (right bar). $f_O/f_I = 1/3$. Ninety percent of maximum output voltage.

of $\frac{1}{3}$ are shown in Figure 7.21. At this particular selected operating condition, the basic open-loop cosine wave crossing method does not produce any subfrequency or d-c terms; thus the firing instants and resulting distortion that it produces here can be considered to be theoretically optimum. It is to be noted, however, that at this particular discrete frequency ratio all the unwanted terms necessarily "conspire together" to become direct harmonics of the wanted output frequency, independent of the control method employed. This is inevitable, because at this frequency ratio each successive output cycle is identical to the previous one.

It can be seen that the amplitudes of the unwanted components for the two control methods are generally close to one another; this confirms the propriety of the integral control method.

7.4 END-STOP CONTROL

7.4.1 General Considerations

The maximum required amplitude or *depth of modulation* of a periodic modulating function is 90°, regardless of its mathematical form; this is the angular deviation of the existence function from its quiescent position that gives the maximum possible average level of voltage at the output of the frequency changer.

Both the cosine wave crossing and integral control schemes theoretically maintain operation virtually up to the maximum required angular deviation of 90°. At this limiting point, however, their operation becomes critically stable; any further increase of the reference voltage above the limiting value results in complete loss of control. This is illustrated by the waveforms of Figure 7.22 for the cosine wave crossing scheme of Figure 7.8. In practice, because of circuit imperfections, loss of

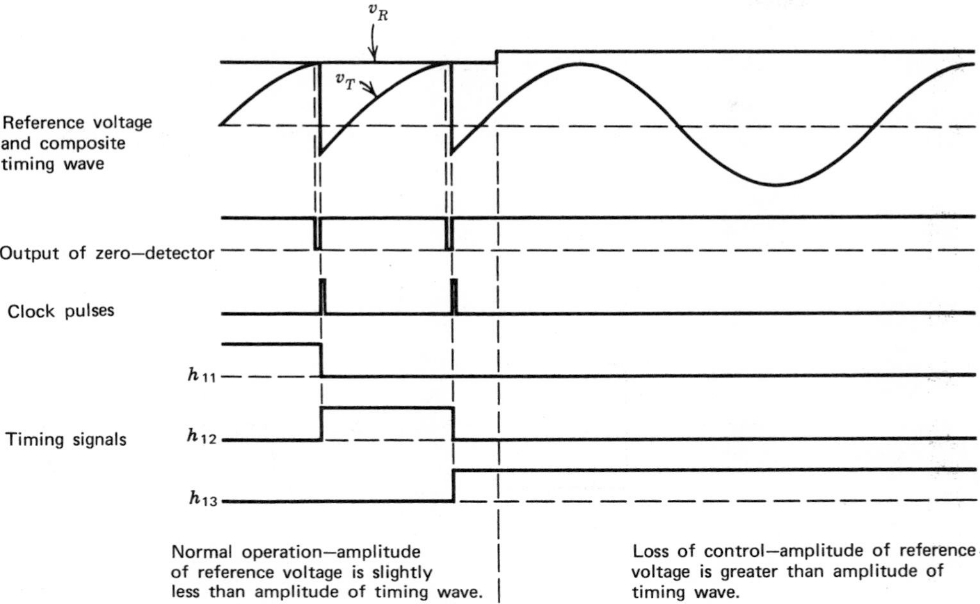

Figure 7.22 Waveforms illustrating loss of control when the amplitude of the reference voltage is made greater than the amplitude of the timing wave—applicable to the basic control scheme of Figure 7.8.

control generally occurs slightly before the theoretical maximum level of reference voltage is reached. In addition, in the naturally commutated cycloconverter, commutation failures inevitably occur in the power circuit before the theoretical 90° delay of the quiescent existence function is attained because commutation does not take place instantaneously, and the power switches require a finite *margin angle* for recovery.

Clearly, in order to prevent improper operation of the control circuits, as well as to avoid commutation failures in the case of the NCC, the need arises for an *end-stop* control that keeps the firing pulses coming in the proper sequence and firmly holds the modulation angle at the desired limit whenever the amplitude of the reference voltage goes beyond a certain limiting level. Since this limiting level generally is a function of the amplitude of the input voltage of the frequency changer (as well as, for the NCC, of the output current), simple clamping of the reference voltage to a fixed level generally is not an acceptable solution. Several ways of achieving the desired result are possible. The general type of circuit arrangement that can be used is illustrated by considering a typical approach.

7.4.2 Typical Functional Approach

The end-stop control method to be described is applicable both to the cosine wave crossing and integral control schemes. It is based upon the use of logic signals derived from and synchronized to the input voltages of the frequency changer that represent the desired range of modulation of each existence function. In the simple case in which the modulation range is exactly 90° (i.e., for the UDFFC and the CDFFC) these logic signals can be derived directly from the input voltage waves, generally with suitable filtering to obviate the effects of distortion and voltage "spikes," as illustrated in Figure 7.23. Similar techniques can be used for the NCC, with varying

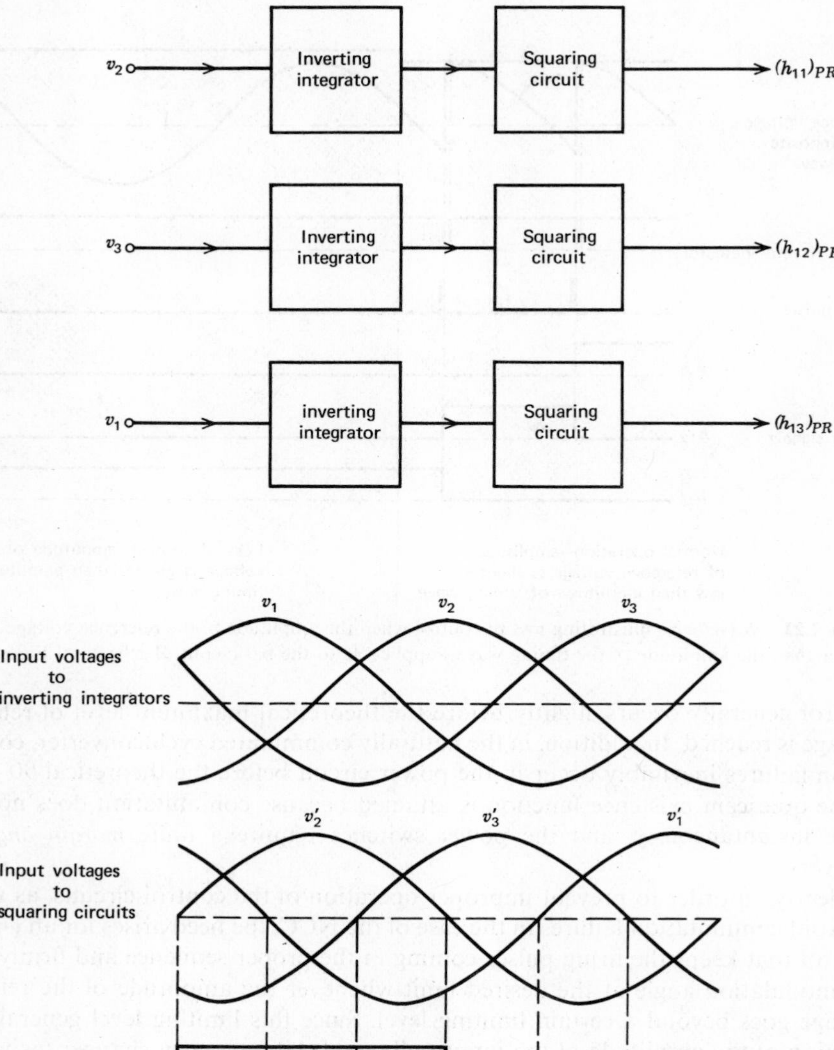

Figure 7.23 Simplified method of derivation of "permissible range of modulation" signals.

degrees of sophistication, to provide the required logic signals, with slightly less than 180° duration, representing the practically permissible range of modulation.

Once the logic signals that represent the desired range of modulation have been obtained, they are injected into the regular timing control circuits in such a way that they affect the operation only when the amplitude of the reference exceeds that corresponding to the desired limits of the modulation range. When this occurs, the modulation angle is held firmly at the desired limit.

A complete functional three-pulse end-stop control scheme is shown in Figure 7.24. The scheme is directly applicable to the three-pulse cosine wave crossing control scheme of Figure 7.8; thus the *zero detector*, *clock pulse generator*, and *shift register* are the same items in Figure 7.24 as they are in Figure 7.8; the end-stop control scheme is simply interposed between these functional blocks. The scheme is also directly applicable to the six-pulse integral control scheme of Figure 7.17; in this case, however, two such three-pulse schemes are required: one for each half of the complete six-pulse circuit. Thus the *zero detector*, *clock pulse generator*, and *shift register* belonging to either one constituent three-pulse channel of Figure 7.17 are the same items as those shown in Figure 7.24.

In normal operation, the output signal of the *zero detector* switches from a 0 to a 1 state at the desired instant of initiation of the corresponding existence function. The *AND gates A1*, *B1*, and *C1*, are supervised by the *permissible range of modulation* signals and the existence functions themselves (as well as the complement of the clock pulse, which is inserted in order to prevent practical "race" conditions) in such a way that the output signal of the zero detector is sent uninhibited to the input of the *clock pulse generator*, provided that this signal is generated within the limits of the permissible modulation range.

In the event that the amplitude of the reference voltage exceeds the positive limiting level (for a positive timing circuit), the output signal of the zero detector switches from a 0 to a 1 level ahead of the corresponding limit of the permitted range of modulation; if the reference is sufficiently large, this signal will assume a permanent 1 value. In either event, each AND gate does not now deliver a 1 signal at its output until the instant at which the corresponding permissible range of modulation signal at its input assumes a 1 value. Thus the generation of the existence functions becomes locked into the *positive end-stop* position.

The *AND gates A2*, *B2*, and *C2* are supervised so that they do not normally produce any output. These gates produce output signals only if the appropriate existence function has not yet been initiated at the latest permissible point. Such a condition, of course, would be caused by an excessive negative reference voltage. In this event, the appropriate gate delivers an immediate 1 signal to the input of the clock pulse generator, and the existence function is gnerated in the *negative end-stop* position.

7.5 CONTROL OF THE UDFFC

7.5.1 Functional Control Schemes

In the previous chapters, it is seen that the unity displacement factor frequency changer consists of two identical power circuits, one continuously generating a positive-type output voltage wave, v_O, the other continuously generating a negative-type output voltage, $v_{O\pi}$. These two constituent voltages are summed together, either by

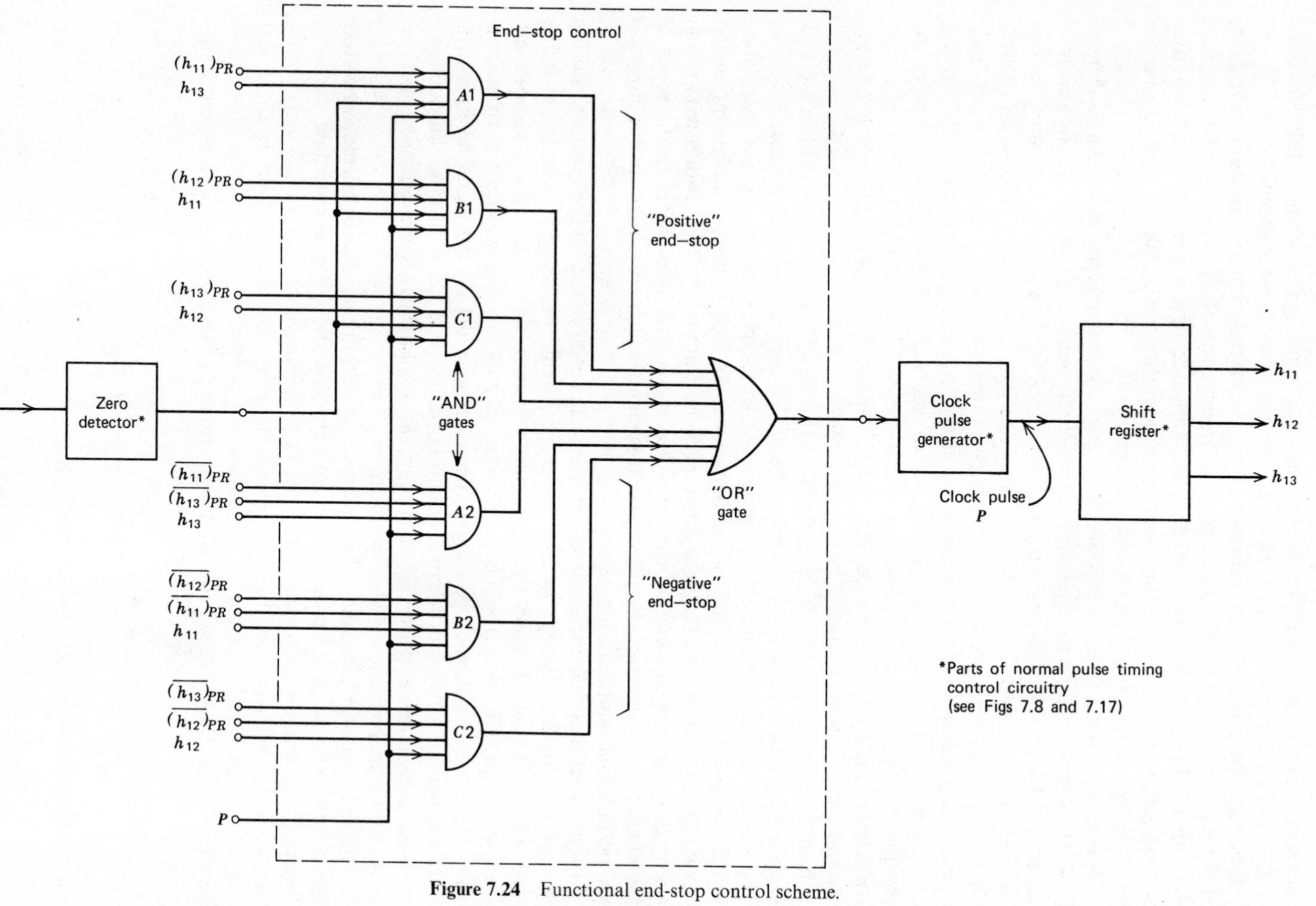

Figure 7.24 Functional end-stop control scheme.

series connection of the constituent power circuits or by parallel connection, through interphase reactors.

In the previous sections of this chapter, individual timing control schemes are presented that continuously produce the positive-type or negative-type output voltage waves by themselves. A complete UDFFC timing control scheme consists simply of separate positive-type and negative-type control schemes, each controlling the corresponding constituent switch array in the power circuit.

Complete functional timing control schemes for the UDFFC are shown in Figure 7.25. The scheme at *a* uses the cosine wave crossing control method with ripple voltage integral feedback; the scheme at *b* uses the integral control method.

7.6 CONTROL OF THE NCC AND CDFFC

7.6.1 General Considerations

Thus far our considerations are essentially limited to separate timing control schemes that continuously produce either the positive-type or the negative-type output voltage wave. In Chapters 3 and 4 it is seen that both the CDFFC and the NCC are controlled so that they generate sections of each of these waveform types, in sequence.

The CDFFC generates each waveform type for half the total period of the wanted output voltage. The phase of the complementary periods of generation of each waveform type depends on the displacement factor desired at the input of the frequency changer.

The NCC operating with no circulating current also generates each waveform type for half the total output period. In this case, the phase position of each waveform type is determined in strict accordance with the phase of the output current. During the positive half-cycle of current, the positive switches of the NCC produce a positive-type output voltage wave, whereas the negative switches remain idle; the converse is true for the negative half-cycle. Sometimes it may be required to overlap the conduction periods of the positive and negative switches of the NCC in the region of the output current crossover. This ensures a smooth transfer of current from one set of switches to the other, at the expense of allowing some current to circulate between the positive and negative groups during the overlap period. At all events, whether or not "overlapping" is employed, the essential requirement for the commutations always to occur naturally is that whenever the positive switches are in conduction, they must always generate a positive-type output voltage wave, and whenever the negative switches are in conduction, they must always generate a negative-type output voltage wave.

Clearly, both the CDFFC and the NCC require some control mechanism for switching from one waveform type to the other. The simplest approach is to use separate, continuously running positive and negative timing circuits, of the types already described, that furnish continuously available positive and negative timing signals. A logic selection is then made between these two sets of timing signals, depending on which output waveform type is currently required.

7.6.2 Derivation of Waveform Switching Signals

A basic control requirement, then, is to derive two complementary supervisory *waveform switching* signals, representing the complementary waveform existence functions,

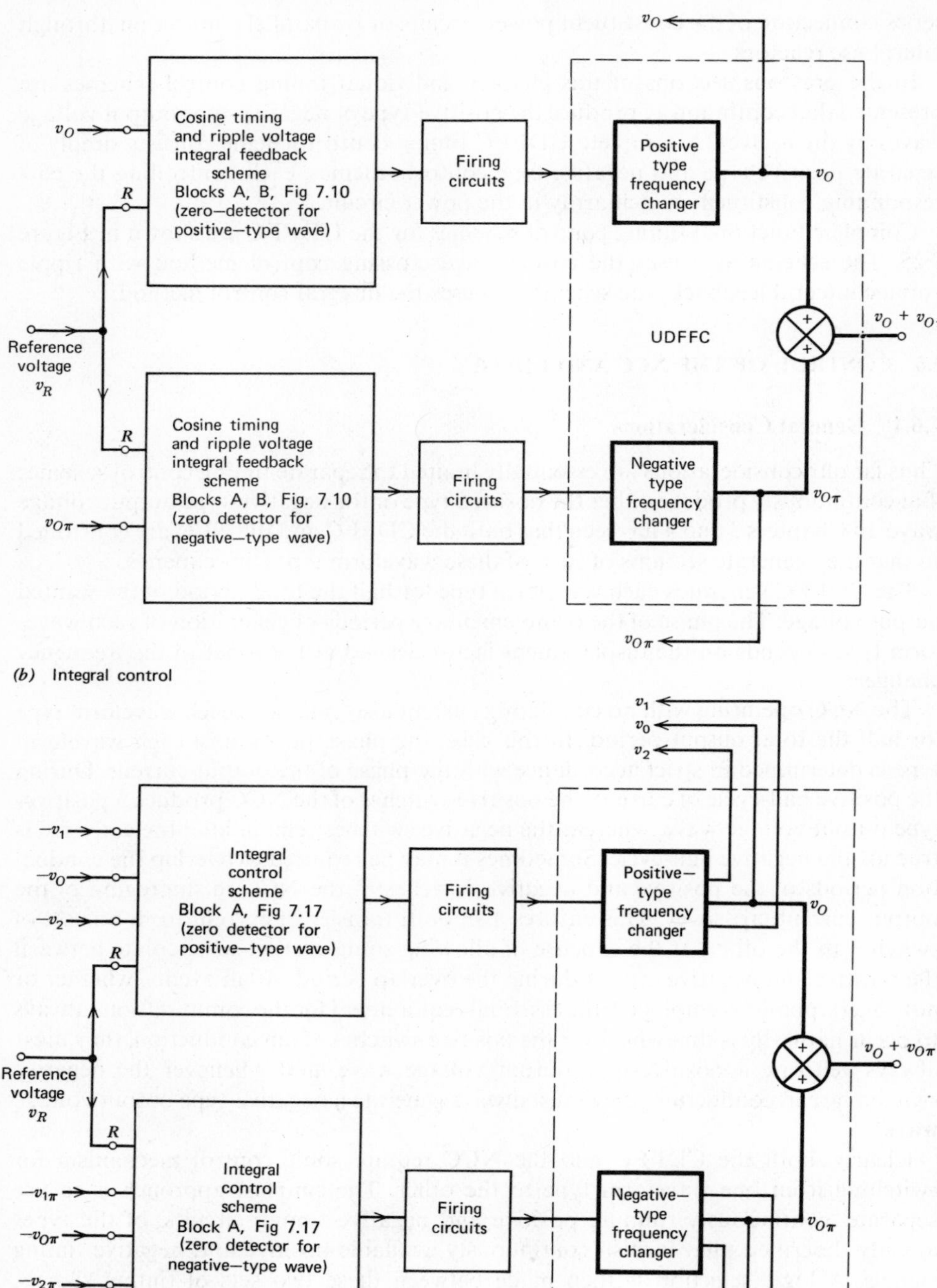

Figure 7.25 Functional control schemes for the UDFFC.

$E(\rho)$ and $E_\pi(\rho)$. The waveform switching signal corresponding to $E(\rho)$ must have unit amplitude whenever the positive-type output voltage wave v_O is required at the output of the frequency changer, and the waveform switching signal corresponding to $E_\pi(\rho)$ must have unit amplitude whenever the negative-type output voltage wave, $v_{O\pi}$, is required.

For the NCC, it is implicit that the complementary waveform switching signals be generated in close correspondence with the output current wave. If this current wave is relatively ripple free, so that it contains no extraneous zero crossings, the waveform switching signals can be derived directly from its actual zero crossings. The functional control scheme of Figure 7.26, with the zero detectors set for "no overlap," provides the desired waveform switching signals. If the output current waveform is likely to contain extraneous zero crossings caused by superimposed ripple, the transfer functions of the zero detectors can be offset as indicated, providing a period of overlap between the two waveform switching signals.

For the CDFFC, the desired phase position of the complementary waveform switching signals is a function of the desired input displacement factor of the frequency changer. Conceivably, the phase of these signals might be controlled in relation either to the voltage reference wave or the output current wave. At first the former might seem to be simpler, because the voltage reference should certainly be "clean" and distortion free, whereas this may not be so for the output current wave. There are good reasons, however, for rejecting this approach.

First, a typical practical application (for example, an induction generator feeding a VSCF frequency changer) may well require that the phase position of the waveform switching signals is shifted either side of the voltage zero crossing as the operating conditions change in order to satisfy the input phase angle requirements. This is practically inconvenient. (It could conceivably be necessary to shift the waveform

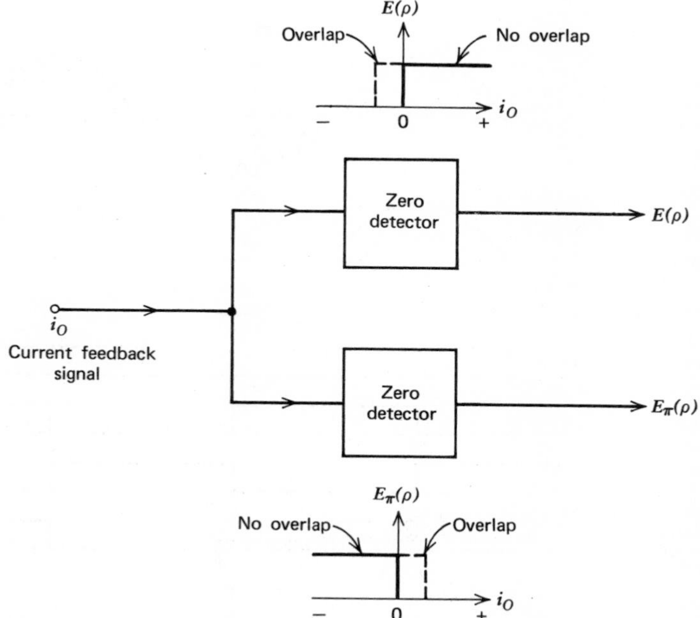

Figure 7.26 Simplified functional scheme for producing waveform switching signals for the NCC.

switching signals either side of the zero crossing of the current wave, but this is less likely in practice.) Second, and fundamentally more objectionable, movement of the phase position of the waveform existence functions in a given direction with respect to the voltage wave does not invariably move the input phase angle in a given direction. The input phase angle theoretically may move either way within different parts of the control range, depending on the phase angle of the load at the output of the frequency changer. Since it would generally be required to provide some form of closed-loop control of the input phase angle of the frequency changer, this behavior is highly undesirable, since it could produce positive feedback and consequent control instability. This phenomenon does not exist, however, if the angle σ of the waveform switching signal is timed with respect to the output current wave. In this case, movement of σ in a given direction invariably produces a given directional movement of the input phase angle. This is evident from the curves of Figures 6.17 and 6.18.

A basic functional control scheme that provides waveform switching signals synchronized to the output current wave with adjustable phase is shown in Figure 7.27. Associated waveforms are shown in Figure 7.28. The output current wave of the frequency changer is passed through a low pass *filter* to remove the main ripple

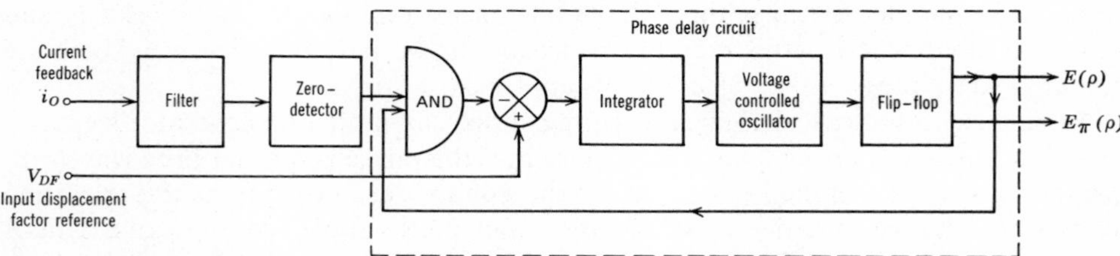

Figure 7.27 Functional scheme for producing waveform switching signals with adjustable phase for the CDFFC.

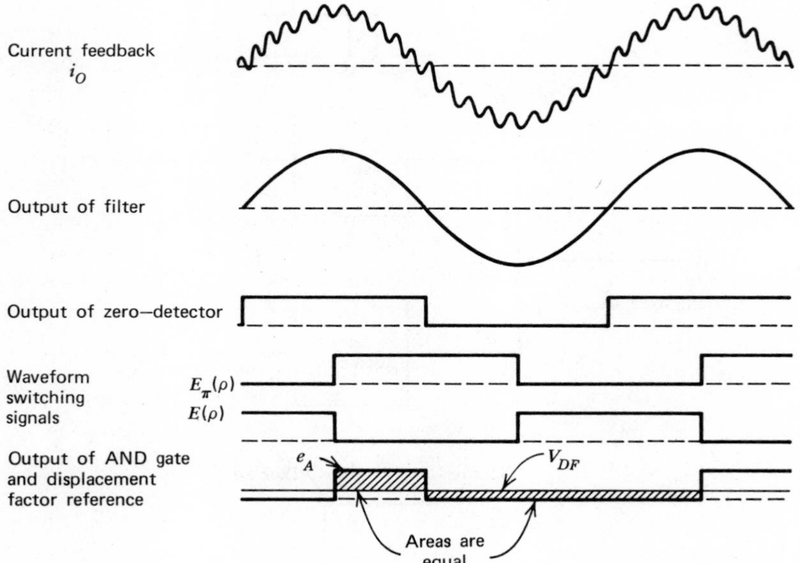

Figure 7.28 Waveforms associated with the functional control scheme of Figure 7.27.

components and present a relatively "clean" wave to the zero detector. The squared output wave of the zero detector is fed to the *phase delay circuit*, which produces two complementary waveform switching signals, $E(\rho)$ and $E_{\pi}(\rho)$, synchronized to the output current, at its output. The phase delay of these output signals with respect to the input signal is controlled by the amplitude of the displacement factor reference, V_{DF}. Increasing V_{DF} advances the phase of the voltage-controlled oscillator and hence of the output signals. Equilibrium is established at the point at which the average value of the voltage pulse at the output of the AND gate just balances the level of V_{DF}, as indicated in Figure 7.28.

It should be noted that this basic scheme will not maintain stable operation if V_{DF} is made too small or too large. Thus, it is necessary either to set strict limits on the maximum and minimum levels of V_{DF} or to provide some additional end-stop control.

7.6.3 Functional Control Schemes for the NCC

Complete functional timing control schemes for the NCC are shown in Figure 7.29. The scheme at *a* uses the cosine wave timing method, with ripple voltage integral feedback. Essentially, the scheme consists of separate free-running positive and negative timing circuits producing complementary sets of positive and negative timing signals. These timing signals are gated to the firing circuits for the positive and negative switches of the NCC, in correspondence with the output signals $E(\rho)$ and $E_{\pi}(\rho)$ of the waveform switching signal generator.

The common output ripple voltage integral feedback acts on both timing channels. The feedback signal is switched from one timing circuit to the other by the waveform switching signals so that it always operates on the timing signals that are currently controlling the output voltage wave. Since the ripple voltage integrator free-runs continuously and thus keeps an "ever-watchful eye" on the output voltage wave, this feedback control scheme inherently must act to suppress objectional low-frequency components in the output.

Since the output ripple voltage has different *direction* for the positive and negative waveform types, the output signal of the integrator is forced to "change direction" at the waveform switching points. The resulting perturbation in the output signal of the integrator can cause misplaced firing pulses at the waveform switching points if the gain of the integrator is too high. For this reason, the maximum permissible gain of the integrator in this type of control scheme—in which waveform switching is employed—may be several times less than that indicated in Table 7.1.

Typical theoretical wavforms applicable to this type of control scheme are shown in Figure 7.30. The change of direction of the ripple voltage integral feedback signal as the control circuit switches from one waveform type to the other is clearly visible.

The scheme in Figure 7.29*b* uses the integral control method. Again, separate free-running positive and negative timing circuits produce complementary sets of positive and negative timing signals. These timing signals are gated to the positive and negative firing circuits, in correspondence with the waveform switching signals, $E(\rho)$ and $E_{\pi}(\rho)$.

In order to keep the positive and negative timing channels in continuous operation, it is necessary to provide these with continuously running positive-type and negative-type voltage waveforms, respectively.

Since neither of these voltage waveforms appears continuously at the output of the NCC, it is necessary to construct these waveforms internally within the control circuits. This is the function of the "*dummy*" *positive-type* and *negative-type waveform*

(a) Cosine wave crossing control with ripple voltage integral feedback

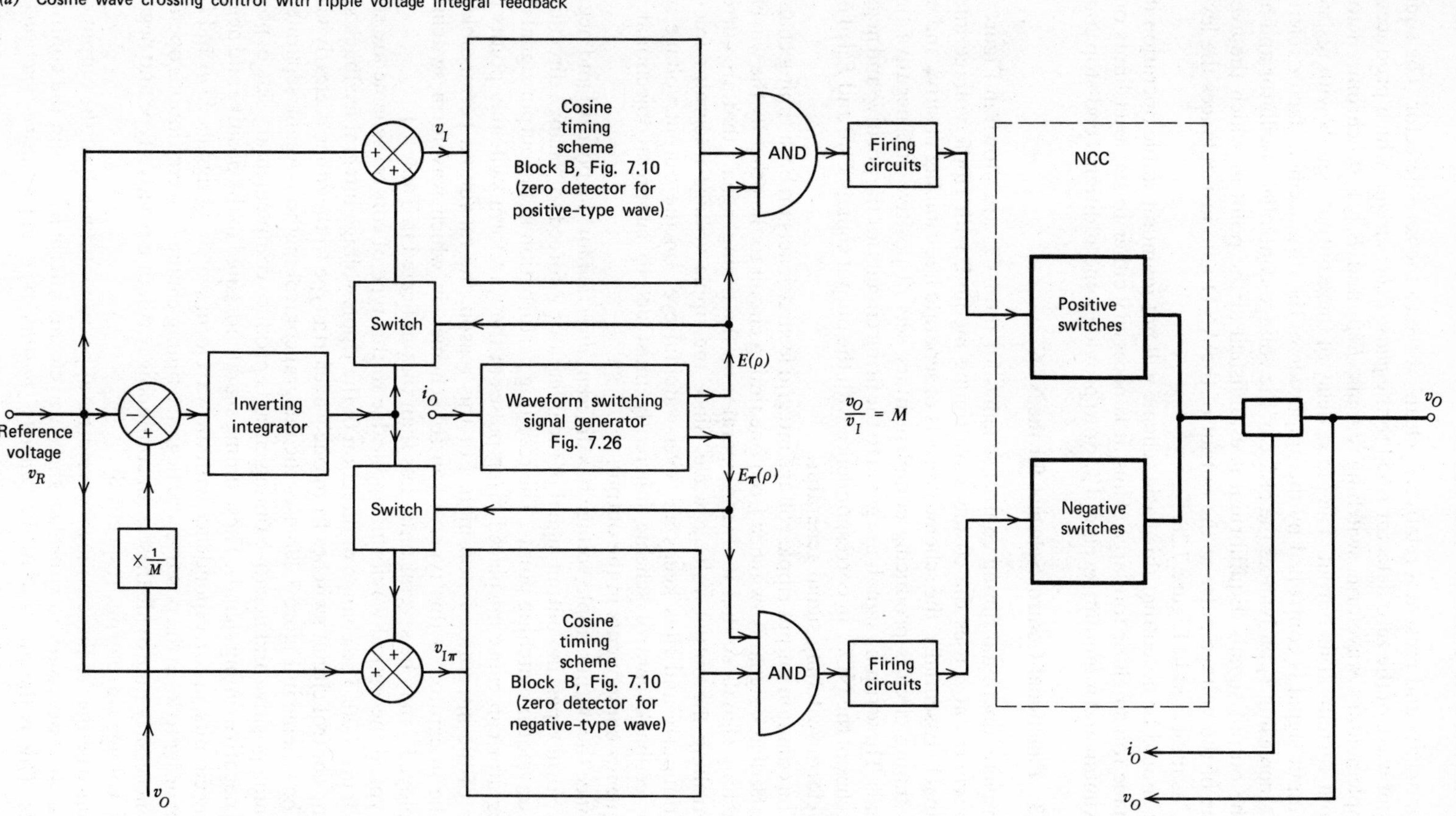

(*b*) Integral control

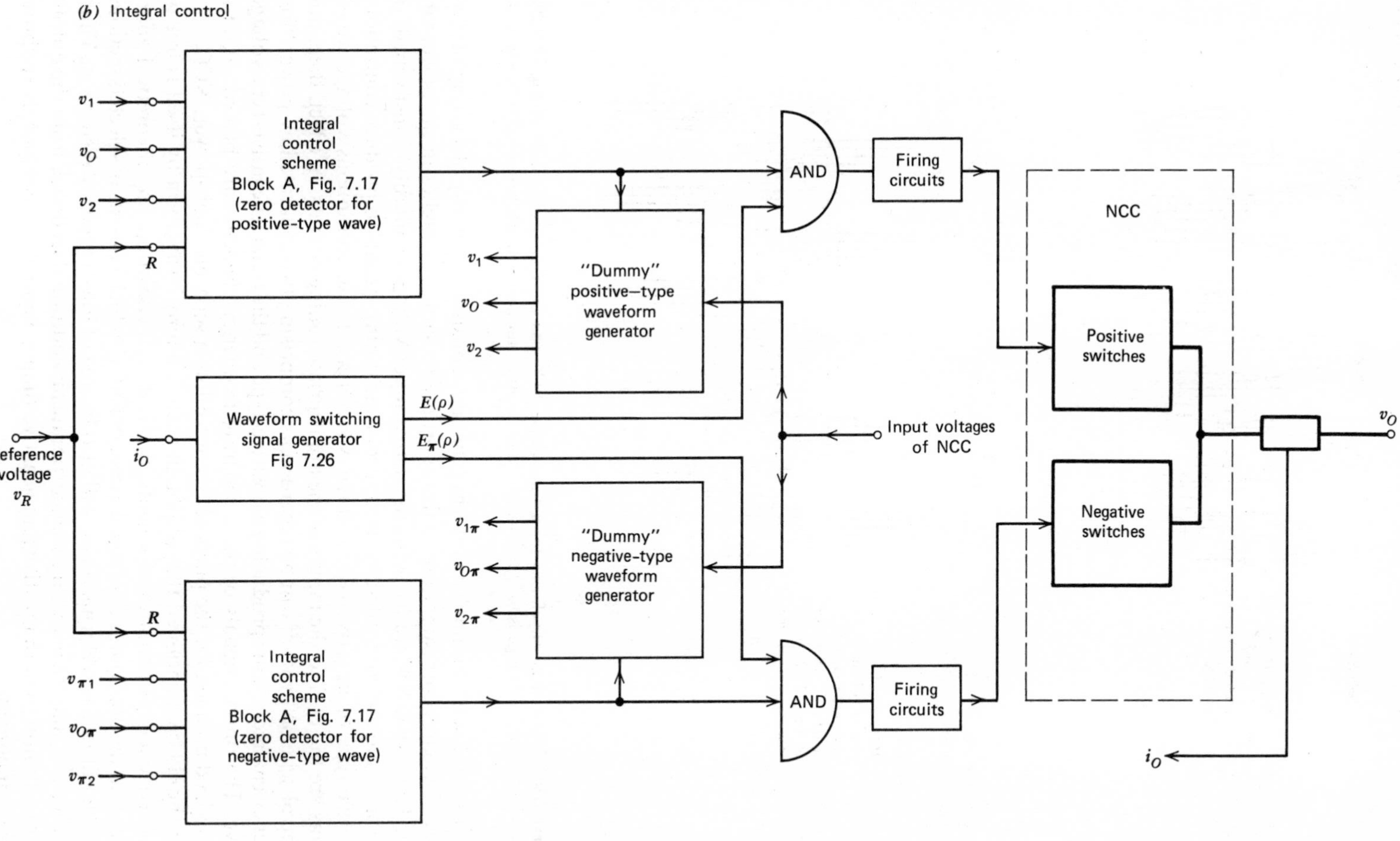

Figure 7.29 Functional control schemes for the NCC.

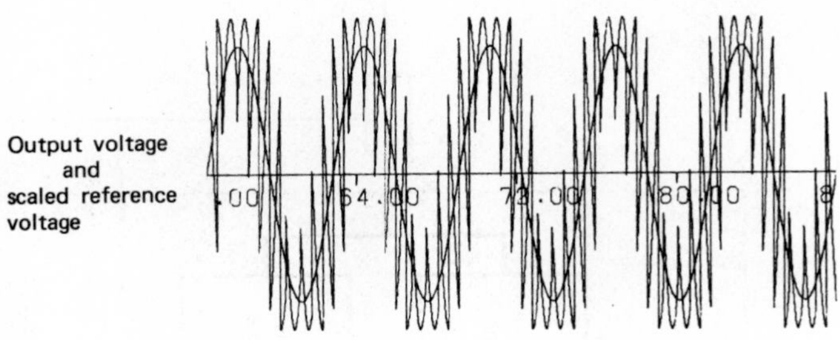

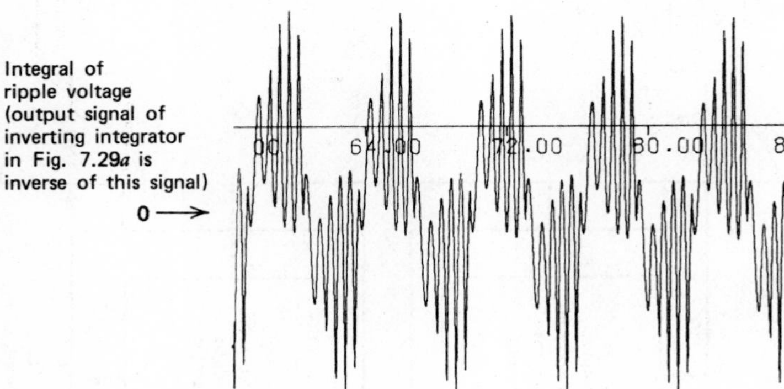

Figure 7.30 Theoretical waveforms for a three-pulse NCC using the control scheme of Figure 7.29*a*. $f_O/f_I = 1/3$. Output voltage is 99% of maximum. $\phi_O = 90°$. Unit-gain frequency of integrator is $0.017\, f_I$.

generators. Each "dummy" waveform generator consists essentially of a group of low-power switches corresponding to the appropriate bank of switches in the power circuit. These switches are fed with the actual input voltages (suitably transformed) of the NCC and are controlled by the appropriate timing signals to produce continuous positive-type or negative-type voltage waveforms. These continuous voltage waveforms are then fed to the inputs of the appropriate timing circuits. In effect, then, this control scheme by itself can be regarded as comprising two separate low-power "frequency changers," one producing a positive-type and the other a negative-type voltage wave. The timing signals of these separate frequency changers are picked off, in a prescribed manner, for the purpose of controlling a separate, high-power, NCC.

It should be mentioned that although each "dummy" waveform by itself is free of low-frequency distortion components, this does not constitute any theoretical guarantee that the final output voltage wave of the NCC, which consists of selected sections of each of these waveforms types, will also be free of low-frequency distortion. Thus, in practice it may be necessary to incorporate an additional feedback from the output itself, common to both positive and negative timing channels, to completely suppress these components.

(a) Cosine wave crossing control with ripple voltage integral feedback

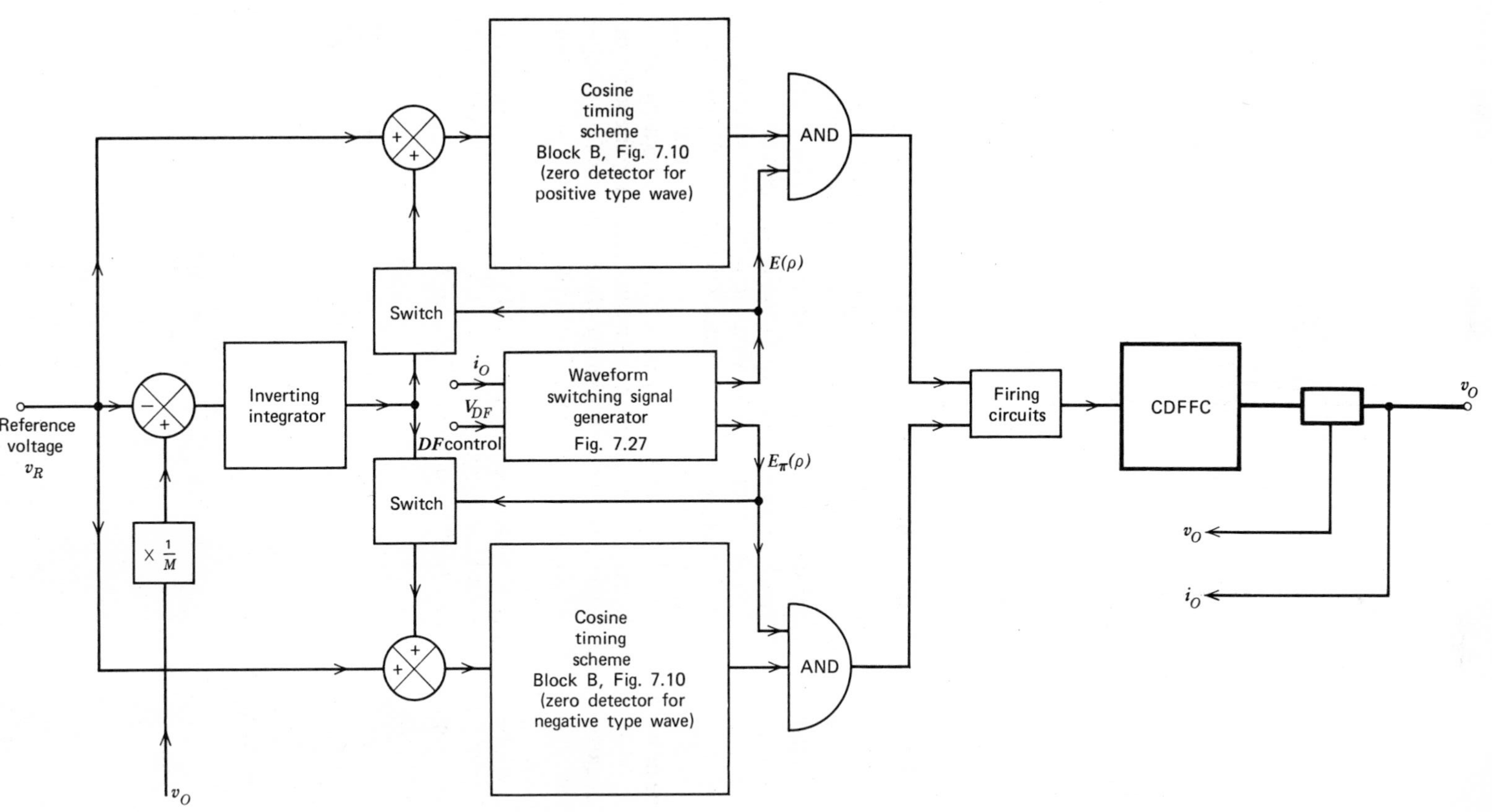

(b) Integral control

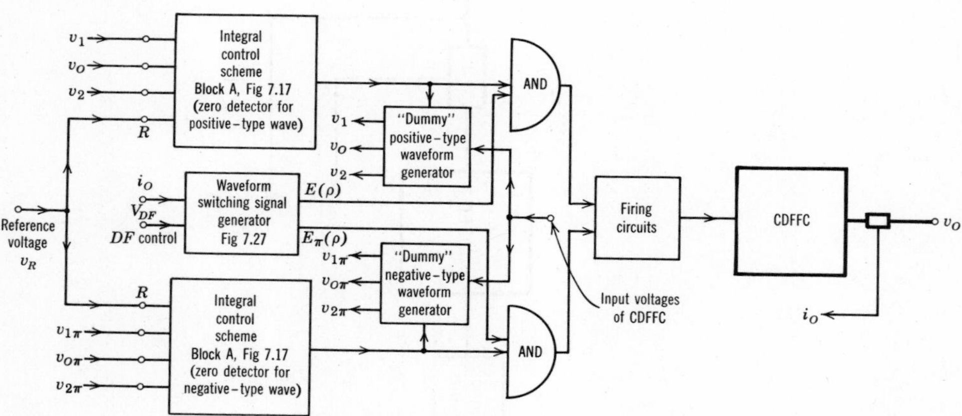

Figure 7.31 Functional control schemes for the CDFFC.

7.6.4 Functional Control Schemes for the CDFFC

As discussed previously, the principles of timing control of the CDFFC are basically similar to those of the NCC. In either case, separate sets of positive and negative timing signals are generated and a selection is made between them in accordance with the complementary waveform switching signals. As far as the control is concerned, the differences lie only in the manner of deriving the waveform switching signals.

Of course the power circuits are different. The CDFFC basically contains a single array of bidirectional switches, whereas the NCC contains separate arrays of positive and negative switches. Thus, whereas the separate positive and negative timing signals for the NCC are channeled into separate firing circuits that serve the separate positive and negative switches, the positive and negative timing signals for the CDFFC are channeled into a single set of firing circuits that serve the single set of bidirectional switches.

Functional timing control schemes for the CDFFC using the cosine wave crossing and integral control methods are shown in Figure 7.31. In view of the basic similarity of these control schemes to those of Figure 7.29, for the NCC, further description is unnecessary.

CHAPTER EIGHT

FORCED COMMUTATION OF FREQUENCY CHANGERS

The thyristor is potentially a candidate as the switching element in frequency changer circuits in which the power requirements are beyond the present capabilities of static switching devices with intrinsic turn-off capability, such as the transistor and the gate-controlled switch. Whereas the thyristor can be turned on at any instant by applying a firing signal to its gate—assuming, of course, that the applied circuit voltage is of the proper polarity—it can be turned off only by reducing its main anode current to zero by external circuit means.

In the naturally commutated cycloconverter, turn-off of the thyristors is achieved naturally through suitable choice of the switching instants; thus firing of the incoming thyristor always tends to apply the appropriate input line-to-line voltage in the reverse direction across the outgoing thyristor, reducing its anode current to zero. More generally, if thyristors are to be applied in the other types of frequency changers considered in this book, the appropriate circuit conditions for natural commutation do not exist at every switching instant, and the main power circuit must therefore be complemented with an auxiliary *force commutating circuit*. The basic function of this force commutating circuit is to provide a temporary diversionary path for the load current, thus allowing the outgoing thyristor to turn off, then to establish the proper circuit conditions for the current to be transferred to the incoming thyristor.

In this chapter, we review the fundamental circuit principles on which the forced commutation of thyristors in a frequency changer circuit may be based. We then briefly illustrate these principles by reference to particular basic embodiments of commutating circuits.

8.1 FUNDAMENTAL PRINCIPLES—HARD AND SOFT COMMUTATION

Each basic bidirectional switch of the frequency changer may consist either of a back-to-back pair of thyristors, as shown in Figure 8.1*a*, or a single thyristor connected within a bridge of diodes, as shown at *b*. A complete frequency changer circuit consists of a multiple array of such switches. A basic three-pulse frequency changer circuit with single-phase output is shown in Figure 8.2.

The first point to bear in mind when considering possible forced commutation techniques is that the load circuit generally smooths the output current wave so that it approximates a sinusoid, with only a relatively small ripple component. Thus the output current of necessity remains substantially constant in magnitude during the relatively short commutation process, because of the natural *inertia* of the load circuit.

In order to turn off a thyristor, it is necessary to reduce its anode current to zero and to impress a reverse voltage across it for a sufficient period (generally in the order

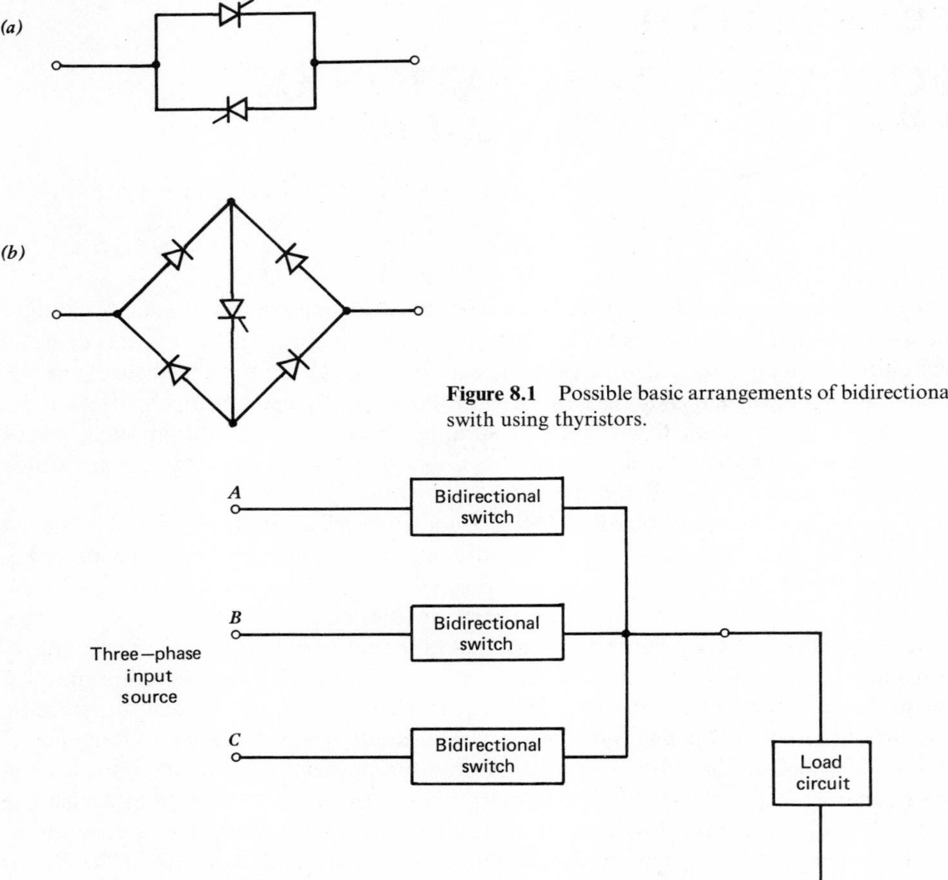

Figure 8.1 Possible basic arrangements of bidirectional swith using thyristors.

Figure 8.2 Basic three-pulse frequency changer circuit with single-phase output.

of tens of microseconds) for it to regain its forward voltage blocking capability. There are two basic mechanisms whereby the auxiliary force commutating circuit may accomplish this function; these are usually referred to as *hard* and *soft* commutation.

The principles of these two basic commutation techniques are illustrated in Figures 8.3 and 8.4, respectively. In order to demonstrate the principles, it is assumed in each case that the commutating circuit is connected directly across the device to be turned off. This is not the only possible point of connection of the commutating circuit into the overall frequency changer circuit, although for soft commutation, it is probably the only practical point of connection. With hard commutation, however, the commutating circuit can be connected at various locations in the frequency changer circuit. At all events, the basic principles involved are unaffected by the actual point of connection of the commutating circuit.

Consider first the hard commutation process, illustrated in Figure 8.3. Thyristor $ThA+$ is the main frequency changer device to be turned off, and initially it carries the output current I_O. Capacitor C is initially charged with the polarity shown. To turn off $ThA+$, commutating thyristor $Th1$ is fired at time t_0. Thyristor $Th2$ may

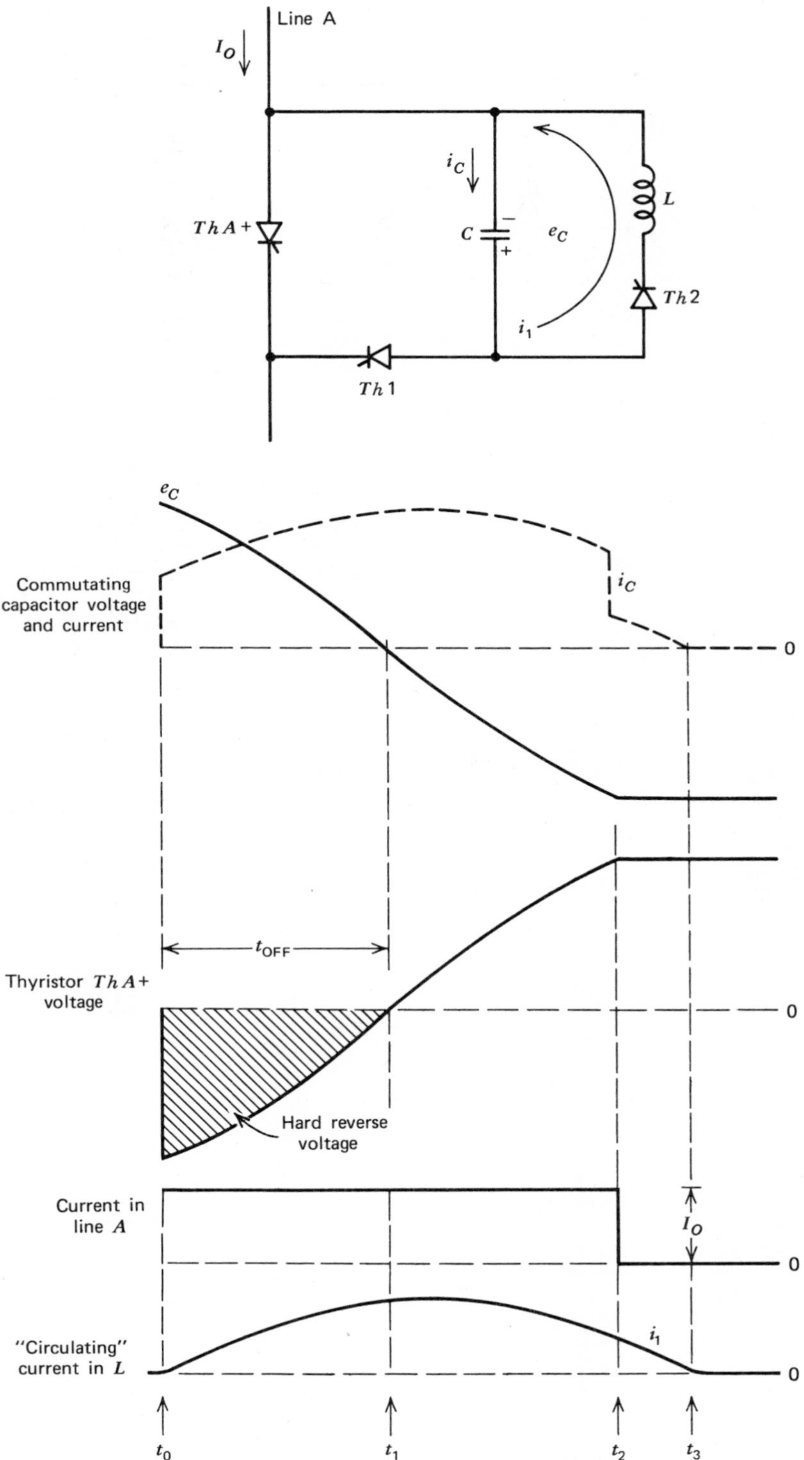

Figure 8.3 Basic principle of hard commutation.

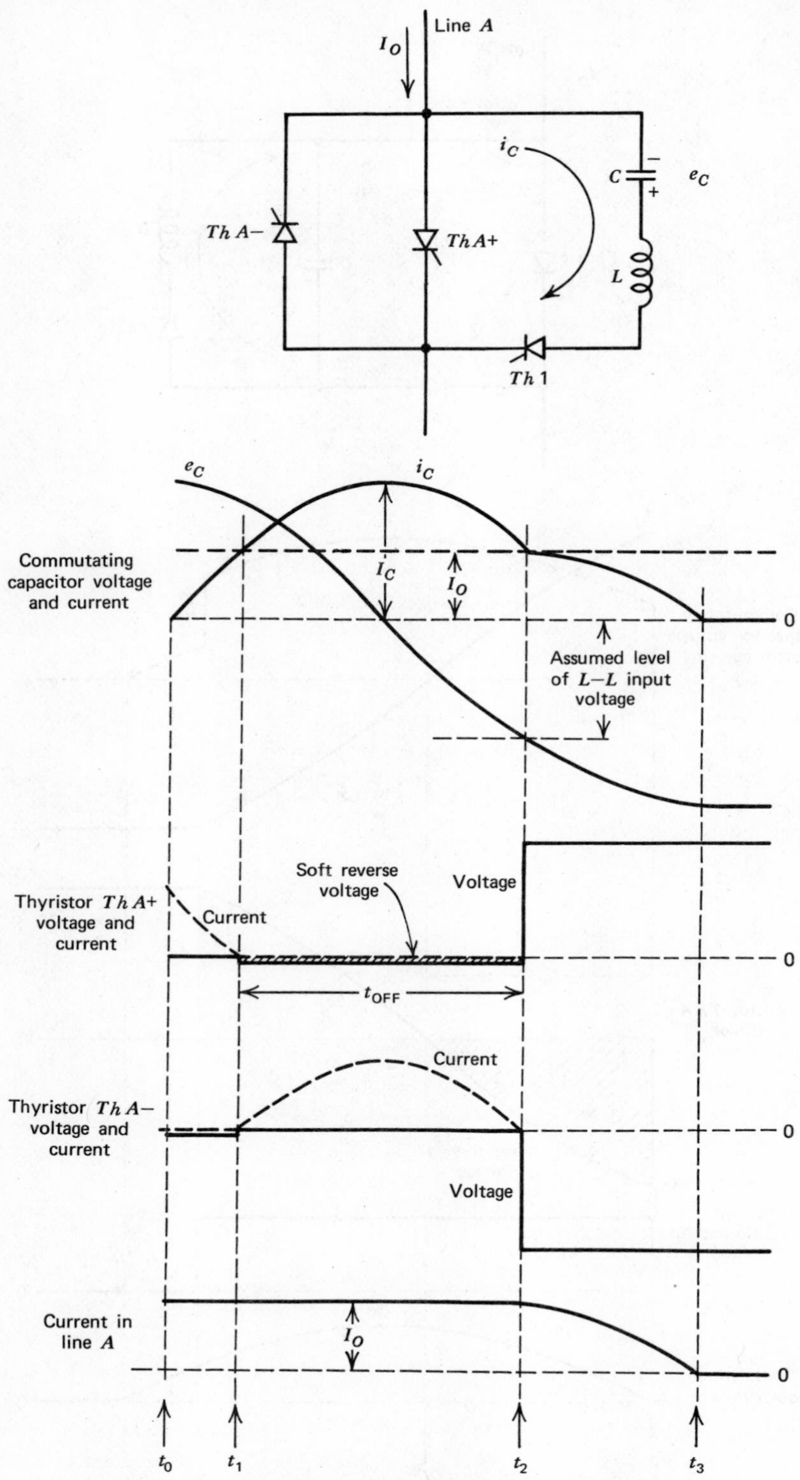

Figure 8.4 Basic principle of soft commutation.

also be fired at this time or at some time shortly thereafter; for simplicity, it is assumed here that it is fired at time t_0. The charged capacitor C is now connected directly across $ThA+$ and applies a reverse voltage across it, thus diverting the output current I_O into C. At the same time, a "circulating" component of current i_1 starts to flow through inductor L and capacitor C. Due to the flow of current through C, its voltage starts to decrease, and at time t_1 this voltage reaches zero. This is the reverse bias *turn-off* time afforded by the commutating circuit to the outgoing thyristor. Currents I_O and i_1 continue to flow through capacitor C, and its voltage now builds up in the opposite direction—that is, in the forward direction across $ThA+$. At time t_2 it is assumed that the voltage across C has reached such a level that the net difference between this voltage and the voltage between the incoming and outgoing input lines is of such polarity that the output current can be diverted away from the commutating circuit and into the incoming input line.

This instantaneous transfer of current out of the commutating circuit is based on the assumption that the impedance of the input source is negligible. In practice, this impedance always has some finite value; thus the transfer of current to the incoming input line from the commutating capacitor is not instantaneous, but it occupies a finite "overlap" period during which the current decays in the commutating circuit as it builds up in the incoming line. At all events, once the output current has been fully transferred to the incoming line, the commutation process, as far as the main frequency changer circuit operation is concerned, is complete.

In general, the point at which the output current is transferred to the incoming input line depends on the instantaneous amplitude and polarity of the relevant input line-to-line voltage and the instant at which the incoming thyristor is fired; in principle this could occur at any time from t_0 onward, depending on the particular circuit conditions.

It is to be noted that, although the process of transferring the output current to the incoming input line is complete at time t_2, the component of current i_1 circulating within the commutating circuit ceases at time t_3. Generally, t_3 will occur after t_2, as is the case in Figure 8.3.

The purpose of this "internal" circulating current circuit may not be immediately evident; without it, the circuit operation would still be quite similar, and the voltage across the commutating capacitor C would still swing from one polarity to the other due to the flow of the output current through it. The rate of change of voltage across the commutating capacitor, however, would then be strictly proportional to the amplitude of the output current; this means that at relatively low levels of output current, the commutation process would take an unacceptably long time. By ensuring that the capacitor voltage always "rings around" through the inductor L, it is guaranteed that the commutation time cannot exceed a given maximum, determined by the natural oscillation period of C and L.

It should be pointed out also that, in principle, the initial voltage on the commutating capacitor need not be of the same order as the final voltage, although this is shown to be so in Figure 8.3. The final capacitor voltage could be made higher or lower than the initial voltage, regardless of the amplitude of the output current, by inserting a d-c source voltage of the appropriate polarity in series with the inductor L.

Finally, it should be pointed out that some additional circuit means for resetting the voltage on the commutating capacitor back to its original amplitude and polarity, in readiness for the next commutation, may be required, depending on the overall arrangement of commutating circuit and main frequency changer power circuit.

Consider now the soft commutation process illustrated in Figure 8.4. Thyristor $ThA+$ is the main frequency changer device to be turned off and initially carries the output current I_O. Connected across $ThA+$ in the reverse direction is the complementary thyristor of the bidirectional switch, $ThA-$. When considering the bidirectional switch arrangement of Figure 8.1*b*, $ThA-$ would be replaced by the bridge connection of diodes, but the basic circuit operating principle remains the same.

Commutating capacitor C is initially charged with the polarity shown. To turn off $ThA+$, commutating thyristor $Th1$ is fired at time t_0. A firing pulse is also applied to $ThA-$ in readiness for this device to pick up current flow from the commutating circuit. Capacitor C initially begins to discharge through inductor L, in the "reverse" direction through $ThA+$, whereas this thyristor continues to carry the output current I_O in the "forward" direction. This situation continues until time t_1, at which the "reverse" discharge current of the commutating circuit i_C becomes equal to "forward" current I_O; at this instant, the net current in $ThA+$ becomes zero. The capacitor discharge current i_C is now greater than the output current I_O; hence i_C transfers as a forward component of current into $ThA-$, whereas I_O transfers as a reverse component of current into this device; the net device current is in the forward direction. During the period t_1 to t_2, a reverse voltage, equal to the forward conduction voltage of $ThA-$, is impressed across $ThA+$; it is this *soft* applied reverse voltage that permits $ThA+$ to turn off and to regain its forward voltage-blocking capability. At time t_2, the net current in $ThA-$ becomes zero. At this instant, the circulating component of current i_C has again become equal to the output current I_O, and the voltage across the capacitor C has now reversed its polarity with respect to its original condition. The output current now flows through the commutating capacitor, and the voltage across $ThA+$ rises sharply in the forward direction to the voltage across this capacitor. In practice, of course, this sharp rate of rise of voltage must be softened to a rate that is tolerable for the thyristor, by means of suitable *snubber* circuitry connected across it.

It is assumed that at this instant the voltage on capacitor C is just equal to the instantaneous voltage between the incoming and outgoing lines; thus any further increase of voltage across capacitor C due to the flow of current through it creates a tendency for this current to be transferred to the incoming line—assuming, of course, that the incoming thyristor is fired at this time.

This assumption with regard to the relative levels of the capacitor voltage and input voltage can be considered to represent the extreme condition when commutating the current from one input line to another, against the maximum instantaneous line-to-line voltage. Generally, at other points in the input cycle, a greater *driving voltage*—that is, the difference between the capacitor voltage and the input line-to-line voltage—would be available at this time to transfer the current to the incoming line. Due to the inductor L, the transfer of current cannot take place instantaneously but occupies the period t_2 to t_3, during which the voltage across the capacitor rises further. At time t_3, the commutation process is complete.

For a given turn-off time, t_{OFF}, the ratio of the peak capacitor discharge current I_C to the peak current to be commutated, I_O, is determined by the values assigned to the commutating capacitor and inductor, and this ratio could theoretically have any value greater than 1.0, as illustrated by the waveforms in Figure 8.5. It can be shown, however, that for the minimum physical sizing of the commutating components, this ratio should be in the region of 1.5:1.

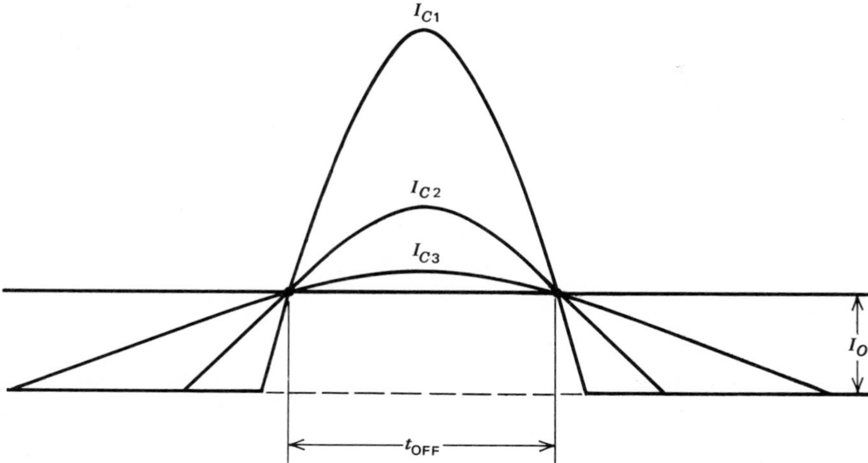

Figure 8.5 Waveforms illustrating that a soft commutating circuit can be designed for different peak capacitor discharge currents, for a given thyristor turn-off time.

Having reviewed the basic processes of hard and soft commutation, the question now arises as to the basic relative merits of the two approaches. This question can be answered generally as follows:

1. In theory, to provide a given turn-off time, t_{OFF}, to the thyristor to be commutated, the required ratings of the passive commutating components (L and C) are smaller for soft commutation than for hard commutation by a factor of about 2:1. In practice, however, actual thyristor switching characteristics can largely nullify this theoretical advantage, because the actual turn-off time required may be substantially longer when the device is subjected to a *soft* reverse biasing voltage of only one or two volts, followed by a relatively rapid rate of rise of applied forward voltage, than when it is subjected to a *hard* reverse biasing voltage, typically in the order of hundreds of volts, followed by a relatively slow rate of rise of applied forward voltage. This is not necessarily so, however, and depends on the particular brand of thyristor in question.

It is generally true, however, that the snubber circuitry required to limit the rate of rise of forward thyristor voltage with soft commutation is more formidable, and hence more dissipative, than that needed (for other reasons) for hard commutation.

(2) The soft commutation process makes use of the complementary reverse connected thyristor of the bidirectional switch of the frequency changer to "ring around" the voltage on the commutating capacitor. This saves additional components in the commutating circuit.

In general, the overall comparison between hard and soft commutation, on the basis of the total circuit complexity, is not this simple.

8.2 POSSIBLE POINTS OF CONNECTION OF THE COMMUTATING CIRCUIT

We have assumed so far, in order to establish the basic principles of the forced commutation process, that the commutating circuit is connected directly across the device to be turned off. As stated, however, this is not the only possible point of connection of the commutating circuit.

We now turn our attention to the question of the various alternative points in the power circuit at which the *commutating impulse* can be applied. Our objective is to establish the basic relative merits of each point of connection in terms of the peak voltages seen by the main frequency changer thrysitors—which generally have an impact on the economics of the main power circuit—and to establish in a general qualitative way the relationship between the peak thryristor voltage, the required size of the commutating capacitor, and the net energy associated with the commutating impulse—which have both a technical and economic impact on the design of the commutating circuit.

For the purposes of this discussion, specific commutating circuitry is not considered. We simply represent the commutating circuit by an equivalent *impulse generator*, which may be connected into the main frequency changer circuit between suitably chosen points. For hard commutation, the equivalent generator produces a voltage impulse of the general form shown in Figure 8.6*a*; it is understood that there is no "reverse current" path across the outgoing thyristor. For soft commutation, the equivalent generator produces the same general form of voltage impulse, but with an "internal" inductive impedance, as shown at *b*; it is understood that a "reverse current" path across the outgoing thyristor is provided. We assume that the commutating voltage impulse varies linearly with time; this is not strictly correct but is sufficiently accurate for the present purposes.

Since we are not considering specific circuitry, the conclusions reached in the following discussion are of a basic nature, unconnected with the circuit details. The practical significance of these conclusions must therefore ultimately be weighed

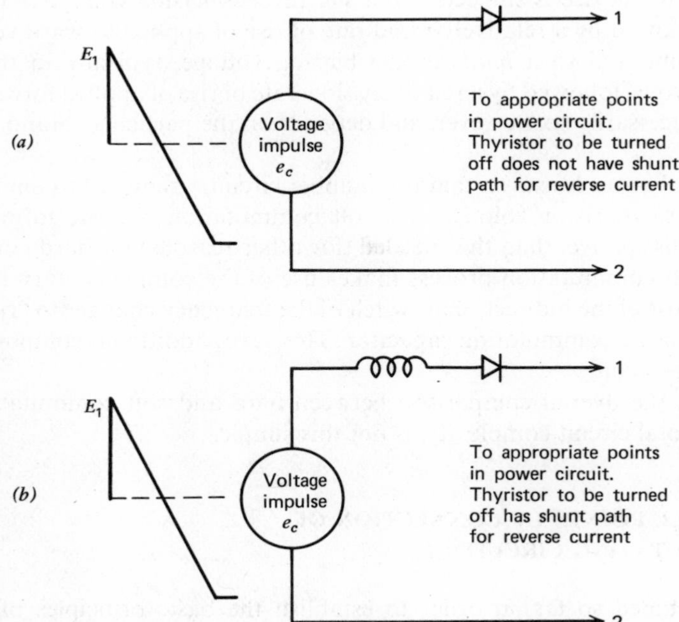

Figure 8.6 Equivalent commutation impulse generators. *a* Hard commutation. *b* Soft commutation.

against considerations of the complexity of the specific commutating circuitry required to implement the commutation at the various alternative points of connection of the commutating impulse.

In general, three possible locations in the main frequency changer circuit can be considered at which the commutating impulse can be connected to effect the commutation. These are:

(1) At the input terminals
(2) Directly across the frequency changer switches
(3) At the output terminals.

In considering the bidirectional switch arrangement of Figure 8.1*b*, it is evident that the only possible point of connection of the commutating circuit is across the thyristor itself. This is because the bridge arrangement of diodes inherently ensures that any and all externally applied circuit voltages or currents are routed in the forward direction to the thyristor; thus no externally applied impulse can find its way to the thyristor in such a direction to turn it off. It is also evident that the presence of the reverse connected diodes across the thyristor precludes the possibility for hard commutation.

When considering the back-to-back arrangement of thyristors of Figure 8.1*a*, however, in principle the commutation can be effected from each of the above points of connection of the commutating voltage impulse. The relative basic merits of these three alternatives are considered in relation to the simple three-pulse circuit of Figure 8.2. The conclusions reached for this simple circuit are generally applicable to all frequency changer circuits.

In order to simplify the discussion, we generally assume that the duration of the commutation process is short in comparison to the periods of the input and output waves; thus the output current and input line-to-line voltages remain constant during the commutation process. We also generally assume that the input source has zero impedance (although in the first case to be considered, we purposefully add an impedance in series with the source as an intrinsic part of the commutating circuit). This assumption is valid because the practical presence of source impedance does not alter the basic operating principles.

8.2.1 Communtation at the Input Terminals

The basic idea is that the commutating circuit should inject an impulse directly between the appropriate input terminals. This impulse temporarily overrides the applied source voltage; thus firing of the incoming thyristor at the instant of impulse injection results in the outgoing thyristor becoming reverse biased, regardless of the instantaneous polarity of the source voltages.

We consider in this case only the possibility of hard commutation, because soft commutation requires that the *antiparallel* thyristor connected across the one to be turned off should be rendered conductive during the commutation process. This raises the possibility of applying a line-to-line short circuit across the input source if the polarity of the appropriate line-to-line voltage is instantaneously in the direction for natural commutation. Conceivably, suitable control logic could be included to bring the forced commutation process into action only at those instants at which natural commutation cannot be accomplished, but this raises difficulties in connection with the reliable detection of such conditions.

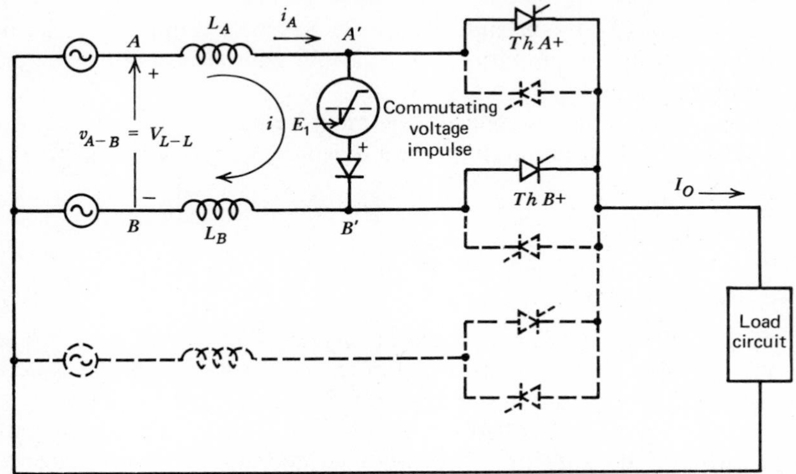

Figure 8.7 Commutation at the input terminals with series inductors. Portion of circuit under consideration when commutating from $ThA+$ to $ThB+$ is shown by full lines.

A basic point when considering commutation at the input terminals is that if we adhere to our stated assumption that the input source itself has zero internal impedance, it will be necessary to insert an impedance of some kind between the source and the frequency changer in order to support an impulse voltage applied at the input terminals. In practice, this impedance could take one of two forms, as discussed in the following sections.

8.2.1.1 *Inductors in Series with Input Source.* The only practical choice of linear passive impedance is a simple inductor connected between each source voltage and the frequency changer input terminals, as illustrated in Figure 8.7.

We consider the basic circuit operation under conditions in which the output current has its maximum positive value, the input source voltage between points A and B has its maximum positive value, and it is required to commutate the output current from thyristor $ThA+$ to thyristor $ThB+$. This is a "worst case" situation because it requires that the full output current be commutated against the maximum input voltage. The portion of the circuit under consideration is as shown by the full lines in Figure 8.7.

In order to commutate the current from thyristor $ThA+$ to thyristor $ThB+$ by the application of a voltage impulse across the input lines, the impulse voltage generator must be connected between input terminals A' and B', with B' initially positive with respect to A'. Assuming that thyristor $ThB+$ is fired at the instant the voltage impulse is applied, the output current will immediately be transferred from $ThA+$ to $ThB+$, and the applied voltage impulse will appear in the reverse direction across $ThA+$. The output current, however, will continue to flow through input line A; in fact, the total current in this line initially will start to increase, because both the input source voltage $v_{A\text{-}B}$ and the initial impulse voltage are of such polarity to produce a "circulating" component of current, *i*, in the direction indicated in Figure 8.7.

Simplified waveforms that describe the subsequent operation of the circuit are shown in Figure 8.8*a*. One basic point is immediately evident from these waveforms: at time T_c', at which the current in input line A has fallen back to its original starting

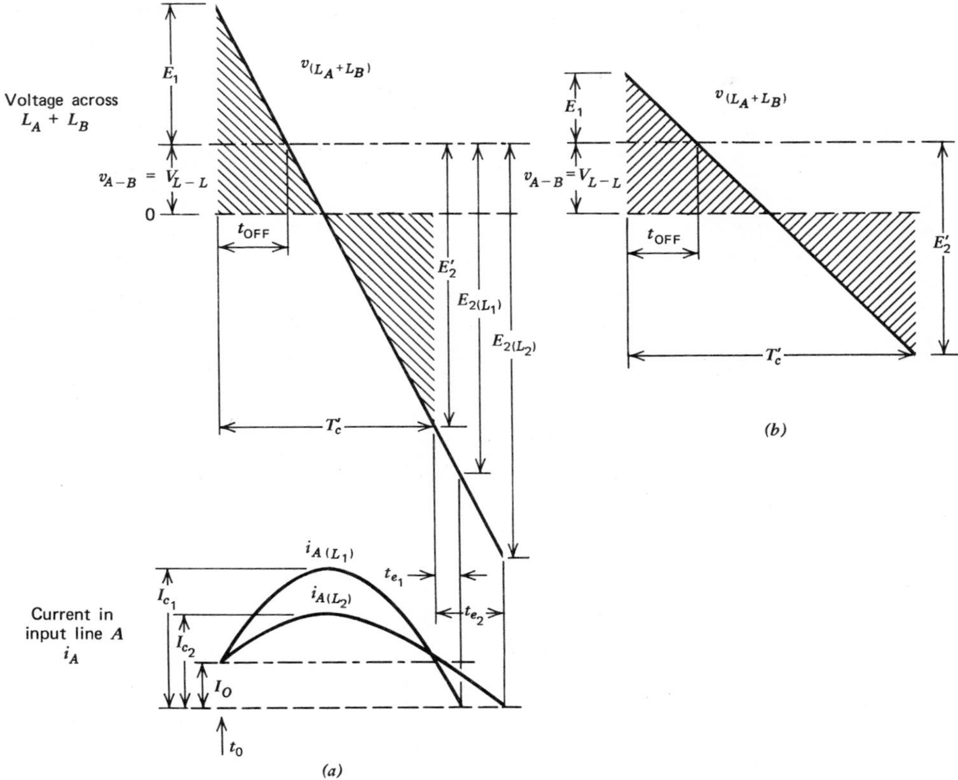

Figure 8.8 Simplified waveforms illustrating the commutating process in the circuit of Figure 8.7. *a* $E_1 = 2V_{L-L}$. *b* $E = V_{L-L}$.

level of I_O—that is, at the time the "circulating" current i has fallen back to zero—the commutating voltage impulse has already attained a higher negative value, E_2', than its initial positive starting value, E_1. This occurs because in order to reduce the circulating current component i to zero, the net integral of the waveform of voltage developed across inductors L_A and L_B must be zero; that is, the positive and negative areas shown shaded under the waveform of voltage across these inductors must be equal. In order to satisfy this condition, it is evident that E_2' must be greater than E_1. This is not a desirable situation, because it implies that the commutating impulse voltage generator must absorb a net component of energy during the commutation interval, since $1/2\, CE_2'^2 > 1/2\, CE_1^2$. In order to set the commutating voltage back to its initial value for the next commutation, this energy must either be dissipated within the commutating circuit, which is generally undesirable, or returned to the source by means of additional circuitry, which may also be undesirable, from the viewpoint of the added circuit complexity.

For given values of $V_{L\text{-}L}$, E_1, and the turn-off time, t_{OFF}, afforded to the outgoing thyristor, the time period T_c' is uniquely determined and is *independent* of the inductance of L_A and L_B.

The value of this inductance, on the other hand, determines the amplitude of the circulating current, i. A relatively small inductance value L_1 results in current waveform $i_{A(L_1)}$ in input line A, whereas a relatively large inductance L_2 results in current waveform $i_{A(L_2)}$. The larger the circulating current, the larger is the impulse of current carried by the commutating circuit; thus, for a given waveform of the commutating impulse voltage, the larger is the required value of the commutating capacitor, and the larger is the energy absorbed by the commutating circuit.

The commutation process is not of course complete at time T'_c, since the current in input line A has still to be reduced to zero, whereas that in input line B must simultaneously be increased up to the level of the output current. As shown, the "extra" time, t_e, necessary to complete the commutation process depends upon the slope of the circulating current wave at time T'_c and hence upon the particular value of inductance used. For t_e to be relatively short, this inductance must be relatively small, and vice versa. (However, we have already seen that if L is small, C must be large, and vice versa.) It is evident, moreover, that the longer is t_e, the larger will be the final amplitude of the commutating impulse voltage, E_2, appearing at the external terminals* (that is, between points 1 and 2 in Figure 8.6) of the impulse generator.

If we neglect this extra time, t_e, required to complete the commutation and assume (optimistically) that the total period of the commutation process is just T'_c, and that the final amplitude of the external impulse voltage is just E'_2, we can make some useful deductions about the relationship between the (assumed) total commutating time, the initial value of the commutating voltage impulse, and its final external value.

The general trend of this relationship is illustrated by the waveform of Figure 8.8*b*, in which it is assumed that the initial value of the commutating voltage E_1 is one-half of that at *a*. In order to maintain the same turn-off time t_{OFF} for the outgoing thyristor, it is evident that the commutation period has increased but the final external value of the commutating impulse voltage has decreased. Evidently, then, a trade-off between these parameters is possible.

The relationships between the total commutating period, expressed as a per-unit value of the required thyristor turn-off time, and the initial and final external values of the commutating voltage impulse expressed as per-unit values of the peak line-to-line source voltage, calculated according to the above simplifying assumptions, are shown graphically in Figure 8.9.

From these relationships, it is evident that little is to be gained, as far as the final external value of the commutating voltage impulse is concerned, by increasing the total commutating period much above five times the required thyristor turn-off time. With this value, this voltage is approximately 2.5 times the peak line-to-line voltage of the input source. Conversely, decreasing the total commutating time below about three times the required turn-off time results in a rapidly increasing impulse voltage level; at this particular value of commutating time, this voltage is already four times the peak line-to-line voltage.

It can be concluded, then, that in practice a peak value of the final external commutating impulse voltage, and correspondingly the peak voltage seen by the thyristors of the frequency changer, will be at least 2.5 times the peak line-to-line voltage of the source, but it could be considerably higher than this.

This is a somewhat unsatisfactory deduction, since peak thyristor voltages of this order of magnitude are certainly undesirably high. It should be mentioned, however,

* It is to be noted that the final *external* voltage of the impulse generator is not necessarily the same as its final *internal* voltage—that is, the voltage "behind" the diode in the equivalent diagram of Figure 8.6*a*. This internal voltage can swing to a higher level than the final external voltage and in general may do so, depending upon the internal operation of the commutating circuit.

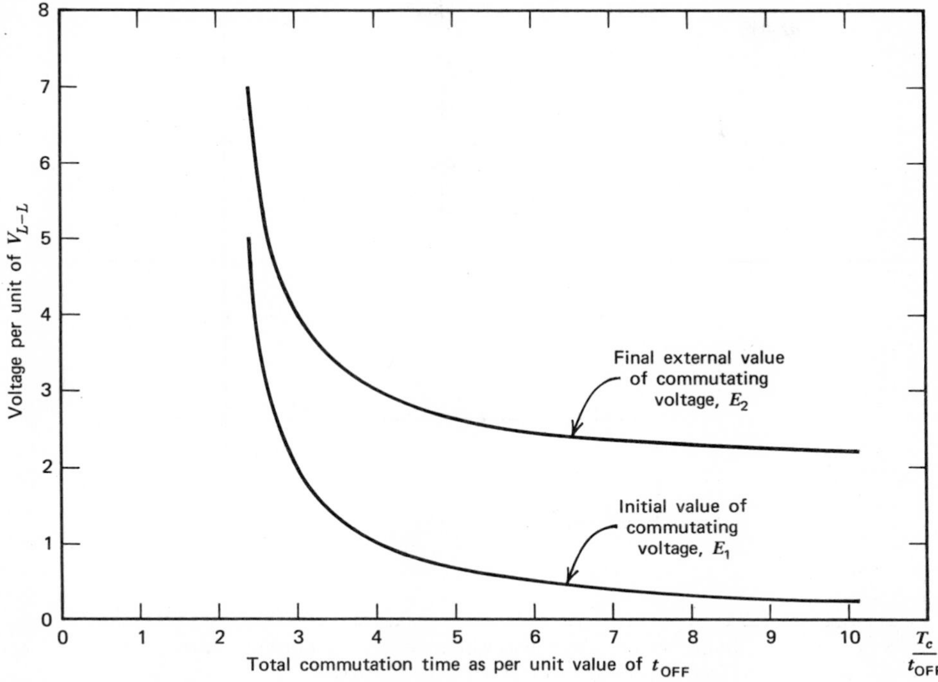

Figure 8.9 Relationships between total commutation time and initial and final external values of commutating voltage for the circuit of Figure 8.7.

that an artifice is possible for substantially alleviating this "voltage" problem, at the expense of increasing the complexity of the commutating circuit. This is to clamp the *reverse* swing of the commutating voltage impulse at some level suitably higher than the peak value of the line-to-line source voltage. This technique reduces the peak value of the commutating voltage impulse, at the expense of increasing the total commutation time.

8.2.1.2 *Diodes in Series with Input Source.* As stated, it is necessary to insert some form of impedance in series with the source voltage to support a commutating voltage impulse applied at the input terminals. The only form of linear passive impedance that can be considered is an inductor.

It is possible, however, to sever the direct connection between the positive and negative thyristors at the input terminals and to connect each thyristor back to the source voltage through an appropriately poled diode, as illustrated in Figure 8.10. To commutate positive output current from one thyristor to the next, an impulse voltage of appropriate polarity can be applied between the anodes of the appropriate positive thyristors; to commutate negative current, an impulse voltage can be applied between the cathodes of the appropriate negative thyristors. In either case, the diodes prevent the commutating voltage impulse from being "shorted" by the source.

It is debatable whether this approach should strictly be classified as commutation at the "input" terminals; it can be argued that the input terminals are in fact the points of connection of the source voltages, and that the diodes are a part of each *bidirectional switch* arrangement. This is a matter of definition, however, and has no bearing on the principles involved.

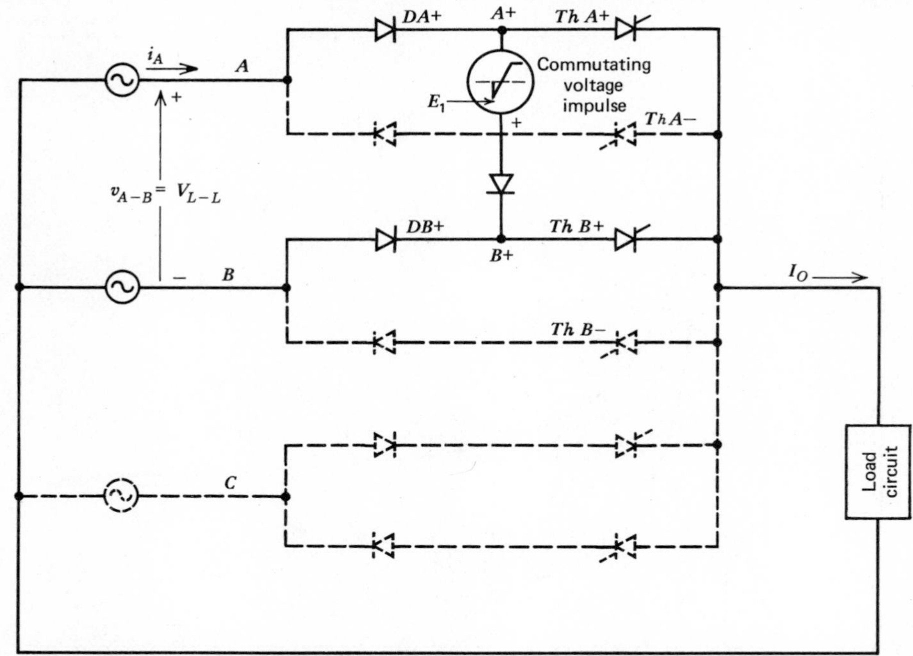

Figure 8.10 Commutation at the input terminals with series diodes. Portion of circuit under consideration when commutating from $ThA+$ to $ThB+$ is shown by full lines.

We now consider the basic circuit operation under the "worst case" condition when the full output current must be commutated against the peak input voltage.

The relevant portion of the circuit to be considered during the commutation interval when transferring the current from thyristor $ThA+$ to thyristor $ThB+$ is shown by the full lines in Figure 8.10. In order to turn off $ThA+$, the impulse voltage is connected between points $A+$ and $B+$, with $B+$ initially positive with respect to $A+$. Assuming that $ThB+$ is fired at the instant the voltage impulse is applied, the output current is transferred immediately from $ThA+$ to $ThB+$, and the voltage impulse appears in the reverse direction across $ThA+$. The output current continues for the time to flow through input line A, because diode $DB+$ is reverse biased by the impulse voltage and the line-to-line source voltage $v_{A\text{-}B}$, acting in series with one another.

Simplified waveforms that illustrate the subsequent operation of the circuit for various initial values of the commutating impulse voltage, $E_{1(1)}$, $E_{1(2)}$, and $E_{1(3)}$ for a given turn-off time t_{OFF} afforded to the outgoing thyristor are shown in Figure 8.11.

The circuit operation is very simple. The output current I_O merely continues to flow through input line A until the commutating voltage impulse reverses and reaches a value equal to the line-to-line voltage, $V_{L\text{-}L}$; at this time diode $DA+$ ceases conduction, and the current is transferred to input line B through diode $DB+$. In practice, of course, the transfer of current from one line to the other is not instantaneous as assumed here, but would take a finite time, depending on the impedance of the input source.

It is evident from these simplified waveforms that the amplitude, E_2, of the external commutating voltage developed across the outgoing thyristor at the completion of the commutation process theoretically is invariably equal to the instantaneous value

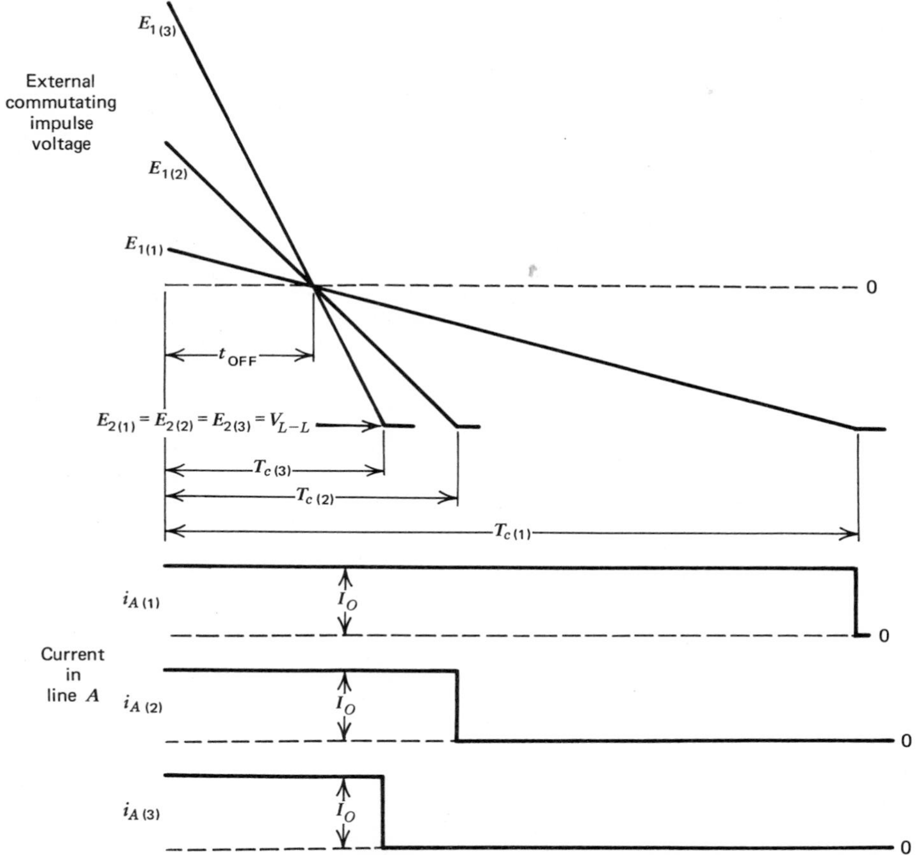

Figure 8.11 Simplified waveforms illustrating the commutating process in the circuits of Figures 8.10 and 8.12, for various values of the initial commutating voltage E_1.

of the line-to-line voltage $V_{L\text{-}L}$. The smaller the initial value, E_1, of the commutating voltage, the longer is the total commutation period T_c ($T_{c(1)} > T_{c(2)} > T_{c(3)}$). In practice, the smaller is E_1 for a given circuit turn-off time, t_{OFF}, the larger is the required value of the commutating capacitance. This follows from the basic fact that for a given current the rate of change of voltage across a capacitor is directly proportional to its capacitance value, and lower values of E_1 obviously require correspondingly lower rates of change of voltage. Thus a value of E, which is, for example, only a small fraction of the peak line-to-line voltage, may not be practicable. A further point to bear in mind is that if E_1 is less than the peak line-to-line voltage, $V_{L\text{-}L}$, then, since the final voltage across the commutating capacitor must be at least $V_{L\text{-}L}$, a net component of energy will be absorbed by the commutating circuit during the commutation process. This energy ultimately must either be dissipated within the commutating circuit, or returned from the commutating circuit to the source by means of additional circuitry. *In principle*, however, it is possible for E_1 to have any desired value; the final voltage on the commutating capacitor, on the other hand, must at least be equal to the peak line-to-line voltage.

We now consider the question of the resulting peak voltages developed across the thyristors of the frequency changer. It is evident that throughout the commutation period, the outgoing thyristor $ThA+$ sees the commutating impulse voltage. The maximum instantaneous device voltage is developed across the thyristor $ThB-$; this occurs at the instant of initiation of the commutation and is equal to $(V_{L\text{-}L} + E_1)$.

It can be deduced readily that the peak voltage across any thyristor can never exceed the sum of the peak line-to-line voltage plus the initial value of the commutating voltage, E_1, regardless of the instant in the input cycle at which the commutation takes place.

Thus, in principle, the peak voltage seen by the thyristors need not be excessive. This voltage is greater than the peak line-to-line source voltage by the initial commutating voltage, E_1; in theory, this *incremental voltage* can be set at any desired level. In practice, however, if it is set too low, this will have an unfavorable impact on the size of the commutating circuit and the energy consumed thereby, as well as on the total commutation time, as explained above.

8.2.2 Commutation Directly Across the Switches

We considered in Section 8.1 the idea of connecting the commutating impulse directly across the thyristor to be turned off. We did not, however, pay any attention to the question of the peak voltage developed across the frequency changer thyristors or to the question of the energy interchange between the main frequency changer circuit and the commutating circuit. These aspects are now reviewed for both hard and soft commutation.

8.2.2.1 *Hard Commutation.* Again we consider the basic circuit operation under the "worst case" condition in which the full output current must be commutated against the peak input voltage.

The relevant part of the circuit to be considered during the commutation interval, when transferring the current from $ThA+$ to $ThB+$, is shown by the full lines in Figure 8.12. In order to turn off $ThA+$, the commutating impulse voltage is con-

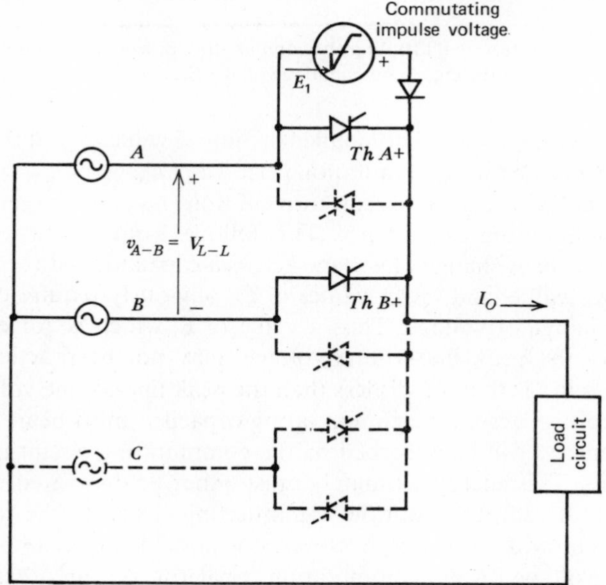

Figure 8.12 Hard commutation across the switches. Portion of circuit under consideration when commutating from $ThA+$ to $ThB+$ is shown by full lines.

nected directly across it, with the initial polarity shown. The output current is immediately transferred from $ThA+$ to the commutating circuit, and the commutating voltage impulse appears in the reverse direction across the outgoing thyristor.

Simplified waveforms that describe the subsequent circuit operation are basically the same as those shown in Figure 8.11 for the circuit arrangement of Figure 8.10. Again, if it is assumed that the incoming thyristor is permitted to turn on as soon as its anode voltage becomes positive, the amplitude of the commutating voltage at the completion of the commutation process theoretically is invariably equal to the instantaneous value of the line-to-line voltage, $v_{L\text{-}L}$, regardless of its initial value, E_1. The smaller is E_1, the longer is the total commutation period T_c, and, for the reasons previously stated, the larger is the required value of the commutating capacitance, and the larger is the net component of energy absorbed by the commutating circuit.

Finally, it can again be deduced that the peak voltage developed across any thyristor can never exceed the sum of the peak line-to-line voltage plus the initial value, E_1, of the commutating voltage, regardless of the instant in the input cycle at which the commutation takes place, provided that the incoming thyristor is always permitted to turn on as soon as it is ready to do so. In practice, this can be ensured simply by applying a continuous firing signal to the incoming thyristor at the instant of initiation of the commutation.

8.2.2.2 *Soft Commutation.* Again we consider initially the basic circuit operation under the "worst case" condition in which the full output current must be commutated against the peak input voltage.

The relevant part of the circuit to be considered during the commutation interval when transferring the current from $ThA+$ to $ThB+$ is shown by the full lines in Figure 8.13.

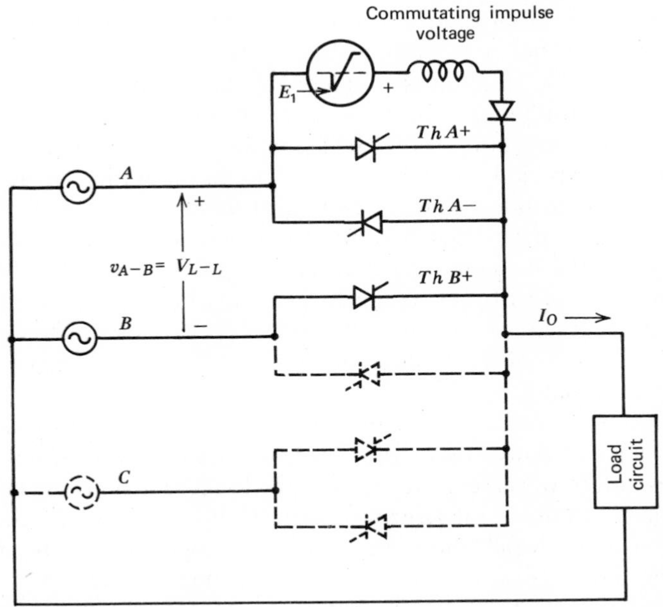

Figure 8.13 Soft commutation across back-to-back thyristor switches. Portion of circuit under consideration when commutating from $ThA+$ to $ThB+$ is shown by full lines.

To turn off $ThA+$, the soft commutating voltage impulse generator is connected directly across it, and a firing pulse is simultaneously applied to thyristor $ThA-$ to allow it to pick up the discharge current from the commutating circuit at the appropriate time. Simplified waveforms that describe the circuit operation are essentially the same as those already shown in Figure 8.4. During the period t_0 to t_1, the current in $ThA+$ decreases to zero. During the period t_1 to t_2, $ThA-$ is in conduction, and the outgoing thyristor $ThA+$ is reverse biased by the soft forward conduction voltage of $ThA-$. At time t_2, $ThA-$ ceases conduction. It is assumed that the incoming thyristor $ThB+$ is fired at this time and that the commutating impulse voltage is instantaneously equal to the line-to-line voltage, $v_{L\text{-}L}$. The output current therefore begins to decrease in the outgoing line, and the voltage across $ThA+$ jumps up to the level of the applied line-to-line voltage. At time t_3 the commutation process is complete.

According to these simplified waveforms, in effect the only *voltage* injected into the main frequency changer circuit by the commutating circuit is the small reverse bias voltage across the outgoing thyristor, due to the forward conduction voltage of $ThA-$. This conclusion depends, however, on the crucial theoretical assumption that the incoming thyristor $ThB+$ is fired coincidentally with the cessation of current in $ThA-$. Unfortunately, this assumption is not practically valid, because this would mean that whenever the input line-to-line voltage is of the appropriate polarity for *natural* commutation, the voltage across the "reverse" device of the outgoing switch would jump *immediately* into the forward direction, rather than into the reverse direction, as in Figure 8.4, once conduction through it ceases. This would cause this device to reconduct and create a line-to-line short circuit.

It might be thought that a solution to this problem is not to force commutate the outgoing switch whenever it can, in any case, be naturally commutated. Difficulties arise, however, in invariably making a reliable logical determination about which type of commutation—that is, forced or natural—should be employed, and such an approach probably is not practically viable.

A practically reliable solution is to allow a period of time, at least equal to the required device turn-off time, to elapse after the reverse device of the outgoing switch has ceased conduction, before the incoming thyristor is fired. Unfortunately, however, during this period, the voltage across the commutating capacitor builds up, above the peak line-to-line voltage. The rate of build-up of voltage depends upon the level of output current, but at full current it could reach a level of around $1.7 \times V_{L\text{-}L}$, before the incoming thyristor is fired. Worse than this, however, if the commutation happens to occur at the most unfavorable point in the input cycle (as of course it could), the total peak voltage developed across the frequency changer devices can be the sum of the peak commutating voltage plus the peak line-to-line voltage—that is, about $2.7 \times V_{L\text{-}L}$.

The problem, of course, is a basic one and has to be accepted as such when considering the "back-to-back" thyristor bidirectional switch arrangement. The basic difficulty does not, however, exist for the bidirectional switch arrangement of Figure 8.1*b*, and in fact with this arrangement of switches it is possible to achieve the near-ideal condition under which the peak voltage developed across the main switches essentially does not exceed the peak line-to-line voltage of the input source.

The simple explanation for this is that, since this switch arrangement does not contain a reverse thyristor, it does not have the problems associated with turning

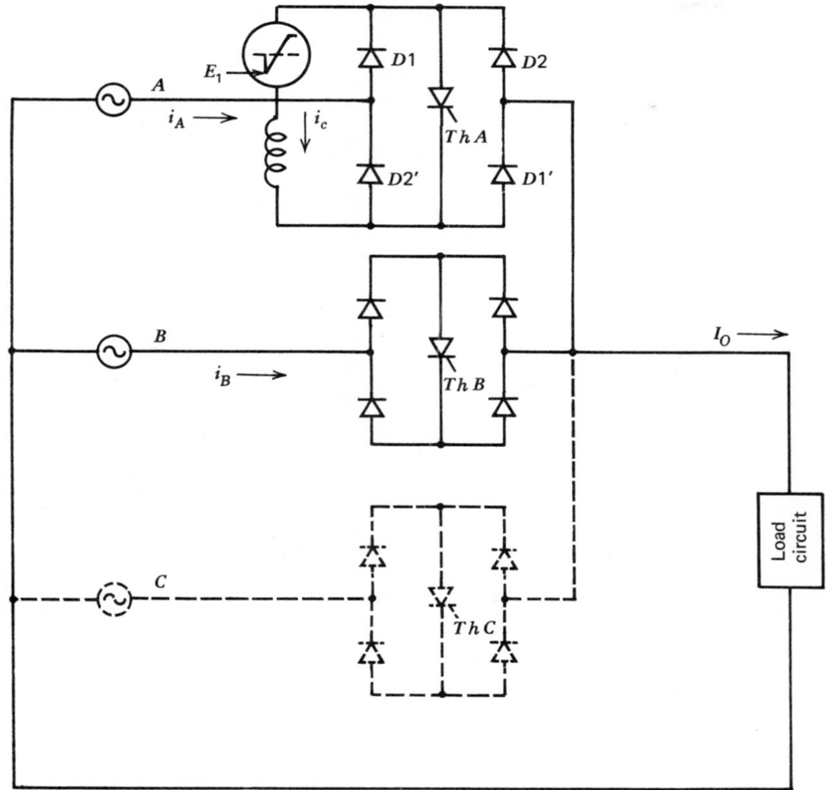

Figure 8.14 Soft commutation of thyristor–diode bidirectional switch arrangement. Portion of circuit under consideration when commutating from *ThA* to *ThB* is shown by full lines.

off this thyristor that give rise to the high peak voltages experienced with the "back-to-back" switch.

We briefly explain this further by reference to the basic three-pulse frequency changer circuit shown in Figure 8.14. It is assumed that the output current I_O is flowing through switch *A* and that it is required to commutate this current to switch *B*. We consider the circuit operation both when the input line-to-line voltage $v_{A\text{-}B}$ has its maximum positive value and when it has its maximum negative value. The part of the circuit under consideration during the commutation is shown by the full lines.

In order to turn off *ThA*, the *soft* impulse generator is connected directly across it, as shown. Waveforms that illustrate the circuit operation are shown in Figure 8.15. At time t_1, the commutating current i_c is equal to the output current I_O, and the net current in the thyristor is zero. The commutating current and the output current I_O then continue to flow through the diode bridge. Diodes $D1$ and $D1'$ carry a current of $(i_c + I_O)/2$, and diodes $D2$ and $D2'$ carry a current of $(i_c - I_O)/2$. During the period t_1 to t_2, *ThA* is reverse biased by the forward conduction voltages of these diodes. At time t_2, *before* the commutating current i_c becomes equal to the output current, the incoming thyristor *ThB* is turned on; it is assumed that by this time *ThA* has regained its ability to block forward voltage. It is assumed further that at this instant

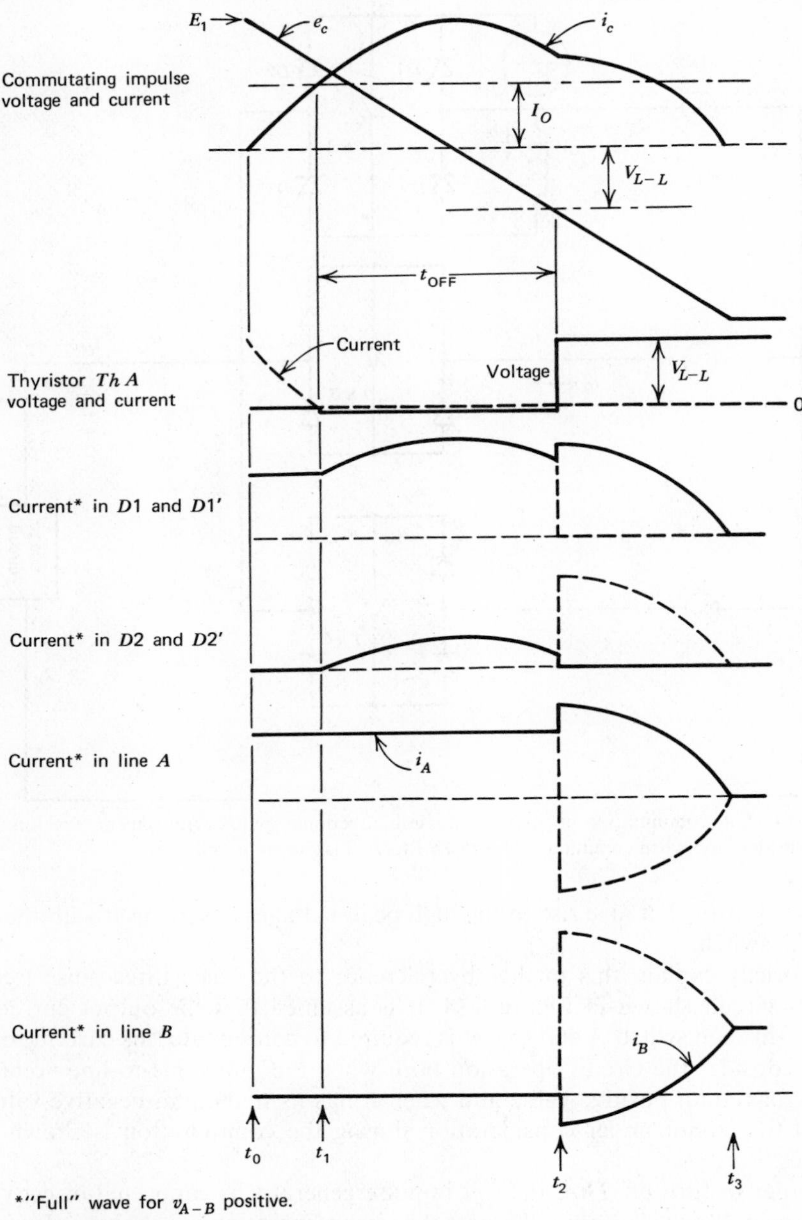

Figure 8.15 Simplified waveforms illustrating the commutating process in the circuit of Figure 8.14.

the commutating impulse voltage is equal to the peak line-to-line source voltage.

If $v_{A\text{-}B}$ has its maximum positive value at this time, diodes $D1$ and $D1'$ continue to conduct and carry the current i_c flowing through the commutating circuit, and $D2$ and $D2'$ become reverse biased by $v_{A\text{-}B}$. This voltage appears in the forward direction across thyristor ThA. The current in line A is now i_c, and the current in line B is $(I_0 - i_c)$. At time t_3, i_c becomes zero, and the commutation process is complete.

If $v_{A\text{-}B}$ has its maximum negative value at time t_2, diodes $D2$ and $D2'$ continue to carry the current i_c flowing through the commutating circuit, and diodes $D1$ and $D1'$ become reverse biased by $v_{A\text{-}B}$. This voltage again appears in the forward direction across thyristor ThA. The current in line A is now $-i_c$, and the current in line B is $(I_O + i_c)$. Again, at time t_3, i_c becomes zero, and the commutation process is complete.

The main point of this discussion has been to demonstrate that the commutating impulse voltage always remains "sheltered" behind the inductor L and is not at any time seen by the main circuit. Thus, from time t_0 to t_2 the voltage across the terminals of the outgoing bidirectional switch is essentially zero. From time t_2 onward, on the other hand, the voltage across the terminals of the outgoing switch is the impressed line-to-line voltage of the input source, and again the commutating impulse voltage is not seen by the main power circuit.

It should be pointed out, as is evident from the waveforms of Figure 8.15, that the final value of the commutating impulse voltage will generally be higher than the initial value E_1 by an amount dependent on the amplitude of the line-to-line voltage of the source at the time of commutation. Thus the need again arises for providing some means of "shedding" the surplus energy absorbed by the commutating capacitor during the commutation process.

8.2.3 Commutation at the Ouput Terminals

The basic idea is that the commutating circuit is connected at the output terminals, and thus the net voltage available for commutating the thyristors is the difference between the commutating impulse voltage and the instantaneous value of the relevant source voltage.

As a practical matter, the possibility of using soft commutation can be ruled out. This is because the circuit for the commutating current pulse now includes the source itself. Apart from the general undesirability of the commutating current pulse flowing through the source, a major practical difficulty is that, with a given initial voltage on the commutating capacitor, the amplitude of the commutating current pulse would depend on the amplitude of the source voltage at the instant of commutation. Thus the amplitude of the capacitor discharge current would typically vary over a range of, for example, five to one, according to the instant in the input cycle at which the commutation takes place. Since the *minimum* amplitude of the commutating current pulse must be at least 1.5 times the peak load current, this is obviously unsatisfactory.

Considering, then, only the possibility for hard commutation, the basic arrangement for a three-pulse circuit is shown in Figure 8.16. The portion of the circuit under consideration when commutating from $ThA+$ to $ThB+$ is shown by the full lines.

The simplified waveforms of Figure 8.17 describe the operation for the condition when v_A has its maximum positive value of V_I, and correspondingly v_B has half-maximum negative value of $V_I/2$. At time t_0, the commutating impulse is applied. The initial value E_1 of the commutating voltage is greater than V_I by ΔE; thus $ThA+$ immediately becomes reverse biased by ΔE, and the output current I_O is transferred to the commutating circuit. At time t_1, the commutating voltage is equal to v_A, and $ThA+$ just becomes forward biased. At time t_2, the commutating voltage is negative and equal to v_B. On the assumption that $ThB+$ already has a firing signal applied

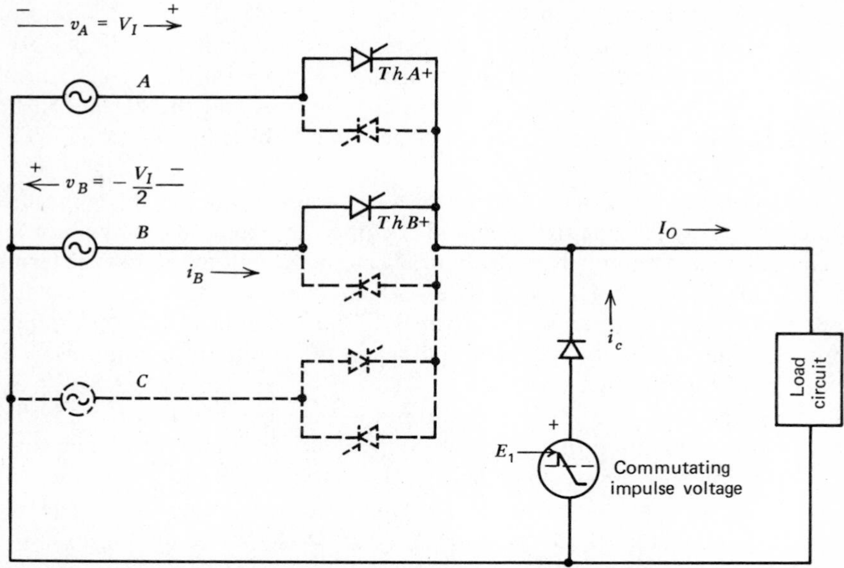

Figure 8.16 Hard commutation at the output terminals. Portion of circuit under consideration when commutating from $ThA+$ to $ThB+$ is shown by full lines.

to its gate, the output current transfers to this thyristor at this time, and the commutation process is complete.

It should be noted that the above case does not yield the highest final external value E_2 of the commutating voltage. The highest value of E_2 is obtained when the commutation takes place at the point at which v_B has its maximum negative value, and in this event $E_2 = V_I$. Of course, if firing of the incoming thyristor is delayed (although there is no theoretical need for this), E_2 could be greater than V_I.

With an initial value E_1 of the commutating voltage of $V_I + \Delta E$, it can easily be shown that the peak voltage seen by the thyristors of the frequency changer is $2V_I + \Delta E = 1.15\ V_{L\text{-}L} + \Delta E$. This assumes that the final external value E_2 does not exceed the initial value (as it will not, unless firing of the incoming thyristor is delayed unduly). Thus, the smaller is ΔE, the smaller will be the peak voltage seen by the thyristors; but, for a given turn-off time, the smaller is ΔE, the larger will be the required value of the commutating capacitor, and the longer will be the total period of the commutation.

Since the initial value $V_I + \Delta E$ of the commutating voltage is greater than the needed maximum final value, V_I, it is evident that there is no fundamental reason why a net component of energy should be absorbed by the commutating circuit during the commutation process.

8.3 SUMMARY AND CONCLUSIONS OF ELEMENTARY DISCUSSION

Before proceeding to a brief review of various possible practical embodiments of commutating circuits, it is useful to summarize the foregoing basic discussion and the conclusions that we have reached:

1. There are two possible basic types of force commutating mechanism, known as *hard* and *soft* commutation.

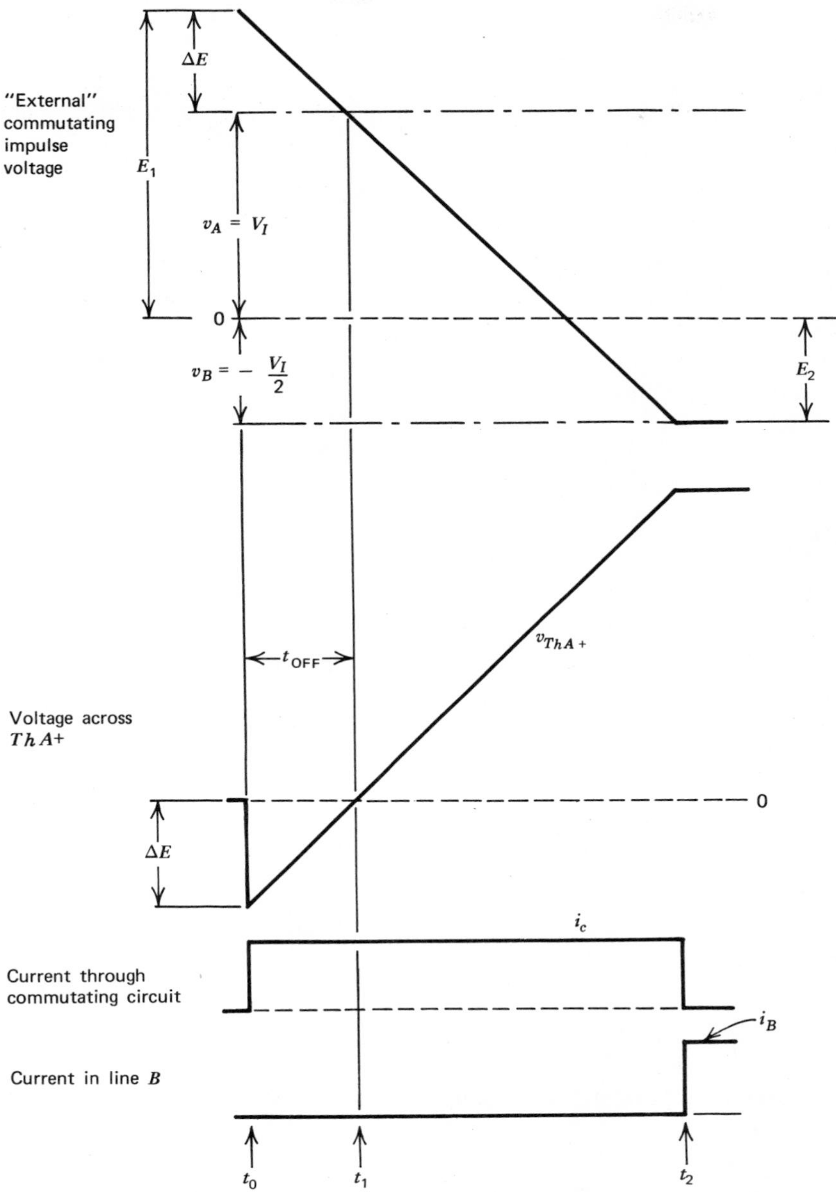

Figure 8.17 Simplified waveforms illustrating the commutating process in the circuit of Figure 8.16.

With hard commutation, the commutating circuit applies a hard reverse voltage across the outgoing thyristor to turn it off; in principle this voltage can have any value within the voltage-blocking capability of the device.

With soft commutation, a path for reverse current flow is provided across the outgoing thyristor either by the complementary *anti parallel* device in the bidirectional switch arrangement of Figure 8.1*a*, or by the bridge of diodes, in the arrangement of Figure 8.1*b*. The commutating circuit discharges a pulse of current into the reverse path, and the resulting soft reverse voltage applied across the outgoing thyristor, to turn it off, is just the conduction voltage drop of this reverse path.

2. The principle of hard commutation can be applied when the commutating circuit is connected either at the input terminals, across the switches themselves, or at the output terminals of the frequency changer. For practical reasons, soft commutation is generally practicable only when the commutating circuit is connected directly across the switches.

3. Hard commutation at the input terminals, with inductors connected in series with the input source to support the commutating impulse voltage, produces a relatively high peak voltage across the thyristors of the main frequency changer. This voltage is typically in the order of two and one-half to four times $V_{L\text{-}L}$. In addition, an appreciable component of energy becomes "trapped" in the commutating circuit.

4. Hard commutation at the input terminals, with diodes connected to support the commutating impulse voltage, gives rise to a peak voltage across the thyristors of the main frequency changer of $V_{L\text{-}L} + E_1$, in which E_1 is the initial value of the commutating voltage. In principle, E_1 can be set at any level. However, the smaller it is, the larger will be the required commutating capacitance, for a given device turn-off time, and the longer will be the total commutating period. Moreover, if E_1 is less than $V_{L\text{-}L}$, a component of energy becomes "trapped" in the commutating circuit.

5. With hard commutation applied directly across the switches of the frequency changer, the conclusions enumerated under (4) apply.

6. Soft commutation of the bidirectional switch arrangement of Figure 8.1*a* produces peak voltages across the thyristors approaching three times $V_{L\text{-}L}$. In addition, a component of energy becomes "trapped" in the commutating circuit.

7. Soft commutation of the bidirectional switch of Figure 8.1*b* (actually the only type of commutation possible for this arrangement), can be controlled in such a way that the peak voltage seen by the thyristors of the main frequency changer essentially does not exceed $V_{L\text{-}L}$. Again, however, a component of energy becomes "trapped" in the commutating circuit.

8. Hard commutation at the output terminals gives rise to peak voltages across the thyristors of the main frequency changer of $1.15\ V_{L\text{-}L} + \Delta E$, in which ΔE is the incremental value of the initial commutating voltage, above the peak source voltage. In principle, ΔE can be set at any level. However, the smaller it is, the larger will be the required commutating capacitance, for a given device turn-off time, and the longer will be the total commutating period. With this type of commutation, however, no energy becomes "trapped" in the commutating circuit.

8.4 SOME BASIC COMMUTATING CIRCUITS

Some basic commutating circuit arrangements are now presented. The intent is to exemplify briefly various possible basic circuit techniques for implementing the principles outlined in the previous sections. Having understood these fundamental principles, the operation of the basic circuits presented becomes largely self-evident; detailed descriptions of the operation of the various circuits are therefore not given.

8.4.1 Commutation at the Input Terminals

8.4.1.1 *Inductors in Series with Input Source.* A basic commutating circuit arrangement for a three-pulse frequency changer is shown in Figure 8.18. At the start of the commutation, the commutating capacitor is charged with the polarity shown. In order to commutate the current from a given frequency changer thyristor to the

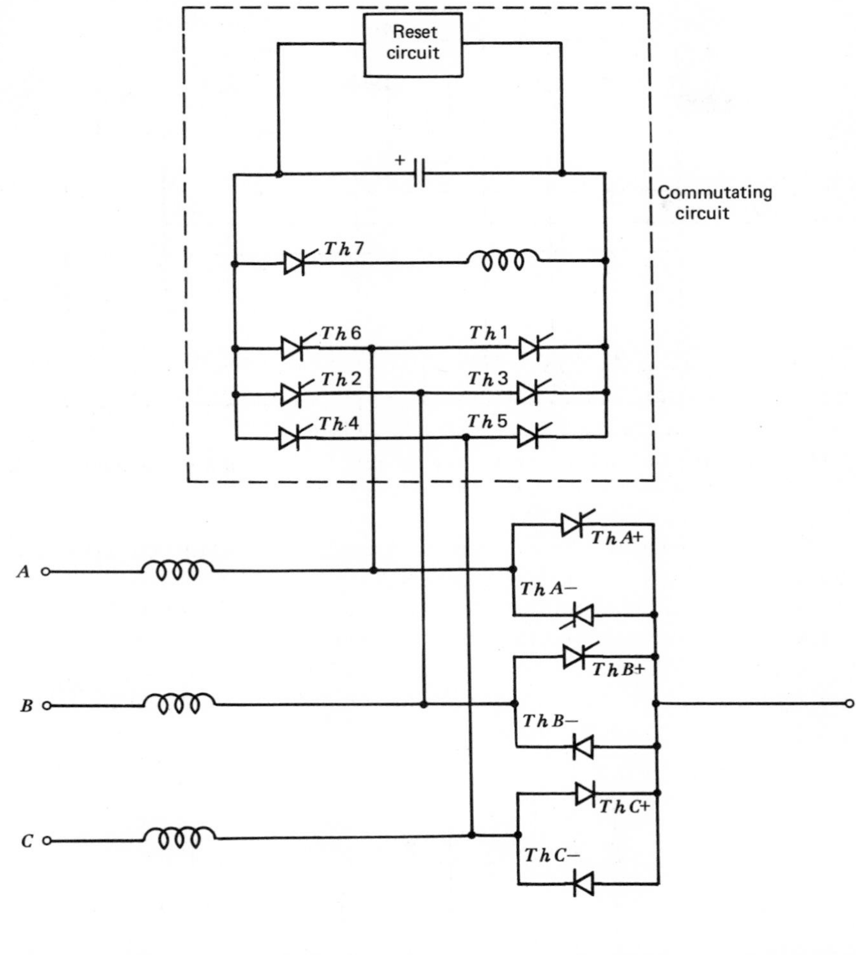

Figure 8.18 Basic circuit for hard commutation at the input terminals of a three-pulse frequency changer, with inductors in series with the input source.

next, the appropriate pair of thyristors in the commutating circuit as well as the incoming frequency changer thyristor are fired. For example, when commutating from $ThA+$ to $ThB+$, this latter thyristor and commutating thyristors $Th1$ and $Th2$ are fired; when commutating from $ThA-$ to $ThB-$, on the other hand, $ThB-$ and commutating thyristors $Th3$ and $Th6$ are fired. Thyristor $Th7$ is also fired during the commutation process to ensure that the voltage on the commutating capacitor always "rings around," regardless of the external circuit conditions.

Once the commutation process has been completed, the *reset circuit* returns the voltage on the commutating capacitor to its original condition in readiness for the next commutation and in so doing absorbs any excess energy "trapped" in the commutating capacitor.

A commutating arrangement for a six-pulse bridge frequency changer is shown in Figure 8.19. The commutating circuit itself is exactly the same as that used for the three-pulse frequency changer— it now simply serves both three-pulse groups of the overall bridge circuit.

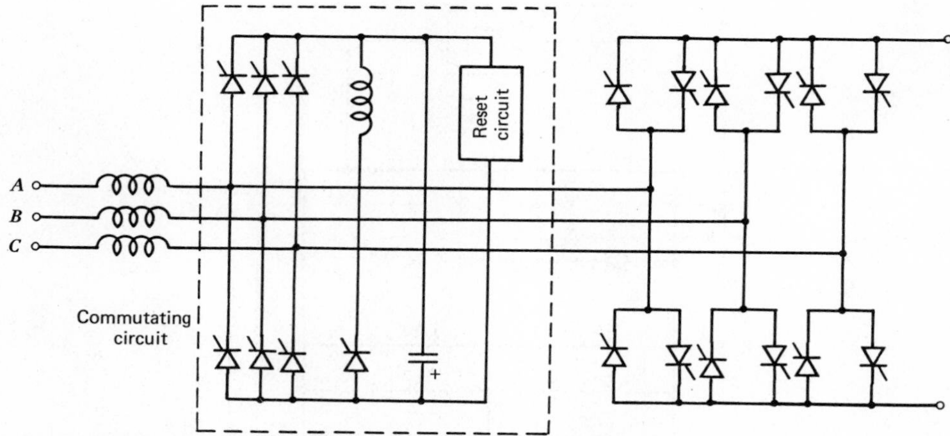

Figure 8.19 Basic circuit for hard commutation at the input terminals of a six-pulse bridge frequency changer, with inductors in series with the input source.

8.4.1.2 *Diodes in Series with Input Source.* A basic commutating circuit for a three-pulse frequency changer is shown in Figure 8.20.

At the start of commutation, the commutating capacitor is charged with the polarity shown. In order to commutate the current from a given thyristor to the next, the appropriate pair of commutating thyristors and the incoming frequency changer thyristor are fired. For example, when commutating from $ThA+$ to $ThB+$, this latter

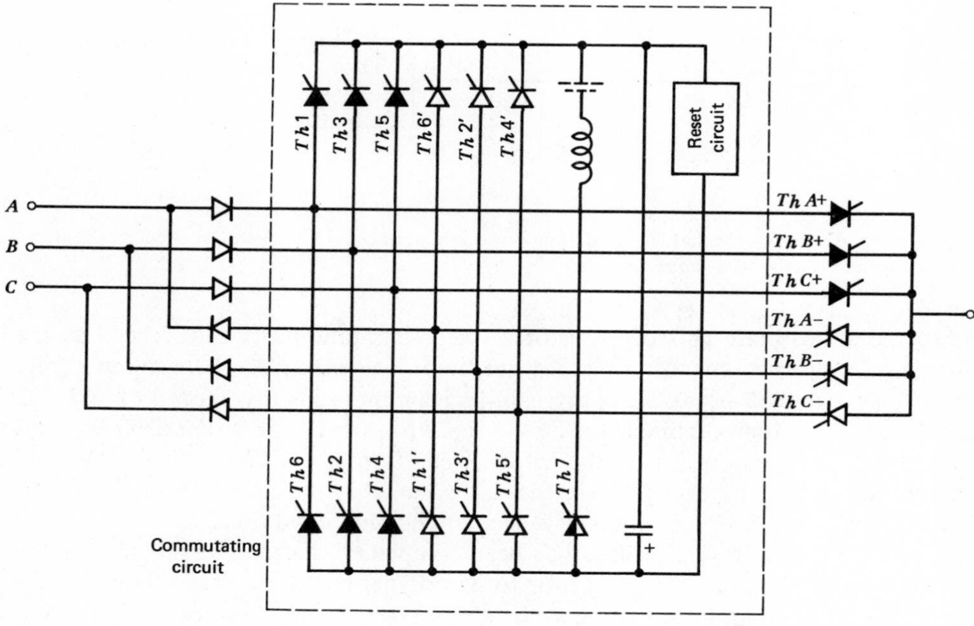

Figure 8.20 Basic circuit for hard commutation at the input terminals of a three-pulse frequency changer, with diodes in series with the input source. Black (white) commutating thyristors correspond to black (white) frequency changer thyristors.

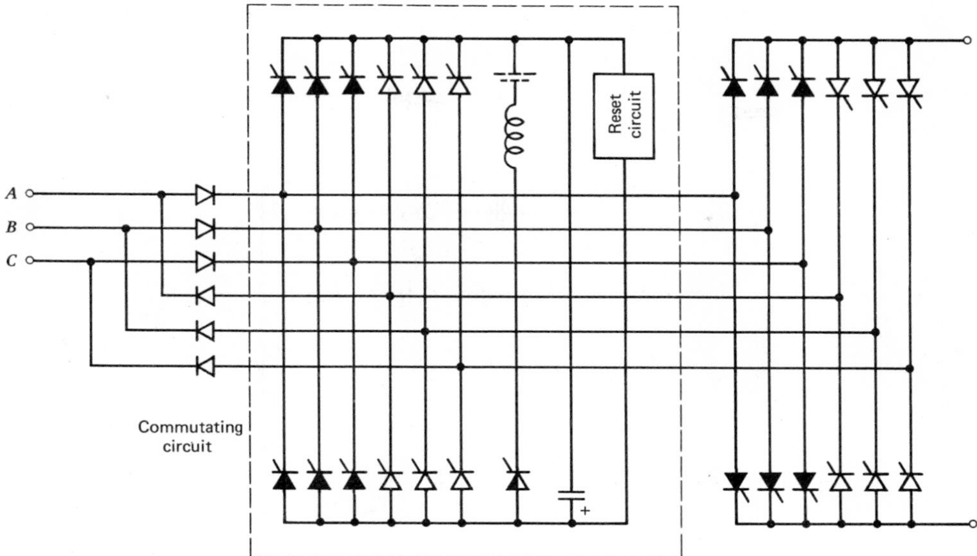

Figure 8.21 Basic circuit for hard commutation at the input terminals of a six-pulse bridge frequency changer, with diodes in series with the input source. Black (white) commutating thyristors correspond to black (white) frequency changer thyristors.

thyristor and commutating thyristors $Th1$ and $Th2$ are fired; when commutating from $ThA-$ to $ThB-$, this latter thyristor and commutating thyristors $Th1'$ and $Th2'$ are fired. Thyristor $Th7$ is also fired during the commutation process to ensure that the voltage on the commutating capacitor always rings around, regardless of the external circuit conditions. The voltage source shown dashed may or may not be present, depending on the desired initial and final values of the commutating voltage impulse.

Once the commutation process has been completed, the *reset circuit* returns the voltage on the commutating capacitor to its original condition in readiness for the next commutation and in so doing absorbs any excess energy trapped in the commutating capacitor.

A commutating arrangement for a six-pulse bridge frequency changer is shown in Figure 8.21. The commutating circuit itself is exactly the same as that used for the three-pulse frequency changer—it now simply serves both three-pulse groups of the overall bridge circuit.

8.4.2 Commutation Directly Across the Switches

8.4.2.1 *Back-to-Back Thyristor Bidirectional Switches.* A basic arrangement providing hard commutation for a three-pulse frequency changer using back-to-back thyristor bidirectional switches is shown in Figure 8.22.

At the start of the commutation, the commutating capacitors are charged with the polarities shown. In order to turn off a given thyristor, the appropriate commutating thyristor is fired. For example, when turning off $ThA+$, commutating thyristor $Th1$ is fired; when turning off $ThA-$, commutating thyristor $Th1'$ is fired. The appropriate "ring around" thyristor, $Th4$ or $Th4'$ is also fired during the commutation process to ensure that the final voltage on the commutating capacitor reaches the desired level, regardless of the level of the load current. The voltage source shown dashed may or

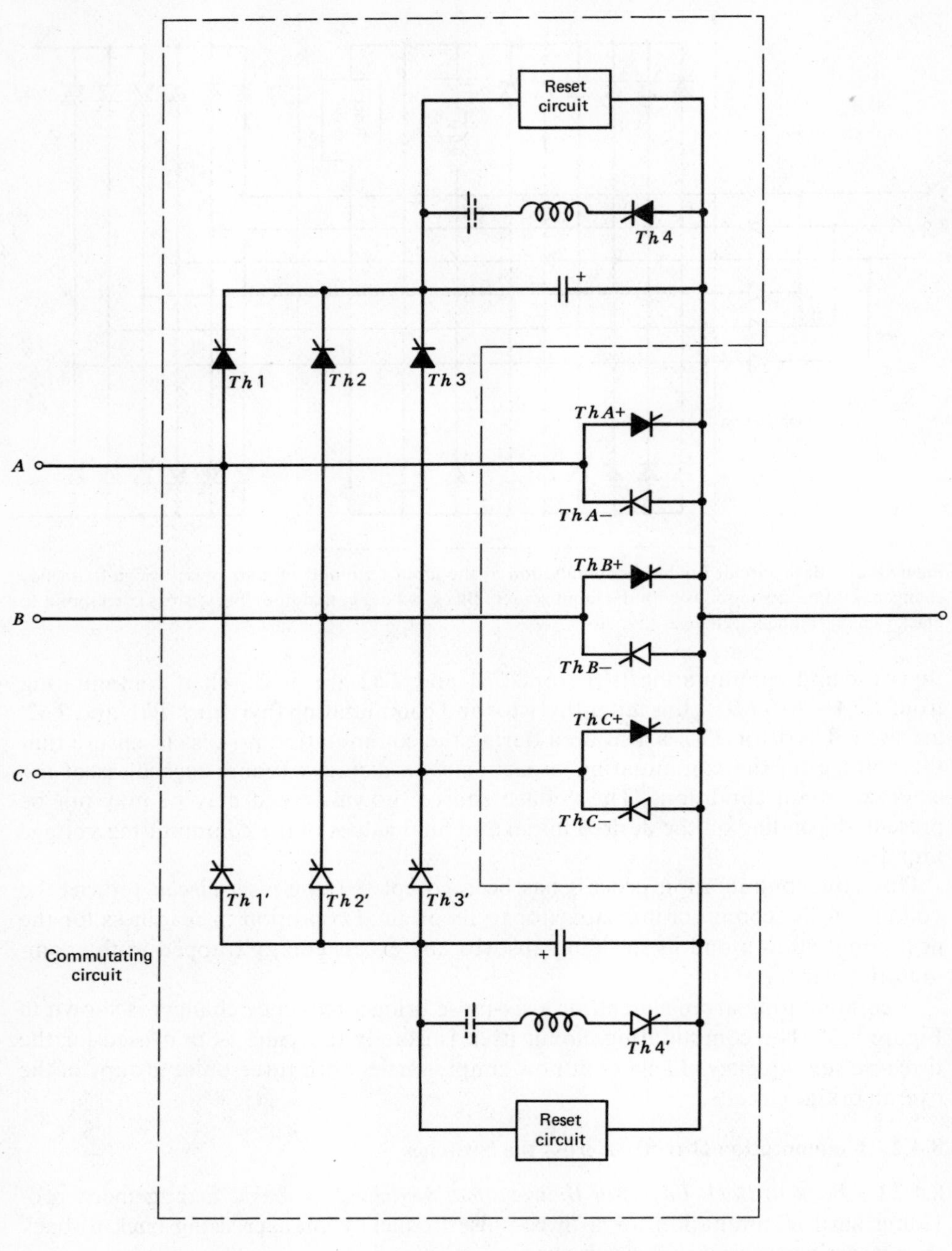

Figure 8.22 Basic circuit for hard commutation directly across the thyristors of a three-pulse frequency changer. Black (white) commutating thyristors correspond to black (white) frequency changer thyristors.

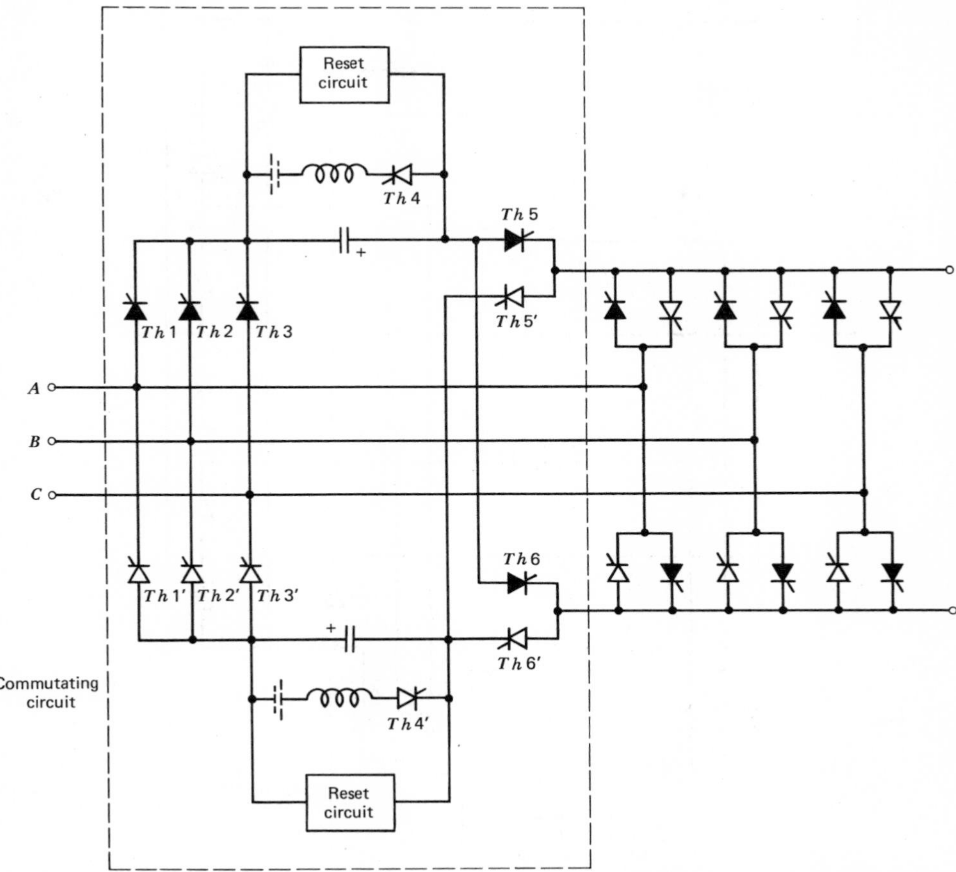

Figure 8.23 Basic circuit for hard commutation directly across the thyristors of a six-pulse bridge frequency changer. Black (white) commutating thyristors correspond to black (white) frequency changer thyristors.

may not be present, depending on the desired initial and final values of the commutating voltage impulse.

Once the commutation process has been completed, the appropriate *reset circuit* returns the voltage on the commutating capacitor to its original condition in readiness for the next commutation and in so doing absorbs any excess energy trapped in the commutating capacitor.

A commutating arrangement for a six-pulse bridge frequency changer is shown in Figure 8.23. The commutating circuit itself is essentially the same as that shown in Figure 8.22. Thyristors *Th*5 and *Th*6, and *Th*5′ and *Th*6′ are added in order to "steer" the commutating impulse to the appropriate "upper" or "lower" thyristor in the main frequency changer circuit.

8.4.2.2 *Thyristor-Diode Bidirectional Switches.* A basic arrangement providing soft commutation for a three-pulse frequency changer using thyristor-diode bidirectional switches is shown in Figure 8.24.

At the start of the commutation, the commutating capacitor is charged with the polarity shown. In order to turn off a given thyristor, the appropriate pair of

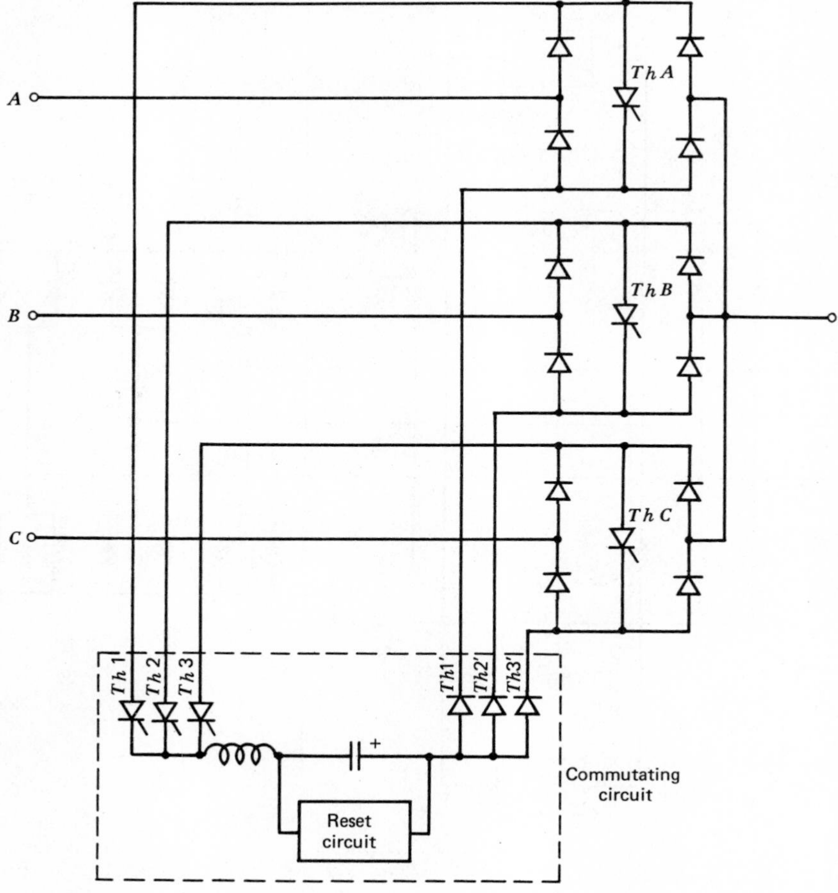

Figure 8.24 Basic circuit for soft commutation of the thyristor–diode bidirectional switches of a three-pulse frequency changer.

commutating thyristors are fired. For example, when turning off ThA, commutating thyristors $Th1$ and $Th1'$ are fixed.

Once the commutation process has been completed, the *reset circuit* returns the voltage on the commutating capacitor to its original condition in readiness for the next commutation and in so doing absorbs any excess energy trapped in the commutating capacitor.

A commutating arrangement for a six-pulse bridge frequency changer using thyristor-diode bidirectional switches is shown in Figure 8.25. The commutating circuit is essentially the same as that shown in Figure 8.24, with additional "steering" thyristors for the additional switches in the bridge circuit.

8.4.3 Commutation at the Output Terminals

8.4.3.1 *Frequency Changers with Single-Phase Output.* A basic commutating circuit for a three-pulse frequency changer is shown in Figure 8.26*a*.

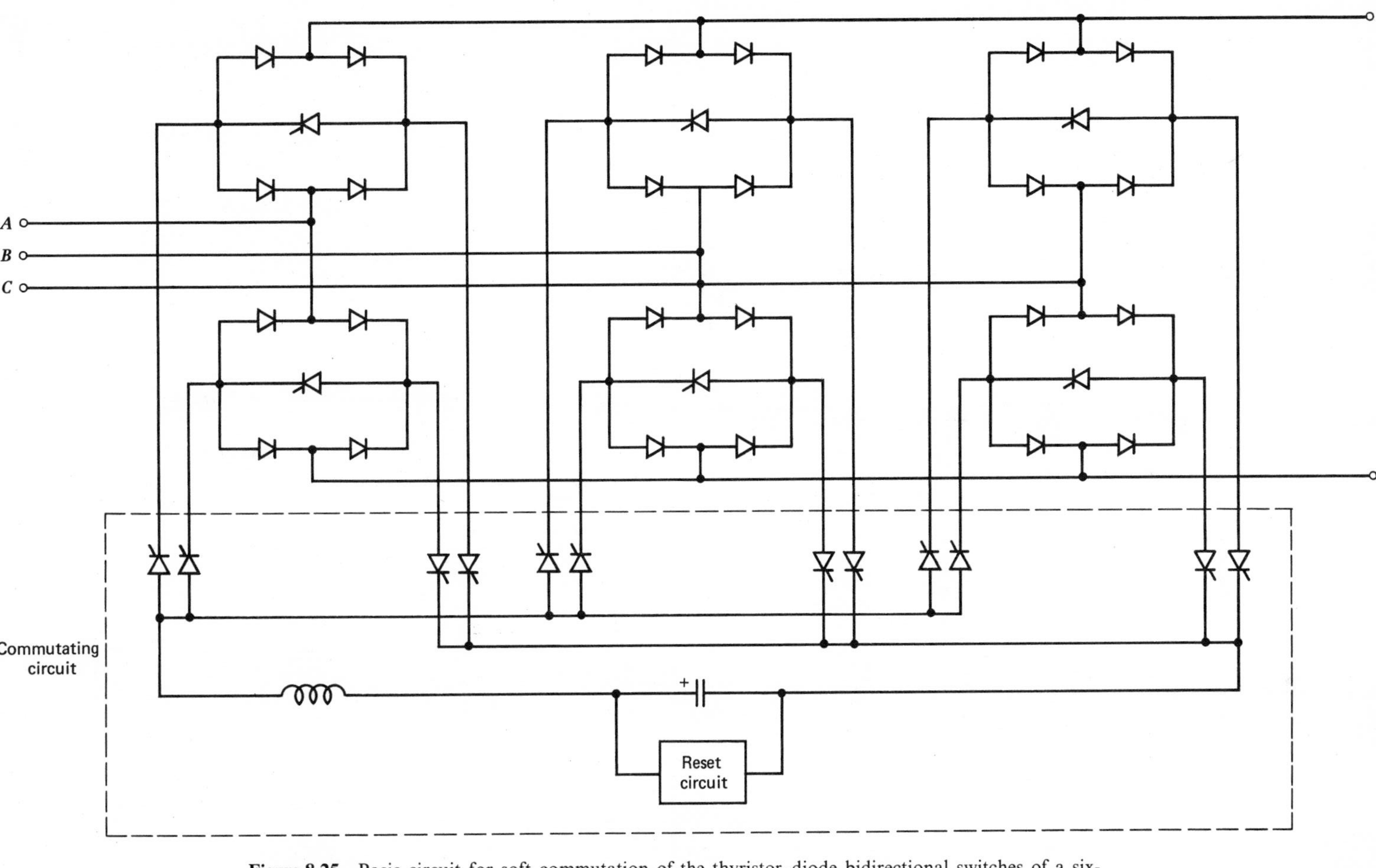

Figure 8.25 Basic circuit for soft commutation of the thyristor–diode bidirectional switches of a six-pulse bridge frequency changer.

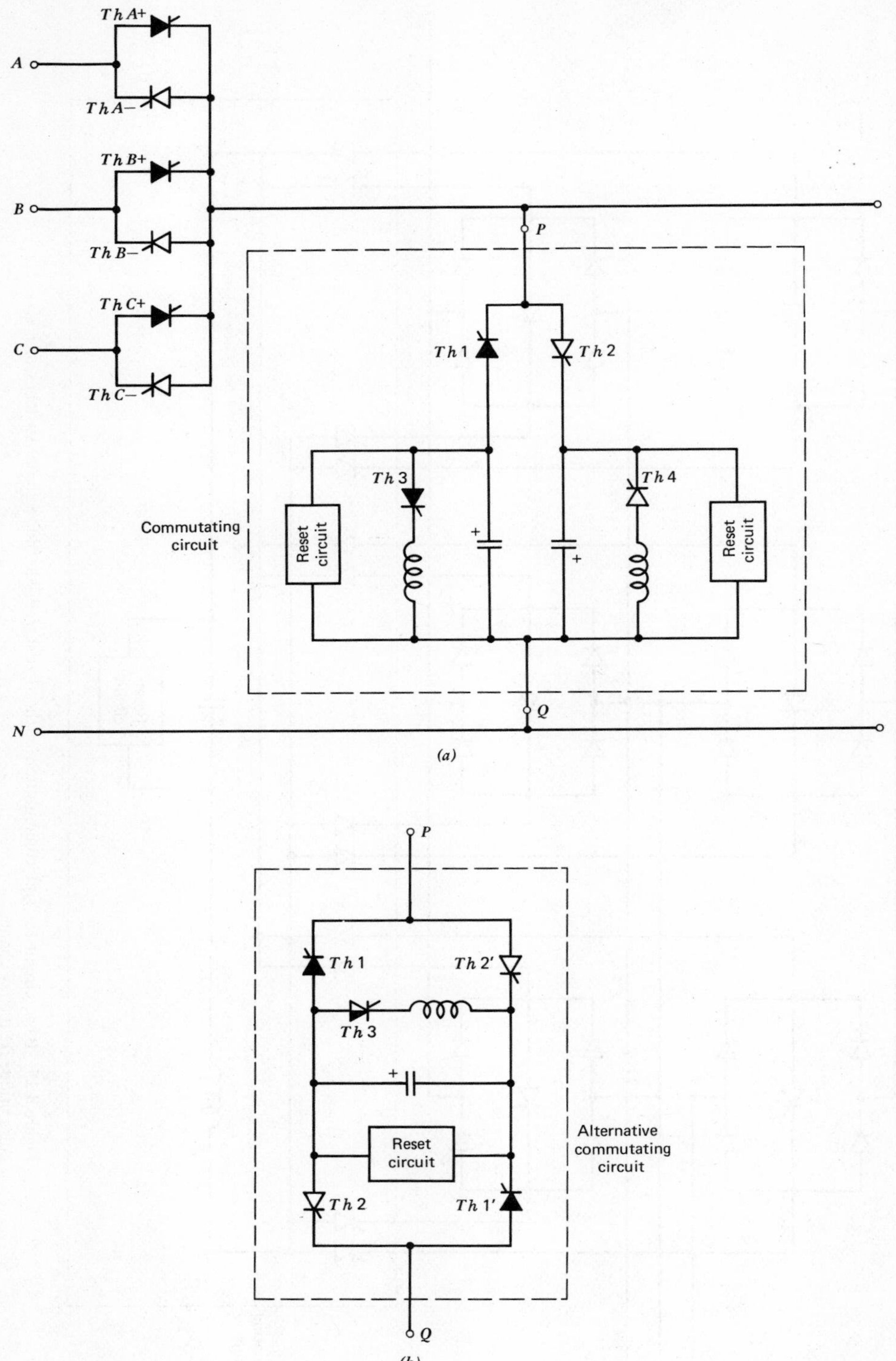

Figure 8.26 Basic circuits for hard commutation at the output terminals of a three-pulse frequency changer. Black (white) commutating thyristors correspond to black (white) frequency changer thyristors.

At the start of the commutation, the commutating capacitors are charged with the polarities shown. In order to turn off any of the positive frequency changer thyristors, commutating thyristor *Th*1 is fired; in order to turn off any of the negative frequency changer thyristors, commutating thyristor *Th*2 is fired. The appropriate "ring around" thyristor, *Th*3 or *Th*4, is also fired during the commutation process to ensure that the final voltage on the commutating capacitor reaches the desired level in a given time, regardless of the level of the load current.

Once the commutation process has been completed, the appropriate *reset circuit* returns the voltage on the commutating capacitor to its original condition in readiness for the next commutation.

An alternative arrangement of commutating circuit that economizes on the number of components is shown in Figure 8.26*b*. In order to turn off any of the positive frequency changer thyristors, commutating thyristors *Th*1 and *Th*1′ are fired, and in order to turn off any of the negative frequency changer thyristors, commutating thyristors *Th*2 and *Th*2′ are fired.

A basic commutating circuit arrangement for a six-pulse bridge frequency changer is shown in Figure 8.27*a*.

At the start of the commutation, the commutating capacitors are charged with the polarities shown. In order to turn off any of the *upper* positive thyristors, commutating thyristor *Th*1 is fired, and in order to turn off any of the *upper* negative thyristors, commutating thyristor *Th*2 is fired. In order to turn off any of the *lower* positive thyristors, commutating thyristor *Th*1′ is fired, and in order to turn off any of the *lower* negative thyristors, commutating thyristors, *Th*2′ is fired. The appropriate "ring around" thyristor, *Th*3 or *Th*4, is also fired during the commutation process to ensure that the final voltage on the commutating capacitor reaches the desired level in a given time.

Again, the *reset circuit* returns the voltage on the commutating capacitor to its original condition in readiness for the next commutation.

An alternative commutating circuit that economizes on the number of components is shown in Figure 8.27*b*.

With this arrangement, pairs of upper and lower frequency changer thyristors are turned off together. Thus, when the output current is positive, firing of commutating thyristors *Th*1 and *Th*1′ turns off both the upper and lower positive thyristors that are in conduction at that time; conversely, when the output current is negative, firing of commutating thyristors *Th*2 and *Th*2′ turns off both the upper and lower negative thyristors that are in conduction at that time. Since the switching pattern of the frequency changer requires that the conduction periods of the upper and lower switches are interlaced with one another, this means that one of the two thyristors turned off at any commutation instant actually is refired for the next conduction period.

Again, the "ring around" thyristor is fired during the commutation process to ensure that the final voltage on the commutating capacitor reaches the desired level, and the *reset circuit* subsequently returns the voltage on the commutating capacitor to its original condition in readiness for the next commutation.

8.4.3.2 *UFC and SSFC with Three-Phase Output.* As seen in earlier chapters, the switching instants for all output phases of a UFC or SSFC supplying a three-phase output occur simultaneously. Thus, rather than commutate each output phase independently of the others, it is possible to provide a commutating circuit that serves all output phases.

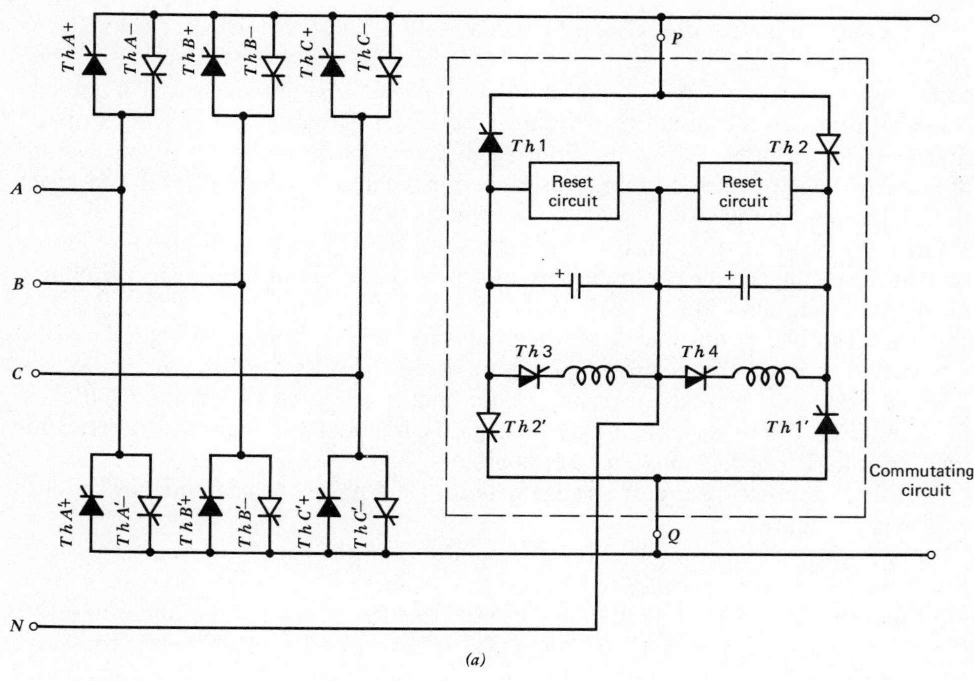

(a)

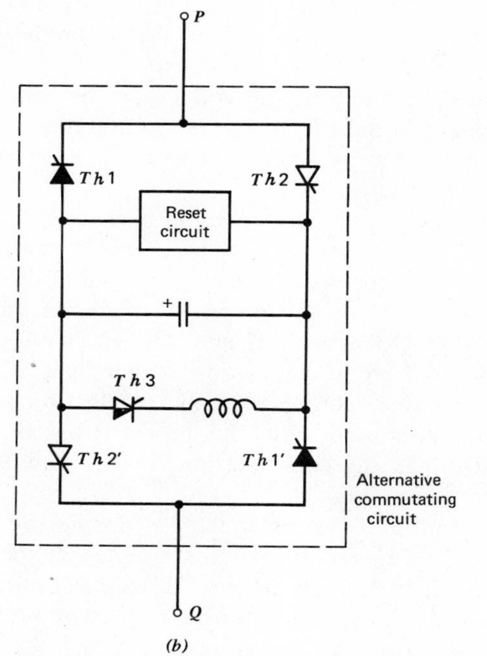

(b)

Figure 8.27 Basic circuits for hard commutation at the output terminals of a six-pulse bridge frequency changer. Black (white) commutating thyristors correspond to black (white) frequency changer thyristors.

One such arrangement for a six-pulse bridge UFC or SSFC with three-phase output[68] is shown in Figure 8.28. At each switching instant, the upper or lower commutating thyristors, as the case may be in each output phase, appropriate to the particular direction of the current of that output phase are fired. Assume, for example, that the directions of the output currents i_{O1}, i_{O2}, and i_{O3} are as shown on the diagram and that $ThA+_1$ in input phase one, $ThC+_2$ in output phase two, and $ThB-_3$ in output phase three are conducting. The polarities of the voltages on the commutating capacitors are as shown. In order to turn off these thyristors, commutating thyristors $Th1_1$, in output phase one, $Th1_2$ in output phase two, and $Th2_3$ in output phase three are fired. Output currents i_{O1} and i_{O2} thus transfer to capacitor C_1, flowing from right to left in the diagram; output current i_{O3} transfers to capacitor C_2, also flowing from right to left, and each of the above frequency changer thyristors turns off. When the voltages on capacitors C_1 and C_2 reach an appropriate level in the opposite direction, the incoming frequency changer thyristors are fired, and the output currents transfer to these devices.

By appropriately timing the firing of the incoming thyristors, it can be arranged that the final reversed voltages across the commutating capacitors are equal in magnitude to the initial values; thus the circuit is now ready to commutate the lower frequency changer thyristors, at the next switching instant. Thus, during any given commutation, the voltage on the commutating capacitors can be set for the next commutation, and a continuously operating auxiliary voltage setting circuit theoretically is not required, as long as there is always a sufficient load at the output of the frequency changer. The initial voltages across the commutating capacitors, prior to system start-up, must, however, be appropriately set by some auxiliary means.

Since the magnitude of the total current flowing through each of the commutating capacitors during any given commutation always lies between 0.866 and 1 times the crest value of the output current wave, this current has a relatively fixed value at all commutations for a given amplitude of alternating output current; thus the "ring around" circuit, shown dashed in Figure 8.28, may not be required, depending on the range of variation of load current to be encountered.

With a balanced three-phase load, the sum of the output current $i_{O1} + i_{O2} + i_{O3}$ is zero, and the neutral connection theoretically does not carry any output current during the commutation process (nor, of course, does it do so during the intervening periods). In practice, however, with three "isolated" output loads, there is no guarantee that the sum of the three output currents will always be precisely zero, and thus the neutral connection cannot be omitted.

It is mentioned that the circuit shown in Figure 8.28 is suitable only for producing full output voltage from the frequency changer. The outputs of two such complete circuits can of course be combined and the net output voltage controlled by means of phase shifting the wanted voltage components of the individual circuits.

The circuit as it stands cannot provide voltage control by pulse-width modulation, because the commutations do not alternate successively between the upper and lower switches of the frequency changer with this control method. Generally, two successive upper commutations are followed by two successive lower commutations, and vice versa. A way around the difficulty is to connect an additional set of commutating thyristors in antiparallel with those shown in Figure 8.28.

An alternative commutating arrangement for a six-pulse bridge UFC or SSFC with three-phase output is shown in Figure 8.29. This circuit is derived from that for single-phase output shown in Figure 8.27*b*.

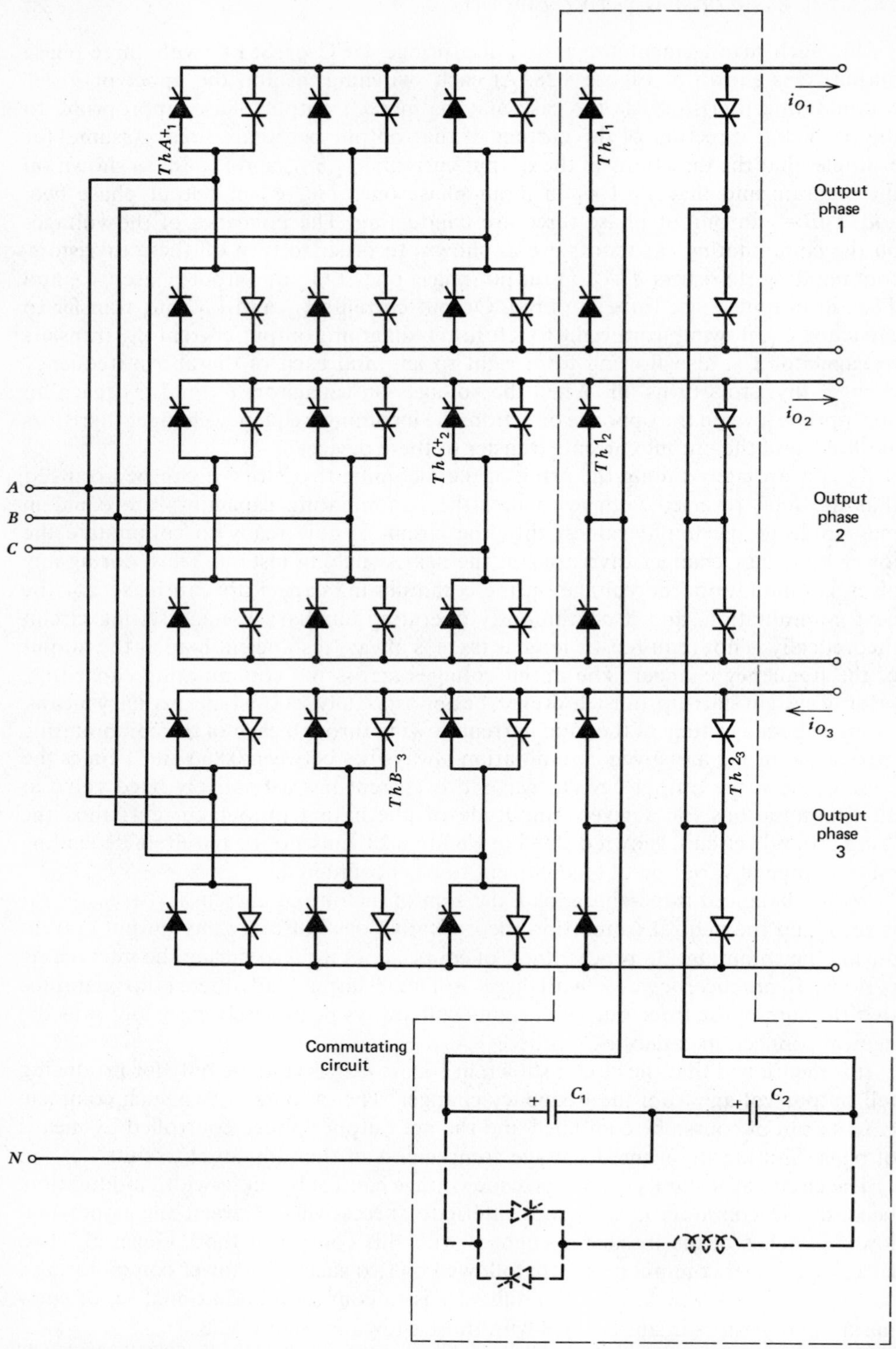

Figure 8.28 Basic circuit for hard commutation at the output terminals of a six-pulse bridge UFC or SSFC with three-phase output. Black (white) commutating thyristors correspond to black (white) frequency changer thyristors.

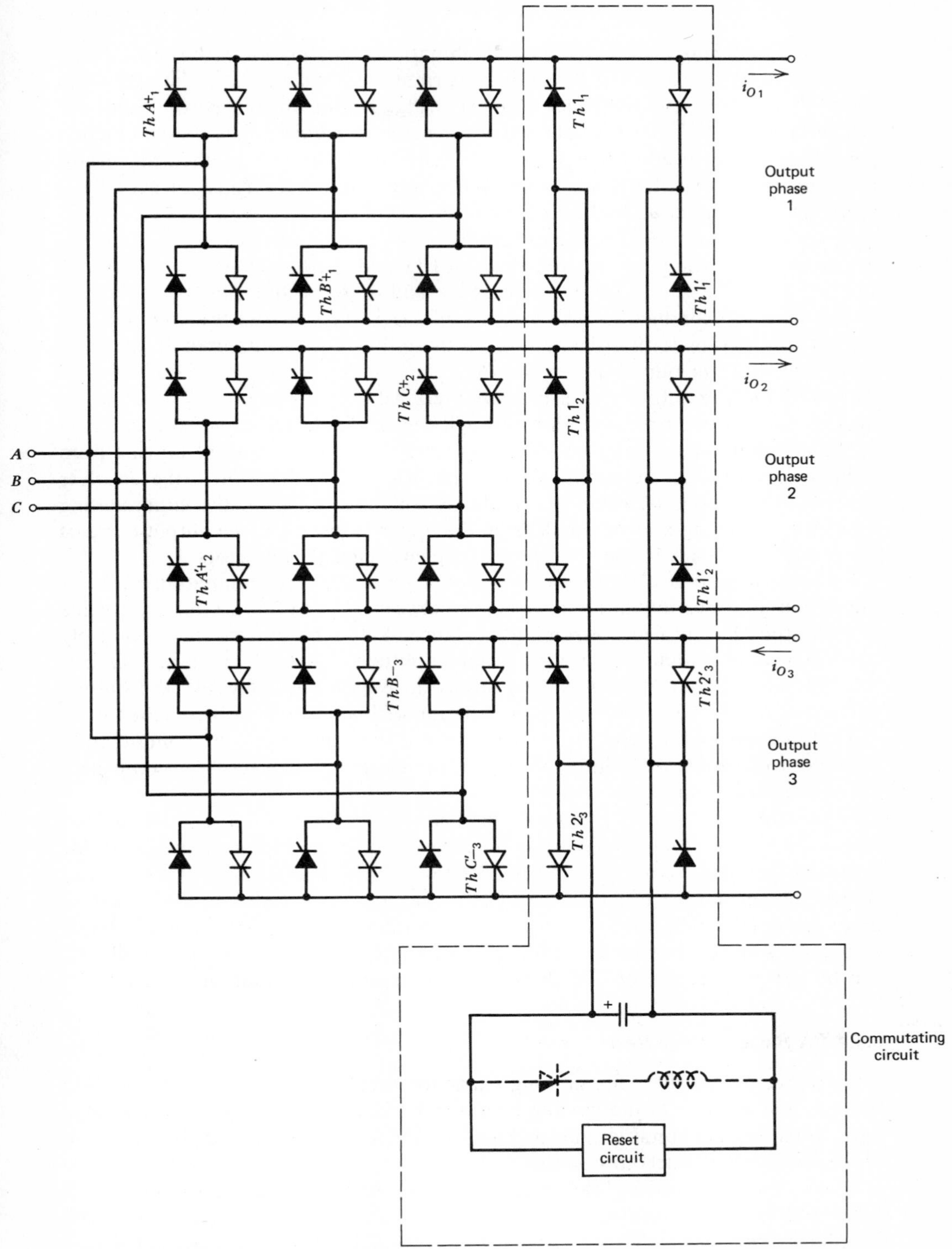

Figure 8.29 Alternative basic circuit for hard commutation at the output terminals of a six-pulse bridge UFC or SSFC with three-phase output. Black (white) commutating thyristors correspond to black (white) frequency changer thyristors.

At each switching instant, pairs of commutating thyristors for each output phase appropriate to the particular direction of current are fired, and both the upper and lower thyristors in the frequency changer bridge circuit are turned off. Since the switching pattern of the frequency changer actually requires that the conduction periods of the upper and lower switches are interlaced with one another, this means that one of the two thyristors turned off at any commutation instant actually is refired at the completion of the commutation period.

Assume, for example, that the directions of the output currents i_{O1}, i_{O2}, and i_{O3} are as shown in the diagram, and that $ThA+$, and $ThB'+$ in output phase one, $ThC+_2$ and $ThA'+_2$ in output phase two, and $ThB-_3$ and $ThC'-_3$ in output phase three are conducting. The polarity of the voltage across the commutating capacitor is as shown. In order to turn off these thyristors, commutating thyristors $Th1_1$ and $Th1'_1$ in output phase one, $Th1_2$ and $Th1'_2$ in output phase two, and $Th2_2$ and $Th2'_3$ in output phase three are fired. All output currents i_{O1}, i_{O2}, and i_{O3} thus transfer in the same direction through the commutating capacitor, and each of the above frequency changer thyristors turns off. The net current flowing from right to left through the commutating capacitor is thus the sum of the absolute values of the individual output currents. When the voltage on the commutating capacitor reaches an appropriate level in the opposite direction, the output currents are commutated back to the appropriate frequency changer thyristors.

Since the magnitude of the total current flowing through the commutating capacitor during any given commutation always lies between $\sqrt{3}$ and 2 times the crest value of the output current wave (assuming a balanced load), this current has a relatively fixed value at all commutations for a given amplitude of alternating output current; thus the "ring around" circuit, shown dashed in Figure 8.29, may not be required, depending on the particular range of variation of load current to be encountered.

The function of the *reset circuit* is to return the voltage on the commutating capacitor to its original condition once the commutation process has been completed, in readiness for the next commutation.

In principle, this circuit is suitable for controlling the amplitude of the output voltage by pulse-width modulation. In practice, however, depending on the particular operating parameters, a fairly appreciable loss of the theoretical 0–100% voltage control range may be obtained, because of the finite commutation and resetting times required, which place practical limits on the maximum and minimum levels of output voltage obtainable within the continuous control range. This difficulty can be largely circumvented by duplicating parts of the commutating circuit.

8.4.4 A Basic Voltage Reset Circuit

The voltage across the commutating capacitor reverses during the commutation process, and in most of the circuits considered it is necessary to reset this voltage back to its original condition, in readiness for the next commutation. It is the task of the *reset circuit* to accomplish this.

So far we have considered this circuit just as a functional unit; we now see how it may typically be implemented, by reference to the specific circuit shown in Figure 8.30. Simplified waveforms that describe the operation of this circuit are shown in Figure 8.31.

The voltage across the commutating capacitor C initially has a reverse value of E_2 as a result of previous operation of the commutating circuit. The main and auxiliary

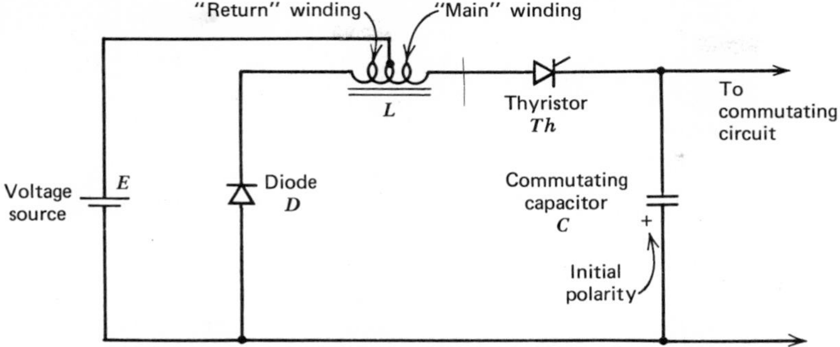

Figure 8.30 Typical basic circuit for resetting the voltage across the commutating capacitor.

Voltage to which
C would charge
without "return"
winding on L and
diode D

$|E_2|$

Current in "main"
winding of L =
current in thyristor
Th

Capacitor
voltage

$2E$

Voltage across
capacitor and
current flowing
through source
voltage E

Source
current

E_2

Current in "return"
winding of L =
current in diode D

Voltage across
thyristor and
diode

Thyristor
voltage

0

Diode
voltage

t_0 t_1 t_2

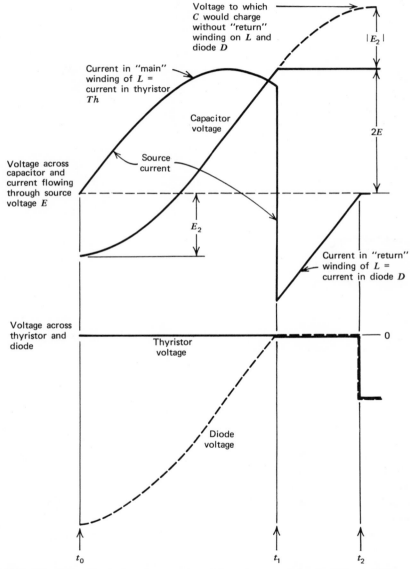

Figure 8.31 Waveforms illustrating the operation of the voltage reset circuit of Figure 8.30.

windings of inductor L have the same number of turns and are tightly coupled to one another. At time t_0, thyristor Th is fired, and a resonant charging current flows to C via the *main* winding of inductor L. From t_0 to t_1, diode D is reverse biased, and no current flows through the *return* winding of inductor L; in the absence of this winding, the final voltage across C would theoretically "ring up" to $2E + |E_2|$, as indicated in Figure 8.31. At the point at which the voltage across C becomes equal to $2E$, however, diode D just becomes forward biased and prevents any further rise of voltage across C. The current previously flowing in the main winding of inductor L now transfers to the return winding, and thyristor Th turns off. The current flowing through the voltage source E now reverses its direction and decays linearly, due to the fixed voltage E impressed across the return winding of inductor L. This current becomes zero at time t_3.

It is evident that whatever the initial value of the reverse voltage across the commutating capacitor, the final voltage—that is, the "initial" voltage for the next commutation—is always $2E$. Thus this voltage can be reset to any desired fixed level by appropriate choice of the amplitude of the voltage source E. If $|E_1|$ is less than $2E$, a net component of energy is delivered from the voltage source E to the commutating capacitor; if $|E_1|$ is greater than $2E$, on the other hand, a net component of energy is absorbed by the voltage source E from the commutating capacitor.

CHAPTER NINE

APPLICATIONS OF STATIC FREQUENCY CHANGERS

The frequency changers treated in this book offer diverse functional characteristics and lend themselves well to many potential applications. From the purely technical viewpoint, their possible use in solving a variety of electrical engineering problems can be said to be limited only by the imagination and ingenuity of the design engineer. We must temper this statement, however, by noting that although certain applications of the naturally commutated cycloconverter in particular have become well established, at present the other members of this frequency changer family have not yet found their way into practical working installations outside of the laboratory, and the diverse functional possibilities that they offer have not yet been commercially exploited.

We believe there are several reasons for this. First, the operating principles, unique performance characteristics, and application advantages of these systems have been established only fairly recently and are not widely appreciated. Indeed, as far as we know, this is the first readily available publication that describes these types of frequency changers. Second, although considerable progress has been made in the last few years in semiconductor device technology, devices with intrinsic gate-controlled turn-off ability of suitable ratings and characteristics are not yet commercially available except for relatively low-power applications. We believe it is inevitable, however, that such devices eventually will become available; undoubtedly, this will give an immediate boost to the practical application of the frequency changers that we describe here. Third, although it appears that the use of conventional thyristors with auxiliary force commutating circuits in some applications would prove to be perfectly viable, both technically and economically, the development of such techniques inevitably requires considerable time and effort, and the day has not yet arrived on which such designs have reached a final mature stage.

We have little doubt that in the future static power frequency changers will become widely accepted items of power electronics equipment. It is indeed a challenge for the present generation of electrical power engineers to develop the tremendous application potential that these systems offer.

The most interesting broad application areas for static power frequency changers, as presently recognized, can be summarized as follows:

1. Variable frequency speed control of a-c machines. A normally fixed frequency input is converted through a frequency changer to a variable frequency variable voltage output, for the purpose of controlling the speed of an a-c motor.
2. Constant frequency power supplies. Variable frequency input power is converted to accurately regulated high-quality constant frequency output power.
3. Controllable VAr generators for voltage support and power factor correction. The frequency changer is operated to provide an essentially similar function to that of

a rotating synchronous condenser. Various interesting schemes using different types of frequency changers have been conceived in recent years. In some, the *frequency changing* capability as such actually is *not* used.

4. A-c system interties. The frequency changer is used to link together two independent power systems and to control the flow of power between them. The frequencies of the two systems may either be nominally the same or different. Again, a particularly interesting scheme using a naturally commutated cycloconverter has been conceived in recent years.

In the first two application areas—variable speed drives, and constant frequency power supplies—the naturally commutated cycloconverter, but not, as yet, the other types of frequency changers, has become well established. A considerable number of variable speed a-c motor drives employing cycloconverters are in practical use. Similarly, considerable effort has been devoted to the development of constant frequency airborne power supplies using naturally commutated cycloconverters. Such systems, although not yet widely in use, are commercially available.

At the research laboratories with which the authors have been associated, each of the above four broad application areas for frequency changers have received attention. In some cases, final fully rated fully functional systems have been developed, whereas in others the more limited objective of demonstrating basic system feasibility on the model level has so far been accomplished.

In order to provide assistance to the reader in measuring the application potential of frequency changers and to encourage the practical use of these schemes, we intend in this "application" chapter to depart from the traditional approach adopted in books of presenting only examples of established equipments and systems that are already in practical use. In addition to state-of-the-art systems, we present new ones, in which basic technical feasibility has been established, but which, for the reasons we have outlined, have not yet found their way into commercial use.

9.1 VARIABLE-SPEED CONTROL OF A-C MACHINES

A static frequency changer in general has the facility for continuous control of both its output frequency and voltage, independent of one another. Furthermore, it is able to operate with loads of any power factor, including regenerative loads. It is thus eminently suited to supply an a-c machine with variable frequency and variable voltage, for the purpose of providing an efficient variable speed drive. Although either a synchronous or an asynchronous machine may be employed, in practice, the latter in the form of a squirrel cage induction motor is generally preferred because of its extreme simplicity, robustness, relatively low cost, and virtually maintenance-free operation.

The basic principles for efficient variable speed control of an induction motor are outlined briefly in the following section.

9.1.1 Basic Principles of Variable-Speed Control of an Induction Motor

Under steady-state operating conditions, with rated voltage applied to the stator windings, the speed of an induction motor is approximately proportional to the frequency of the applied voltage and is practically independent of the load on the machine, within the normal load range. Thus, by controlling the frequency and amplitude of the stator voltage, in such a relationship to one another as to maintain a constant airgap flux in the machine, an a-c drive system with characteristics similar to those of a separately excited d-c machine with armature voltage control—for example, a Ward-Leonard system—can be obtained.

In the case of the d-c machine, the torque developed is proportional to the armature current, which is determined by the difference between the applied voltage and the induced e.m.f. of the machine, which is itself proportional to the machine speed. In the case of the induction motor, with the voltage to frequency ratio controlled so as to maintain a constant flux in the machine, the torque developed is determined only by the absolute difference or *slip frequency* between the applied stator frequency and the output "shaft frequency" irrespective of the speed.

The torque/slip frequency characteristic for an induction motor with constant excitation flux is shown in Figures 9.1*a* and *b*. Also shown plotted alongside is the corresponding stator current/slip frequency characteristic. Both of these characteristics are "universal" and are generally applicable to any induction motor, independent of the applied frequency or speed. It should be noted that these characteristics show both positive and negative values of slip, torque, and current; that is, they are applicable to operation of the machine both in its *motoring* and in its *regenerating* mode.

Considering the motoring region of operation, it can be seen that as the slip frequency increases so the torque and current increase, up to a certain maximum torque. Thereafter, further increase in the slip frequency results in a reduced torque with increased current. The absolute slip frequency that results in the maximum torque of which the machine is capable—the *pullout torque*—depends on the resistance of the rotor circuit and is usually a few percent (or less) of the rated frequency. This frequency is referred to here as the *pullout slip frequency*.

The normal steady-state operating range of an induction machine is over the portion of the torque/slip characteristic that has a positive slope. However, in the base in which the supply frequency is fixed, it is clear that, at starting, the slip frequency must inevitably be much greater than that which results in maximum torque. A typical operating point, with a fixed frequency supply, with the rotor at standstill, is at *A* (Figure 9.1*b*). At this point, the torque is considerably less than the pullout torque, and the current is relatively high. It can be seen, in order to increase the starting torque, that it is necessary for the starting point *A* to be moved to the left. This implies that the absolute value of the pullout slip frequency must be increased, which, in turn, implies that the resistance of the rotor circuit must also be increased. This is undesirable for a squirrel cage induction motor, since it is necessarily accompanied by a reduced full-load efficiency. Thus it can be seen that the squirrel cage induction motor, when fed from a fixed frequency supply, has the undesirable, yet inevitable, characteristic that the available starting torque is less than the pullout torque, and the starting current is relatively high.

If, on the other hand, the frequency and voltage of the power source can be controlled at will, there is no longer any need to operate the machine outside of that portion of the torque-slip characteristic with a positive slope, either in the *motoring* or *regenerating* region of operation. In other words, the applied frequency can now be controlled so as always to keep the absolute slip frequency less than (or equal to) the *pullout* slip frequency, and the machine can therefore be made to operate on the most favorable portion of its torque-slip characteristic, under all conditions. Thus it is possible to realize the maximum driving and braking torques of which the machine is capable, at all speeds, including standstill. Moreover, due to this possibility, there is no longer any need for the resistance of the rotor circuit to have an artifically high

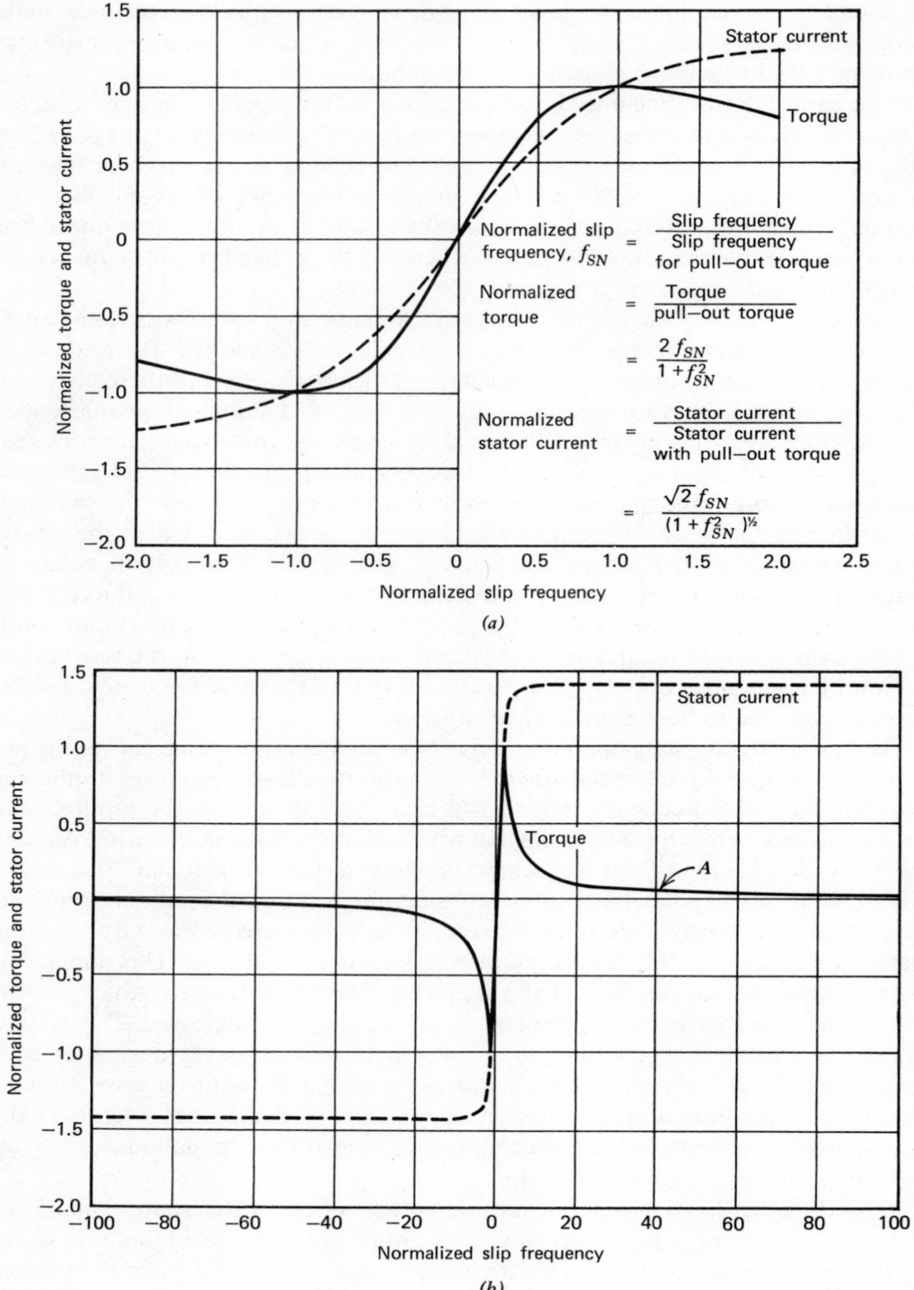

Figure 9.1 Universal characteristics for an induction motor with constant excitation flux.

value simply to provide a given starting torque capability. Thus it is possible to design the rotor circuit to have the minimum possible resistance—which implies, also, the minimum possible pullout slip frequency. These features are desirable, not only from the viewpoint of increased efficiency, but also, because of the low slip, the speed of the machine becomes almost exactly proportional to the applied frequency over a wide range of operation. In this way it is possible to control the speed with a fairly high degree of accuracy, without resort to a closed-loop speed control, by accurately controlling the applied frequency.

As mentioned, in order to maintain a constant flux in the machine, it is necessary to control the amplitude of the applied voltage in accordance with the frequency. For an "ideal" machine, in which the resistance and leakage inductance of the stator winding are assumed to be zero, and hence the "airgap" voltage is equal to the applied voltage, a constant ratio between the voltage and the frequency would be required. For a practical machine, in order to maintain a constant ratio between the "airgap" voltage and the frequency, it is necessary to adjust the applied voltage beyond the proportional value in order to offset the voltage drop across the series impedance of the winding, due to the stator current. This voltage drop is actually a relatively small proportion of the full rated voltage of the machine, and hence the required amount of adjustment of the voltage with load is small by comparison to the full voltage. Thus, under conditions in which the applied stator voltage and frequency are relatively high, the effect of a small adjustment of the amplitude of the applied voltage with load may have little practical effect upon the operation. At low operating frequencies, however, under conditions in which the applied voltage is relatively small, the voltage drop across the series resistance of the stator winding becomes a large proportion of the applied voltage, and the adjustment of the voltage with load, so as to maintain the full airgap flux, and hence also the maximum torque capability of the drive, now has a critical effect upon the performance of the system. Thus, in order to realize the maximum torque capability of the machine at low speeds, it is essential to adjust the voltage to frequency ratio beyond the proprotional value.

All the static a-c to a-c frequency changers described in this book can be used in variable-frequency induction motor speed control systems. Here we consider just two types for this application—the naturally commutated cycloconverter and the unrestricted frequency changer.

The naturally commutated cycloconverter can provide an economic solution for large variable-speed motor drives, in which the required upper limit of the operating frequency range is appropriately less than the industrial supply frequency.

The unrestricted frequency changer offers a technically elegant solution for applications in which the required operating frequency range extends above the supply frequency.

Variable-speed drive schemes for induction motors using these two alternative approaches are briefly discussed in the following sections.

9.1.2 An NCC Variable-Speed Control System for an Induction Motor

The basic elements of a variable frequency speed control system using a naturally commutated cycloconverter are illustrated in Figure 9.2. The cycloconverter provides three-phase variable frequency output power, with reversible phase sequence, from a fixed frequency three-phase power input. Taken in conjunction with its *pulse timing and firing circuits* (see Figures 7.29*a* and *b*), the cycloconverter can be regarded as a

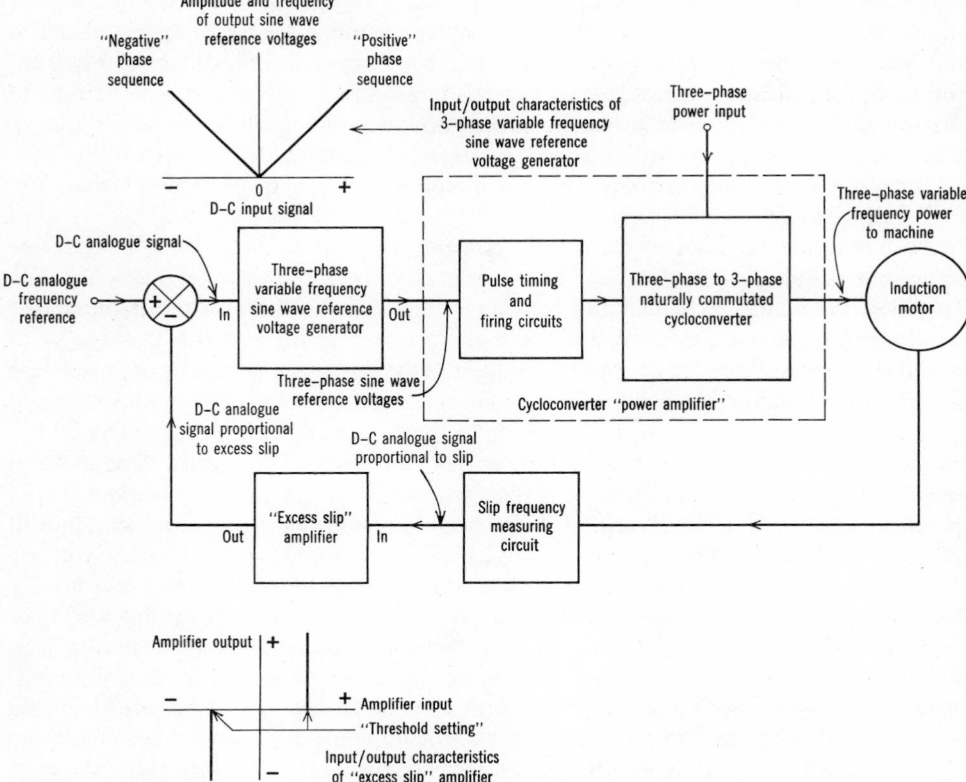

Figure 9.2 Schematic representation of a variable-frequency speed control system for an induction motor, using a naturally commutated cycloconverter.

three-phase power amplifier. Thus the output voltages of the cycloconverter are proportional to the three-phase analogue sine wave reference voltages, obtained from the *reference voltage generator*, which are used as input signals to the pulse timing and firing circuits. The frequency and amplitude of these reference sine waves are controlled to achieve the desired output speed and torque.

There are various ways of realizing a three-phase variable-frequency, variable-voltage sine wave reference generator. With the present-day highly sophisticated integrated circuit technology, the best approach is perhaps to synthesize the sine waves from "stepped" square waves using digital switching circuits. This method can provide an inherently balanced three-phase output with negligible distortion, assuming that an appropriately large number of switching steps are used in the waveform synthesis.

In the simplified representation shown in Figure 9.2, it is assumed that a constant flux can be maintained in the machine by providing a linear ratio between the output voltage and the output frequency. As has been explained, in order to achieve this result in practice, it is necessary to adjust the applied voltage beyond the proportional value, especially at low frequency.

Under steady-state operating conditions, the output signal from the *excess slip amplifier* is zero; hence the only input signal to the three-phase variable-frequency sine wave reference voltage generator is the d-c analogue reference voltage representing the desired output frequency, and the speed of the machine is appropriate to this frequency. A positive frequency reference at the input results in a positive phase sequence at the output of the cycloconverter and hence a positive direction of rotation of the machine. A negative frequency reference, on the other hand, results in a negative phase sequence at the output and hence a negative direction of rotation.

The *slip measuring circuit* provides a d-c analogue signal proportional to the slip frequency. For the positive direction of rotation, a positive voltage signal proportional to the slip frequency is provided when the speed of the machine is less than the synchronous speed, that is, the machine is motoring. Conversely, when the machine acts as an induction generator and delivers power to the cycloconverter, the speed is greater than the synchronous speed, and a negative voltage signal proportional to the negative slip frequency is provided. For the negative direction of rotation, the polarities of the slip signal for the motoring and generating conditions are interchanged.

The *threshold* setting of the excess slip amplifier is less than, or in the limiting case, equal to, the pullout slip frequency of the machine. Since, under normal steady-state conditions, the actual slip frequency is less than the pullout slip frequency, the output voltage of the slip-measuring circuit is therefore less than the threshold setting of the excess slip amplifier, and thus there is no output from this amplifier.

If, however, the slip frequency should attempt to exceed a level corresponding to the threshold setting of the excess slip amplifier—this might be caused, for example, by a sudden change in the demanded stator frequency—this amplifier produces a sharply increasing output signal that opposes the analogue input voltage to the sine wave reference generator. The gain of the excess slip amplifier is sufficiently high that, under this condition, its output signal effectively overrides the frequency reference, and the system now operates with a virtually constant slip frequency, corresponding to the threshold setting of the excess slip amplifier. Thus it can be seen that the actual slip frequency can never exceed the pullout slip frequency, and therefore the machine always operates on the most favorable positive-slope portion of its torque-slip characteristic. It therefore produces the maximum torque of which it is capable, at all speeds, in both directions of rotation, in both the motoring and regenerating modes of operation. Furthermore, since the magnitude of the stator current is directly related to the slip frequency, as shown by the curve of Figure 9.1, it is clear that this automatic slip limit control also constitutes, in effect, an automatic stator current limit. Thus it can be seen that the performance characteristics of this variable speed a-c drive are, for all practical purposes, equivalent to those of a high-performance d-c drive.

The performance of an NCC variable-speed induction motor drive of this type is illustrated by the oscillograms shown in Figures 9.3–9.7. These oscillograms were obtained in a 50 HP cycloconverter drive operated in the speed range of 0–2330 rpm, forward and reverse. The cycloconverter is fed from a three-phase, 220-volt, 60-Hz source; its output frequency is variable between 0 and 40 Hz. The cycloconverter comprises three six-pulse dual-bridge converters (for reference see Figure 1.24), each supplying one isolated stator winding of the motor. The inputs of all three converters are connected to the common three-phase source. The firing pulses for the cycloconverter are generated by cosine wave crossing control, with ripple voltage integral feedback, as illustrated in Figure 7.29*a*.

Figures 9.3–9.5 show oscillograms of the output voltage of one phase of the cycloconverter and the corresponding stator current for output frequencies of 10, 20, and

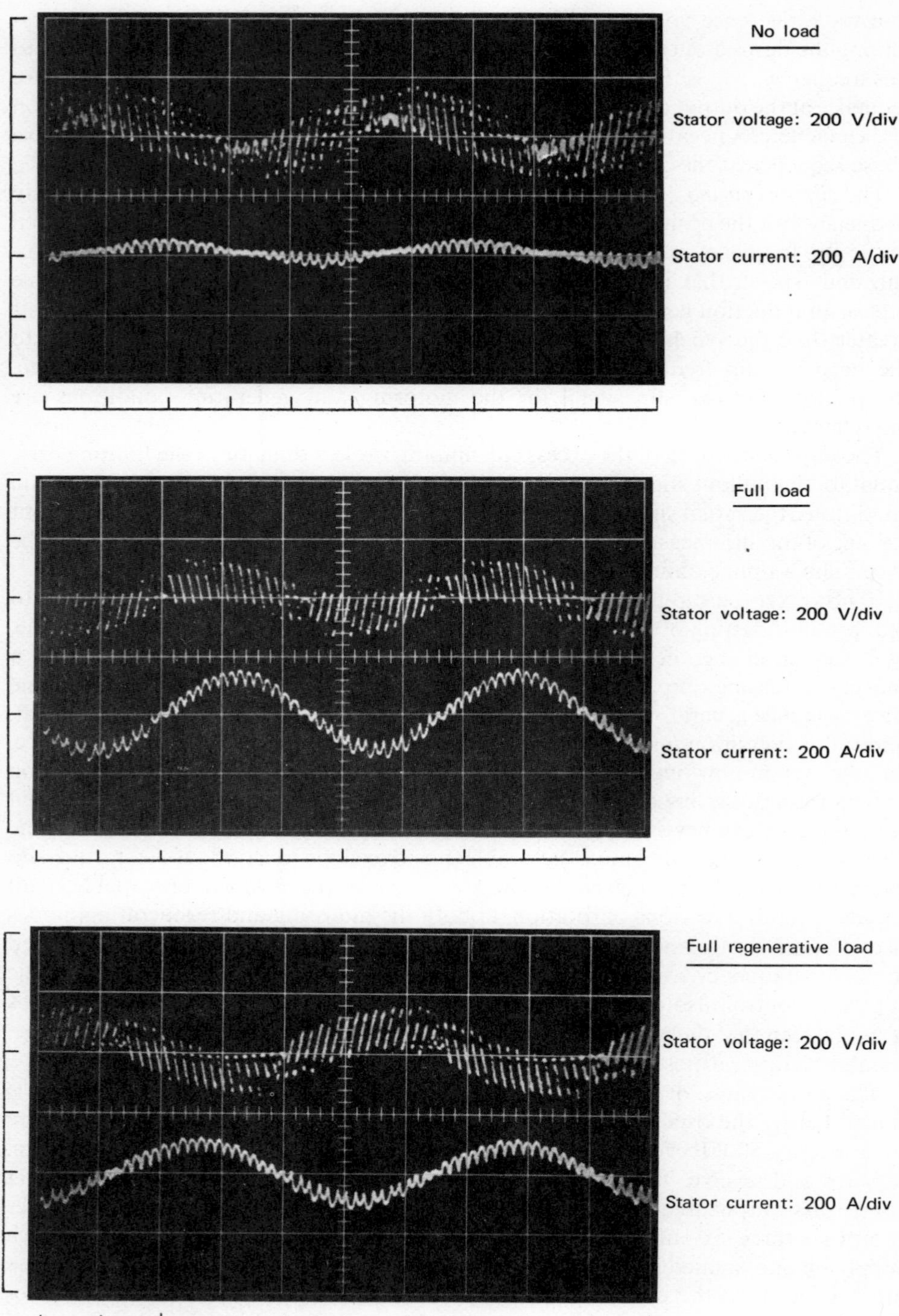

Figure 9.3 Stator voltage and current waveforms obtained in a naturally commutated cycloconverter induction motor drive. Machine rating: 30 HP at 25 Hz. Supply Frequency: 60 Hz. NCC output frequency: 10 Hz approx.

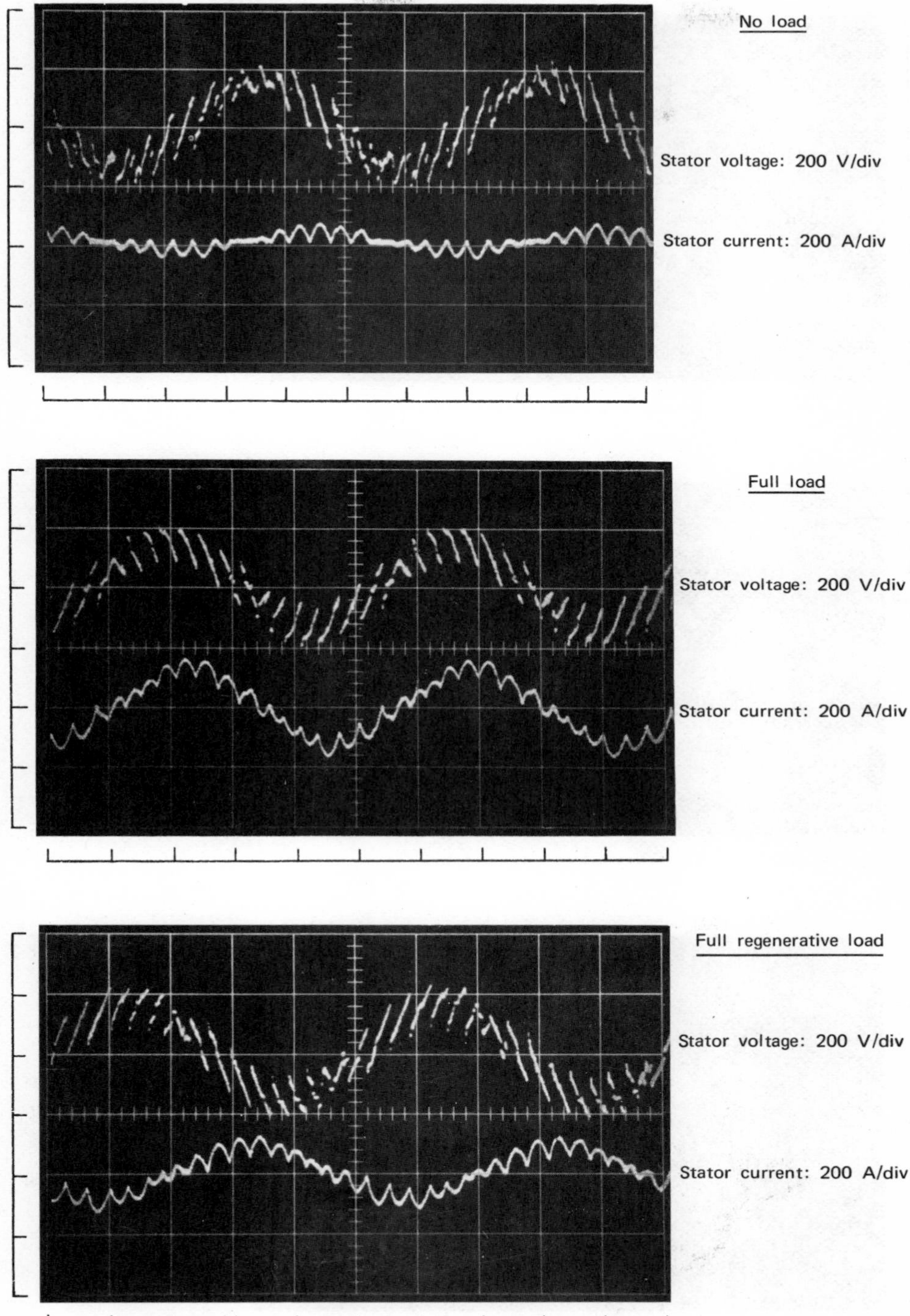

Figure 9.4 Stator voltage and current waveforms obtained in a naturally commutated cycloconverter induction motor drive. Machine rating: 30 HP at 25 Hz. Supply frequency: 60 Hz. NCC output frequency: 20 Hz approx.

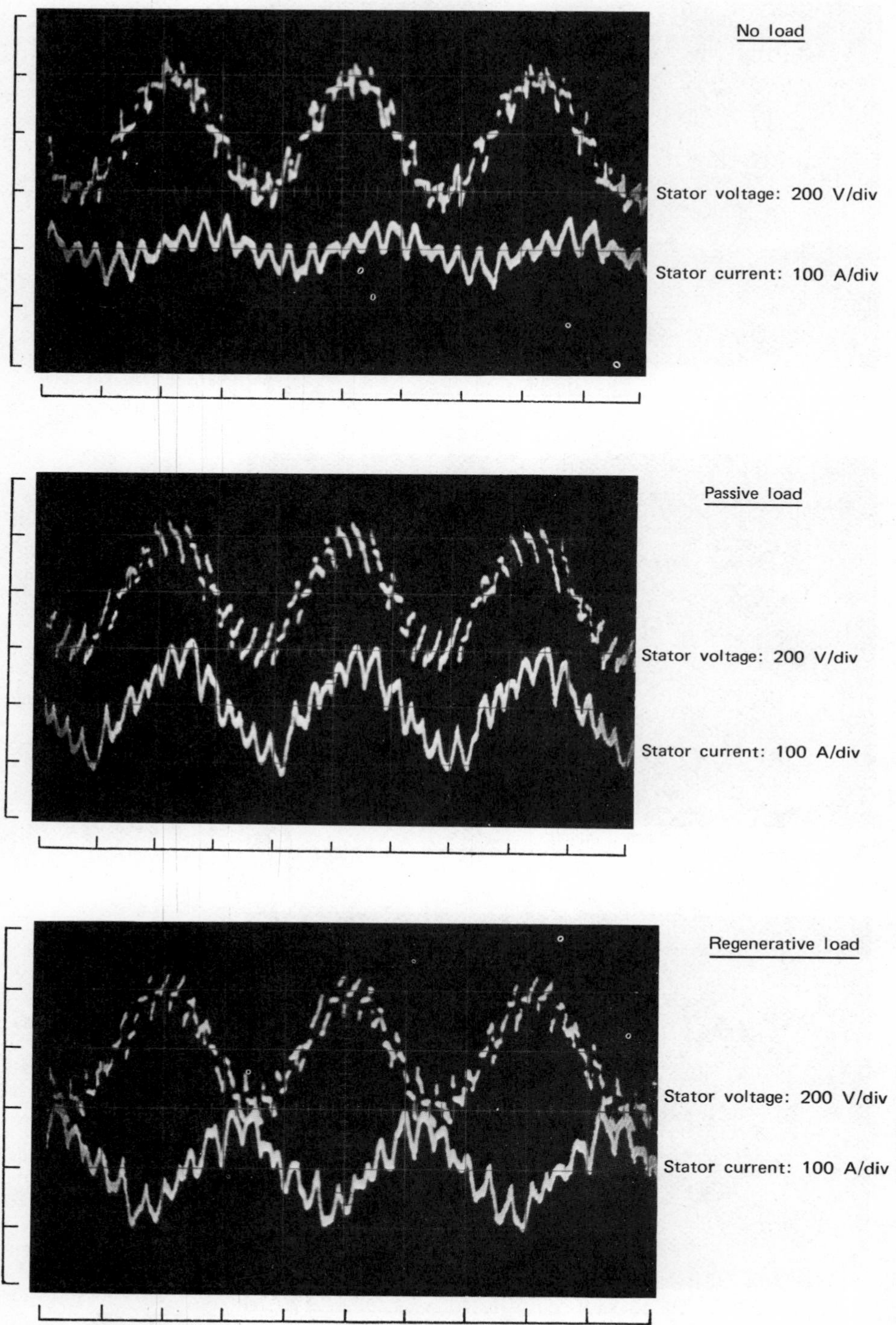

Figure 9.5 Stator voltage and current waveforms obtained in a naturally commutated cycloconverter induction motor drive. Machine rating: 30 HP at 25 Hz. Supply frequency: 60 Hz. NCC output frequency: 40 Hz approx.

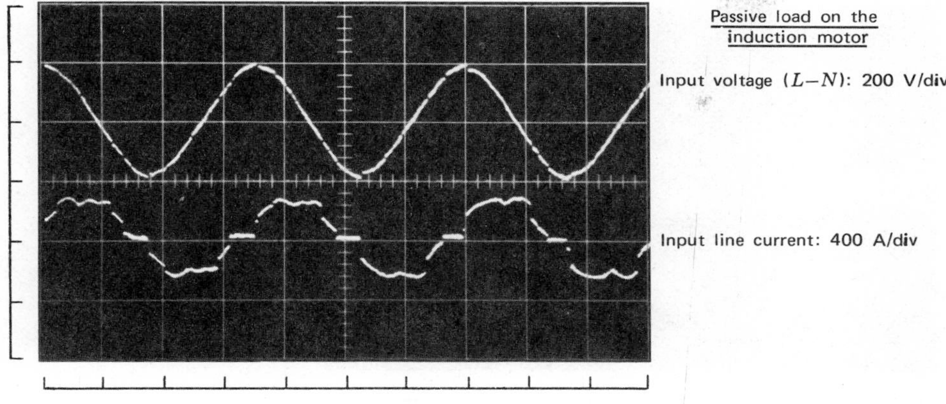

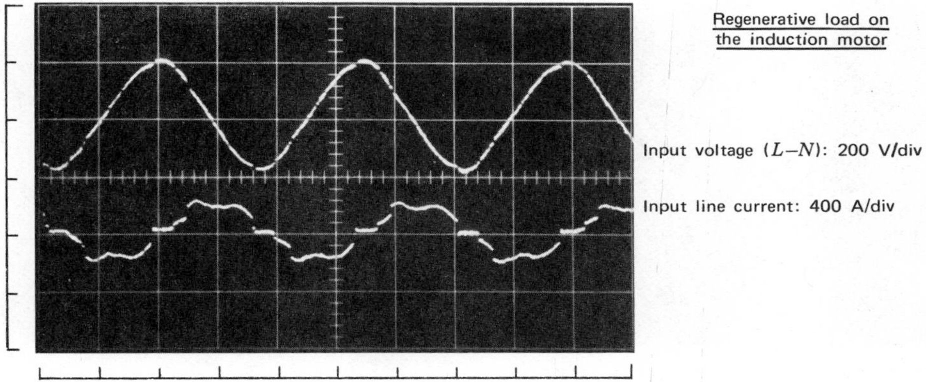

Figure 9.6 Input voltage and current waveforms obtained in a naturally commutated cycloconverter induction motor drive. Machine rating: 30 HP at 25 Hz. Supply frequency: 60 Hz. NCC output frequency: 20 Hz approx.

40 Hz, respectively. In each case, the waveforms are shown for the unloaded condition, as well as for the conditions of full motoring and full braking torque. It is seen that for no-load, the stator current lags the applied voltage by almost 90 degrees. With full motoring torque, the stator current is almost in phase with the voltage, which of course indicates that the cycloconverter is supplying power to the motor. With full braking torque, the stator current is almost 180 degrees out of phase with the voltage, which indicates that the power flow is in the reverse direction through the cycloconverter; in other words, the machine is operating as an induction generator.

Figure 9.6 shows oscillograms of typical voltage and current waveforms at the input of the cycloconverter, for both the forward and reverse directions of power flow.

Figure 9.7 shows oscillograms that illustrate the system performance when a step change is made in the speed reference from 1200 rpm forward to 1200 rpm reverse. The constant deceleration/acceleration characteristic of the machine and the near-constant magnitude of the stator current during the speed reversal illustrate the effectiveness of the automatic slip limitation.

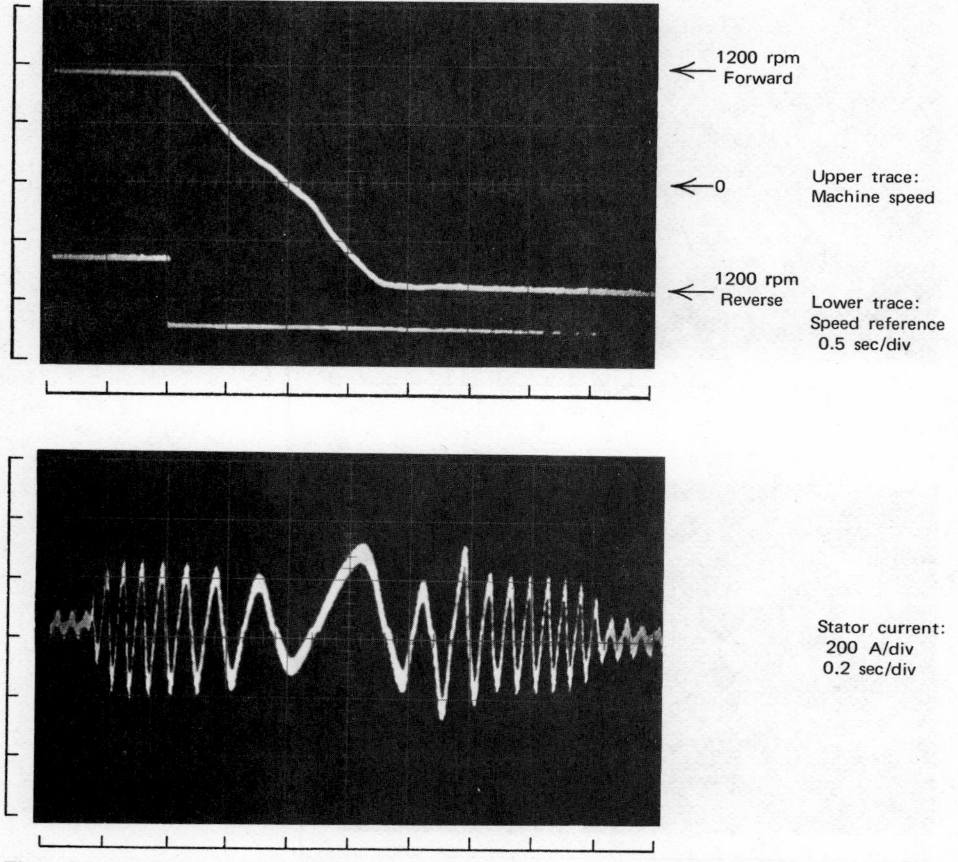

Figure 9.7 Oscillograms illustrating system performance when a step change is made in the speed reference from 1200 rpm forward to 1200 rpm reverse. No load on machine. (Note different time scales for speed and current oscillograms.)

9.1.3 A UFC Variable-Speed Control System for an Induction Motor

The basic components of a variable-frequency speed control system using an unrestricted frequency changer are illustrated in Figure 9.8. This motor control scheme is functionally quite similar to the system employing a naturally commutated cycloconverter (Figure 9.2), although for simplicity only one direction of shaft rotation is considered. Again, the d-c analogue input signal, which controls the frequency and hence speed of the induction machine, is derived as the difference of the d-c frequency reference signal and the excess slip signal. Thus, as in the NCC scheme, a single analogue signal controls the output frequency and voltage; the internal control mechanism by which the output frequency and voltage are actually varied, however, is significantly different. In the NCC control system, the analogue d-c signal is converted into a set of three balanced reference voltage sine waves, the frequencies and amplitudes of which are proportional to the magnitude of the analogue input signal. The naturally commutated cycloconverter merely acts as a linear power amplifier. In the UFC control scheme, on the other hand, the analogue input signal is converted into two mutually displaced pulse trains, P_1 and P_2, whose frequencies are propor-

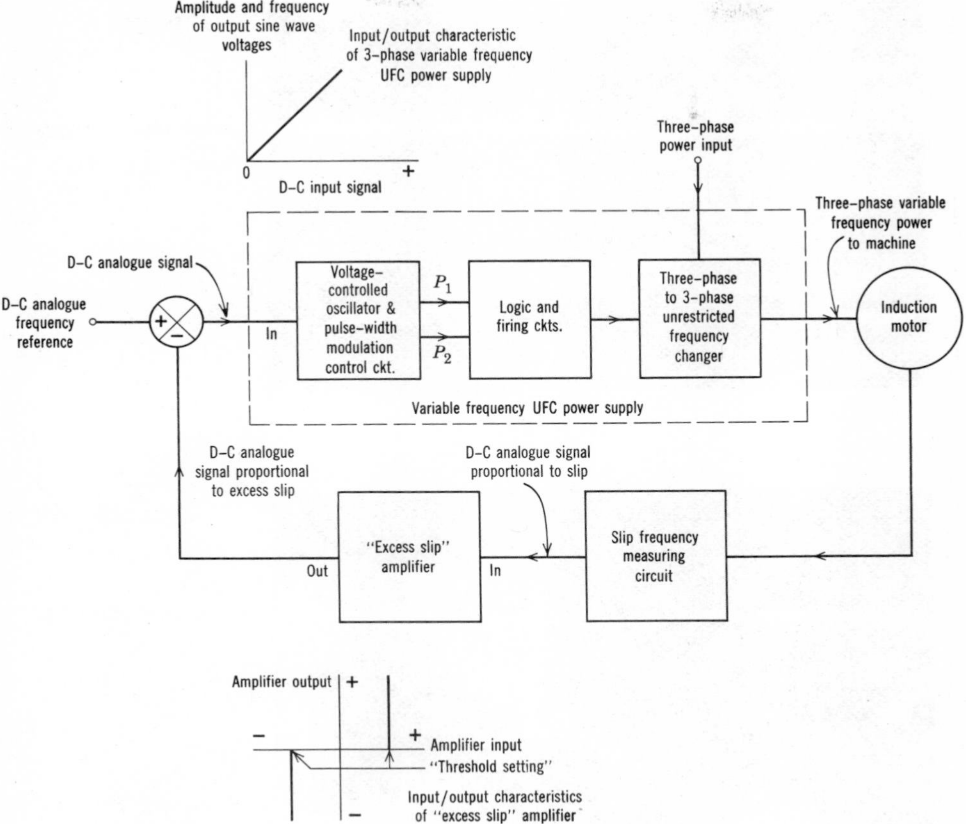

Figure 9.8 Schematic representation of a variable-frequency control system for an induction motor, using an unrestricted frequency changer.

tional to the amplitude of this input signal. These pulses control the output frequency and voltage of the UFC via appropriate logic circuitry, as described in Chapter 7 and illustrated in Figures 7.3 and 7.4.

The performance of a UFC variable-speed induction motor drive is illustrated by the oscillograms shown in Figures 9.9–9.15. In this drive, a 5 kVA, six-pulse UFC, comprising three bridge converters employing gate-controlled switches, with a frequency range of 0–180 Hz, is used. The UFC is directly fed from a three-phase, 220-volt, 60-Hz source; each bridge feeds a separate isolated stator winding. The induction motor used is a three-phase 10 pole, class C (high-slip) machine, delivering 3 HP at the top speed of 2160 rpm, at 210 volts, 180 Hz.

Figures 9.9–9.13 show oscillograms of the output voltage of one phase of the UFC and the corresponding stator current for output frequencies of approximately 10, 30, 60, 120, and 180 Hz, respectively. In each case, the waveforms are shown at no load, full motoring torque (positive slip), and full braking torque (negative slip). Because the reactive magnetizing current is comparable to the real stator current under rated load conditions, and the losses are relatively high-characteristics of small motors—the phase position of the stator current changes only moderately between the motoring and braking modes of operation.

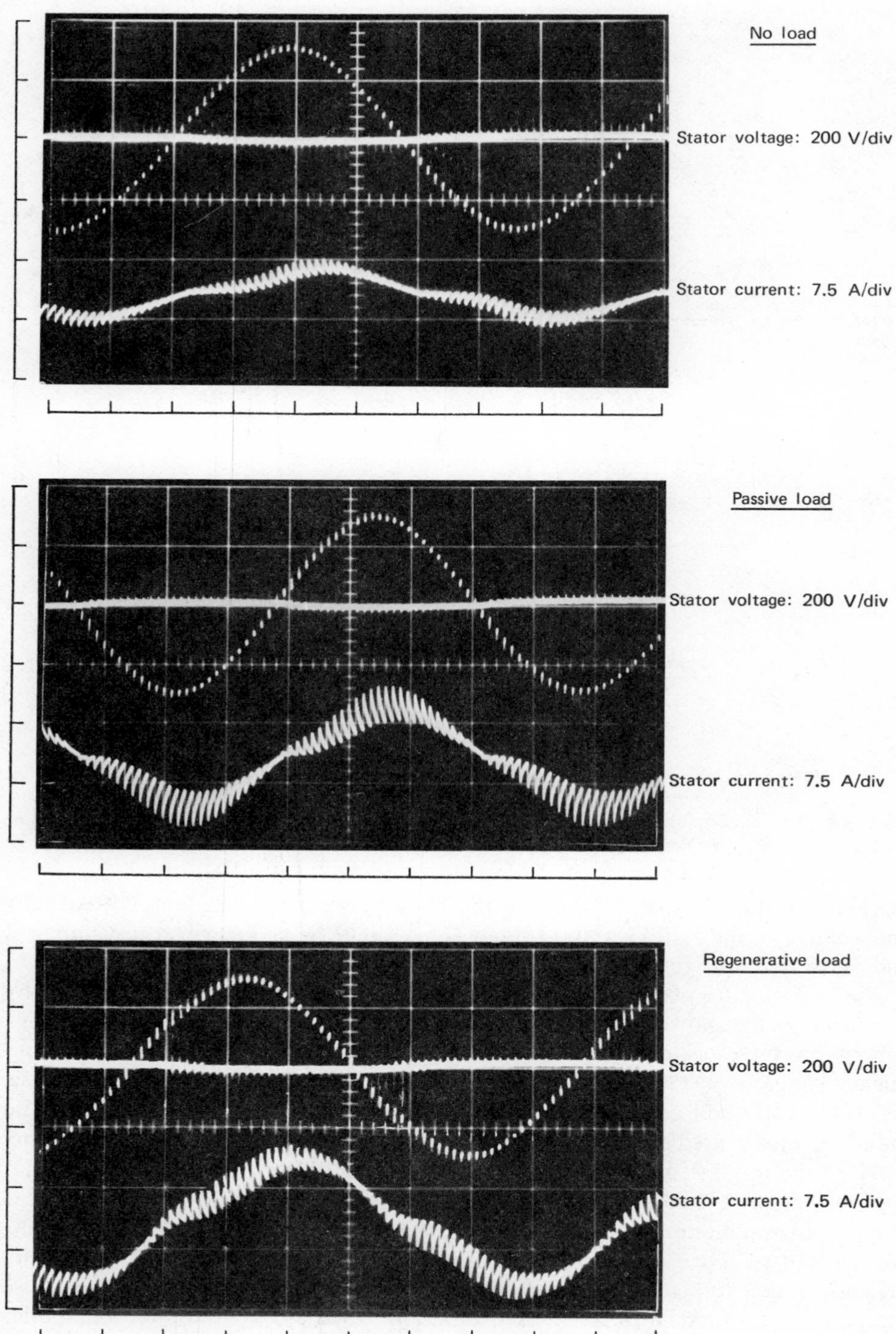

Figure 9.9 Stator voltage and current waveforms obtained in an unrestricted frequency changer (PWM output voltage control) induction motor drive. Machine rating: 3 HP at 180 Hz. Supply frequency: 60 Hz. UFC output frequency: 10 Hz approx.

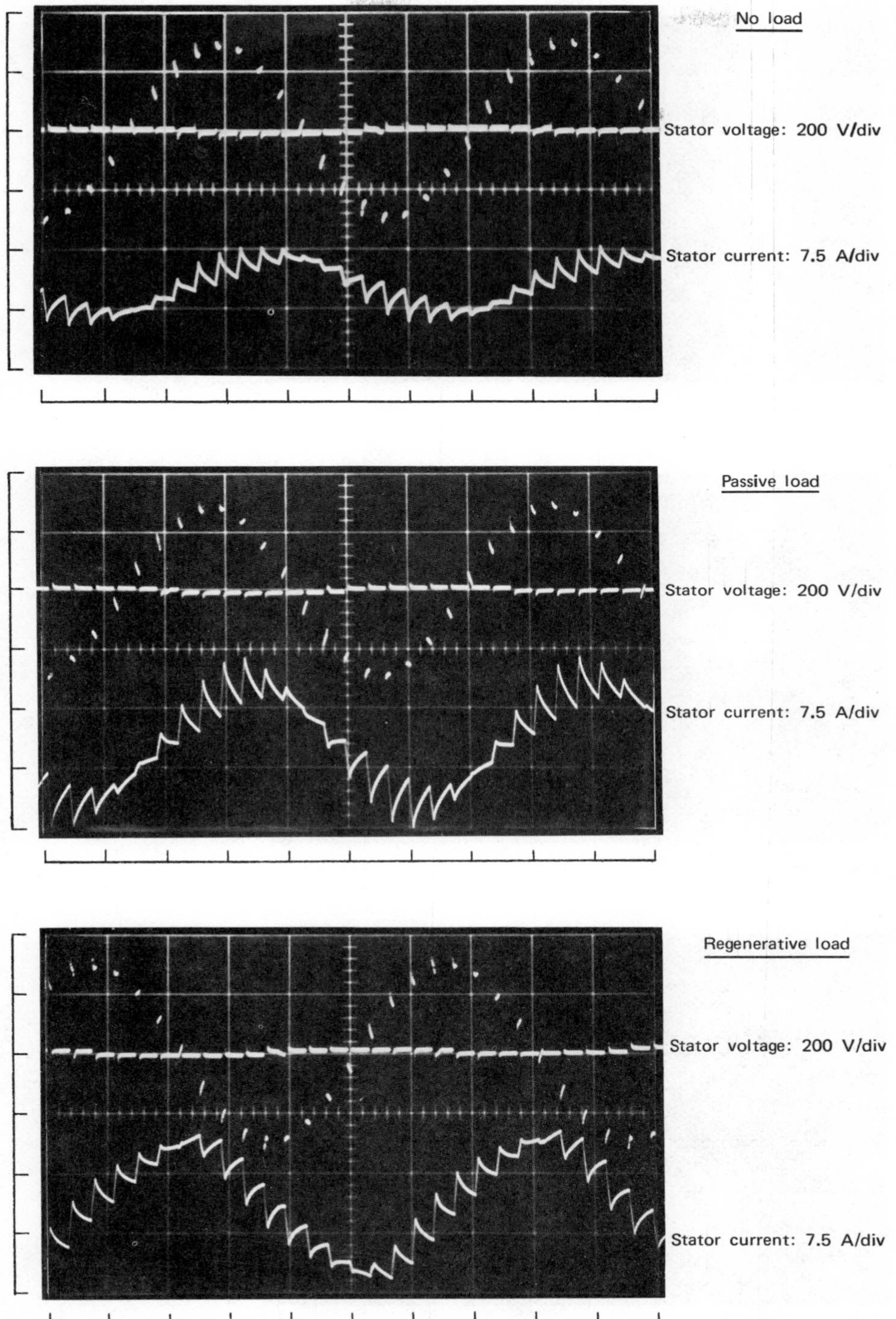

Figure 9.10 Stator voltage and current waveforms obtained in an unrestricted frequency changer (PWM output voltage control) induction motor drive. Machine rating: 3 HP at 180 Hz. Supply frequency: 60 Hz. UFC output frequency: 30 Hz approx.

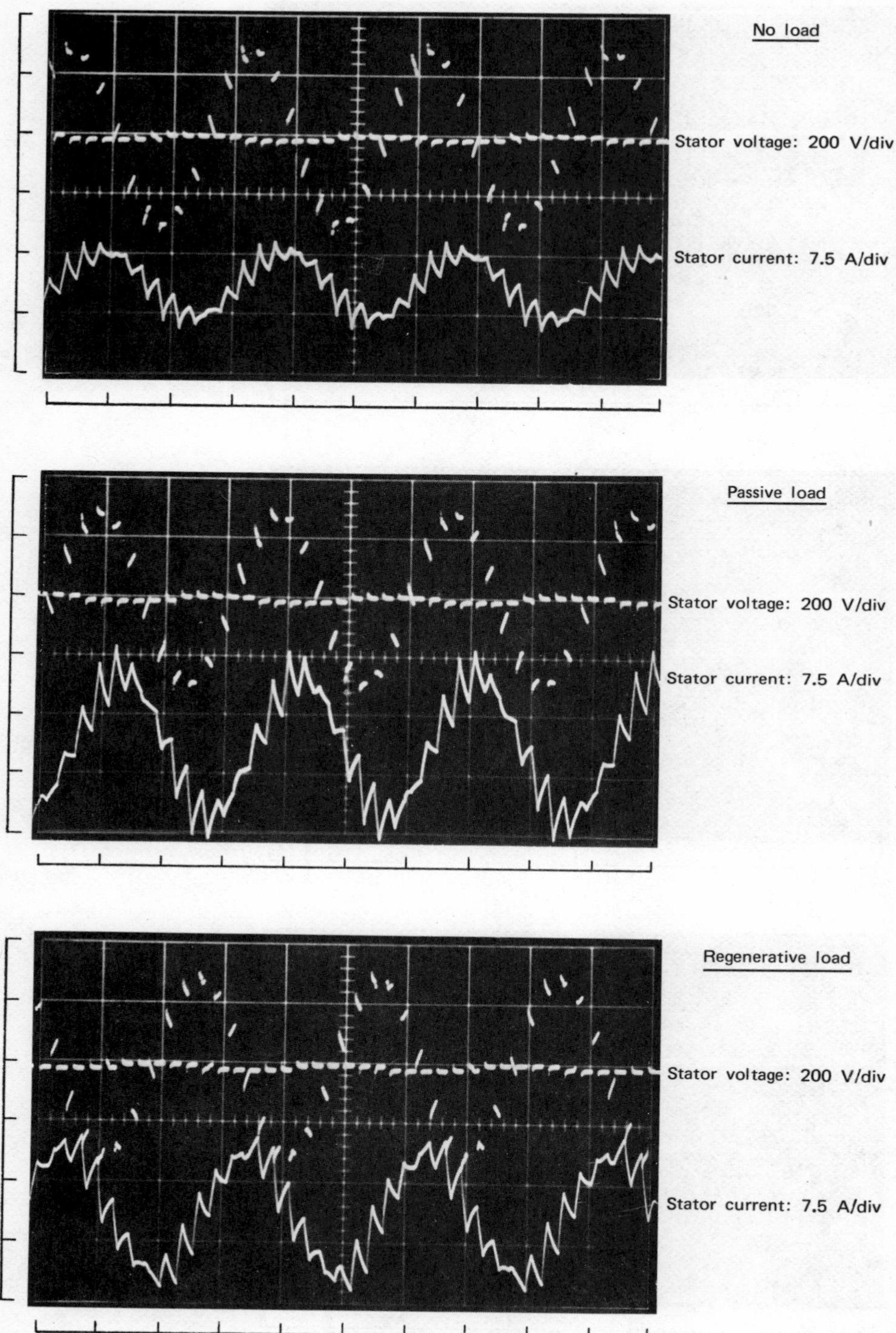

Figure 9.11 Stator voltage and current waveforms obtained in an unrestricted frequency changer (PWM output voltage control) induction motor drive. Machine rating: 3 HP at 180 Hz. Supply frequency: 60 Hz. UFC output frequency: 60 Hz approx.

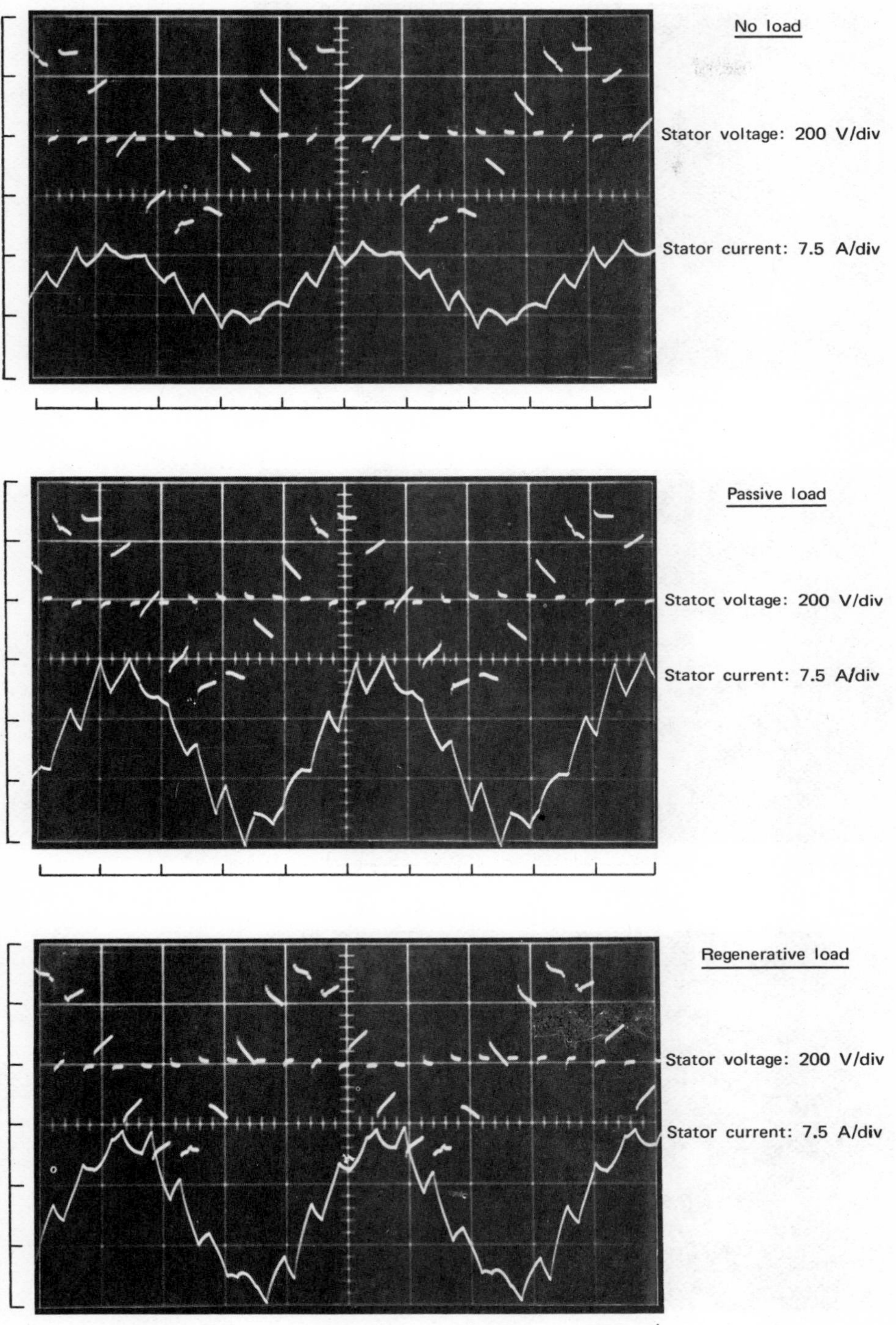

Figure 9.12 Stator voltage and current waveforms obtained in an unrestricted frequency changer (PWM output voltage control) induction motor drive. Machine rating: 3 HP at 180 Hz. Supply frequency: 60 Hz. UFC output frequency: 120 Hz approx.

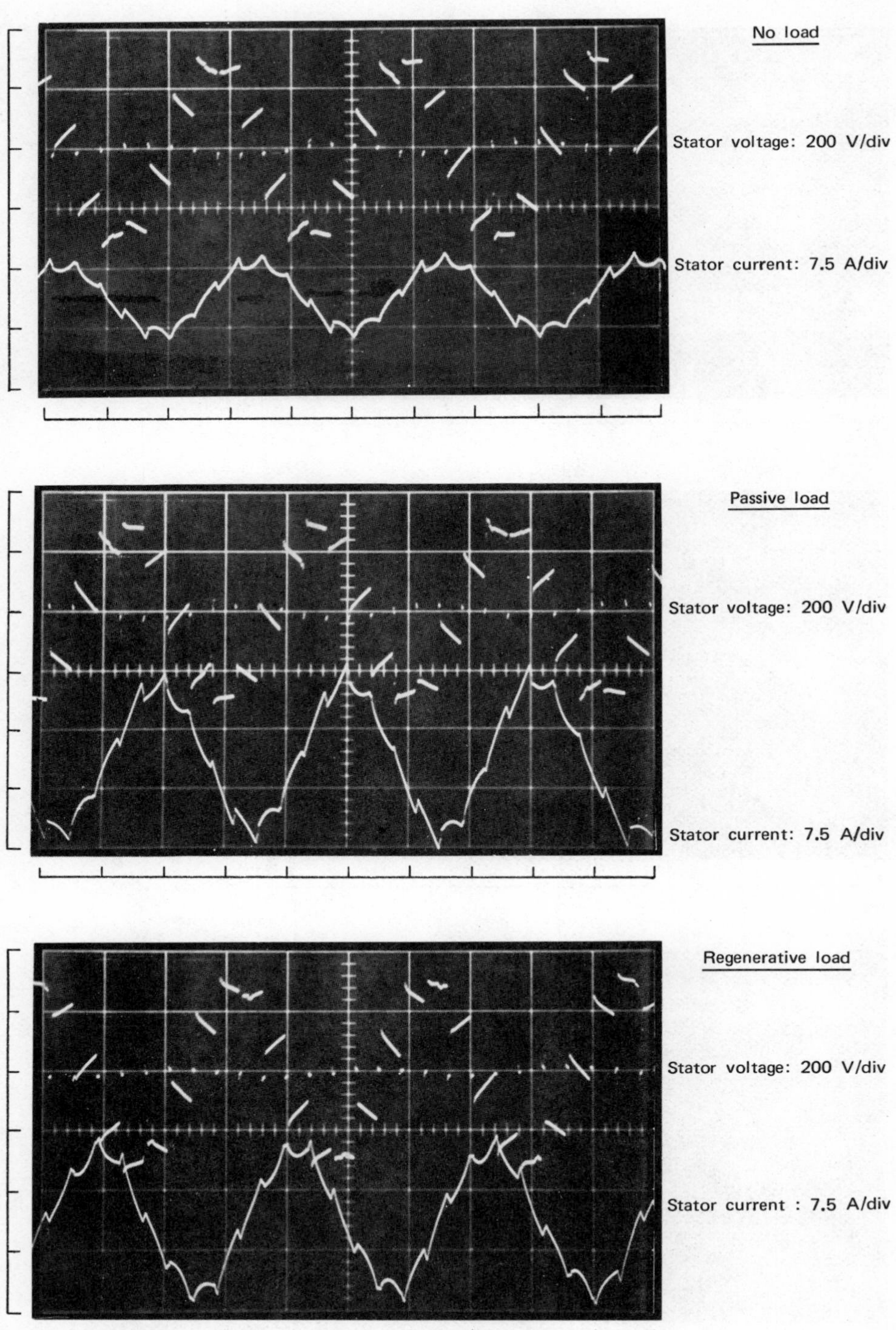

Figure 9.13 Stator voltage and current waveforms obtained in an unrestricted frequency changer (PWM output voltage control) induction motor drive. Machine rating: 3 HP at 180 Hz. Supply frequency: 60 Hz. UFC output frequency: 180 Hz approx.

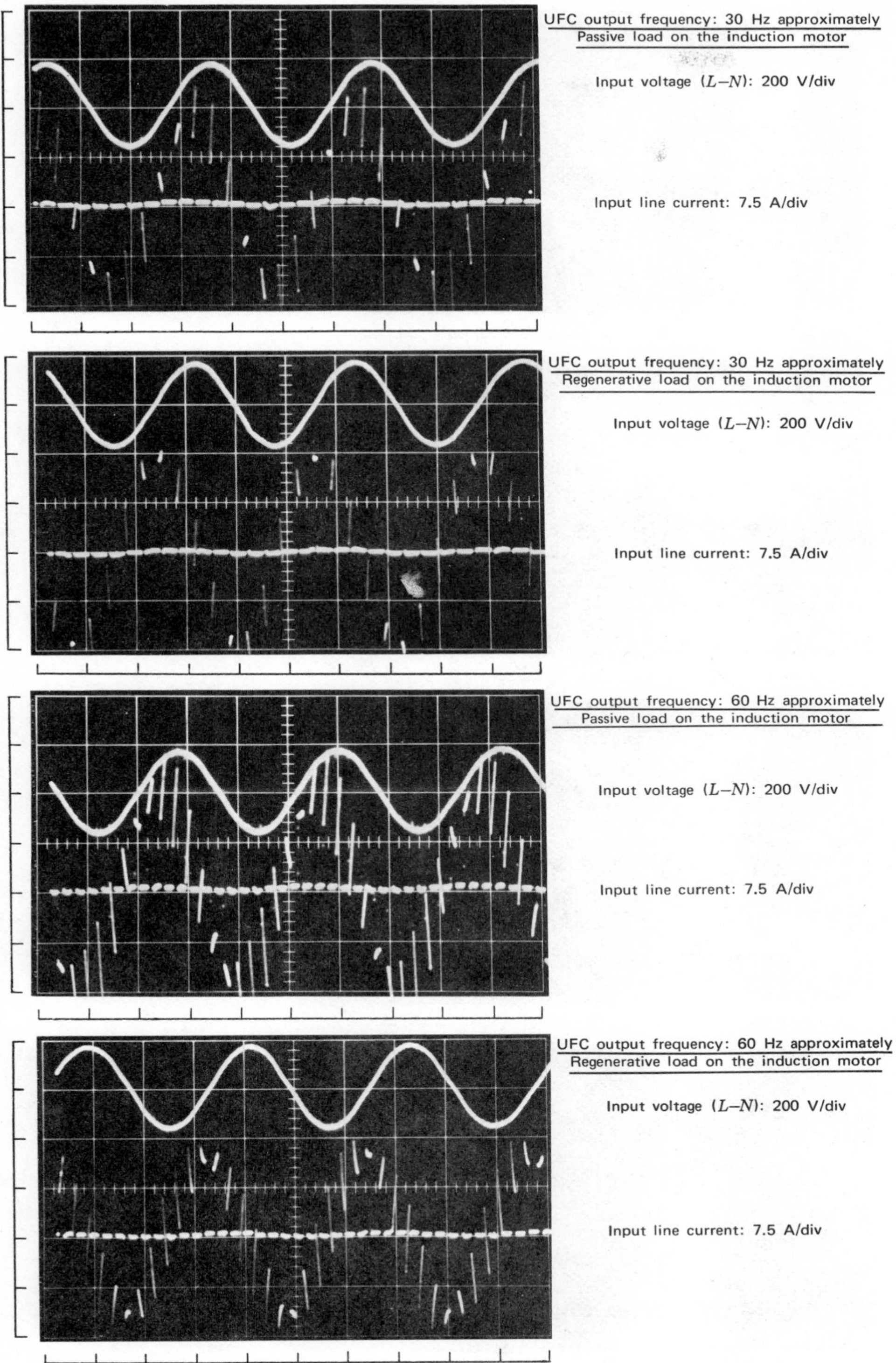

Figure 9.14 Input voltage and current waveforms obtained in an unrestricted frequency changer (PWM output voltage control) induction motor drive. Machine rating: 3 HP at 180 Hz. Supply frequency: 60 Hz.

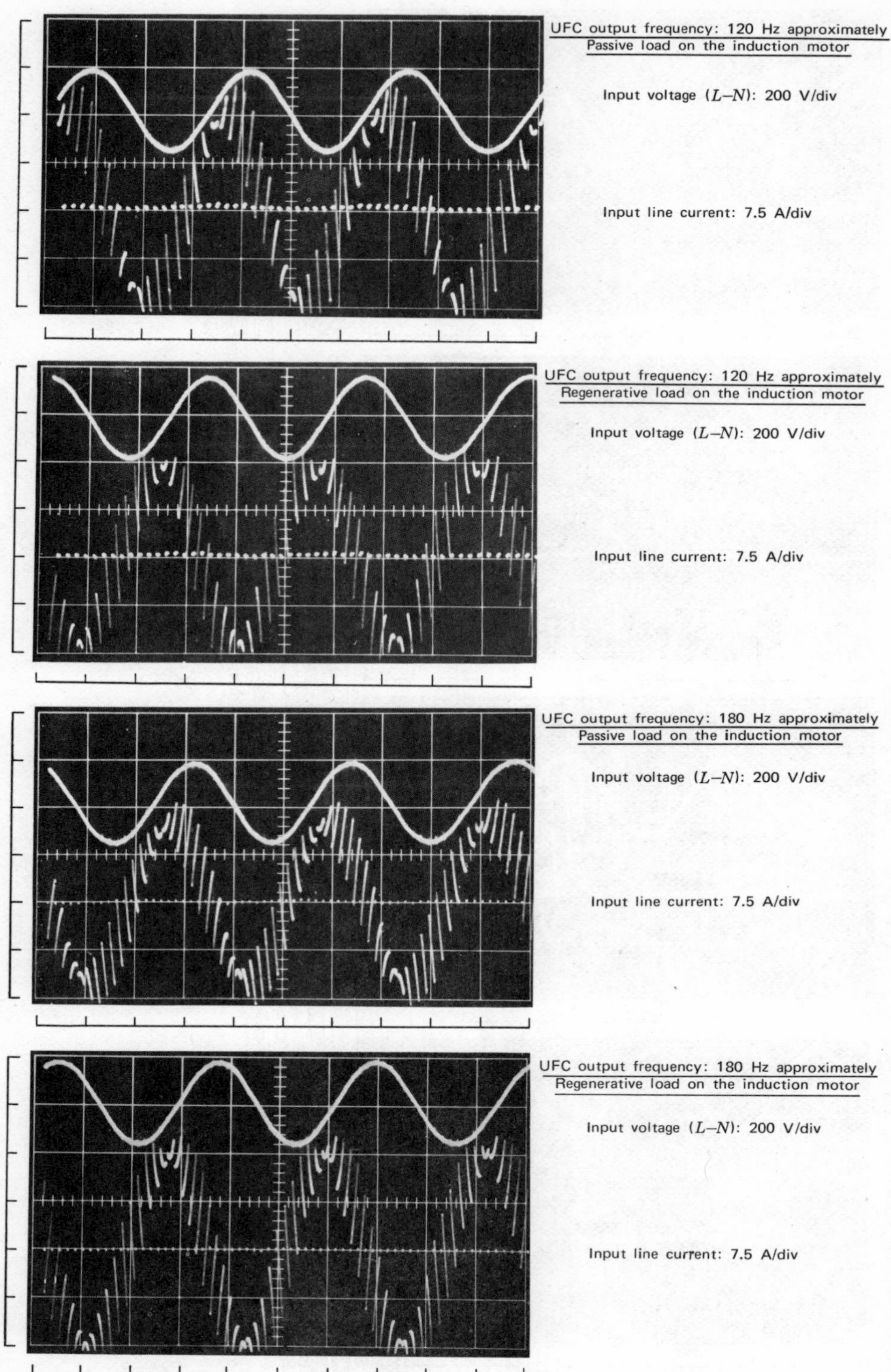

Figure 9.15 Input voltage and current waveforms obtained in an unrestricted frequency changer (PWM output voltage control) induction motor drive. Machine rating: 3 HP at 180 Hz. Supply frequency: 60 Hz.

Figures 9.14 and 9.15 show oscillograms of typical input voltage (L-N) and current waveforms for both forward and reverse power flow (positive and negative slip). Note that the input current *leads* the corresponding input voltage, since the induction machine presents a *lagging* load to the UFC, and the basic property of the UFC is that it transfers the negative of the load phase angle to the input.

9.2 CONSTANT-FREQUENCY POWER SUPPLIES

Several applications require the production of an accurately regulated fixed frequency power output from a variable-frequency power source. In this type of application, the static frequency changer offers an ideal means of frequency conversion.

One application in this category is aircraft power conversion. Here the prime source of electrical power is an alternator that receives its mechanical power input from the engine of the aircraft. Clearly, since the engine speed varies—usually over a 2:1 range—it is not possible for the alternator to produce a constant frequency output if coupled directly to the engine. Hitherto the generally accepted practice has been to insert a hydraulic constant-speed coupling device between the engine and the alternator, thereby enabling the generator to be driven at a constant speed and hence to deliver a constant-frequency output power. Such a system has several disadvantages, not least of which is the frequent and costly maintenance required.

An alternative system approach to aircraft power generation is to couple the alternator directly to the aircraft engine; thus it produces variable-frequency power at its output, as dictated by the engine speed. This variable-frequency power is then converted to accurately regulated constant-frequency output power by means of a static frequency changer in conjunction with a suitable electrical filter. This type of system is generally known as a variable-speed constant frequency (VSCF) power converter.

Another application in this category is power conversion in mobile a-c power supplies. Traditionally, diesel engine-driven alternators having the required 50, 60, or 400 Hz output power have been used. These systems have the disadvantages that a separate generator is needed for each output frequency, they are heavy, and have regulation, maintenance, and reliability problems.

An alternative system utilizes a high-speed turbine that drives a high-frequency, low-weight generator. The high-frequency output power of the generator is converted by a static frequency changer in conjunction with a filter to precisely regulated a-c power, with any of several desired selectable frequencies—typically 50, 60, and 400 Hz. Since the output to input frequency ratio is low, even at the highest output frequency (400 Hz), a relatively small output filter can remove the unwanted components of the frequency changer's output waveform and provide an essentially sinusoidal output.

In the above applications, the use of certain types of frequency changers leads to power-generating systems of rather unique characteristics. The most "conventional" approach, of course, is to use a naturally commutated cycloconverter, and at present this probably provides the most economical solution for relatively high power levels.

In airborne VSCF systems the unrestricted frequency changer may be advantageous for any one or more of the following reasons:

1. The input frequency can be chosen independently of the desired output frequency; thus the generator design can be optimized with regard to mechanical, weight, and reliability considerations without being constrained to a specific frequency range.

2. Since the input phase angle is the negative of the output phase angle, the generator "automatically" receives an extra excitation in the form of a leading current whenever heavy lagging loads are applied to the output terminals—for example, during start-up of motors connected at the output. This helps to maintain the generator voltage, and hence the output voltage, even under transient overload conditions, and allows a reduction in the rating of the generator exciter.
3. A high-quality sinusoidal output can be provided with a small amount of filtering, due to the superior spectrum of the UFC output voltage waveform. This can result in appreciable weight reduction, as well as inherently low output voltage regulation.

The unity displacement factor frequency changer can be advantageous in either airborne or ground power supply applications, by virtue of providing unity displacement factor to the generator, independent of the load power factor. This characteristic allows the generator to be rated essentially only for the required real output power. This system also exhibits a superior voltage regulation under transient (lagging or leading) overload conditions, since the reactive load current does not flow through the generator and therefore does not require a corresponding increased machine field excitation.

The controllable displacement factor frequency changer can be used to best advantage in a mobile ground power generating system. As mentioned, in this application the mechanical power is provided by a high-speed turbine that may be operated at speeds in excess of 50,000 rpm. This requires a generator with a mechanical construction that allows reliable operation at such a high speed. Suitable machines are solid rotor inductor generators, squirrel-cage induction generators, and permanent magnet generators. The induction machine, however, cannot be internally excited; the "internal" excitation of the permanent magnet generator is constant, and thus its external voltage is a function of the amplitude and phase of the applied load current.

Either of these types of machine can be combined with a controllable displacement factor frequency changer to provide a unique power-generating system. The CDFFC is used both for converting the variable high-frequency input power to fixed frequency output power *and* for providing controllable excitation for the generator by maintaining the proper amount of leading reactive current in the stator windings. In such a system, the output voltage and the input phase angle of the frequency changer are independently controlled.

In the following sections, airborne VSCF power converters employing an NCC, a UDFFC, and a UFC, and mobile ground power VSCF systems using an NCC and a CDFFC are described.

9.2.1 Airborne VSCF Power-Generating System Using an NCC

A block diagram illustrating the basic elements of a VSCF power-generating system using a naturally commutated cycloconverter is shown in Figure 9.16. The generator, which typically would be operated over a speed range of 10,000–20,000 rpm, provides variable-frequency input power to the cycloconverter, typically over a 1200–2400 Hz frequency range. The NCC converts this variable-frequency power to precisely regulated fixed-frequency output power, typically at 400 Hz. A simple *LC* filter is usually used to remove the unwanted components and provide an essentially sinusoidal output voltage. The cycloconverter, in conjunction with its *pulse timing and firing circuits*, can again be considered as a high-power three-phase amplifier, the

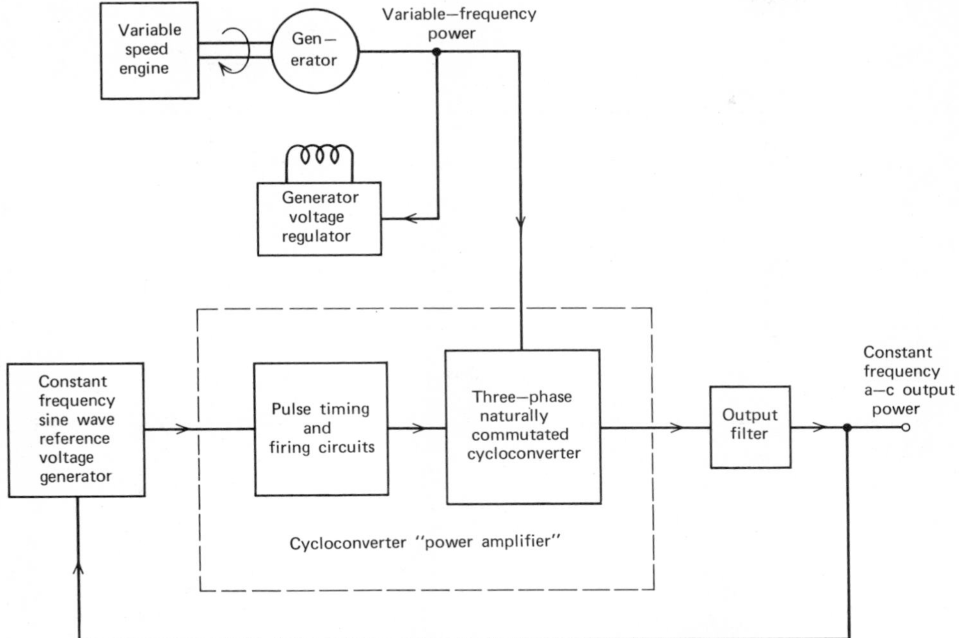

Figure 9.16 Schematic representation of a variable-speed constant-frequency (VSCF) power-generating system using a naturally commutated cycloconverter.

output voltages of which are proportional to the reference input voltages provided by the three-phase *sine wave reference generator.*

The three constant-frequency (400 Hz) sinusoidal reference waves are usually generated first as multiple-step square waves, using digital circuits that are controlled from a very accurate and stable master clock oscillator. The multiple-step square waves are then filtered to obtained the final reference signals.

The amplitude of the output voltage of each phase is independently regulated by comparing it with a reference signal representing the desired output voltage and using the error signal to control the amplitude of the corresponding sinusoidal reference wave. The relative phase positions of the sinusoidal reference waves may also be controlled by feedback from the output, to balance the output voltages under unbalanced load conditions. Under short-circuit conditions at the output, the cycloconverter is typically controlled to maintain approximately 3 PU output current. This is accomplished by appropriately controlling the amplitudes of the reference sine waves from a current-limiting circuit.

The performance of a practical 60 kVA VSCF power-generating system, using an NCC, is illustrated by the oscillograms shown in Figure 9.18*a–d.*

The cycloconverter in this particular system is comprised of three six-pulse thyristor circuits, each composed of four three-pulse groups with two interphase reactors, as shown in Figure 9.17. The input power is provided by a six-phase generator. The integral control scheme described in Chapter 7 and illustrated in Figure 7.29*b* is employed to control the timing of the cycloconverter firing pulses.

Figure 9.18 *a* and *b* show oscillograms of the "raw" (i.e., unfiltered) and filtered output voltage waveforms of one phase of the cycloconverter, with no load, and with 60 kW load at unity power factor, respectively.

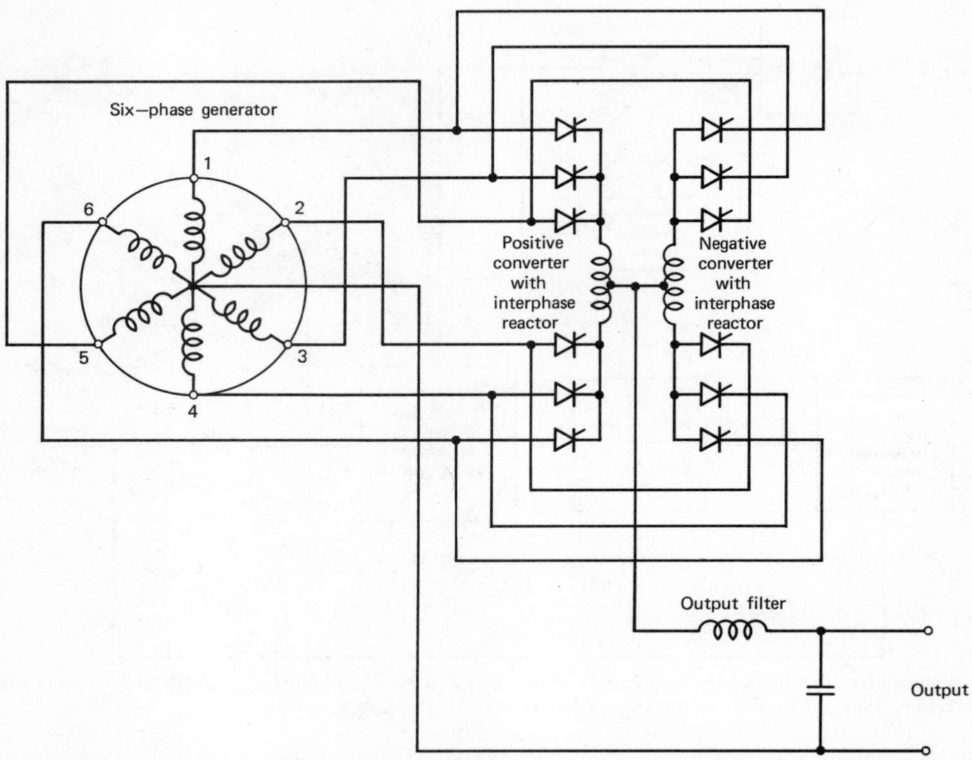

Figure 9.17 VSCF naturally commutated cycloconverter power circuit (shown for single output phase).

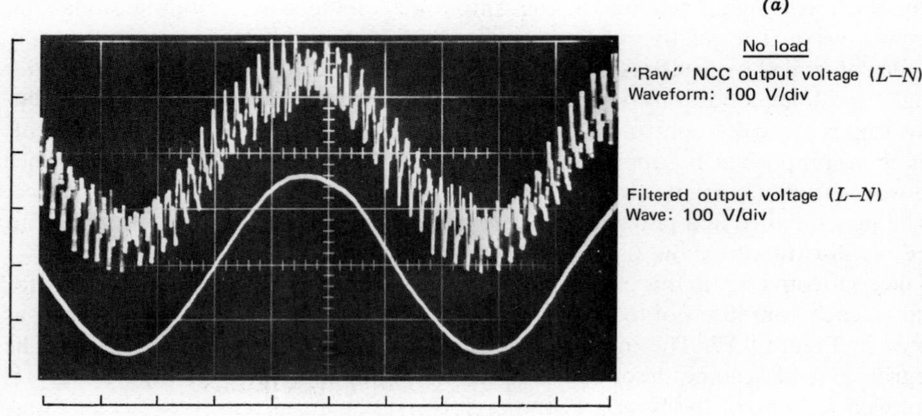

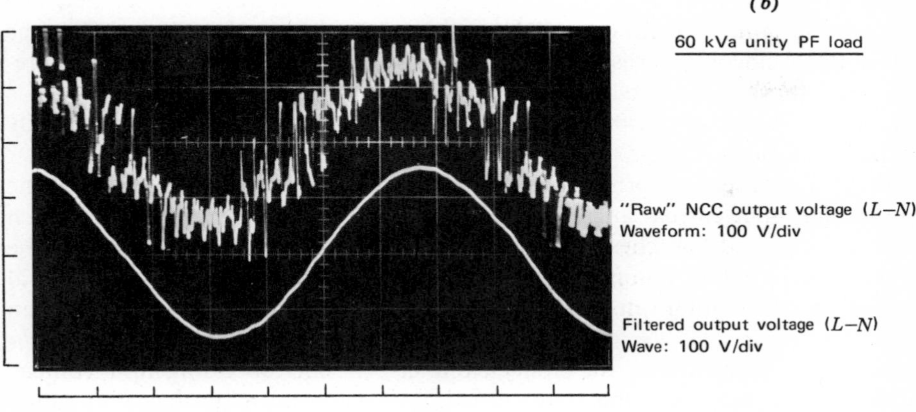

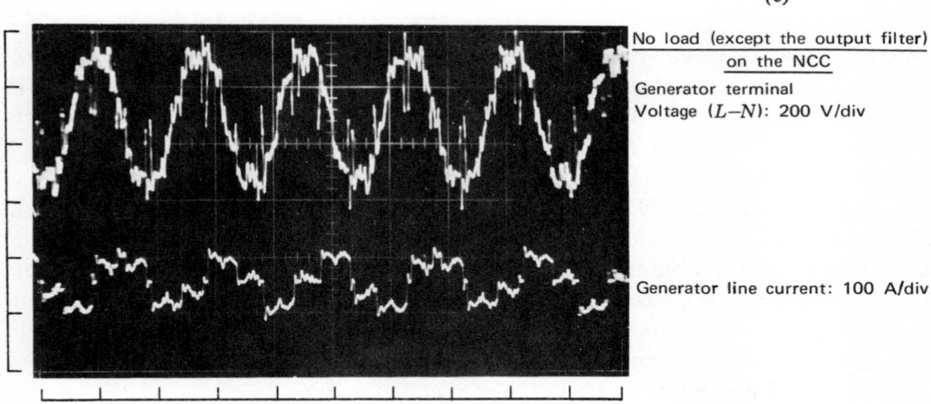

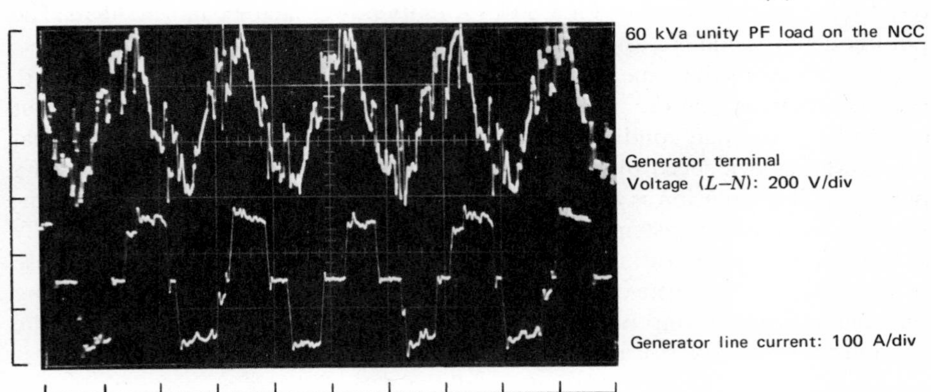

Figure 9.18 Output voltage, input voltage, and input line current waveforms obtained in a VSCF power-generating system, using a naturally commutated cycloconverter. Input (generator) frequency: 1800 Hz approx. Output frequency: 400 Hz.

Figure 9.18*c* and *d* show one phase of the generator terminal voltage and line current for the same load conditions. Note that under the "no load" condition, the output of the cycloconverter is actually loaded by the *LC* output filter, which represents a nearly pure capacitive load.

The output frequency is 400 Hz, and the generator frequency is approximately 1800 Hz, for all cases shown.

Although the generator terminal voltage is considerably distorted because of the nonsinusoidal input current and the natural commutations of the thyristors, which produce pronounced "notches" on the input voltage wave, precise timing of the firing pulses required for minimum output distortion is still provided by the integral control scheme. The total r.m.s. distortion of the filtered voltage waves is less than 2.5%.

It may also be observed that the input current lags the corresponding input voltage, regardless of the output load; this characteristic is typical of the naturally commutated cycloconverter.

9.2.2 Airborne VSCF Power-Generating System Using a UDFFC

Since the unity displacement factor frequency changer is controlled from a low-power sinusoidal reference wave generator, similarly to the naturally commutated cycloconverter, the overall functional scheme for these two frequency changers in a VSCF power-generating system is the same. Thus, the *NCC power amplifier*, in Figure 9.16 can be substituted with a *UDFFC power amplifier* to give the representative functional block diagram. A block diagram giving details of the timing and firing control circuits applicable to the UDFFC in a VSCF application is shown in Figure 7.25.

The actual waveforms illustrating the performance of a six-pulse UDFFC in a 60 kVA VSCF system, obtained by computer simulation, are shown in Figure 9.19*a* and *b*. Here again a six-phase generator is used, and the output waveforms of four basic three-pulse converters are combined with interphase reactors. The output voltage is filtered by a low-pass *LC* filter.

Figure 9.19*a* shows the three filtered output (*L-N*) voltage waves (v_{O1F}, v_{O2F}, v_{O3F}), together with the "raw" output voltage waveform of phase 1 (v_{O1}); also shown are the three output currents (i_{O1}, i_{O2}, i_{O3})—that is, the load currents and the filter currents combined—and one generator terminal voltage (v_{I1T}) together with the corresponding line current (i_{I1}), for a 60 kVA unity power factor balanced load. The output frequency is 400 Hz, and the generator frequency is 1200 Hz.

Figure 9.19*b* shows the same quantities for a 60 kVA, 0.7 lagging power factor load.

It can be observed that the input current is in phase with the corresponding input voltage under both load conditions; thus the generator has to supply only the real output power, as evidenced by the smaller input current obtained with the lagging output load. This situation is a considerable improvement over the naturally commutated cycloconverter system, in which the generator has to supply substantially more input VA than the rating of the load—typically $VA_{\text{IN}}/VA_{\text{OUT}} = 1.6$—because of the lagging input displacement factor of the NCC. In the UDFFC power-generating system, the required rating of the generator is only marginally greater than the required output rating—typically $VA_{\text{IN}}/VA_{\text{OUT}} = 1.1$.

9.2.3 Airborne VSCF Power-Generating System Using a UFC

A functional block diagram of a VSCF system using an unrestricted frequency changer is shown in Figure 9.20. Here again the generator provides a variable-frequency

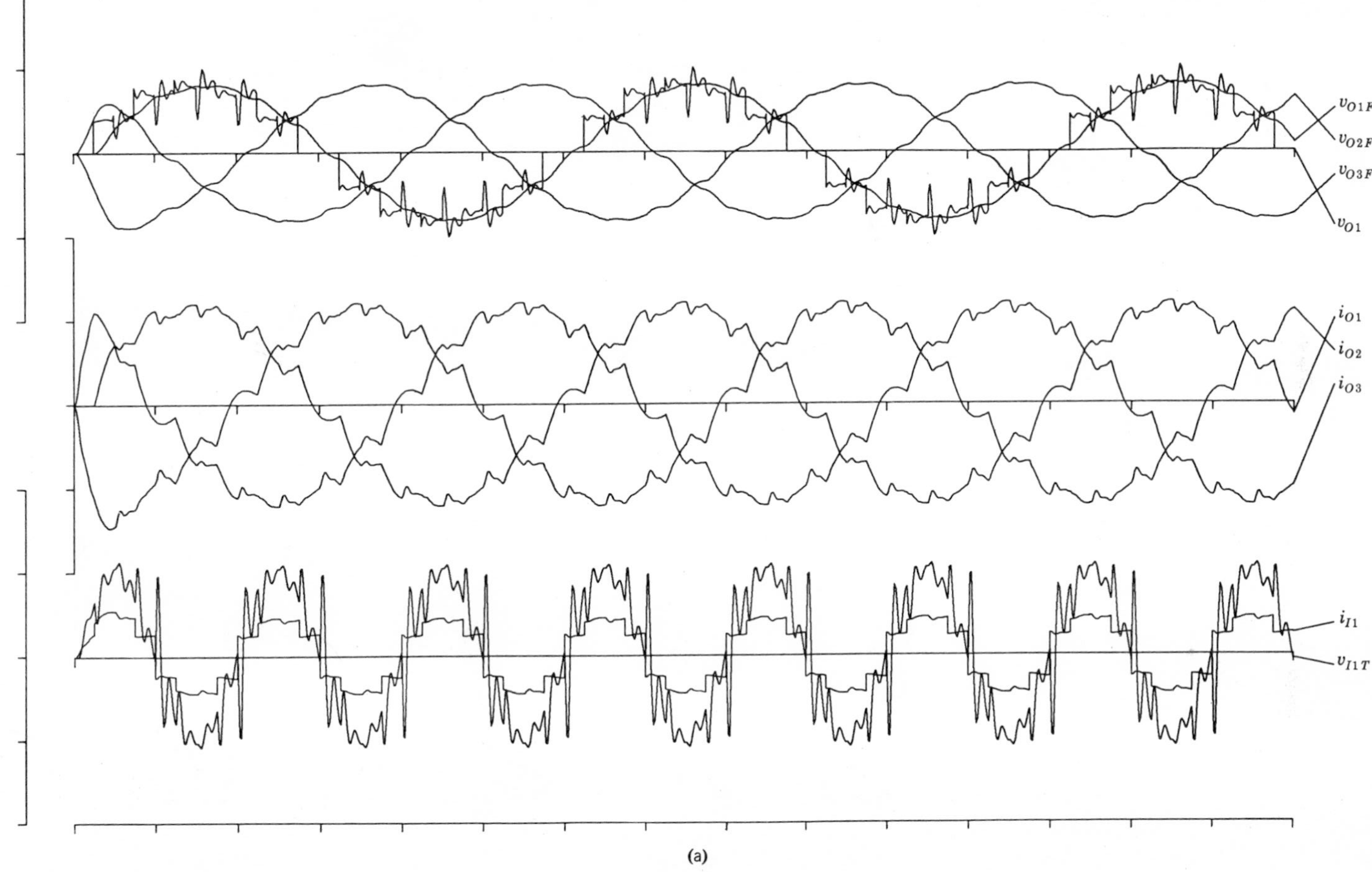

(a)

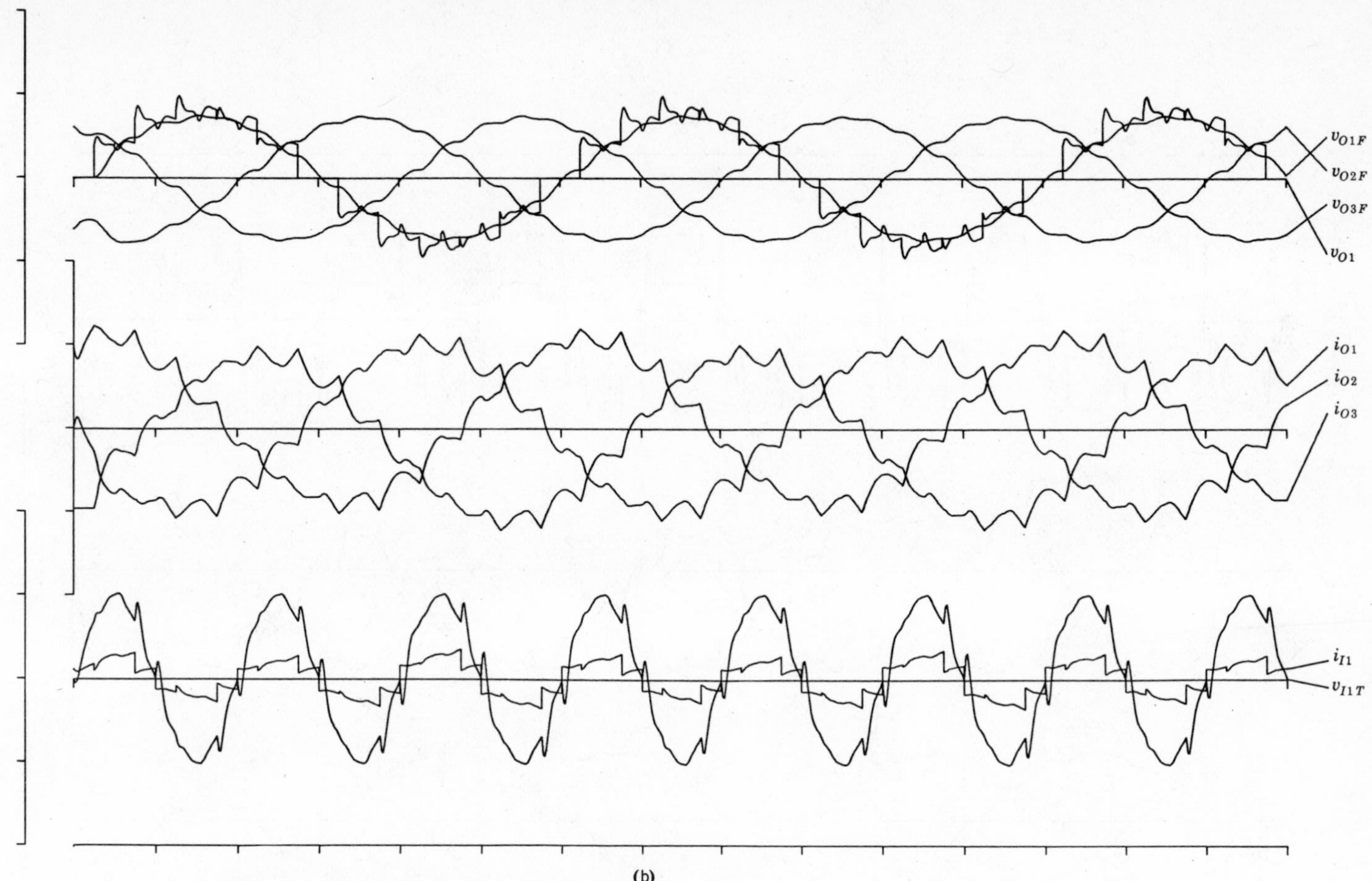

Figure 9.19 Output voltage, generator terminal voltage (*L-N*) and input line current waveforms obtained in a simulated VSCF power-generating system, using a unity displacement factor frequency changer. Input (generator) frequency: 1200 Hz. Output frequency: 400 Hz. Quantities are shown in per units. [(a) 60 kVA unity PF load (b) 60 kVA 0.7 PF load.]

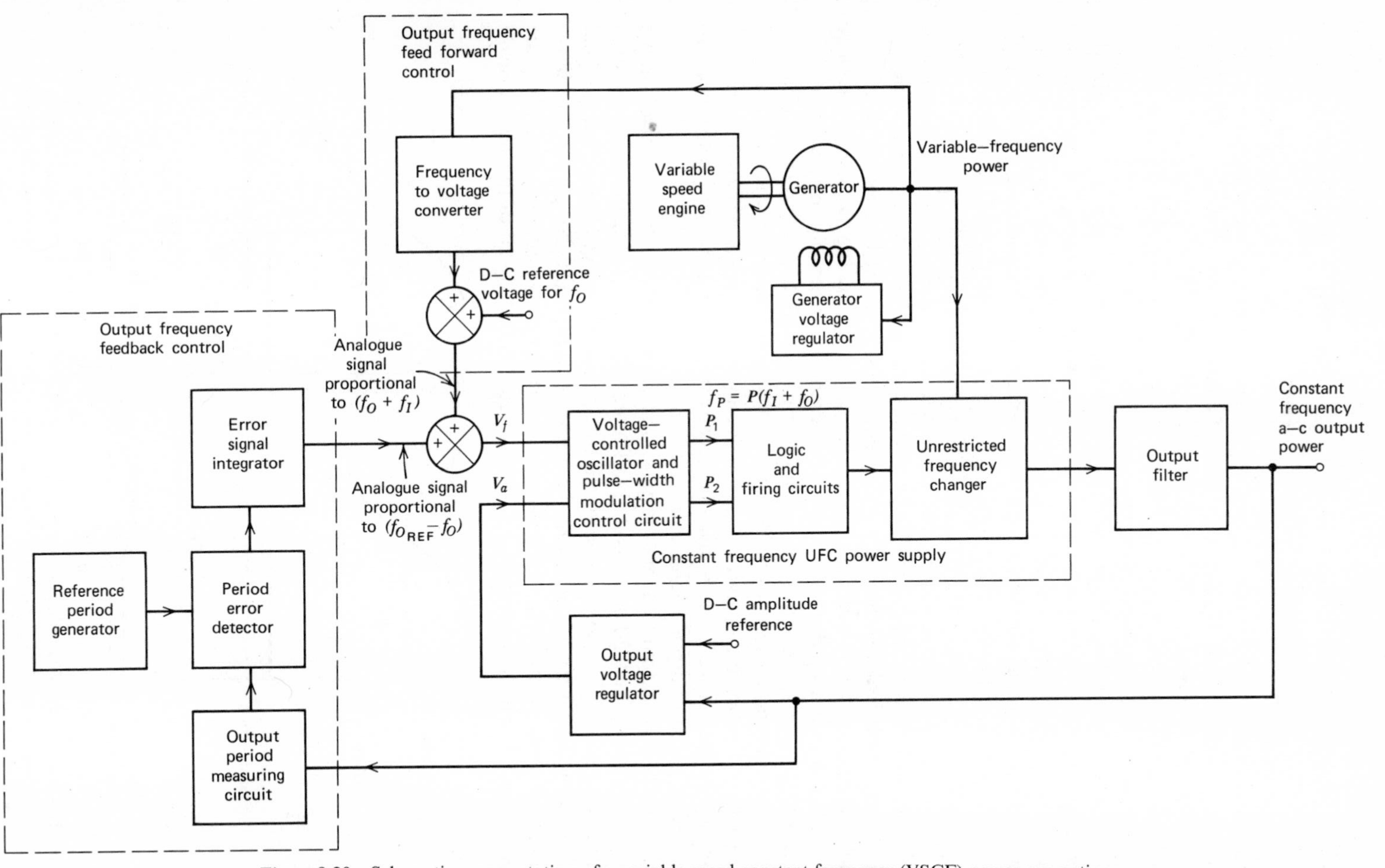

Figure 9.20 Schematic representation of a variable-speed constant-frequency (VSCF) power-generating system using an unrestricted frequency changer.

power that the UFC converts to a fixed-frequency output power. In this system, however, there is no restriction on the generator frequency; it may be lower, higher, or equal to the wanted output frequency.

As described, the output frequency and voltage of the UFC are varied by two mutually displaced pulse trains, P_1 and P_2, which in turn may be controlled by two analogue signals, V_f and V_A, using the type of control scheme outlined in Chapter 7 and illustrated in Figure 7.3. In a VSCF system, therefore, the control must provide analogue signals V_f and V_A, such that the output frequency and voltage remain constant under varying input frequency and load conditions.

It has been established [equation (3.44)] that the output frequency f_O is the difference between the repetition rate at which the switches of the UFC are operated and the input frequency, namely, $f_O = f_S - f_I$. Therefore the correct switching frequency for a wanted output frequency at a given input frequency is $f_S = f_I + f_O$. The frequency f_P of pulse train P_1 (and hence also of pulse train P_2) thus has to be proportional to f_S; that is, $f_P = Pf_S = P(f_I + f_O)$, in which P is the pulse number. To obtain a constant output frequency, theoretically it is enough to vary analogue signal V_f, and thereby frequency f_P, in proportion to the generator frequency f_I. This is accomplished by the *output frequency feed forward control*, in which the generator frequency is converted to an analogue voltage by the *frequency to voltage converter* and summed with a constant d-c reference representing the wanted output frequency. If the frequency to voltage conversion ($f_I + f_O$ to V_f) and then voltage to frequency conversion (V_f to f_P) could be done with negligible error, this simple control scheme would provide constant output frequency at any generator frequency. In a practical system, however, it is usually necessary to use a corrective feedback to accomplish precise output frequency regulation.

The principle of output frequency regulation by corrective feedback control shown functionally in Figure 9.20 is illustrated in Figure 9.21. The half-period of the filtered output voltage is measured and compared to a period reference (square wave) signal generated by digital techniques from the output of a highly stable crystal oscillator. The period error in the form of a pulse is converted into an analogue signal by the *error integrator*, which is summed to the analogue output signal of the *feed forward*

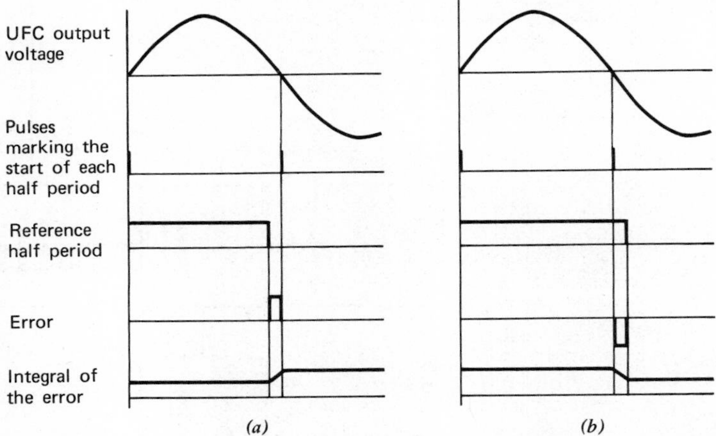

Figure 9.21 Waveforms illustrating the operating principles of the output frequency control in the functional scheme of Figure 9.20, [(a) output frequency lower than reference (b) output frequency higher than reference].

control, providing the analogue frequency control signal, V_f. With this technique, highly accurate and stable output frequency can be maintained, even during dynamic acceleration or deceleration of the generator.

The amplitude of the output voltage of each phase is regulated independently by comparing a rectified sample of the output voltage to the amplitude reference and using the amplified error signal V_a to control the position of the P_2 pulse relative to the P_1 pulse, and hence the depth of the pulse-width modulation in the output voltage waveform. Thus the P_2 pulses for each output phase generally do not occur precisely together, although a common P_1 pulse serves all output phases.

The performance of a VSCF system using a UFC is illustrated by the oscillograms in Figures 9.22–9.25. These oscillograms are applicable to a 5 kVA model VSCF system, using a 6 kVA, six-phase generator, operated in the 300–600 Hz frequency range, with a six-pulse UFC with three output phases. The power circuit comprises three pairs of three-pulse circuits; each pair provides one output phase, via an interphase reactor, as illustrated in Figure 1.26*b*.

Figure 9.22 shows oscillograms of the unfiltered and filtered output voltage waves of one phase of the UFC. The output frequency is 400 Hz, the generator frequency is approximately 380 Hz, and the output load is 5 kW at unity power factor.

The oscillograms in Figure 9.23 illustrate the speed of response of the frequency control. A step error representing a 20-Hz increase in the generator frequency is introduced in the feedback loop (lower trace). The upper trace shows the output of the *error integrator*. It can be observed that 90% of the error is corrected during the first half-period.

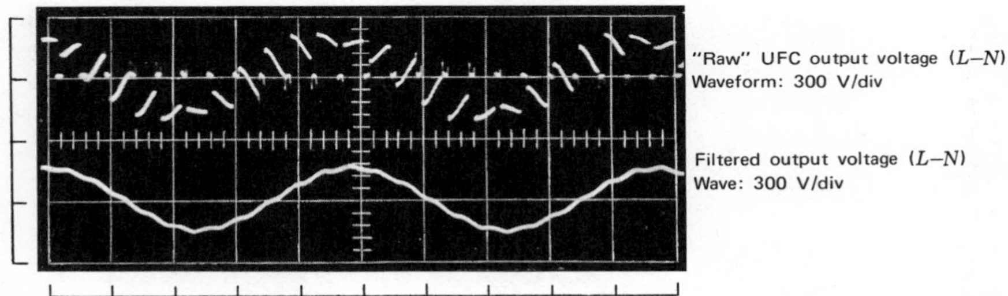

Figure 9.22 Unfiltered and filtered output voltage waveforms of the unrestricted frequency changer in a VSCF system. Input (generator) frequency: 380 Hz approx. Output frequency: 400 Hz.

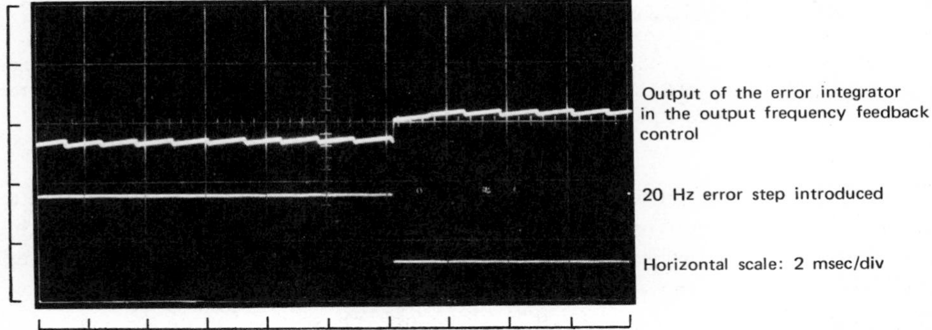

Figure 9.23 Oscillogram illustrating the performance of the output frequency feedback control in a VSCF system using an unrestricted frequency changer.

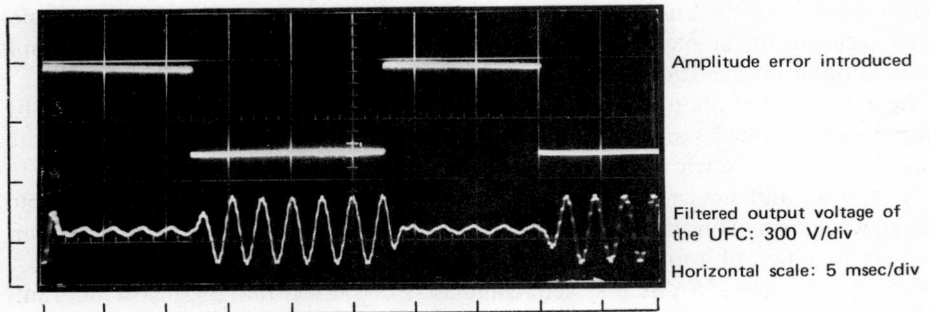

Figure 9.24 Oscillogram illustrating the performance of the output voltage control in a VSCF system using an unrestricted frequency changer.

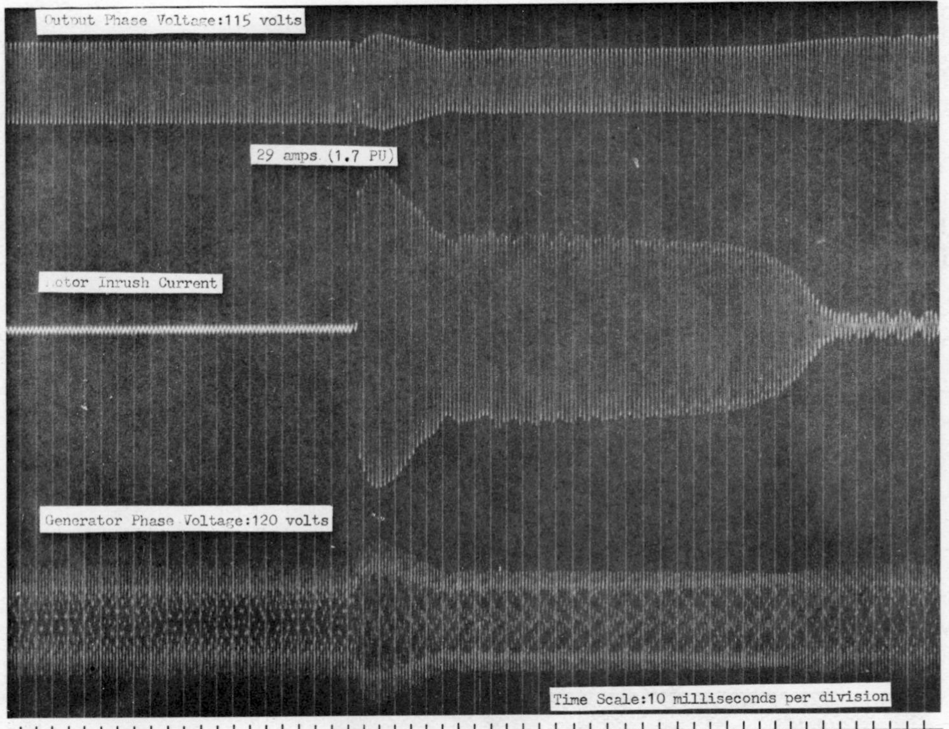

Figure 9.25 Motor-starting performance of the unrestricted frequency changer in a VSCF system. Input (generator) frequency: 500 Hz approx. Output frequency: 400 Hz. Motor rating: 1.6 HP. (Generator voltages are regulated; UFC output voltages are unregulated.)

The oscillogram in Figure 9.24 illustrates the speed of response of the amplitude control of the output voltage. A large steplike amplitude error is introduced in the output voltage regulator feedback loop (top trace). As can be seen, the actual filtered output voltage (lower trace) responds almost instantly.

The recordings given in Figure 9.25 show one phase voltage of the generator (lower trace) during the start-up of a 1.6-HP induction motor connected at the

400-Hz output. The frequency of the generator is about 500 Hz. The upper trace shows the motor inrush current. Initially the generator voltage increases because, until the generator voltage regulator becomes effective, the generator "sees" the lagging output load as leading, due to the load phase angle-inverting property of the UFC. This recording was taken with the internal voltage control loop of the UFC disconnected; thus the amplitude of the output voltage is proportional to the amplitude of the generator voltage. This is the reason why the motor current is high during the first few cycles while the generator voltage is also high.

9.2.4 Mobile Ground Power-Generating System Using an NCC

A mobile ground power generating system is functionally quite similar to the VSCF system shown in Figure 9.16. The major difference is that the speed of the alternator, and consequently the frequency of the electric power generated, is fairly well regulated; a typical speed and frequency variation is within 10%. Another difference is in the characteristic of the generator. In an airborne VSCF system a wound-rotor synchronous generator usually is employed. In the ground power system a rotor without windings generally has to be employed, because of the extremely high operating speed (usually in excess of 50,000 rpm.). Although various types of machines have been considered for this application, the solid rotor *inductor* generator has the required mechanical ruggedness, as well as the capability of providing regulated terminal voltages. This machine, however, has considerably higher subtransient—leakage—impedance than a wound-rotor synchronous generator, which would make the commutation of the cycloconverter, particularly under heavy load conditions, problematical. Fortunately, since the frequency of the generator is nearly constant, this problem can be overcome simply by shunting the generator terminals with appropriately sized capacitors. In fact, these capacitors may be dimensioned to cancel, or greatly reduce, the lagging reactive current demand of the NCC on the generator. This approach would not be practical in an airborne VSCF system because of the variation of the generator frequency over a wide range, typically of two to one.

The performance of a 60 kVA mobile ground power system using a naturally commutated cycloconverter that is fed by a generator of high subtransient reactance, the terminals of which are shunted by power factor-correcting capacitors, is illustrated by the oscillograms shown in Figure 9.26*a–d*.

The power circuit configuration of the cycloconverter is essentially the same as shown in Figure 9.17—that is, a six-pulse circuit with interphase reactors. The input power is provided by a six-phase generator, shunted by capacitors to cancel the reactive input current of the cycloconverter at the rated output load of 60 kW. The generator operates in the frequency range of 1800–2000 Hz, and the output frequency is 400 Hz.

Figures 9.26*a* and *b* show oscillograms of the "raw" (unfiltered) and filtered output voltage waveforms of one phase of the cycloconverter, with no load and full load at unity power factor, respectively.

Figure 9.26*c* shows the generator terminal voltage (with shunting capacitors) and the cycloconverter input current waveforms at full output load of 60 kW, at unity power factor.

Figure 9.26*d* shows, with expanded horizontal scale, the generator terminal voltage (with shunting capacitors) and the generator line current, at the above full load condition.

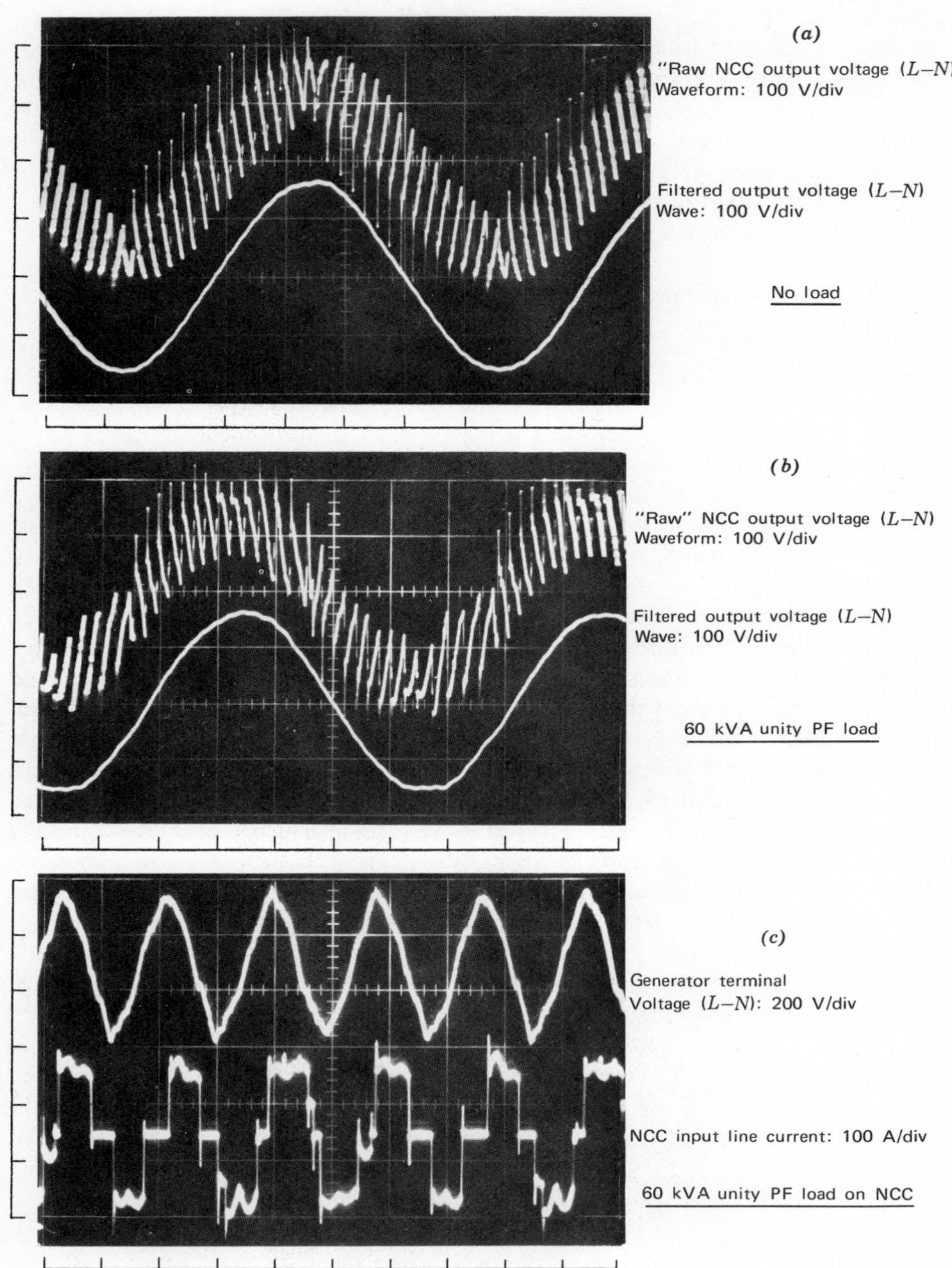
(a)
"Raw NCC output voltage (L–N)
Waveform: 100 V/div
Filtered output voltage (L–N)
Wave: 100 V/div
No load
(b)
"Raw" NCC output voltage (L–N)
Waveform: 100 V/div
Filtered output voltage (L–N)
Wave: 100 V/div
60 kVA unity PF load
(c)
Generator terminal
Voltage (L–N): 200 V/div
NCC input line current: 100 A/div
60 kVA unity PF load on NCC

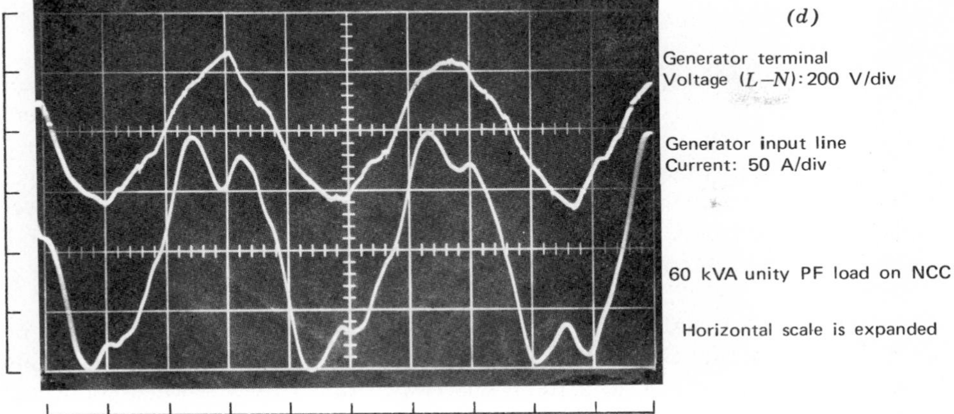

Figure 9.26 Output voltage, generator voltage, NCC input current, and generator current waveforms obtained in a mobile ground power-generating system, using a naturally commutated cycloconverter. Input (generator) frequency: 1800 Hz approx. Output frequency: 400 Hz. Each generator terminal is shunted by a capacitor to the neutral.

It can be observed that the shunt capacitors are effective in providing a "stiff" voltage source for commutation; the subtransient reactance of the generator actually plays no part in the commutation; indeed, small inductances are added into the input lines of the cycloconverter to limit the rate of rise of current during commutation. The output voltage waveforms resemble well the typical ideal cycloconverter waveforms. It is interesting to compare the oscillograms shown in Figure 9.26 to those shown in Figure 9.18 to see the effect of the input shunt capacitors on the waveforms.

It can also be seen that the input shunt capacitors effectively cancel the quadrature lagging component of the cycloconverter input current; furthermore, they provide low-impedance shunt paths—that is, filtering—for the majority of extrabasal components, thereby considerably reducing the total distortion of the generator line currents.

9.2.5 Mobile Ground Power-Generating System Using an Induction Generator and a CDFFC

The use of a squirrel-cage induction generator in conjunction with the controllable displacement factor frequency changer constitutes a unique and most interesting power-generating system.

The advantages of the squirrel-cage induction machine—simplicity, ruggedness, low cost, and the possibility for operating at high speeds—have long been recognized. Hitherto, however, induction machines have largely been restricted to "motoring" duty because of their inability to supply lagging reactive power when used as generators. The squirrel-cage induction generator, when properly supplied with lagging reactive power, however, is capable of supplying *real* power to an external load connected to it. The lagging reactive power (VAr) demand of the load *and* the reactive power of the machine must be supplied by external means. A number of methods have been suggested for providing the lagging VAr demand of an induction generator. These include schemes using fixed and switched capacitors, synchronous condensers, and various types of static solid-state VAr generators connected in parallel with the machine. None of these schemes, however, appears to be totally satisfactory.

The unique operating characteristic of the controllable displacement factor frequency changer—that is, the facility for controlling the quadrature component of the fundamental input current that it draws from the a-c source between prescribed leading and lagging values—offers the possibility of using this frequency changer for a double purpose: first, to convert the high (and variable) frequency power supplied by an induction generator to a fixed lower-frequency output power; second, to supply the generator with a controlled lagging reactive power and thus simultaneously to control its excitation.

In order to understand the basic operating principles of such a system, let it be assumed that a multiphase squirrel-cage induction machine is driven by an engine at the proper speed and is, in a traditional way, excited by a parallel connected synchronous generator. Assume that a controllable displacement factor frequency changer is employed to produce multiphase output waveforms with the wanted frequency from this machine combination. Assume further that an *LC* output filter, inserted between the frequency changer and the output terminals, is used as usual to remove the inevitable "ripple" produced by the static frequency conversion process. Since the output frequency and voltage are normally fixed, this filter will draw a constant reactive (leading) component of current from the frequency changer. Assume now that a load with an arbitrary lagging, leading, or unity power factor is applied at the output terminals, and that the frequency changer is controlled so as to produce unity input displacement factor. In this case, the fundamental current drawn from the two generators by the frequency changer is in phase with the corresponding terminal voltage. If the excitation of the synchronous generator is appropriately set, the total fundamental current to the frequency changer—and thus the total *real* power to the load—can be supplied by the induction machine alone, and the synchronous generator supplies only the needed reactive excitation current of the induction generator. Suppose now that the frequency changer is controlled to draw some leading quadrature current and thus provide a slightly *leading* input displacement factor. (It is reiterated that this displacement factor control does *not* affect the output frequency and voltage of the frequency changer.) Assuming that the terminal voltage of the machine combination is not allowed to change as a result of this perturbation, this means that the excitation of the synchronous generator must be decreased, since the excitation current of the induction machine is now partially provided by the frequency changer itself. Evidently, if the frequency changer is controlled to provide the total excitation, the current in the synchronous machine can be reduced to zero. The synchronous generator may now be disconnected, and the induction generator-frequency changer combination becomes self-sufficient. Keeping in mind that the frequency changer can generate fixed output frequency from variable input frequency, and that the input displacement factor can be controlled independently of the input and output frequencies, it is easy to visualize that this self-sufficient state of the generating system can be maintained under practical conditions of changing output loads and varying shaft speeds.

Assume, for example, that a heavier load is applied to the output, at a given engine speed. In order to satisfy the higher power demand, the slip of the induction generator must increase; thus its frequency will decrease slightly. To maintain the terminal voltage under this condition, the induction generator must be supplied with an increased lagging component of current. The frequency changer controls therefore must be adjusted to generate the same constant output frequency from the lower generator frequency and, at the same time, to *draw* the exact leading component of current—that is, to *supply* the exact lagging component of current required to maintain the terminal voltage of the generator. In a similar manner, it can also be visualized that, under engine-speed variations, the output frequency and voltage, and the generator voltage, can be maintained by appropriate control of the frequency changer.

Two particular aspects, however, require further explanation. One is operation with open circuit output—that is, with no external load—and the other is the initial excitation of the induction generator.

Considering the first problem, one must realize that a frequency changer is always loaded with its output filter. The filter current is capacitive at the output; thus the CDFFC can be controlled to *draw* a corresponding capacitive current *from* the generator—that is, to *supply* a corresponding lagging current *to* the generator. Depending on the particular filter design, however, it could happen that this current is insufficient to excite the induction generator. This problem can be solved by shunting the generator with appropriately sized capacitors. This usually does not mean the addition of "extra" components to the system, since in practice input capacitors are generally needed for frequency changers employing turn-off devices or force commutated thyristors to suppress the transient voltages at the input terminals, which would otherwise be produced by the forced, rapid current change in the generator subtransient impedance at each commutation. (As we saw in the previous section, input capacitors can also be advantageous for the NCC.) As well as providing suppression of the switching transients, these capacitors also decrease the distortion of the generator line currents and thereby improve the terminal voltage waveshapes. Thus, indirectly, the input filter capacitors also reduce the distortion of the output voltage waveforms that are constructed from segments of the terminal voltage waves.

To ensure proper no-load excitation, it is necessary that the total generator current, composed of the input capacitor current plus the maximum obtainable capacitive input current of the CDFFC due to its output filter current, must be equal to or greater than the no-load excitation current of the induction generator, at the minimum operating speed. In practice, this criterion will generally be satisfied "naturally"; thus the size of the filter capacitors does not have to be increased beyond that which is required for other reasons.

The second aspect to be considered is the initial start-up. It might be thought that, since the induction machine initially has no internally established voltages, passive components cannot provide the initial excitation required. It is a fact, however, that induction machines do have some magnetic remanence (and even if they did not, this could easily be established by a single current pulse injected into the stator winding). This remanence ensures that initial self-excitation in fact takes place naturally, by *positive feedback* action. Due to the remanence, a small voltage is developed in the stator by the rotating rotor. This voltage drives some current into the input filter capacitors, which in turn increases the generator voltage. When the generator terminal voltage exceeds some convenient level, the frequency changer is activated and begins to supply current to the output filter. If the displacement factor of the frequency changer is closed-loop controlled to maintain a desired generator voltage, at start-up the input displacement factor would be automatically set as leading as possible, thereby ensuring the rapid completion of the initial excitation

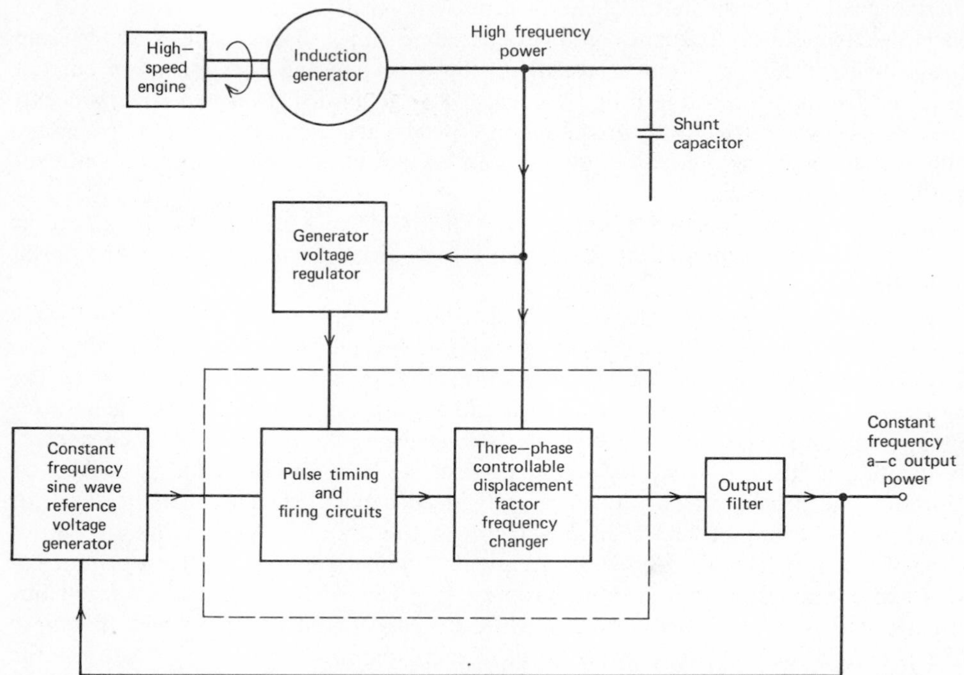

Figure 9.27 Schematic representation of a power-generating system using an induction generator and a controllable displacement factor frequency changer.

of the generator. Once the required terminal voltage is reached, the closed-loop control of the frequency changer continuously adjusts the reactive component of the input current so as to maintain the correct excitation of the machine.

A functional block diagram illustrating the basic elements of a VSCF generating system using an induction generator and a controllable displacement factor frequency changer is shown in Figure 9.27. Ignoring the problem of the generator excitation, the control mechanism of this system is identical to that employing an NCC in Figure 9.16. The excitation of the generator and the input terminal voltages of the CDFFC are controlled by comparing the generator phase voltages to a reference and using the analogue error signal to vary the phase position of the waveform switching signals. The *waveform switching signal generator* is an integral part of the *pulse timing and firing circuit* unit (see Figure 9.27); its functional elements are shown in Figure 7.31, and its operation is explained in Section 7.6.4.

The operation of a power-generating system using a squirrel-cage induction machine and a controllable displacement factor frequency changer is illustrated by the oscillograms shown in Figures 9.28–9.30. These oscillograms are applicable to a 5 kVA system, comprising a 7.5 HP, six-phase induction generator and a six-pulse CDFFC with three output phases. Each output phase is supplied by two three-pulse circuits via an interphase reactor (Figure 1.26*b*) and an *LC* filter. The machine speed varies to provide variable-frequency output in the range of 170–220 Hz. The output frequency of the CDFFC is kept at 60 Hz.

Figures 9.28*a* and *b* show oscillograms of the "raw" and filtered output voltage, the total output current of the CDFFC, and the external load current, with a 5 kW unity power factor load at input frequencies of 170 and 220 Hz, respectively.

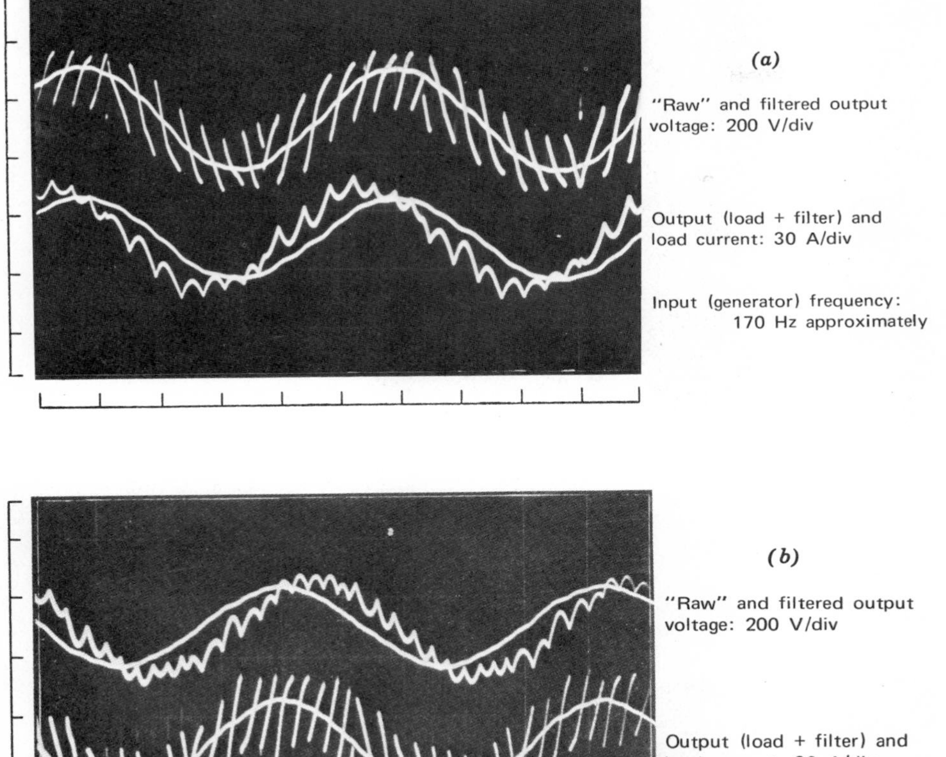

Figure 9.28 Output voltage and current waveforms obtained in a power-generating system using a squirrel-cage induction generator and a controllable displacement factor frequency changer. Output frequency: 60 Hz. 5 kVA unity PF load on the CDFFC.

Figures 9.29 and 9.30 show oscillograms of the output and input voltage and current waveforms under different load conditions, for generator frequencies of 170 and 220 Hz, respectively. At the minimum operating frequency of 170 Hz, the input shunt capacitors do not supply enough VArs to excite the induction generator. The generator voltage regulator error signal therefore makes the frequency changer operate with an appropriately leading input displacement factor, thereby assisting the excitation of the machine. The input current waveforms therefore *lead* the corresponding generator voltage waves in Figure 9.29. By contrast, at the maximum operating frequency of 220 Hz, the input shunt capacitors actually overexcite the induction generator. The generator voltage regulator therefore produces an error signal of opposite polarity, which forces the frequency changer to operate with an appropriately *lagging* input displacement factor, thereby reducing the excitation of the machine to the required level. Consequently the input current waveforms lag the corresponding generator voltage waves in Figure 9.30.

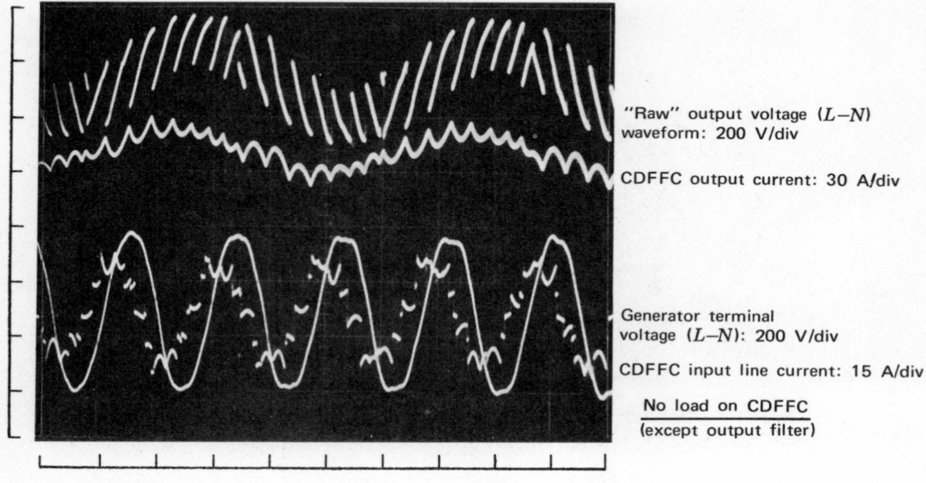
"Raw" output voltage (L–N) waveform: 200 V/div
CDFFC output current: 30 A/div
Generator terminal voltage (L–N): 200 V/div
CDFFC input line current: 15 A/div
No load on CDFFC
(except output filter)

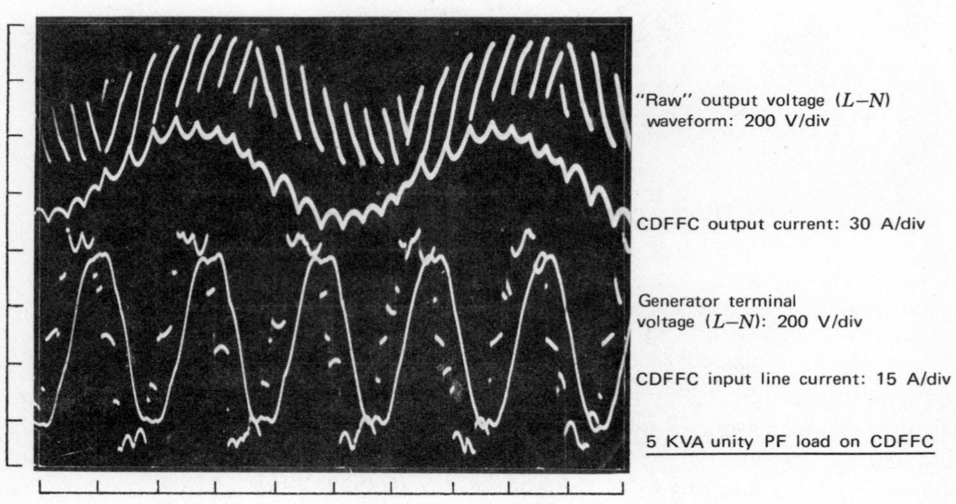
"Raw" output voltage (L–N) waveform: 200 V/div
CDFFC output current: 30 A/div
Generator terminal voltage (L–N): 200 V/div
CDFFC input line current: 15 A/div
5 KVA unity PF load on CDFFC

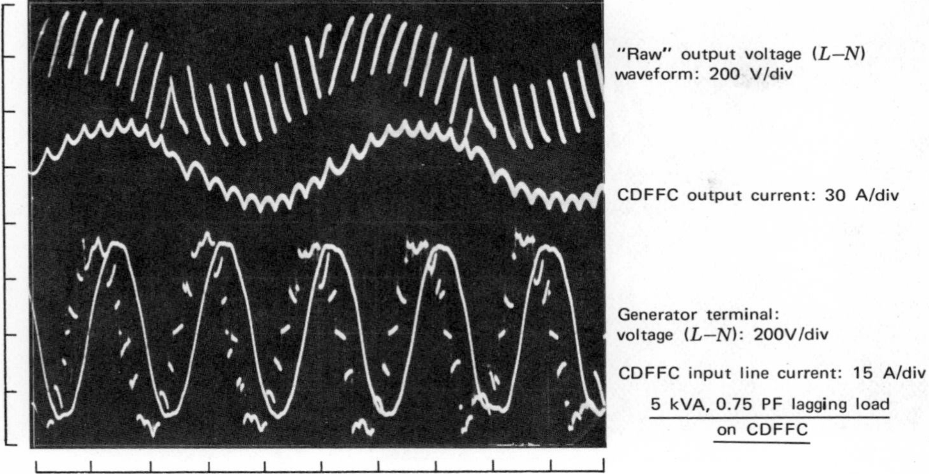

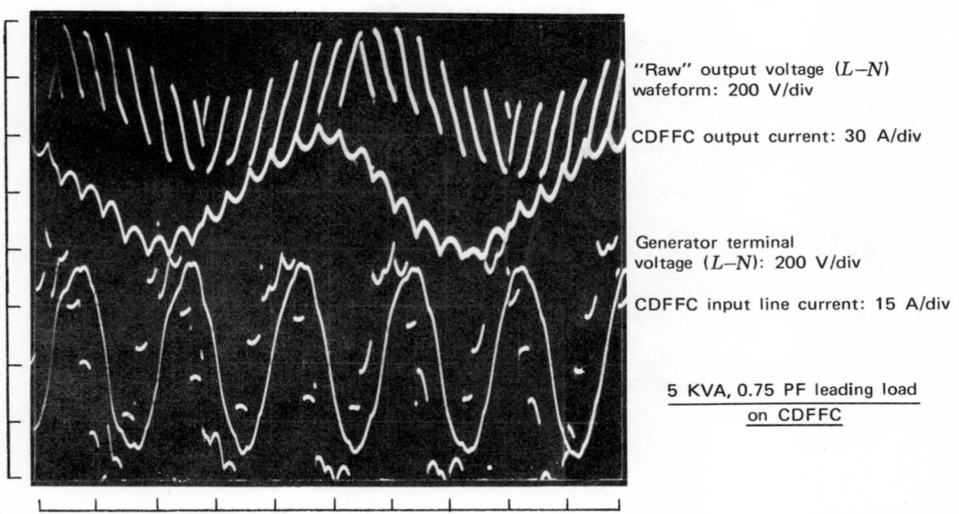

Figure 9.29 Output voltage and current, input voltage and current waveforms obtained in a power-generating system using a squirrel-cage induction generator and a controllable displacement factor frequency changer. Input (generator) frequency: 170 Hz approx. Output frequency: 60 Hz.

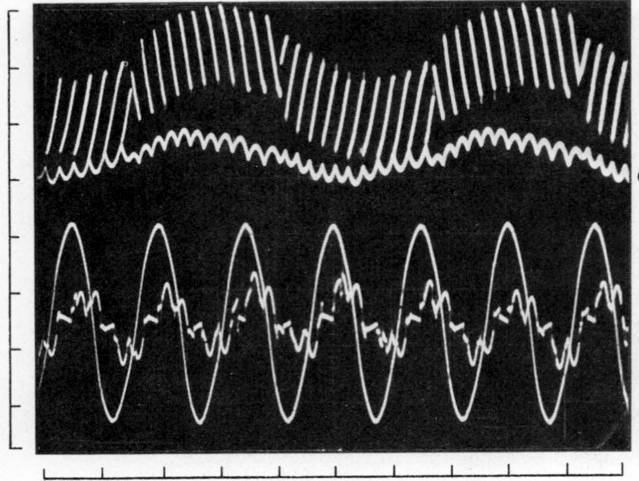
"Raw" output voltage (L–N)
waveform: 200 V/div
CDFFC output current: 30 A/div
Generator terminal
voltage (L–N): 200 V/div
CDFFC input line current: 15 A/div
No load on CDFFC
(except output filter)

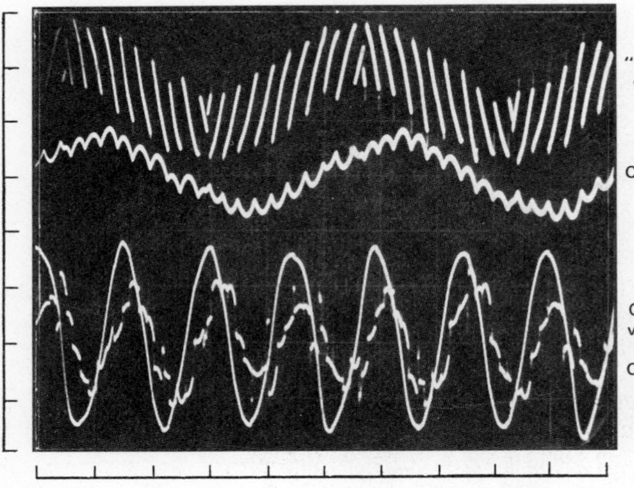
"Raw" output voltage (L–N)
waveform: 200 V/div
CDFFC output current: 30 A/div
Generator terminal
voltage (L–N): 200 V/div
CDFFC input line current: 15 A/div
5 kVA, 0.75 PF lagging
on CDFFC

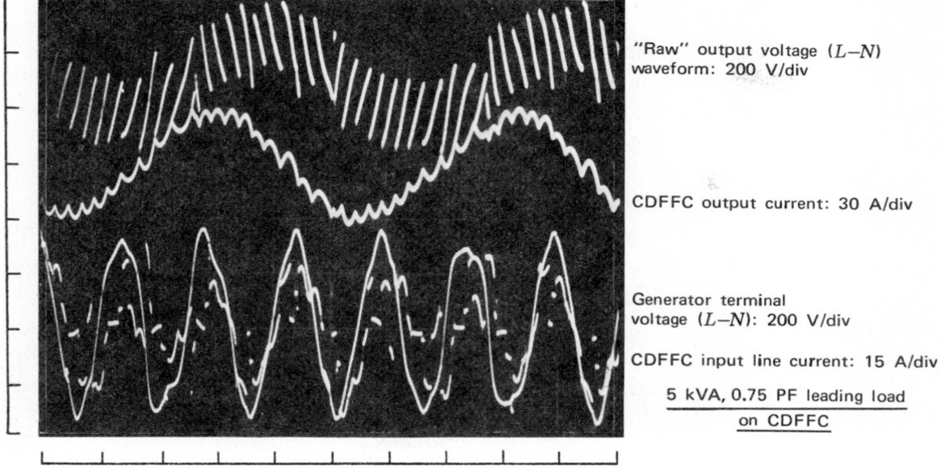

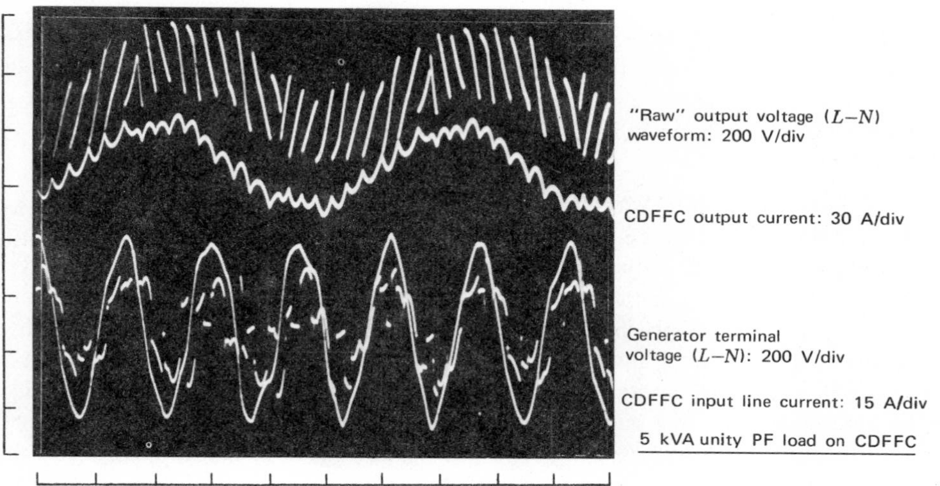

Figure 9.30 Output voltage and current, input voltage and current waveforms obtained in a power-generating system using a squirrel-cage induction generator and a controllable displacement factor frequency changer. Input (generator) frequency: 220 Hz approx. Output frequency: 60 Hz.

9.3 STATIC VAr GENERATORS

In recent years, there has been a greatly increased demand for controllable power factor correction in industrial power systems due to the growing use of electrical machines, the rapidly increasing popularity of the electric arc furnace in steel production, and the general acceptance of line (naturally) commutated thyristor drives and power controllers throughout the industry.

Traditionally, power factor correction has been accomplished by rotating synchronous condensers and fixed or mechanically switched capacitor banks. Recent advances in high-power thyristor technology and electronic circuitry have prompted the development of controllable static power factor correctors, and several large installations are presently in service. These systems are conceptually simple; they usually comprise shunt capacitors and inductors in conjunction with thyristor "on/off" or phase-controlled switches. Their commercial success is due to their acceptable cost, coupled with their desirable technical features such as extremely fast response time—the reactive current supplied can be controlled from zero to maximum within a period, or less, of the supply frequency—flexibility in control, and continuous operation with virtually no maintenance.

In principle, static frequency changers could also be used for reactive power generation and control, and for some applications they offer potential advantages over the more conventional static approaches. Their performance would generally be equivalent and in many respects superior to that of the rotating synchronous condenser.

In the following two sections some novel controllable VAr generator schemes, using static frequency changers, are outlined.

9.3.1 VAr Generators Using Frequency Changers Operated from a High Frequency Base

The basic principles of a VAr generator using a frequency changer with a *high-frequency* (HF) *base* can be introduced by considering a conventional rotating synchronous condenser, shown schematically in Figure 9.31*a*. For purely reactive power flow, the three-phase induced e.m.f.s, e_1, e_2, and e_3, of the synchronous rotating machine are in phase with the system voltages v_1, v_2, and v_3. By controlling the excitation of the machine, and hence the amplitude, E, of its voltages, the reactive power can be controlled; increasing E above the amplitude, V, of the system voltages causes leading (capacitive) current to be drawn from the a-c system, whereas decreasing E below V produces a lagging (inductive) load on the a-c system. Under either operating condition, a small amount of real power flows from the a-c system to the machine to supply its mechanical and electrical losses.

An alternative method of implementing the same principle of VAr control is illustrated in Figure 9.31*b*. Here a generator of relatively high frequency feeds a static frequency changer that converts the generator frequency f_B to the a-c system frequency f. The output terminals of the frequency changer are connected to the a-c system via small inductors. Assuming that the frequency changer is controlled to produce output voltage waves v_{O1}, v_{O2}, and v_{O3}, whose wanted components are in phase with the corresponding system voltages v_1, v_2, and v_3, respectively, it is evident, as for the synchronous condenser at *a*, that reactive power can be supplied in either direction to the a-c system by simple amplitude control of the frequency changer voltages. Thus the frequency changer will draw leading current from—that

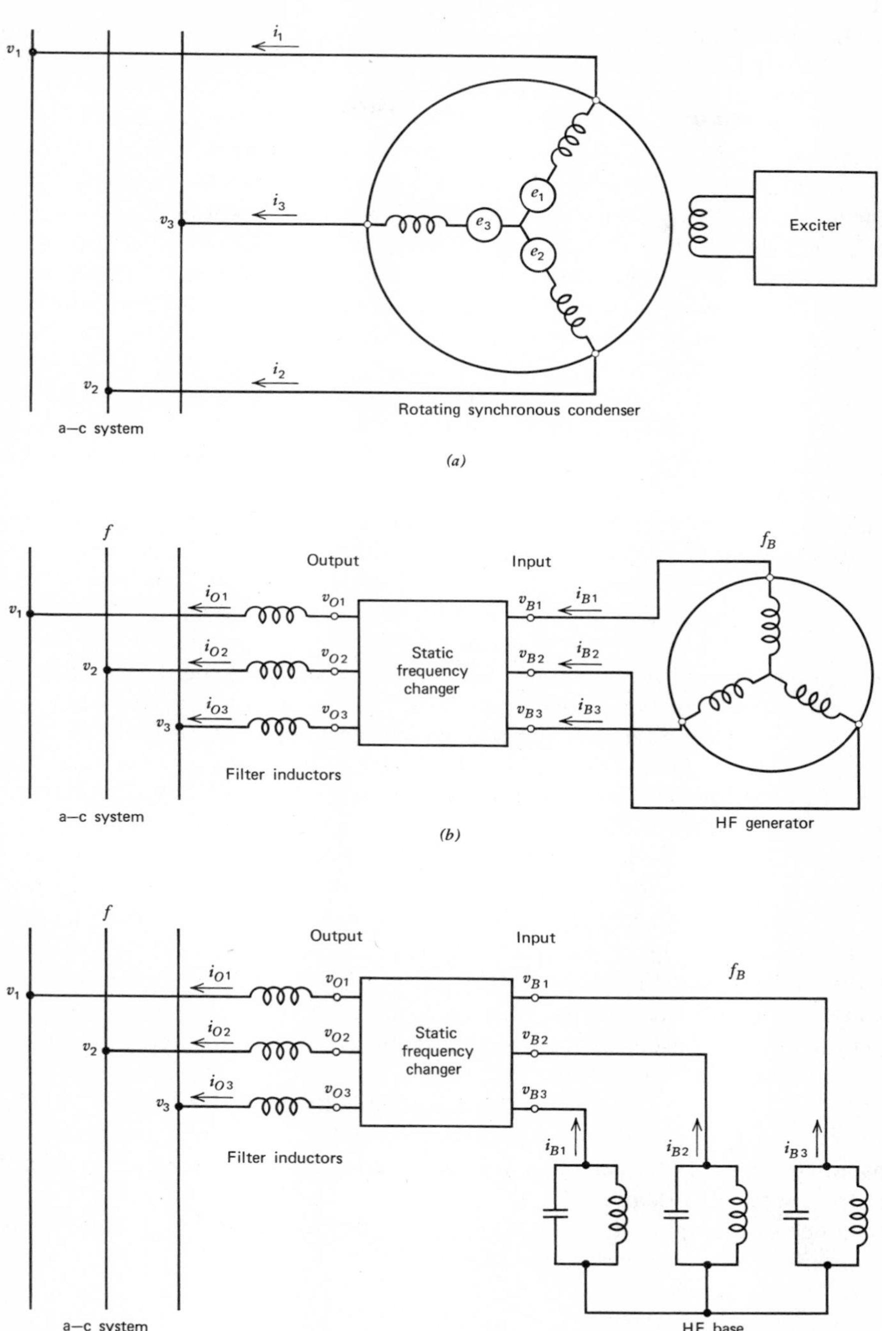

Figure 9.31 Conceptual explanation of the high-frequency-base frequency changer approach to controllable VAr generation. *a* Schematic representation of a controllable VAr generator using a rotating synchronous condenser. *b* Schematic representation of a controllable VAr generator using a high-frequency generator in conjunction with a static frequency changer. *c* Schematic representation of a controllable VAr generator using a static frequency changer with a high-frequency-base tank circuit.

is, it *supplies* lagging current to—the a-c system when the amplitude, V_O, of its wanted output voltages is greater than that of the system voltages, V. Conversely, it will draw lagging current whenever V_O is smaller than V.

As the amplitude V_O of the wanted output voltage of the frequency changer is varied in order to control the reactive system current, it might naturally be assumed that this varying reactive power would be reflected through the frequency changer to the machine. It is shown in this book, however, that each type of frequency changer has its own special characteristic for reactive power transfer, and therefore different types of frequency changers would impose completely different VAr demands on the machine, when supplying identical output VArs. For example, both leading and lagging VArs supplied by an NCC would appear as lagging VArs on the machine; leading VArs supplied by a UFC would appear as lagging VArs on the machine, and vice versa; and a UDFFC could supply either leading or lagging VArs without any reactive power demand on the machine. All frequency changers, because of their nonsinusoidal input currents, would draw some extrabasal (harmonic) current from the machine.

Since the machine in Figure 9.31*b* theoretically handles only reactive and/or harmonic power, it can be replaced by a multiphase static oscillating *LC* tank circuit—which we call a *high-frequency base*, or *HF base*—as shown at *c*. As with the scheme at *b*, control of the reactive power at the a-c system side can be obtained through control of the voltage generated at the output terminals of the frequency changer. The varying reactive load that may be reflected to the tank circuit by the frequency changer, as the reactive power at the a-c system side is varied, has the same effect as a variable reactance (inductance or capacitance, depending on the type of frequency changer) connected in parallel with the passive *LC* circuit; that is, it causes a variation in the natural operating frequency of the HF base. Since frequency changers can operate from a variable-frequency source without any difficulty, this frequency variation of the HF base, provided it is kept within reasonable limits by appropriate design of the tank circuit, does not affect the operation of the system.

In an actual system, the amplitude of the oscillation in the tank circuit, and thus the amplitude of the input voltage of the frequency changer, cannot be maintained without replenishing the energy used up by losses. The power required for this purpose can be obtained by establishing a sufficient real power flow from the a-c system to the HF base. This can be accomplished quite simply by introducing an appropriate small phase shift between the output voltages of the frequency changer and the a-c system voltages. In a practical scheme this phase shift would be closed-loop controlled, so as either to maintain the voltage of the oscillating tank circuit constant or possibly to vary this voltage in an incremental manner in sympathy with the output VAr demand.

In order to exemplify this general approach further, we now consider the use of two specific types of frequency changers—the NCC and the UDFFC—in such a scheme. From the standpoint of the a-c system, the performance of the NCC and the UDFFC are similar; either can provide continuously variable leading and lagging VArs, with practically negligible distortion of the current wave. In both cases, the magnitude of the reactive current supplied to the a-c system is controlled by varying the amplitudes of the reference voltage waves; thus the response time for each approach is similar. From the viewpoint of the HF base, however, the two types of frequency changers differ significantly.

The NCC always presents a lagging reactive load to the HF base, regardless of whether the reactive power supplied to the a-c system is lagging or leading. As the reactive current (leading or lagging) supplied to the a-c system by the NCC is varied, the reactive lagging load on the HF base also varies. Thus, to a first approximation, the NCC can be regarded as constituting a variable inductive load on the HF base. As a consequence, the HF base frequency increases as a function of the reactive output power supplied to the system. It is therefore essential to have an *LC* tank circuit with a sufficiently large "reservoir" of internal oscillating energy to keep the frequency variation within practical limits.*

The UDFFC, on the other hand, requires no reactive input power under any load condition. Thus the total reactive power supplied to the a-c system is essentially circulated within the UDFFC. As explained, the operation of a static frequency changer always results in extrabasal input current components with frequencies different from the input frequency, which flow through the input source. Thus, when considering the use of a UDFFC in such a system, the input current wave is entirely composed of extrabasal components, which have to flow through the HF base. Thus the main requirement for the HF base is to provide input voltages, but no reactive power to the UDFFC, at a fixed base frequency, and to provide a low-impedance path for the extrabasal current components. The required rating of the *LC* tank circuit to be used with a UDFFC to provide essentially the extrabasal power is theoretically much smaller than that required for an NCC, where both reactive and extrabasal power must be provided.

When compared to a more conventional type of static controllable VAr generator using shunt capacitors and inductors in conjunction with thyristor switches, the HF base scheme generally has the potential advantage of reduced size and possibly reduced cost, because the reactive elements operate at higher than the a-c system frequency. In addition, when the UDFFC is employed, the total rating of the reactive elements may be substantially less than that required for the more conventional approach. The system is free from the problem of energizing large capacitor banks directly from the a-c system, and from possible problems of resonance of such banks with the a-c system. In addition, the output currents supplied by the HF base scheme have little distortion and require little or no filtering.

The basic elements of a static VAr generator using a frequency changer (either an NCC or UDFFC) with an HF base are illustrated in Figure 9.32. The frequency changer in conjunction with the *pulse timing and firing circuits* can again be regarded as a high-power amplifier, producing output voltages that are proportional to the reference input voltages. Assuming first an oscillating lossless *LC* tank circuit for the HF base, the output VArs supplied to the a-c system could be controlled simply by varying the amplitudes of the in-phase reference voltages derived from the a-c system voltages, by a step-down transformer. For the purpose of replenishing the losses of the *LC* tank circuit, the requisite real power flow from the a-c system to the HF base must also be established. As explained, this can be accomplished by appropriately phase shifting the output voltages of the frequency changer with respect to the a-c system voltages. Thus power flows from the a-c system to the HF base if the output voltages *lag* the corresponding system voltages, and vice versa. To achieve the necessary phase shift, a variable-amplitude reference voltage

* Techniques[66] are available to minimize the variation of the reactive load on the link. Their essence is to circulate a controllable amount of current through the converters constituting the NCC, thereby controlling its input displacement factor so that the total current drawn from the HF base remains constant under all output load conditions. Further description of such techniques is beyond the scope of this book.

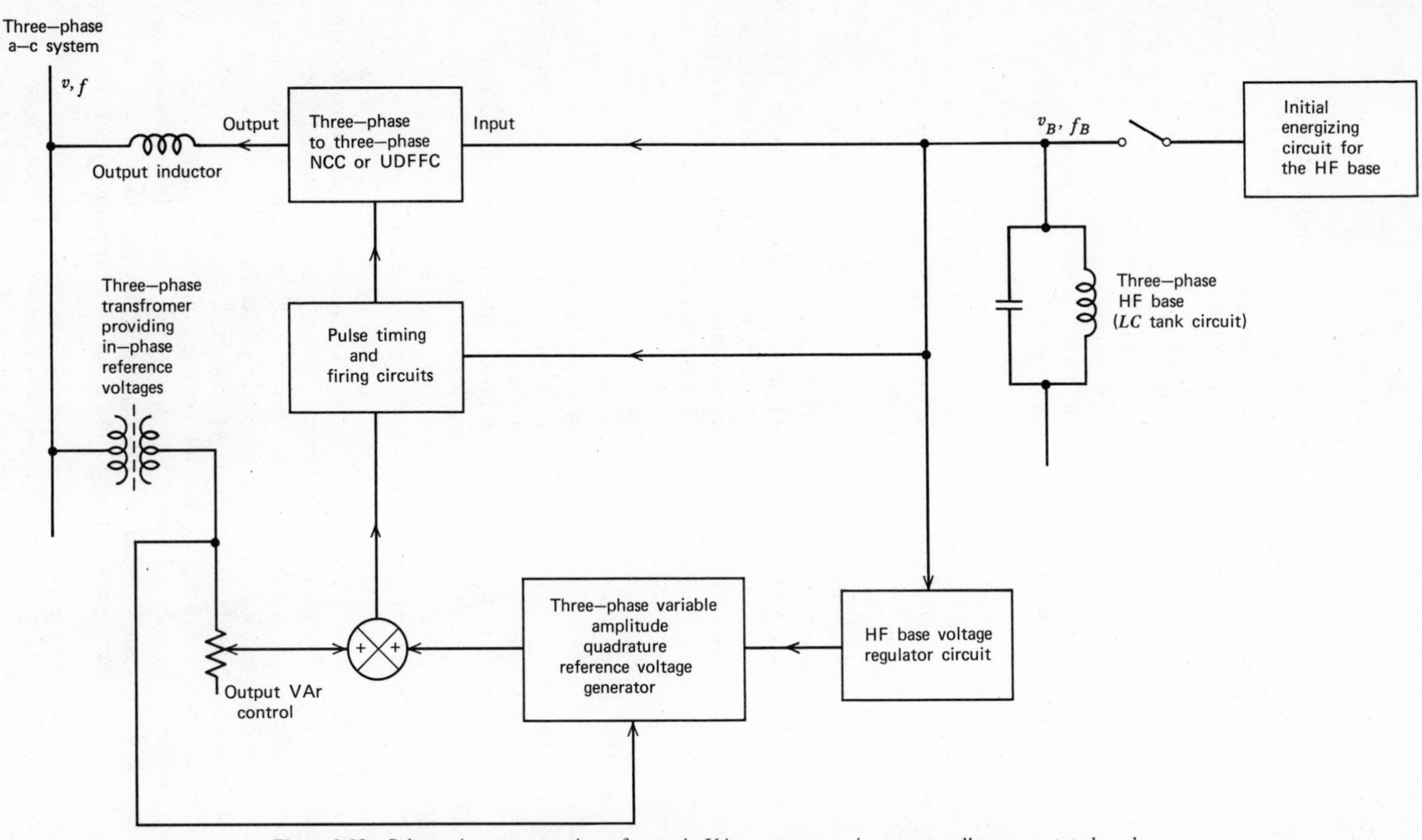

Figure 9.32 Schematic representation of a static VAr generator using a naturally commutated cycloconverter or a unity displacement factor frequency changer operated from a high-frequency base.

that is in quadrature with the a-c system voltage is generated and summed to the in-phase reference voltage controlling the reactive VAr output. The amplitude of this quadrature reference voltage is controlled by the *HF base voltage regulator circuit*; thus it provides sufficient real power to the *LC* tank circuit to maintain a constant voltage across it. A somewhat different control strategy would be to vary the HF base voltage incrementally about a nominal level, in sympathy with the required output VArs, to maintain only the minimum voltage necessary for the operation of the frequency changer at that particular setting of external VArs.

The initial energization of the *LC* tank circuit can be accomplished by various means. One approach is to use a small synchronous generator and charge the tank circuit by slowly increasing the excitation of the machine. When the HF base voltage reaches the normal operating level, the frequency changer is brought into operation, and the machine may be disconnected. Various types of static circuits—for example, an inverter—could also be used for initial energization. In principle it is also possible to energize the tank circuit initially through appropriate control of the frequency changer itself. With a UDFFC, in which at least one of the constituent circuits is force commutated, this should be accomplished easily.

The operation of a static VAr generator employing an NCC with a passive HF base is illustrated by the oscillograms in Figure 9.33*a* and *b*. These oscillograms are appropriate to a 30-kVAr three-phase model using a simple three-pulse NCC and a three-phase HF base comprising three *LC* tuned tank circuits. The nominal HF base frequency is 450 Hz.

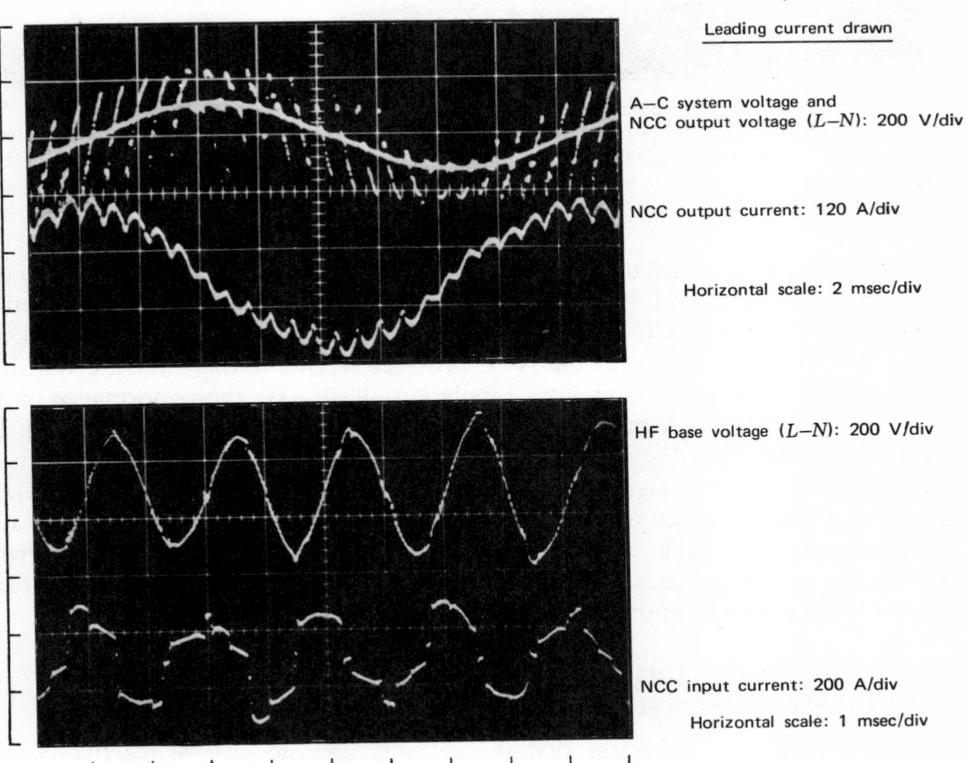

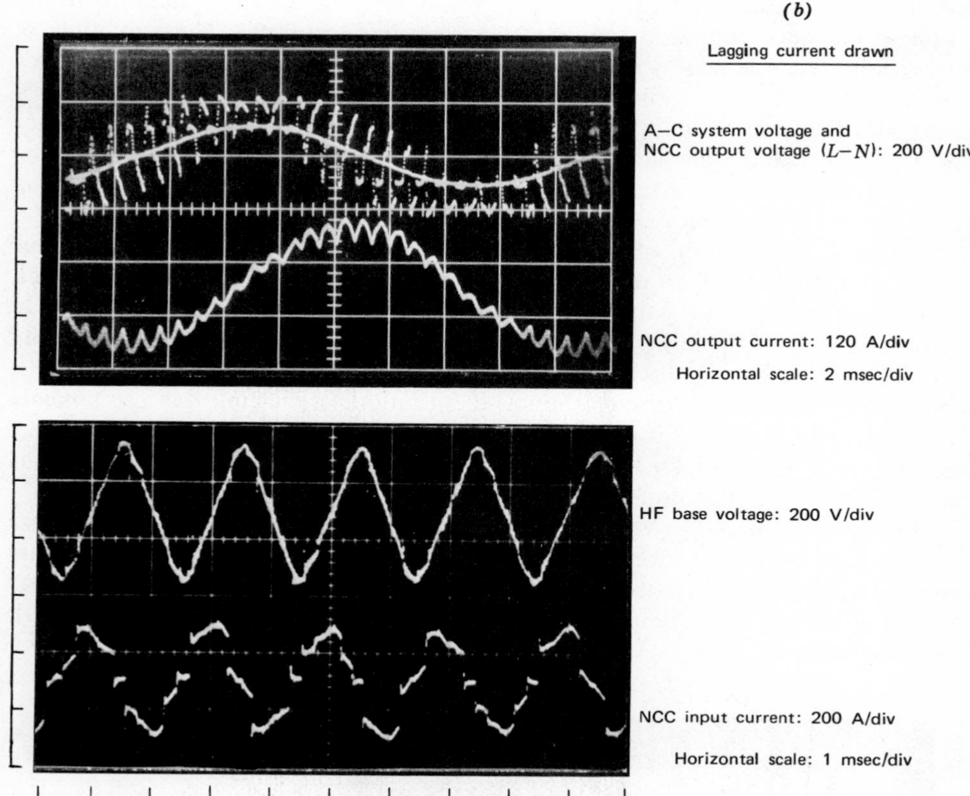

Figure 9.33 Oscillograms illustrating the operation of the VAr generator using a naturally commutated cycloconverter operated from a high-frequency base, as shown in Figure 9.32. *a* Leading and *b* lagging reactive current is drawn from the a-c system. A-C system frequency: 60 Hz. High-frequency-base frequency: 450 Hz approx.

Figure 9.33*a* shows oscillograms of typical output voltage and current waveforms of the NCC, together with the corresponding HF base (input) voltage and current waveforms, when the NCC supplies leading VArs to the a-c system. Figure 9.33*b* shows similar waveforms when the NCC provides lagging VArs to the a-c system.

Waveforms obtained by computer simulation, illustrating the performance of a VAr generator using a six-pulse unity displacement factor frequency changer with a HF base, are shown in Figure 9.34. At *a*, leading VArs, and at *b*, lagging VArs are supplied to the system. Here the HF base frequency is kept constant at 360 Hz, that is, at six times the a-c system frequency of 60 Hz. The amplitudes of the HF base voltages are varied in sympathy with the supplied VAr output. It can be seen that full leading or lagging reactive output current is provided without any reactive current being drawn from the HF base.

9.3.2 VAr Generators Using Frequency Changers in Power-Doubling Connection

A unique static VAr generator that theoretically uses no passive reactive components—capacitors or inductors—can be realized with a so-called *power-doubling*

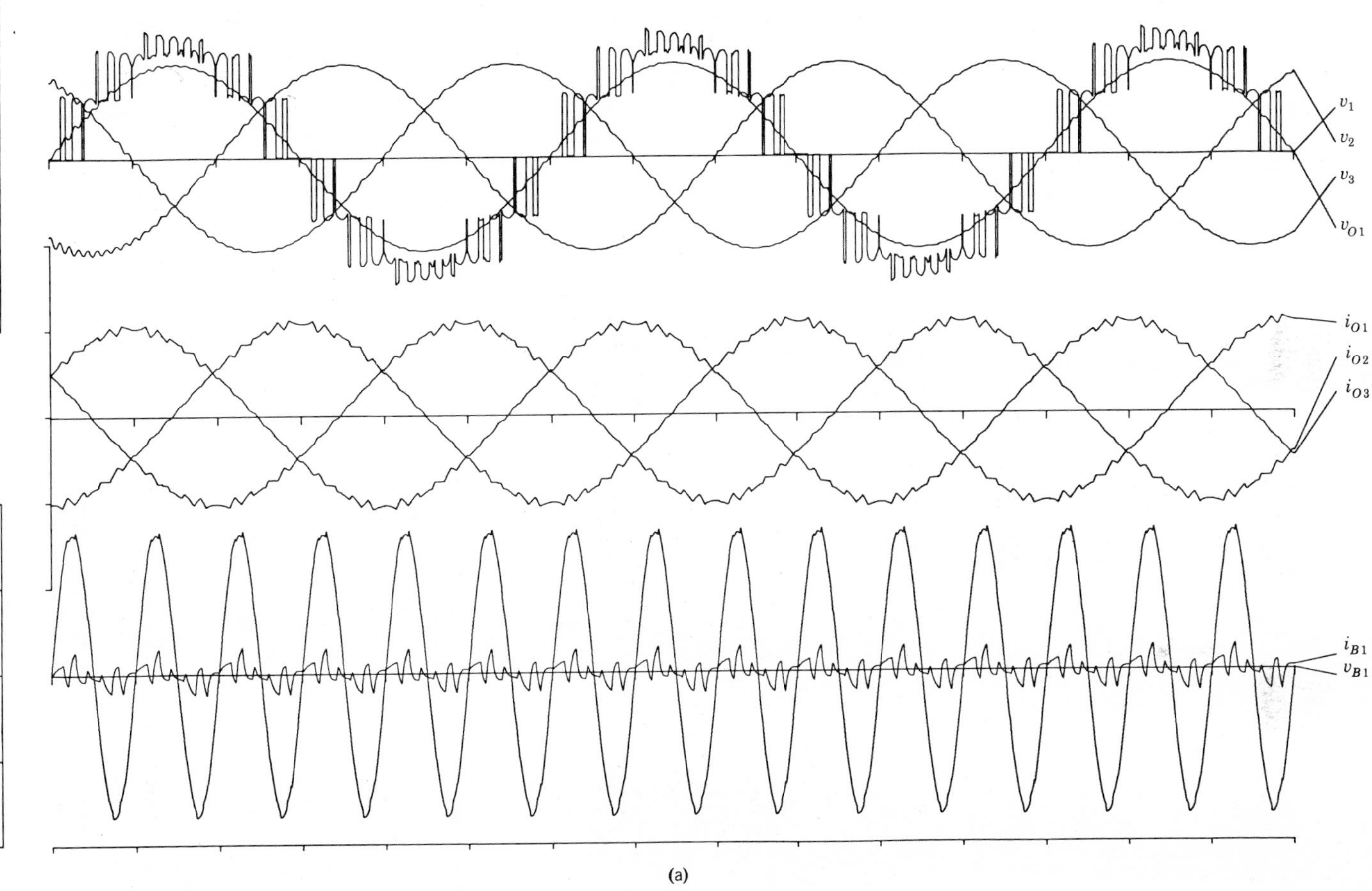

(a)

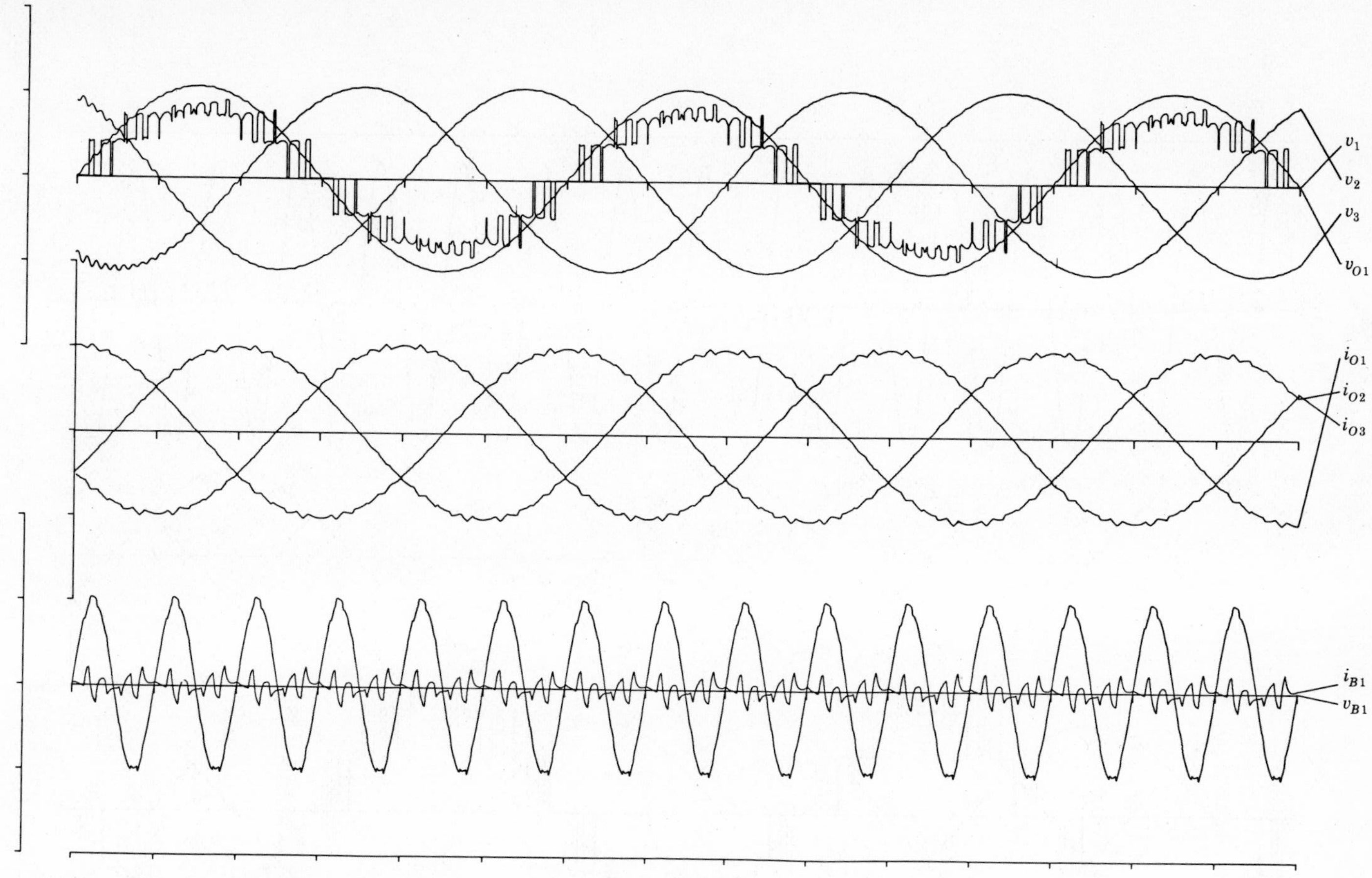

(b)

Figure 9.34 Waveforms obtained by computer simulation for the VAr generator shown in Figure 9.32, with a unity displacement factor frequency changer. *a* Leading and *b* lagging reactive current is drawn from the a-c system. A-C system frequency: 60 Hz. High-frequency-base frequency: 360 Hz. *Note*: Plots show UDFFC output currents; these are opposite to the a-c system currents.

scheme. Such a scheme employing an NCC is treated in a rudimentary way in Chapter 1.

In this scheme, the input and output sides of the frequency changer are *both* connected to the a-c system; thus both the input and output frequencies are equal to the system frequency. The main function of the frequency changer is to reflect the same phase angle at both its input and output terminals, as viewed by the common system voltage applied to both sets of terminals. This operating mode makes it possible to provide *twice* as much reactive VA for the a-c system, as the actual VA rating of the frequency changer. Thus, a frequency changer of 1/2 PU VA rating (throughput) can supply 1 PU reactive VA to the a-c system.

The operation of the power-doubling scheme is explained conceptually with reference to Figure 9.35. Consider first Figure 9.35*a*, in which a static frequency changer converts the three-phase a-c system voltages (v_{I1}, v_{I2}, v_{I3}) to three-phase output voltages (v_{O1}, v_{O2}, v_{O3}). Let it be assumed that the frequency changer can be operated under the following conditions:

1. The generated angular output frequency, ω_O, is equal to the angular input frequency, ω_I.
2. The wanted components, v_{Ow1}, v_{Ow2}, and v_{Ow3}, of the generated output voltages, v_{O1}, v_{O2}, and v_{O3}, are in phase with the respective a-c voltages, v_{I1}, v_{I2}, and v_{I3}.
3. The amplitude of the wanted components of the generated output voltage waves is variable with respect to the nominally fixed amplitude of the input voltages.
4. The input displacement angle, ϕ_I, between the input phase voltage and the fundamental component of the input current is the negative of the output phase angle, ϕ_O, between the wanted components of the output voltage and current. Thus, $\phi_I = -\phi_O$.

With the above stipulations and symbols, the following relationships between the output and input quantities may be written:

$$\left.\begin{aligned} v_{Ow1} &= V_O \sin \omega_O t = c_1 V_I \sin \omega_I t \\ v_{Ow2} &= V_O \sin\left(\omega_O t - \frac{2\pi}{3}\right) = c_1 V_I \sin\left(\omega_I t - \frac{2\pi}{3}\right) \\ v_{Ow3} &= V_O \sin\left(\omega_O t - \frac{4\pi}{3}\right) = c_1 V_I \sin\left(\omega_I t - \frac{4\pi}{3}\right) \end{aligned}\right\} \tag{9.1}$$

$$\left.\begin{aligned} i_{IF1} &= I_I \sin(\omega_I t + \phi_I) = c_2 I_O \sin(\omega_I t - \phi_O) \\ i_{IF2} &= I_I \sin\left(\omega_I t - \frac{2\pi}{3} + \phi_I\right) = c_2 I_O \sin\left(\omega_I t - \frac{2\pi}{3} - \phi_O\right) \\ i_{IF3} &= I_I \sin\left(\omega_I t - \frac{4\pi}{3} + \phi_I\right) = c_2 I_O \sin\left(\omega_I t - \frac{4\pi}{3} - \phi_O\right) \end{aligned}\right\} \tag{9.2}$$

where V_I is the amplitude of the input (a-c system) voltage,
V_O is the amplitude of the wanted component of the output voltage,
I_I is the amplitude of the fundamental input current,
I_O is the amplitude of the wanted component of the output current,
$c_1 = V_O/V_I$, and $c_2 = I_I/I_O$

Assume now that the outputs of the frequency changer are connected to a three-phase external voltage source (v_1, v_2, v_3)—which could be another a-c power

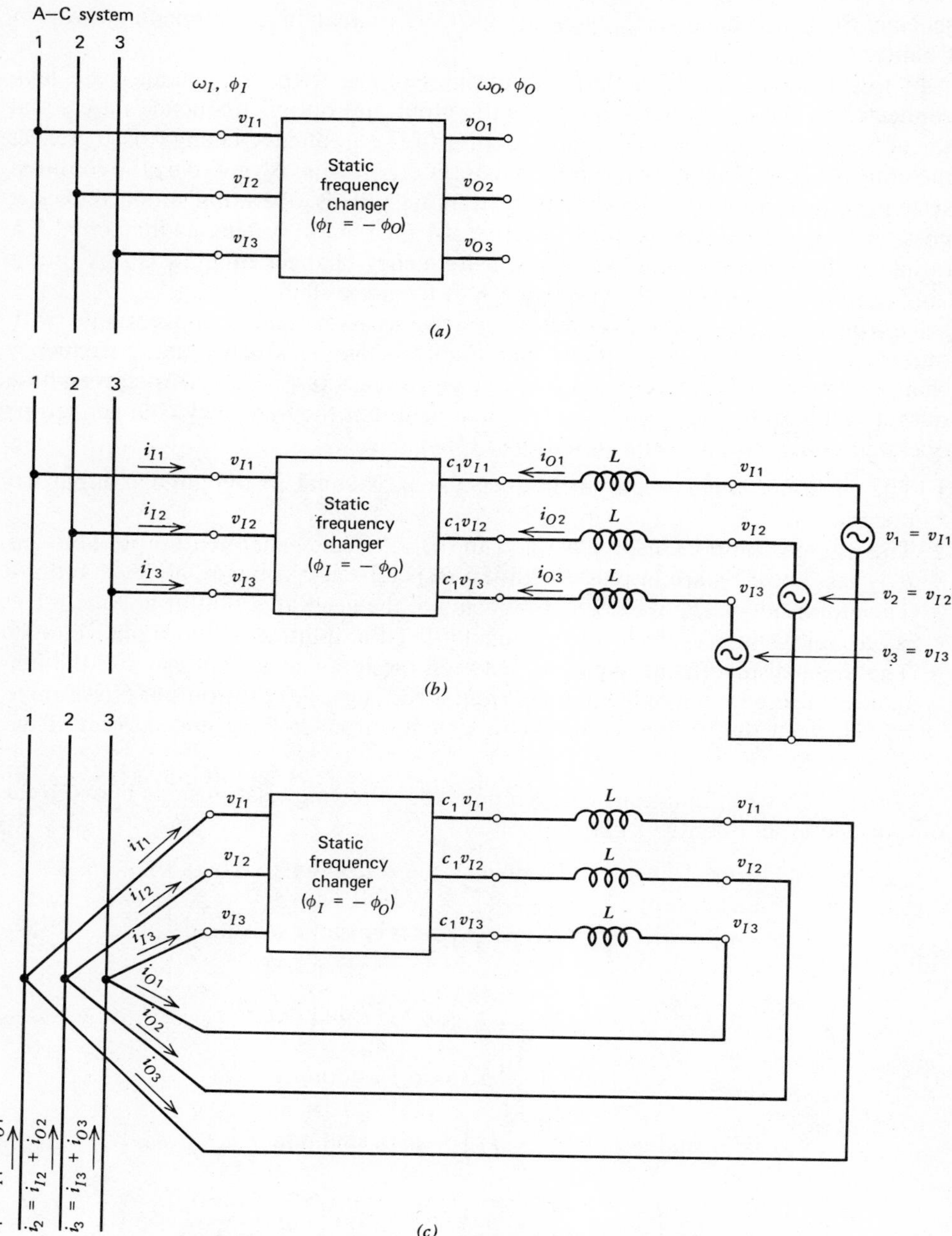

Figure 9.35 Conceptual explanation of the notion of *power doubling*.

system—via three small inductors, the values of which are theoretically unimportant. The arrangement is shown in Figure 9.35*b*. Assume further that the three voltages of the external source are in fact replicas of the input voltages—that is, $v_1 = v_{I1}$, $v_2 = v_{I2}$, and $v_3 = v_{I3}$. The frequency changer, whose output voltages are stipulated to be proportional to the input voltages, can be made to supply either lagging or leading VArs to this external source; that is, if $c_1 > 1$, the frequency changer supplies lagging current to the external source, and if $c_1 < 1$, the frequency changer supplies leading current to the external source. In the first case, the output currents of the frequency changer *lag* the corresponding wanted output voltages, which means that the frequency changer is *inductively* loaded, whereas the external source is *capacitively* loaded. In the second case, the output currents of the frequency changer *lead* the output voltages, which means that the frequency changer is *capacitively* loaded, whereas the external source is *inductively* loaded. Of course, when $c_1 = 1$, no current of fundamental frequency flows.

To proceed further with the explanation of the power-doubling concept, it is necessary to consider the fundamental input currents, i_{IF1}, i_{IF2}, and i_{IF3}, drawn by the frequency changer from the a-c system, for the three cases of $c_1 > 1$, $c_1 < 1$, and $c_1 = 1$.

As explained, if $c_1 > 1$, the wanted output currents of the frequency changer *lag* the corresponding wanted output voltages; that is, the output phase angle, ϕ_O, is $-90°$. It was stipulated at the outset that the frequency changer has the characteristic of reflecting the negative of the output phase angle to the input. Thus $\phi_I = -\phi_O = -(-90°) = 90°$. Consequently, the fundamental input currents lead the corresponding a-c system voltages by 90°. Similarly, if $c_1 < 1$, the fundamental output currents lead the output voltages of the frequency changer; that is, the output phase angle, ϕ_O, is $+90°$. The input currents now *lag* the input voltages by 90°; that is, $\phi_I = -90°$. At $c_1 = 1$, the fundamental components of the input currents are zero, since the frequency changer supplies no output currents.

On the basis of the above deductions, it can be concluded that whenever $c_1 > 1$ the currents flowing from the a-c system to the input terminals of the frequency changer *as well as* those flowing from the external source to the output terminals of the frequency changer *lead* the corresponding voltages by 90°. Similarly, whenever $c_1 < 1$, the currents flowing from the a-c system *as well as* those flowing from the external source *lag* the corresponding voltages by 90°.

These conclusions lead directly to the essence of the power-doubling concept. Since we stipulated that the voltages of the three-phase external source are perfect replicas of the a-c system voltages, it follows that the above-described current/voltage relationships will not change if the outputs of the frequency changer are removed from the external source (which was introduced only to aid the explanation) and connected instead to the a-c system, as shown in Figure 9.35c. Since both the input and output currents of the frequency changer can simultaneously be made to lead or lag the a-c system voltages, it is evident that the total reactive current supplied to the a-c system will be the sum of these currents. Thus $i_1 = i_{I1} + i_{O1}$, $i_2 = i_{I2} + i_{O2}$, and $i_3 = i_{I3} + i_{O3}$. Therefore, the total reactive power supplied to the a-c system is

$$\begin{aligned} P_Q &= 3V_{I,\mathrm{RMS}}(I_{I,\mathrm{RMS}} + I_{O,\mathrm{RMS}}) \\ &= 3V_{I,\mathrm{RMS}}\left(1 + \frac{1}{c_2}\right) I_{I,\mathrm{RMS}} \\ &= 3V_{I,\mathrm{RMS}}(1 + c_2)I_{O,\mathrm{RMS}} \end{aligned} \tag{9.3}$$

where $V_{I,\mathrm{RMS}}$ is the r.m.s. input (a-c system) voltage,
$I_{I,\mathrm{RMS}}$ is the r.m.s. value of the fundamental input current, and
$I_{O,\mathrm{RMS}}$ is the r.m.s. value of the wanted component of the output current.

If the inductance L is relatively small and thus c_1 is reasonably close to unity, the input and output currents will be approximately equal ($c_2 \cong 1$). Therefore the total reactive power may be expressed by:

$$\begin{aligned} P_Q &\cong 3V_{I,\text{RMS}} \times 2I_{I,\text{RMS}} \\ &\cong 3V_{I,\text{RMS}} \times 2I_{O,\text{RMS}} \end{aligned} \tag{9.4}$$

The VA rating (throughput) of the frequency changer, on the other hand, is

$$\begin{aligned} (VA)_{FC} &= 3V_{I,\text{RMS}} \times I_{I,\text{RMS}} \\ &\cong 3V_{I,\text{RMS}} \times I_{O,\text{RMS}} \\ &= \frac{P_Q}{2} \end{aligned} \tag{9.5}$$

Thus the VA rating (throughput) of the static frequency changer is only one-half of the maximum leading or lagging VArs supplied to the a-c system.

The principle of power-doubling has been based on the assumption that the frequency changer has special characteristics—that is, $\phi_I = -\phi_O$, and $\omega_I = \omega_O$. In fact, only the unrestricted frequency changer can unreservedly meet these requirements. However, the naturally commutated cycloconverter can also be employed in this type of scheme if the objective is to provide continuously variable *lagging* reactive power. We stated this in Chapter 1, and we explain it in a little more detail below.

A static VAr generator employing a three-phase, six-pulse UFC in the power-doubling configuration is shown schematically in Figure 9.36, and its operation is described with reference to Figure 9.37.

In practice, in order to control the reactive current supplied to the system, it is necessary to control the output voltage of the UFC. In order to simplify the theoretical waveforms of Figure 9.37, which illustrate the operation when both lagging and leading VArs are supplied to the system, it is assumed that the UFC operates at full voltage in both cases. This amounts to a tacit assumption of a slightly different turns ratio on the transformer, for the two modes of operation.

The line-to-neutral voltages of the a-c system v_1, v_2, and v_3 are illustrated in Figure 9.37*a*. The UFC is operated so that its wanted output voltages v_{Ow1}, v_{Ow2}, and v_{Ow3} (shown at *b*, *c*, and *d*) are in phase with v_1, v_2, and v_3, respectively. This can be accomplished by synchronizing the operation of the switches of the power circuit to the a-c system voltages to follow the conduction sequence indicated. For example, switches A_{11} and B_{12}, C_{21} and A_{22}, B_{31} and C_{32} are made to conduct at the instants when the voltage v_3 crosses zero. The conduction interval for any pair of switches is 1/12 of the period time, or 30 degrees; for an individual switch it is 1/6 of the period time, or 60 degrees. Thus, after a 30-degree conduction interval, that is, when voltage v_{23} crosses zero, the conduction is transferred to the following pair of switches: A_{11} and C_{12}, C_{21} and B_{22}, B_{31} and A_{32}, and so on. The amplitudes of the output voltages v_{O1}, v_{O2}, and v_{O3} are approximately equal to the amplitudes of the line-to-line voltages; the reduction factor is $3/\pi$. Therefore theoretically a $1:\sqrt{3}/\pi$ step-down ratio is required on the transformer to match the output voltages of the UFC to the a-c system voltages, assuming negligible voltage drop across the inductor L.

Consider first the case in which the amplitudes of the wanted components of the three output voltage waves, at the secondary of the transformer, are somewhat greater than those of the line-to-neutral a-c system voltages. A lagging current will flow from each output phase of the frequency changer to the corresponding phase of

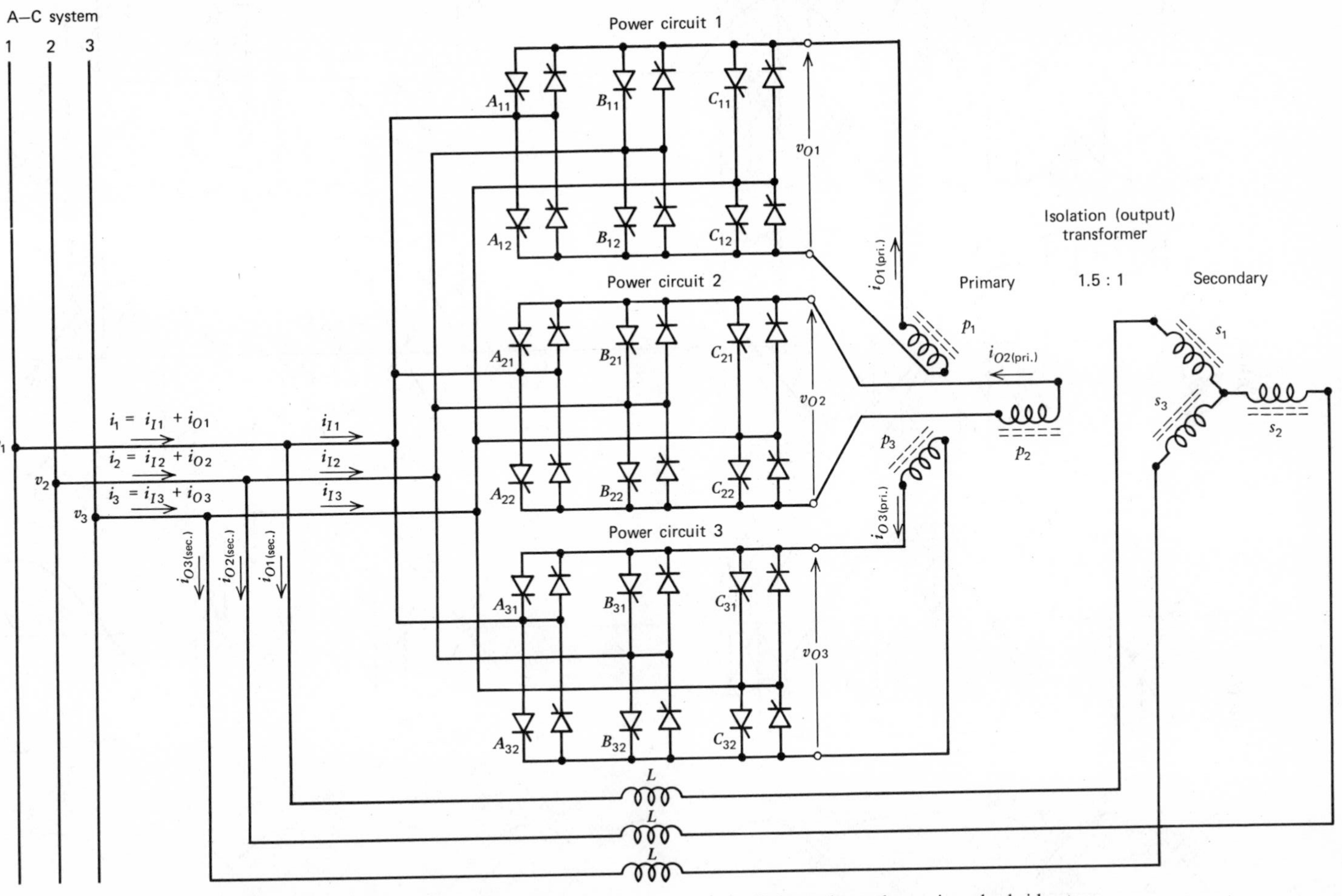

Figure 9.36 Schematic of a power-doubling VAr generator utilizing a three-phase, six-pulse bridge type unrestricted frequency changer.

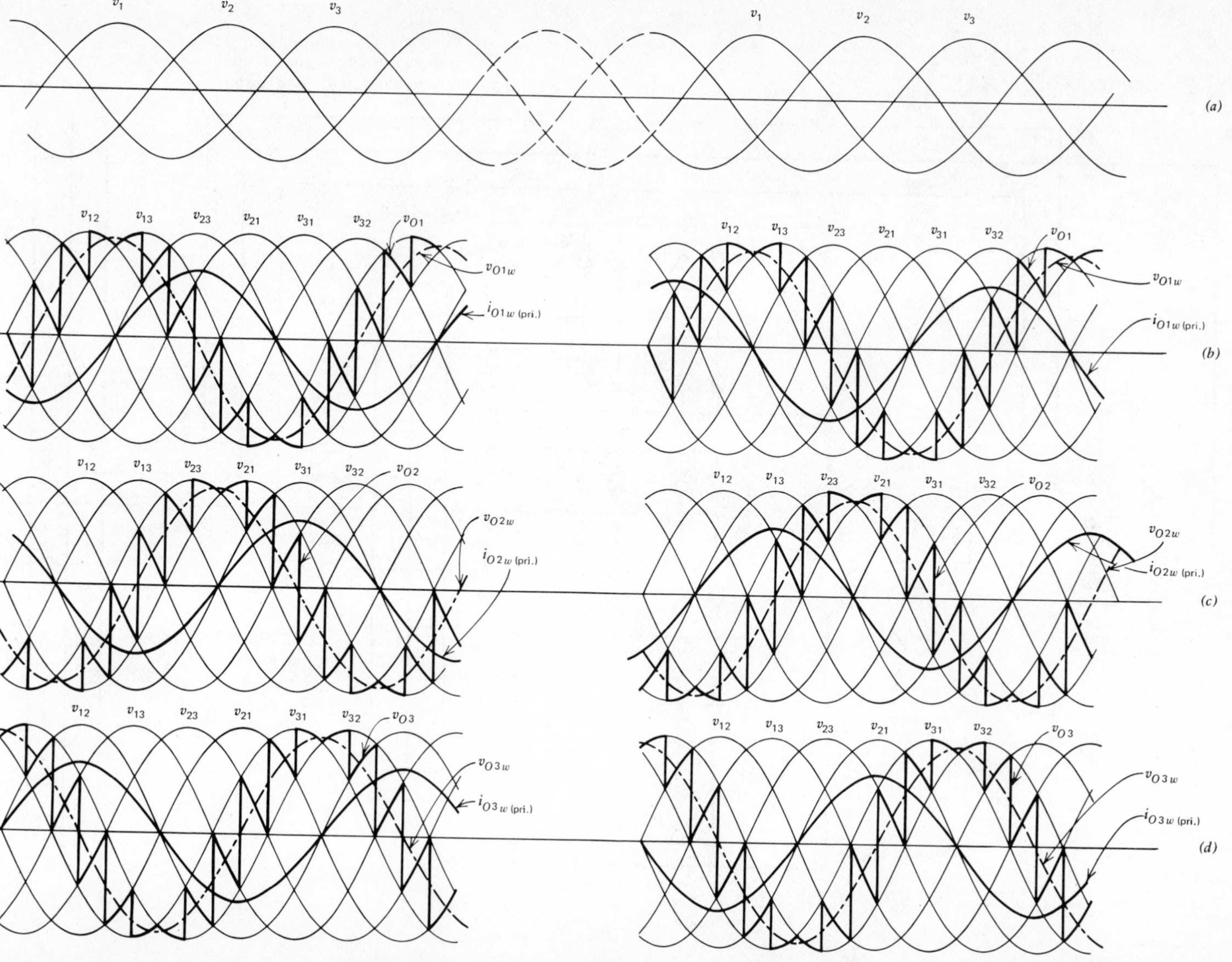

v_1
v_2
v_3
v_1
v_2
v_3
(a)
v_{12}
v_{13}
v_{23}
v_{21}
v_{31}
v_{32}
v_{O1}
v_{O1w}
$i_{O1w\,(\text{pri.})}$
(b)
v_{12}
v_{13}
v_{23}
v_{21}
v_{31}
v_{32}
v_{O2}
v_{O2w}
$i_{O2w\,(\text{pri.})}$
(c)
v_{12}
v_{13}
v_{23}
v_{21}
v_{31}
v_{32}
v_{O3}
v_{O3w}
$i_{O3w\,(\text{pri.})}$
(d)

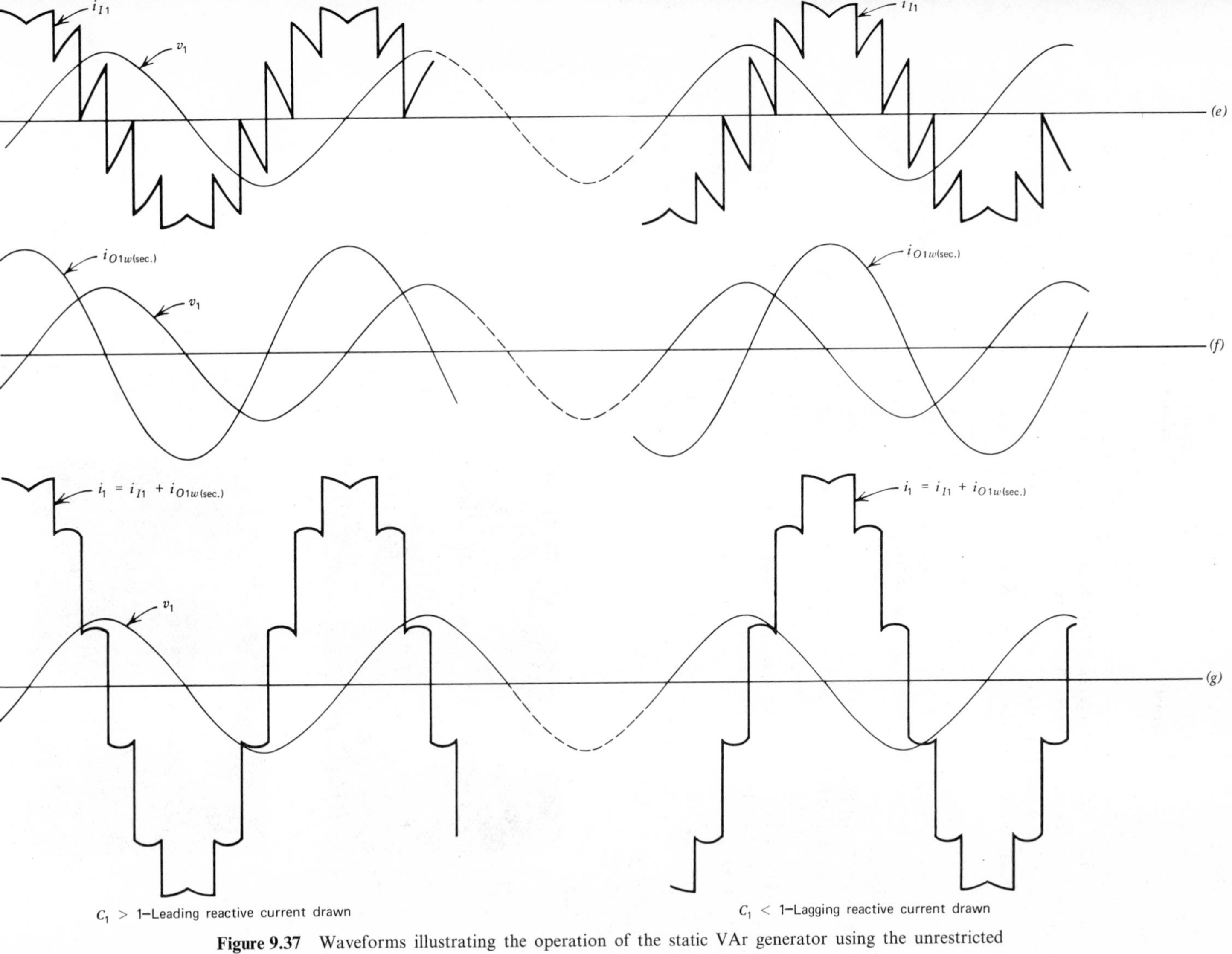

Figure 9.37 Waveforms illustrating the operation of the static VAr generator using the unrestricted frequency changer in the power-doubling scheme as shown in Figure 9.36.

the a-c system. In other words, the frequency changer constitutes a corresponding leading load on the system. The wanted components of the three output currents i_{Ow1}, i_{Ow2}, and i_{Ow3} are shown at the left-hand side of Figure 9.37 at *b*, *c*, and *d*. The three input currents i_{I1}, i_{I2}, and i_{I3} can be derived graphically from the output current waveforms shown at *b*, *c*, and *d*. One input current waveform, i_{I1}, is illustrated together with the corresponding voltage v_1 at *e*, on the left-hand side, for the case under consideration. As can be seen, the input current i_{I1} leads the corresponding voltage v_1.

One wanted output current, i_{Ow1}, flowing into the secondary of the transformer from phase 1 of the a-c system, is shown together with the corresponding voltage v_1 at *f*.

The total current flowing from line 1 of the system into the frequency changer, $(i_{I1} + i_{Ow1(\text{sec})})$, is shown at *g*. Evidently, this total current is approximately twice as large as the current "flowing through" the UFC, and it leads the corresponding system voltage.

The operation of the scheme when drawing lagging current from the a-c system is similar. In this case, the amplitudes of the output voltages of the UFC, at the secondary side of the output transformer, must be lower than those of the system voltages. The operation under this condition is illustrated in a self-explanatory manner on the right-hand side of Figure 9.37.

The operation of a static VAr generator employing an unrestricted frequency changer in the power-doubling configuration is illustrated by the oscillograms in Figure 9.38. These oscillograms are appropriate to a model system using a 6-kVA, six-pulse UFC, in the arrangement as shown in Figure 9.36. The output voltage of the

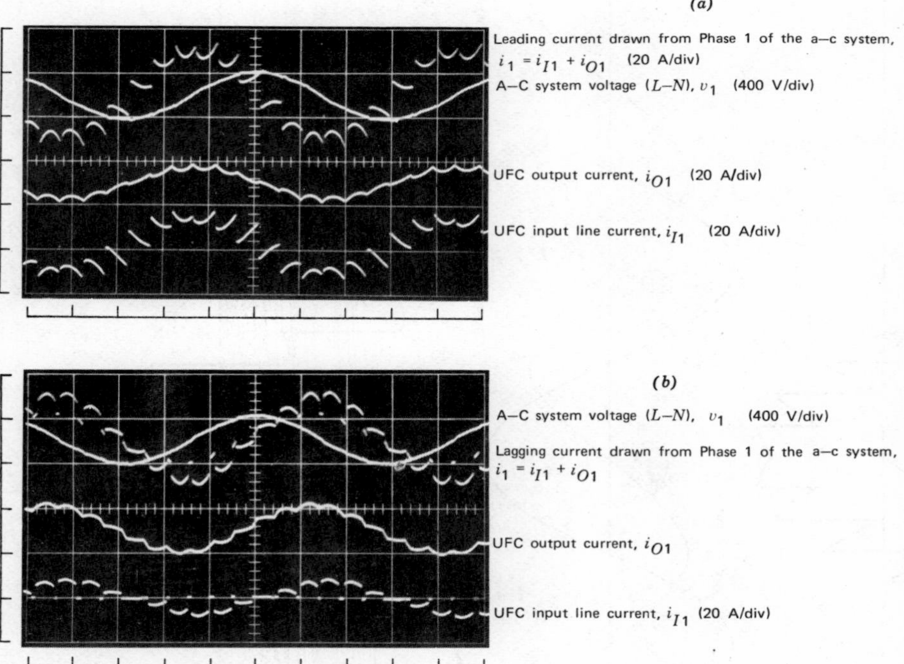

Figure 9.38 Oscillograms illustrating the operation of the power-doubling VAr generator shown in Figure 9.36. *a* Leading and *b* lagging reactive current is drawn from the a-c system.

UFC is controlled by the technique of pulse-width modulation. As can be seen, the practical waveforms are quite similar to the ideal ones shown in Figure 9.37.

As established above, an unrestricted frequency changer of 1/2 PU rating (VA throughput) can provide 1 PU leading and lagging reactive power. The operating characteristics of this general scheme are summarized for reference in Figure 9.39*a*. However, in many practical applications the generation of lagging VArs is not required. In this case, the rating of the UFC can be reduced to 1/4 PU by the *hybrid* arrangement shown in Figure 9.39*b*. A fixed capacitor of 1/2 PU VA rating is connected to the input lines, and a UFC of 1/4 PU rating is used either to "buck" or "boost" the leading VArs consumed by this fixed capacitor. Thus, continuous control from 1 PU to zero of the net leading VArs consumed by this arrangement is possible. In addition to reducing the VA rating of the frequency changer in relation to the maximum VArs, the fixed capacitor also functions as a harmonic filter.

Turning now to the possibility of using a naturally commutated cycloconverter in this type of scheme, inspection of Figure 9.37 indicates that when the frequency changer consumes *lagging* reactive power from the a-c system ($c_1 < 1$) the requirements for natural commutation of the switches of the power circuit (as outlined in Chapter 1) are satisfied. Thus the output waveforms at *b*, *c*, and *d*, on the right-hand side, show that the *incoming* voltage is always more positive than the *outgoing* one during the positive current half-cycles, and that this relationship reverses during the negative current half-cycles. Consequently, a naturally commutated cycloconverter with 1/2 PU VA rating could be employed to consume *lagging* reactive power, up to 1 PU, from the a-c system. The operating characteristics of a NCC power-doubling arrangement are summarized in Figure 9.40*a*.

Since the naturally commutated cycloconverter cannot be operated in the manner illustrated by the waveforms on the left-hand side of Figure 9.37, this arrangement as it stands cannot consume leading VArs from the system. It can, however, be used in a hybrid arrangement in conjunction with a fixed capacitor, as shown in Figure 9.40*b*, to consume controllable leading VArs from the system. Note that in this arrangement, the required VA rating of the NCC, as well as that of the fixed capacitor, is twice as high as the rating of these components in the similar scheme employing a UFC (compare Figure 9.39*b* to Figure 9.40*b*).

9.4 INTERTIES (LINKS) BETWEEN A-C POWER SYSTEMS

Another, and historically important, application of static frequency changers—the last to be considered in this book—is to tie (link) together two asynchronous a-c power systems, for the purpose of controlling power flow between them. The naturally commutated cycloconverter was originally developed for this application, that is, to tie a 50-Hz, three-phase power system to a $16\frac{2}{3}$-Hz single-phase distribution system supplying electric railroads in Germany during the 1930s.

The use of the cycloconverter as a general asynchronous tie between power systems has, however, been seriously hindered by the restriction that the frequencies of the two systems to be tied could not be too close to one another; in fact, the ratio of the two frequencies should not be greater than about $\frac{2}{3}$ is reasonable performance is to be achieved.

All frequency changers except the UFC have similar restrictions on the output to input frequency ratio. In any case, no frequency changer that requires semiconductor

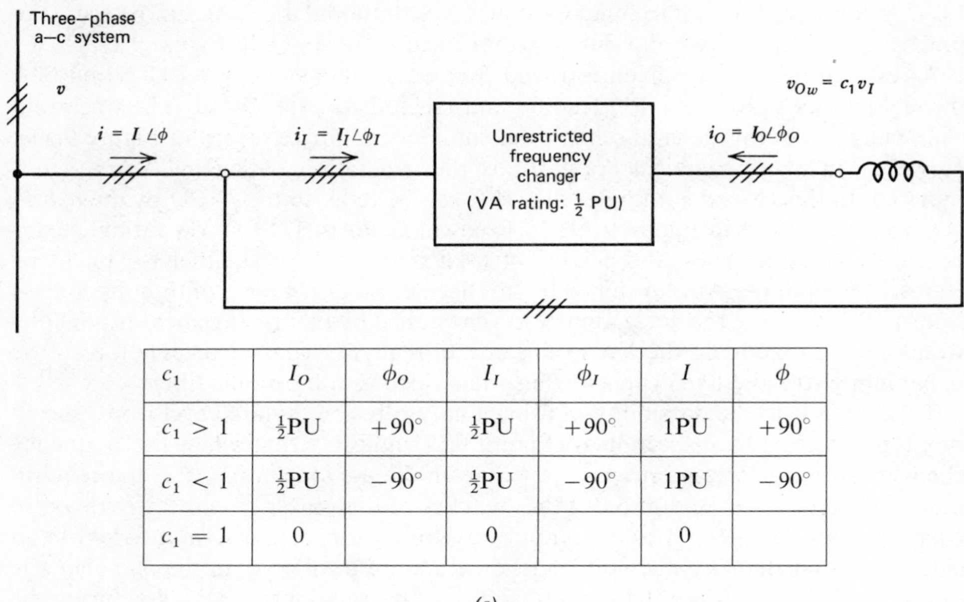

c_1	I_O	ϕ_O	I_I	ϕ_I	I	ϕ
$c_1 > 1$	$\frac{1}{2}$PU	$+90°$	$\frac{1}{2}$PU	$+90°$	1PU	$+90°$
$c_1 < 1$	$\frac{1}{2}$PU	$-90°$	$\frac{1}{2}$PU	$-90°$	1PU	$-90°$
$c_1 = 1$	0		0		0	

(a)

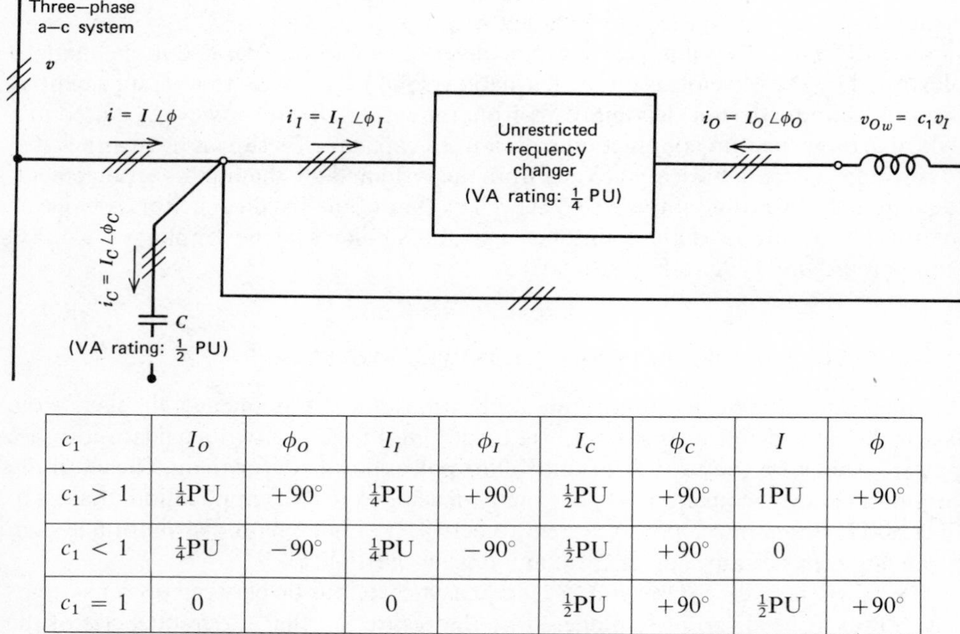

c_1	I_O	ϕ_O	I_I	ϕ_I	I_C	ϕ_C	I	ϕ
$c_1 > 1$	$\frac{1}{4}$PU	$+90°$	$\frac{1}{4}$PU	$+90°$	$\frac{1}{2}$PU	$+90°$	1PU	$+90°$
$c_1 < 1$	$\frac{1}{4}$PU	$-90°$	$\frac{1}{4}$PU	$-90°$	$\frac{1}{2}$PU	$+90°$	0	
$c_1 = 1$	0		0		$\frac{1}{2}$PU	$+90°$	$\frac{1}{2}$PU	$+90°$

Note: All phase angles are referred to the input (A-C system) voltages, output phase angle ϕ_O is opposite to that shown with respect to the wanted output voltage v_{Ow}.

(b)

Figure 9.39 Characteristics of the *a* basic and *b* hybrid power-doubling VAr generator using the unrestricted frequency changer.

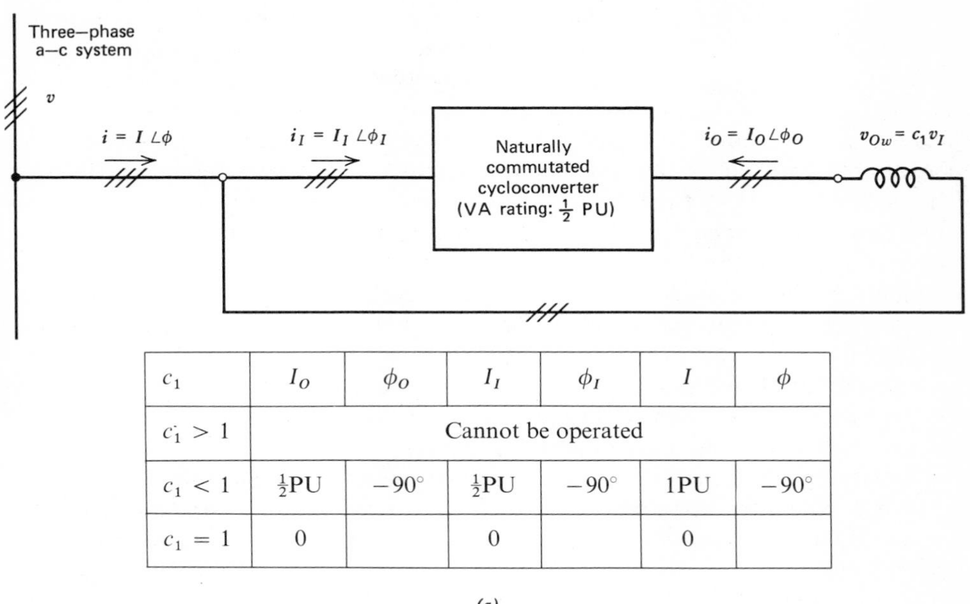

c_1	I_O	ϕ_O	I_I	ϕ_I	I	ϕ
$c_1 > 1$	Cannot be operated					
$c_1 < 1$	½PU	−90°	½PU	−90°	1PU	−90°
$c_1 = 1$	0		0		0	

(a)

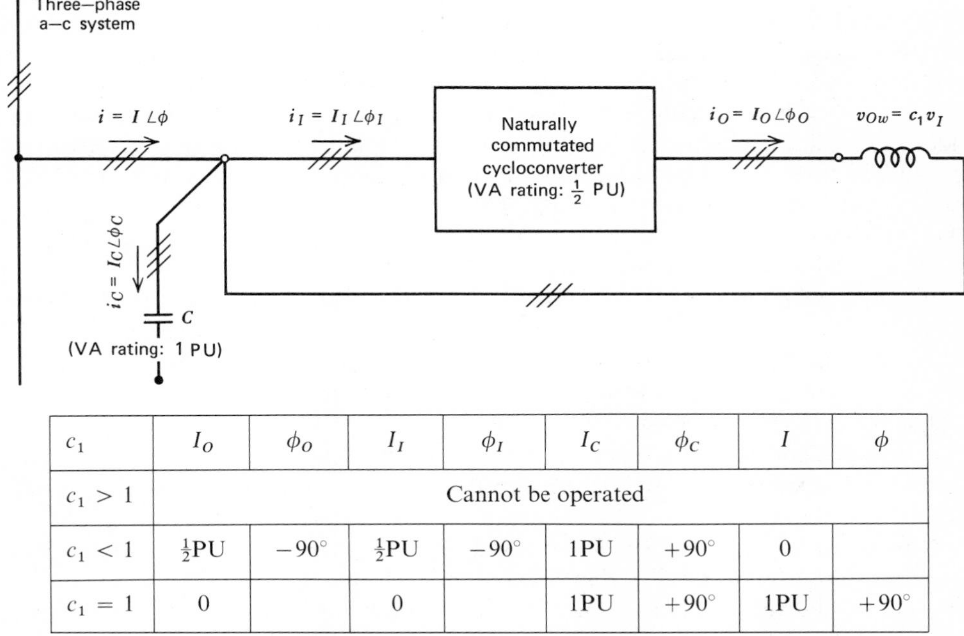

c_1	I_O	ϕ_O	I_I	ϕ_I	I_C	ϕ_C	I	ϕ
$c_1 > 1$	Cannot be operated							
$c_1 < 1$	½PU	−90°	½PU	−90°	1PU	+90°	0	
$c_1 = 1$	0		0		1PU	+90°	1PU	+90°

Note: All phase angles are referred to the input (A-C system) voltages. Output phase angle ϕ_O is opposite to that shown with respect to the wanted output voltage v_{Ow}.

(b)

Figure 9.40 Characteristics of the *a* basic and *b* hybrid power-doubling VAr generator using the naturally commutated cycloconverter.

switches with intrinsic turn-off ability, or force commutated power circuits, including the UFC, could presently be considered as viable candidates for a high-power system.

These technical difficulties can be overcome, and theoretically a perfect static intertie can be realized, by employing the *high-frequency-base* concept, introduced in the previous section. The basic idea is to use two naturally commutated cycloconverters in tandem, each with its input terminals connected to a common HF base. The output terminals of the two cycloconverters are connected to the two systems to be tied. Thus power flows from one system to the other from the output to the input terminals of the first cycloconverter, and then from the input to the output terminals of the second cycloconverter. Both cycloconverters are naturally commutated from the voltages of the HF base. As long as the base frequency is appropriately higher than that of either system, the two system frequencies can be nominally equal, although they can also be different. The power factor at either side of the tie can be maintained at unity or any other desired value. Moreover, the distortion of the current at both sides of the intertie is relatively low.

The basic principles of this scheme are explained by reference to the simplified functional diagrams shown in Figure 9.41. At *a*, two naturally commutated cycloconverters have their input terminals—that is, the terminals from which the commutation is effected—connected to a common high-frequency-base voltage generator.

Let it be assumed, first, that the high-frequency-base voltage generator delivers power to the input terminals of both cycloconverters, as illustrated at *a*. Let it be assumed further that cycloconverter 1 delivers power P_1 at frequency f_1 at its output terminals, and that cycloconverter 2 delivers power P_2 at frequency f_2 at its output terminals. Frequency f_1 may be equal to f_2 but the base frequency must be appropriately higher than either of these frequencies. Under these conditions, the total real component of current delivered from the high-frequency-base voltage generator is $i_{IR1} + i_{IR2}$, in which these currents correspond to P_1 and P_2, respectively. In addition, each cycloconverter consumes, as usual, a lagging quadrature component of current from the input supply to which it is connected, regardless of the load power factor at its output terminals. The high-frequency-base voltage generator therefore also supplies two lagging quadrature components of current, i_{IQ1} and i_{IQ2}, associated with cycloconverters 1 and 2, respectively.

Finally, each cycloconverter also draws extrabasal currents from the high-frequency-base voltage generator, although, as has been seen with a balanced three-phase output, these extrabasal currents are relatively insignificant. These currents are designated i_{E1} and i_{E2}, for cycloconverters 1 and 2, respectively.

The state of affairs discussed so far is not unusual; the situation is simply that of two independent, naturally commutated cycloconverters connected to a common input source, supplying separate, independent, loads at output frequencies f_1 and f_2.

Now consider the situation if the power flow, P_1, through cycloconverter 1 is reversed. This simply implies that a-c system 1 is now a source of power, and it delivers this power into the output terminals of cycloconverter 1. As far as the operation of the cycloconverter is concerned, this is a "natural" event, since the cycloconverter inherently is capable of accepting "regenerative" power flow—indeed, it is capable of operating at any power factor at its output terminals. Let it be assumed, furthermore, that $P_1 = P_2$. In this event, as indicated at *b*, the real power handled by the high-frequency-base voltage generator is the difference between P_1 and P_2, and this is zero; thus $i_{IR1} + i_{IR2} = 0$. In other words, power now is transmitted

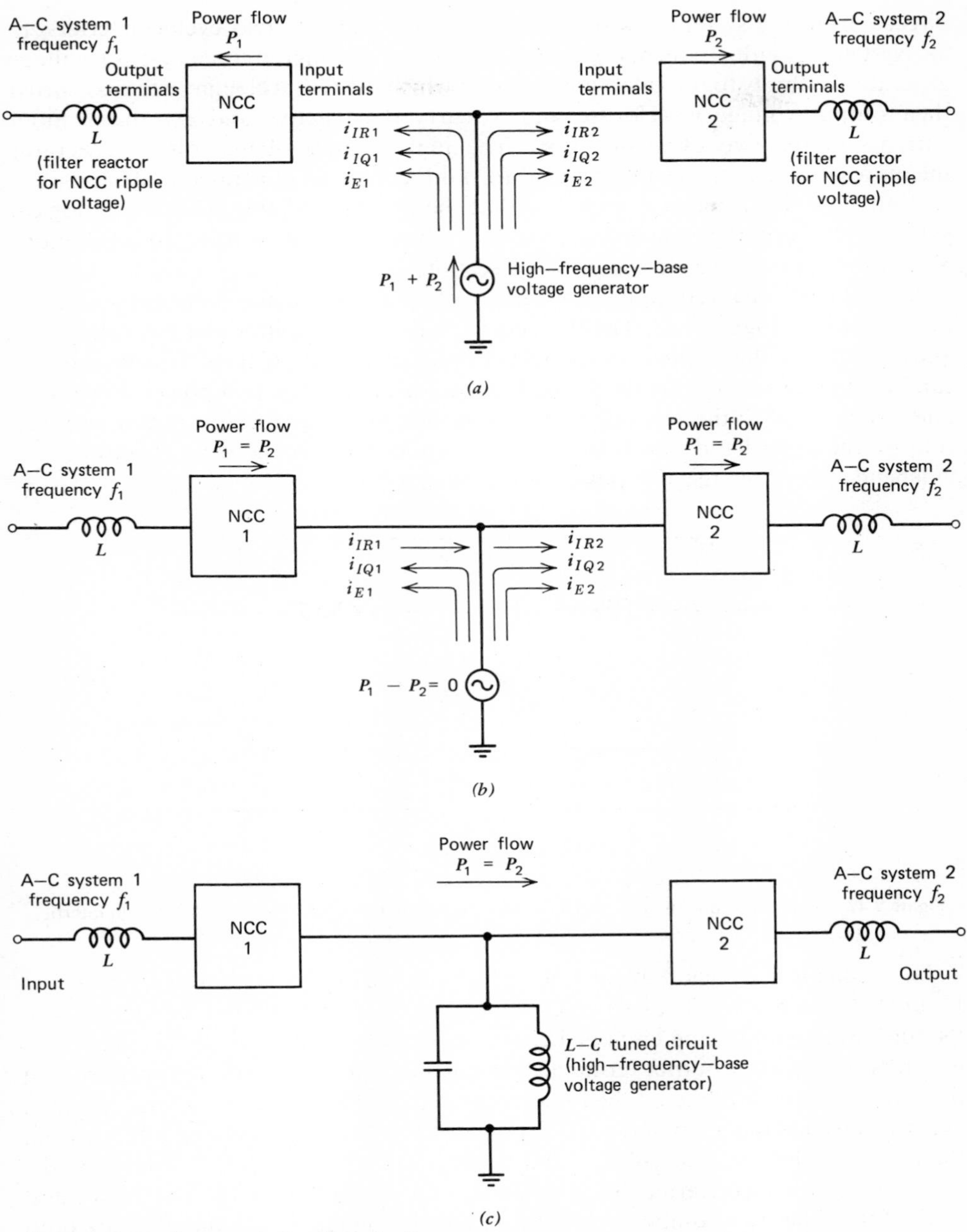

Notes: 1. Power flow may be in either direction.
2. f_1 may be equal to or different from f_2.

Figure 9.41 Simplified functional diagram explaining the concept of the high-frequency-base cycloconverter a-c system intertie.

directly from a-c system 1 with frequency f_1, through the two cycloconverters, to a-c system 2, with frequency f_2; the function of the high-frequency-base voltage generator is simply to provide a voltage from which the two cycloconverters construct their output voltage waveforms, and to carry the reactive and extrabasal input currents of the two cycloconverters. The high-frequency-base voltage generator therefore could be replaced by a tuned *LC* tank circuit, as illustrated at *c*.

With this conclusion it is apparent that the principle of this scheme is a logical generalization of the simple high-frequency-base concept applied to continuous VAr control, introduced in the previous section.

A simplified idealized equivalent circuit of a high-frequency-base asynchronous tie is shown in Figure 9.42. The frequency, phase, and amplitude of the voltages v_1 and v_2—that is, the wanted components of output voltage of the cycloconverters—can be adjusted independently of one another, as long as the real power flow out of one side is equal to the real power flow into the other. The reactive power at either side, on the other hand, can be controlled in either the lagging or leading direction, independently of the reactive power at the other side.

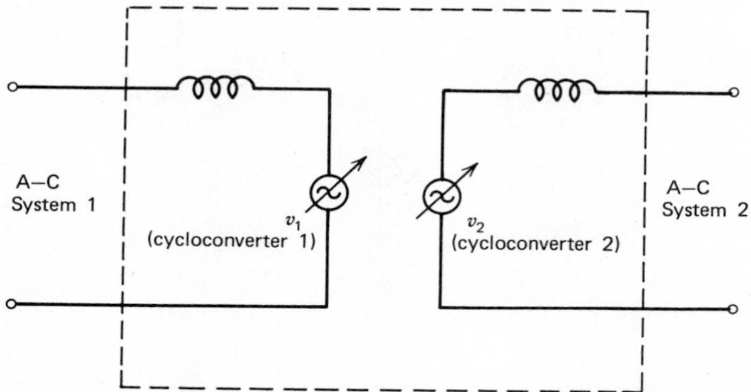

Figure 9.42 Simplified equivalent circuit of a high-frequency-base cycloconverter a-c system intertie.

The elements of a basic control scheme for this type of system intertie are shown in Figure 9.43. As previously explained, each cycloconverter, taken in conjunction with its pulse timing and firing circuits, behaves essentially as a linear voltage amplifier, which produces at its output terminals a wanted component of voltage proportional to, and in phase with, the applied reference voltage. The reference voltage for each cycloconverter is made up of three components. The first, v_S^*, is derived directly from the corresponding system voltage, and it produces a component of voltage at the output of the cycloconverter that is equal to, and in phase with, the system voltage. Thus, if the other two components of the reference voltage, $v_{0,180}^*$ and $v_{\pm 90}^*$ are both zero, no current flows at the output terminals of the cycloconverter.

The component of reference voltage $v_{0,180}^*$ is derived from the 0°/180° *sinewave generator*, and this voltage is either in phase or in antiphase with v_S^*, depending on the polarity of a d-c signal applied at the input of this functional block. Thus variation of the amplitude and sign of this component of reference voltage produces a corresponding variation in the reactive component of current drawn from the system.

The d-c input signal to the 0°/180° sinewave generator is the sum of the quadrature current reference signal I_Q^*, representing the desired quadrature current, and a

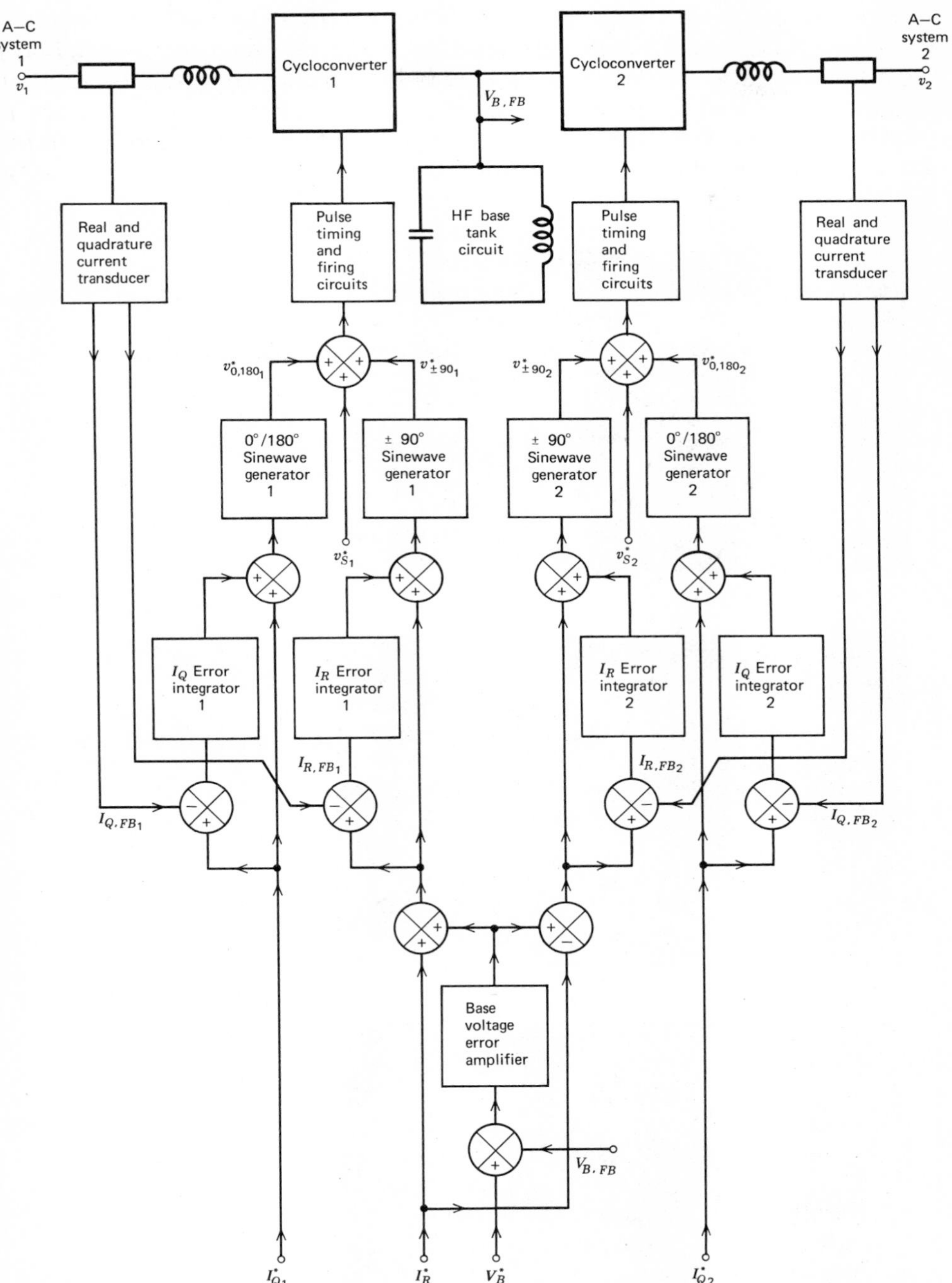

Figure 9.43 Simplified schematic representation of a basic control scheme for a high-frequency-base cycloconverter a-c system intertie.

correction signal that is the integrated error between I_Q^* and a feedback signal representing the actual quadrature component of current flowing in the system, $I_{Q,FB}$. The action of this feedback loop is such as to force the actual system quadrature current to correspond to the reference value.

The component of reference voltage $v_{\pm 90}^{\circ}$ is derived from the $\pm 90°$ *sinewave generator*, and this voltage either leads or lags v_S^* by 90°, depending on the polarity

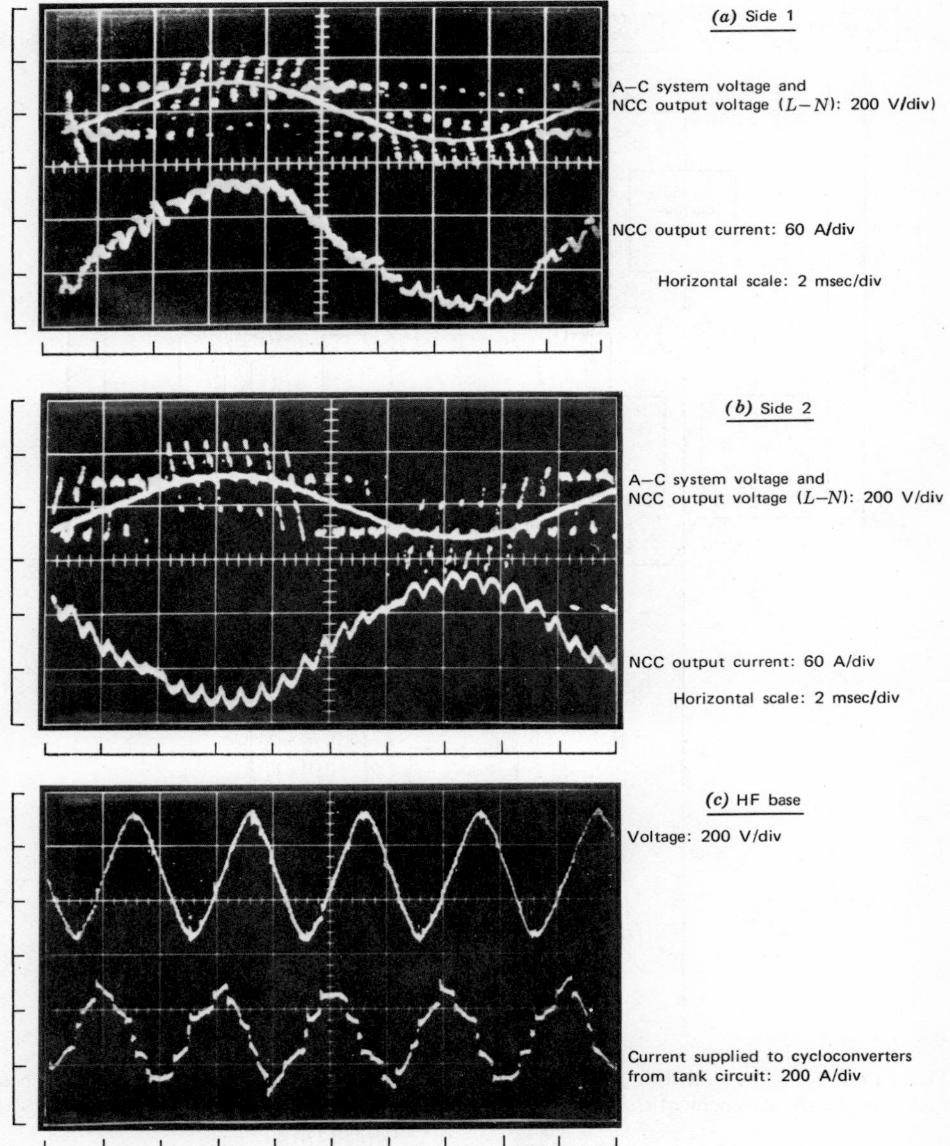

Figure 9.44 Oscillograms illustrating the operation of a high-frequency-base cycloconverter a-c system intertie when all phases at side 1 of the intertie draw full current at 0° from a-c system 1, and all phases at side 2 of the intertie deliver full current at 0° to a-c system 2.

of a d-c signal applied at the input of this functional block. Thus variation of the amplitude and sign of this component of reference voltage produces a corresponding variation in the real component of current supplied to, or drawn from, the a-c system.

The d-c input signal to the $\pm 90^\circ$ sinewave reference generator is essentially the sum of the real current reference signal, I_R^*, and a correction signal that is the integrated error between I_R^* and a feedback signal representing the actual real component of current flowing in the system, $I_{R,FB}$. Again, the action of this feedback loop is such as to force the actual real component of current to correspond to the reference value.

In theory, all that is necessary to make the real power flowing into one side equal to the real power flowing out of the other is to apply a common real current reference to both cycloconverters, but with opposite polarity. On the assumption that the system voltages at both sides are equal, this will produce the desired equal but opposite power flow at the two sides. The quadrature currents at each side, on the other hand, can be adjusted independently of one another, since these do not contribute to any net real power flow through the intertie.

In practice, since the basic requirement is for substantially equal *power* at each side, some means of modifying the real *current* reference signals against changes of *voltage* at the two sides must be included; in addition, some means of automatically trimming the reference signals to take care of the losses both in the tank circuit and the cycloconverters must be incorporated so that the proper power balance is maintained between the two sides.

The level of voltage across the high-frequency-base tank circuit is a direct indicator of the state of power balance of the system. A tendency for the base voltage to decrease below the desired level is indicative of a tendency for the input power to be less than the output power, whereas the reverse is true for a higher than normal base voltage. Thus the necessary automatic correction of the real current reference signals, which forces the proper power balance between the two sides, can be based on a comparison of a signal representing the actual tank circuit voltage $V_{B,FB}$ with a preset reference signal, V_B^*, representing the desired value, with the error being applied in the proper sense to the real current reference signals of the two sides, so as to eliminate itself.

The operation of a model scheme of this type is illustrated by the oscillograms shown in Figure 9.44. These oscillograms are applicable to a 15-kVA (throughput) experimental system using simple three-pulse three-phase naturally commutated cycloconverters, with a passive three-phase, 450-Hz base. The output voltage and current waveforms of one phase of cycloconverter 1 absorbing real power at unity power factor from system 1 are shown at *a*; those of cycloconverter 2 supplying real power at unity power factor to system 2 are shown at *b*. The voltage waveform across one phase of the tank circuit and the corresponding waveform of the total base current drawn by the two cycloconverters are shown at *c*. It is of interest to note that this current is indeed essentially reactive.

APPENDIX

TABLE A.1. Values of the Coefficients of the Harmonic Series Described by Expression (4.30)

r	$a_{2,0}$	$a_{2,2}$	$a_{4,0}$	$a_{4,2}$	$a_{4,4}$	$a_{8,0}$	$a_{8,2}$	$a_{8,4}$	$a_{8,6}$	$a_{8,8}$	$a_{10,0}$	$a_{10,2}$	$a_{10,4}$	$a_{10,6}$	$a_{10,8}$	$a_{10,10}$
1.0	0.000	1.000	0.000	0.000	1.000	0.000	0.000	0.000	0.000	1.000	0.000	0.000	0.000	0.000	0.000	1.000
0.9	0.190	0.810	−0.272	0.616	0.656	−0.043	0.139	−0.334	0.808	0.430	−0.109	0.197	−0.108	−0.146	0.818	0.349
0.8	0.360	0.640	−0.331	0.922	0.410	0.237	−0.466	0.307	0.755	0.168	−0.119	0.302	−0.479	0.585	0.604	0.107
0.7	0.510	0.490	−0.240	1.000	0.240	0.172	−0.478	0.769	0.480	0.058	0.205	−0.355	0.050	0.777	0.294	0.028
0.6	0.640	0.360	−0.051	0.922	0.130	−0.129	0.050	0.823	0.239	0.017	0.227	−0.562	0.660	0.561	0.107	0.006
0.5	0.750	0.250	0.188	0.750	0.063	−0.363	0.656	0.609	0.094	0.004	−0.100	−0.029	0.820	0.278	0.029	0.001
0.4	0.840	0.160	0.437	0.538	0.026	−0.329	0.967	0.334	0.028	0.001	−0.377	0.685	0.591	0.096	0.006	0.000
0.3	0.910	0.090	0.664	0.328	0.008	−0.010	0.876	0.129	0.005	0.000	−0.268	0.977	0.270	0.021	0.001	0.000
0.2	0.960	0.040	0.845	0.154	0.002	0.451	0.520	0.029	0.000	0.000	0.218	0.712	0.067	0.002	0.000	0.000
0.1	0.990	0.010	0.960	0.040	0.000	0.846	0.152	0.002	0.000	0.000	0.765	0.231	0.005	0.000	0.000	0.000

TABLE A.2. Values of the Coefficients of the Harmonic Series Described by Expression (4.31)

r	$b_{5,1}$	$b_{5,3}$	$b_{5,5}$	$b_{7,1}$	$b_{7,3}$	$b_{7,5}$	$b_{7,7}$	$b_{11,1}$	$b_{11,3}$	$b_{11,5}$	$b_{11,7}$	$b_{11,9}$	$b_{11,11}$	$b_{13,1}$	$b_{13,3}$	$b_{13,5}$	$b_{13,7}$	$b_{13,9}$	$b_{13,11}$	$b_{13,13}$
1.0	0.000	0.000	1.000	0.000	0.000	0.000	1.000	0.000	0.000	0.000	0.000	0.000	1.000	0.000	0.000	0.000	0.000	0.000	0.000	1.000
0.9	−0.530	0.693	0.591	0.276	−0.417	0.785	0.478	−0.300	0.284	−0.208	−0.050	0.810	0.314	0.285	−0.313	0.353	−0.349	0.134	0.775	0.254
0.8	−0.403	0.922	0.328	−0.306	0.103	0.826	0.210	0.012	0.110	−0.384	0.664	0.532	0.086	−0.374	0.356	−0.248	−0.107	0.729	0.402	0.055
0.7	0.036	0.875	0.168	−0.624	0.649	0.600	0.082	0.488	−0.508	0.294	0.716	0.226	0.020	0.058	0.089	−0.401	0.607	0.551	0.131	0.010
0.6	0.538	0.691	0.078	−0.409	0.890	0.348	0.028	0.017	−0.306	0.758	0.434	0.071	0.004	0.498	−0.540	0.317	0.692	0.238	0.030	0.002
0.5	0.938	0.469	0.031	0.164	0.820	0.164	0.008	−0.612	0.419	0.693	0.177	0.016	0.000	−0.133	−0.195	0.766	0.390	0.067	0.005	0.000
0.4	1.142	0.269	0.010	0.771	0.572	0.060	0.002	−0.454	0.863	0.381	0.048	0.002	0.000	−0.674	0.613	0.603	0.130	0.012	0.000	0.000
0.3	1.119	0.123	0.002	1.128	0.298	0.015	0.000	0.406	0.734	0.127	0.008	0.000	0.000	−0.092	0.862	0.246	0.024	0.001	0.000	0.000
0.2	0.883	0.038	0.000	1.086	0.101	0.002	0.000	1.107	0.328	0.021	0.001	0.000	0.000	0.933	0.476	0.045	0.002	0.000	0.000	0.000
0.1	0.485	0.005	0.000	0.659	0.014	0.000	0.000	0.943	0.051	0.001	0.000	0.000	0.000	1.045	0.082	0.002	0.000	0.000	0.000	0.000

TABLE A.3. Values of the Coefficients of the Harmonic Series Described by Expression (4.32)

r	$a_{1,0}$	$a_{1,2}$	$a_{1,4}$	$a_{1,6}$	$a_{1,8}$	$a_{1,10}$	$a_{1,12}$	$a_{1,14}$	$a_{1,16}$
1.0	0.637	0.424	−0.085	0.036	−0.020	0.013	−0.009	0.007	−0.005
0.9	0.746	0.277	−0.277	0.005	−0.001	0.000	0.000	0.000	0.000
0.8	0.813	0.198	−0.012	0.002	0.000	0.000	0.000	0.000	0.000
0.7	0.863	0.142	−0.006	0.000	0.000	0.000	0.000	0.000	0.000
0.6	0.903	0.100	−0.003	0.000	0.000	0.000	0.000	0.000	0.000
0.5	0.934	0.067	−0.001	0.000	0.000	0.000	0.000	0.000	0.000
0.4	0.959	0.042	0.000	0.000	0.000	0.000	0.000	0.000	0.000
0.3	0.977	0.023	0.000	0.000	0.000	0.000	0.000	0.000	0.000
0.2	0.990	0.010	0.000	0.000	0.000	0.000	0.000	0.000	0.000
0.1	0.997	0.003	0.000	0.000	0.000	0.000	0.000	0.000	0.000

r	$a_{5,0}$	$a_{5,2}$	$a_{5,4}$	$a_{5,6}$	$a_{5,8}$	$a_{5,10}$	$a_{5,12}$	$a_{5,14}$	$a_{5,16}$
1.0	0.127	−0.303	0.707	0.579	−0.163	0.085	−0.053	0.037	−0.028
0.9	−0.014	−0.079	0.921	0.187	−0.019	0.004	−0.001	0.000	0.000
0.8	−0.260	0.460	0.727	0.077	−0.004	0.001	0.000	0.000	0.000
0.7	−0.360	0.840	0.490	0.031	−0.001	0.000	0.000	0.000	0.000
0.6	−0.290	0.987	0.291	0.011	0.000	0.000	0.000	0.000	0.000
0.5	−0.083	0.929	0.150	0.004	0.000	0.000	0.000	0.000	0.000
0.4	0.201	0.733	0.065	0.001	0.000	0.000	0.000	0.000	0.000
0.3	0.502	0.476	0.021	0.000	0.000	0.000	0.000	0.000	0.000
0.2	0.763	0.233	0.004	0.000	0.000	0.000	0.000	0.000	0.000
0.1	0.938	0.061	0.000	0.000	0.000	0.000	0.000	0.000	0.000

r	$a_{7,0}$	$a_{7,2}$	$a_{7,4}$	$a_{7,6}$	$a_{7,8}$	$a_{7,10}$	$a_{7,12}$	$a_{7,14}$	$a_{7,16}$
1.0	−0.091	0.198	−0.270	0.686	0.594	−0.175	0.094	−0.061	0.043
0.9	0.169	−0.322	0.193	0.828	0.142	−0.013	0.002	−0.001	0.000
0.8	0.208	−0.513	0.736	0.526	0.045	−0.002	0.000	0.000	0.000
0.7	−0.043	−0.102	0.857	0.274	0.014	0.000	0.000	0.000	0.000
0.6	−0.304	0.483	0.697	0.120	0.004	0.000	0.000	0.000	0.000
0.5	−0.377	0.890	0.443	0.043	0.001	0.000	0.000	0.000	0.000
0.4	−0.203	0.971	0.220	0.012	0.000	0.000	0.000	0.000	0.000
0.3	0.154	0.764	0.080	0.002	0.000	0.000	0.000	0.000	0.000
0.2	0.563	0.420	0.017	0.000	0.000	0.000	0.000	0.000	0.000
0.1	0.881	0.118	0.001	0.000	0.000	0.000	0.000	0.000	0.000

r	$a_{11,0}$	$a_{11,2}$	$a_{11,4}$	$a_{11,6}$	$a_{11,8}$	$a_{11,10}$	$a_{11,12}$	$a_{11,14}$	$a_{11,16}$
1.0	−0.058	0.120	−0.133	0.165	−0.246	0.667	0.609	−0.187	0.104
0.9	0.075	−0.181	0.277	−0.437	0.547	0.641	0.083	−0.007	0.001
0.8	−0.209	0.430	−0.418	0.169	0.753	0.259	0.016	0.001	0.000
0.7	0.038	0.016	−0.325	0.717	0.472	0.080	0.003	0.000	0.000
0.6	0.278	−0.566	0.371	0.697	0.200	0.019	0.000	0.000	0.000
0.5	0.070	−0.341	0.803	0.405	0.060	0.003	0.000	0.000	0.000
0.4	−0.308	0.438	0.704	0.154	0.012	0.000	0.000	0.000	0.000
0.3	−0.348	0.954	0.357	0.035	0.001	0.000	0.000	0.000	0.000
0.2	0.105	0.797	0.095	0.004	0.000	0.000	0.000	0.000	0.000
0.1	0.719	0.274	0.007	0.000	0.000	0.000	0.000	0.000	0.000

r	$a_{13,0}$	$a_{13,2}$	$a_{13,4}$	$a_{13,6}$	$a_{13,8}$	$a_{13,10}$	$a_{13,12}$	$a_{13,14}$	$a_{13,16}$
1.0	0.049	−0.100	0.108	−0.124	0.158	−0.240	0.662	0.613	−0.190
0.9	0.064	−0.110	0.042	0.103	−0.360	0.646	0.555	0.064	−0.005
0.8	0.044	−0.132	0.271	−0.465	0.444	0.652	0.178	0.010	0.000
0.7	−0.221	0.459	−0.441	0.128	0.723	0.308	0.042	0.001	0.000
0.6	0.078	−0.054	−0.296	0.703	0.466	0.095	0.007	0.000	0.000
0.5	0.279	−0.604	0.473	0.651	0.181	0.020	0.001	0.000	0.000
0.4	−0.061	−0.118	0.815	0.318	0.043	0.003	0.000	0.000	0.000
0.3	−0.394	0.756	0.547	0.085	0.005	0.000	0.000	0.000	0.000
0.2	−0.102	0.923	0.169	0.010	0.000	0.000	0.000	0.000	0.000
0.1	0.619	0.367	0.013	0.000	0.000	0.000	0.000	0.000	0.000

TABLE A.4. **Values of the Coefficients of the Harmonic Series Described by Expression (4.33)**

r	$b_{2,1}$	$b_{2,3}$	$b_{2,5}$	$b_{2,7}$	$b_{2,9}$	$b_{2,11}$	$b_{2,13}$	$b_{2,15}$	$b_{2,17}$	$b_{4,1}$	$b_{4,3}$	$b_{4,5}$	$b_{4,7}$	$b_{4,9}$	$b_{4,11}$	$b_{4,13}$	$b_{4,15}$	$b_{4,17}$
1.0	0.849	0.509	−0.121	0.057	−0.033	0.022	−0.015	0.012	−0.009	−0.340	0.728	0.566	−0.154	0.078	−0.049	0.033	−0.024	0.019
0.9	1.094	0.273	−0.029	0.006	−0.001	0.000	0.000	0.000	0.000	−0.249	0.966	0.215	−0.022	0.004	−0.001	0.000	0.000	0.000
0.8	1.141	0.169	−0.011	0.001	0.000	0.000	0.000	0.000	0.000	0.199	0.845	0.101	−0.006	0.001	0.000	0.000	0.000	0.000
0.7	1.109	0.104	−0.004	0.000	0.000	0.000	0.000	0.000	0.000	0.638	0.647	0.046	−0.002	0.000	0.000	0.000	0.000	0.000
0.6	1.023	0.062	−0.002	0.000	0.000	0.000	0.000	0.000	0.000	0.964	0.447	0.020	−0.001	0.000	0.000	0.000	0.000	0.000
0.5	0.901	0.034	−0.001	0.000	0.000	0.000	0.000	0.000	0.000	1.134	0.276	0.008	0.000	0.000	0.000	0.000	0.000	0.000
0.4	0.750	0.017	0.000	0.000	0.000	0.000	0.000	0.000	0.000	1.143	0.148	0.002	0.000	0.000	0.000	0.000	0.000	0.000
0.3	0.579	0.007	0.000	0.000	0.000	0.000	0.000	0.000	0.000	1.003	0.065	0.001	0.000	0.000	0.000	0.000	0.000	0.000
0.2	0.394	0.002	0.000	0.000	0.000	0.000	0.000	0.000	0.000	0.741	0.020	0.000	0.000	0.000	0.000	0.000	0.000	0.000
0.1	0.199	0.000	0.000	0.000	0.000	0.000	0.000	0.000	0.000	0.393	0.002	0.000	0.000	0.000	0.000	0.000	0.000	0.000

r	$b_{8,1}$	$b_{8,3}$	$b_{8,5}$	$b_{8,7}$	$b_{8,9}$	$b_{8,11}$	$b_{8,13}$	$b_{8,15}$	$b_{8,17}$	$b_{10,1}$	$b_{10,3}$	$b_{10,5}$	$b_{10,7}$	$b_{10,9}$	$b_{10,11}$	$b_{10,13}$	$b_{10,15}$	$b_{10,17}$
1.0	−0.162	0.185	−0.261	0.679	0.599	−0.179	0.097	−0.063	0.045	0.129	−0.140	0.170	−0.250	0.670	0.606	−0.185	0.102	−0.067
0.9	0.391	−0.397	0.304	0.780	0.124	−0.011	−0.002	0.000	0.000	−0.286	0.345	−0.449	0.480	0.686	0.095	−0.008	0.001	0.000
0.8	0.158	−0.367	0.788	0.444	0.035	−0.002	0.000	0.000	0.000	0.362	−0.290	−0.004	0.787	0.311	0.021	0.001	0.000	0.000
0.7	−0.442	0.221	0.776	0.203	0.009	0.000	0.000	0.000	0.000	0.327	−0.503	0.631	0.571	0.109	0.004	0.000	0.000	0.000
0.6	−0.631	0.736	0.534	0.076	0.002	0.000	0.000	0.000	0.000	−0.339	0.043	0.788	0.284	0.030	0.001	0.000	0.000	0.000
0.5	−0.235	0.889	0.281	0.023	0.000	0.000	0.000	0.000	0.000	−0.658	0.680	0.568	0.103	0.006	0.000	0.000	0.000	0.000
0.4	0.460	0.716	0.111	0.005	0.000	0.000	0.000	0.000	0.000	−0.197	0.879	0.274	0.026	0.001	0.000	0.000	0.000	0.000
0.3	1.025	0.407	0.030	0.001	0.000	0.000	0.000	0.000	0.000	0.648	0.634	0.085	0.004	0.000	0.000	0.000	0.000	0.000
0.2	1.141	0.146	0.004	0.000	0.000	0.000	0.000	0.000	0.000	1.151	0.260	0.013	0.000	0.000	0.000	0.000	0.000	0.000
0.1	0.738	0.020	0.000	0.000	0.000	0.000	0.000	0.000	0.000	0.881	0.039	0.000	0.000	0.000	0.000	0.000	0.000	0.000

SELECTED BIBLIOGRAPHY

BOOKS

1. Rissik, H., *Mercury Arc Current Convertors*, Sir Isaac Pitman & Sons, 1935.
2. Rissik, H., *The Fundamental Theory of Arc Convertors*, Chapman & Hall, 1939.
3. Pelly, B. R., *Thyristor Phase-Controlled Converters and Cycloconverters*, Wiley-Interscience, 1971.
4. McMurray, W., *The Theory and Design of Cycloconverters*, The MIT Press, 1972.

EARLY LITERATURE

5. Hazeltine, L. A., "An Improved Method of and Apparatus for Converting Electric Power," British Patent No. 218.675, Jan. 4, 1926.
6. Schenkel, M., "Eine unmittelbare Asynchrone Umrichtung für niederfrequente Bahnnuetze," *Electr. Bahnen*, **8**, 69–73 (1932).
7. Von Issendorff, J., "Der Gesteuerte Umrichter," *Wiss. Veröff. Siemens*, **14**, 1–31 (1935).

RECENT LITERATURE

8. Chirgwin, K. M., and Stratton, L. J., "Variable-Speed Constant-Frequency Generator System for Aircraft," *AIEE Trans. Appl. Ind.*, **78**, pt. II, 304–310 (1959).
9. Jessee, R. D., and Spaven, W. J., "Constant-Frequency AC Power Using Variable Speed Generation," *AIEE Trans. Appl. Ind.*, **78**, pt. II, 411–418 (1959).
10. Chirgwin, K. M., Stratton, L. J., and Toth, J. R., "Precise Frequency Power Generation from an Unregulated Shaft," *AIEE Trans. Appl. Ind.*, **79**, pt. II, 442–451 (1960).
11. Caldwell, S. C., Peaslee, L. R., and Plette, D. L., "The Frequency Converter Approach to a Variable Speed Constant Frequency System," *AIEE Conf. Paper*, CP 60–1076, August 1960.
12. Ward, L. J. and Sinclair, W., "Production of Constant Frequency Electrical Power for Aircraft Using Static Equipment," Paper given at the Joint Conference of the Royal Aeronautical Society and the IEE in 1962.
13. VanEck, R. A., "Frequency-Changer Systems Using the Cycloconverter Principle," *IEEE Trans. Appl. Ind.*, 163–168, May 1963.
14. Heck, R., and Meyer, M., "A Static Frequency-Changer-Fed Squirrel-Cage Motor Drive for Variable Speed and Reversing," *Siemens Rev.*, No. 11, 401–405, November 1963.
15. Plette, D. L., and Carlson, H. G., "Performance of a Variable-Speed Constant Frequency Electrical System," *IEEE Trans. Aerospace*, Vol. AS-2, 957–970, April 1964.
16. Faust, W., "Static Frequency Changers for $16\frac{2}{3}$ c/s Railway Networks," *Brown Boveri Rev.*, Vol. 51, No. 8/9, 519–525 (1964).
17. Schönung, A., "Varying the Speed of Three-Phase Motors by Means of Static Frequency Changers," *Brown Boveri Rev.*, Vol. 51, No. 8/9, 540–554 (1964).
18. Guyeska, J. C., and Jordan, H. E., "Cycloconverter Adjustable Frequency Drives," *IEEE Textile Ind. Conf.*, October 1–2, 1964.
19. Guyeska, J. C., and Jordan, H. E., "Static AC Variable Frequency Drive," *Proc. Nat. Elec. Conf.*, Vol. 20, 358–365 (1964).
20. Brown, M., and Harvery, W. T., "A Variable Frequency Supply for Induction Motors," *Proc. Conf. Appl. Large Ind. Drives*, London, England, 120–123, May 5–7, 1965.
21. Amato, C. J., and Diczhazy, R. B., "Lower Order Distortion Terms in Frequency Converters," *Proc. IEEE Nat. Aerospace Elect. Conf.*, 165–172, May 10–12, 1965.

22. Chirgwin, K. M., "A Variable-Speed Constant Frequency Generating System for a Supersonic Transport," *Suppl. IEEE Trans. Aerospace*, 387–392, June 1965.

23. Lawson, L. J., "Precisely Controlled Three-phase Squirrel Cage Induction Motor Drives for Aerospace Applications," *Suppl. IEEE Trans. Aerospace*, 93–97, June 1965.

24. Amato, C. J., "Sub-Ripple Distortion Components in Practical Cycloconverters," *Suppl. IEEE Trans. Aero space*, 98–106, June 1965.

25. Slabiak, W., and Lawson, L. J., "Precise Control of a Three-phase Squirrel Cage Induction Motor Using a Practical Cycloconverter," *Proc. Nat. Elect. Conf.*, Vol. 21, 938–943 (1965) (or *IEEE Trans. Ind. Gen. Appl.*, Vol. IGA-2, 274–280, July/August 1966).

26. Hamilton, R. A., and Lezan, G. R., "Thyristor Adjustable Frequency Power Supplies for Hot Strip Mill Run-out Tables," IEEE Pub. 34C20, *Record IEEE Industrial Static Power Conversion Conf.*, 69–77, Nov. 1–3, 1965 (or *IEEE Trans. Ind. Gen. Appl.*, Vol. IGA-3, 168–175, March/April 1967).

27. Amato, C. J., "Variable Speed with Controlled Slip Induction Motor," IEEE Pub. 34C20, *Record IEEE Ind. Static Power Conversion Conf.*, 181–185, Nov. 1–3, 1965.

28. Slabiak, W., and Lawson, L. J., "Optimizing Control Systems for Land Vehicles," IEEE Pub. 34C20, *Record IEEE Ind. Static Power Conversion Conf.*, 186–189, Nov. 1–3, 1965.

29. Abraham, L., Forster, J., and Schliephake, G., "AC Motor Supply with Thyristor Converters," IEEE Pub. 34C20, *Record IEEE Ind. Static Power Conversion Conf.*, 210–216, Nov. 1–3, 1965 (or *IEEE Trans. Ind. Gen. Appl.*, Vol. IGA-2, No. 5,334–340, Sept./Oct. 1966).

30. Bowler, P., "The Application of a Cycloconverter to the Control of Induction Motors," *Conf. Power Applications of Controllable Semiconductor Devices*, London, England, IEEE Pub. No. 17, 137–145, Nov. 10–11, 1965.

31. Slabiak, W., "An AC Electric Individual Wheel Drive System for Land Vehicles," S.A.E. Paper No. 660134, *S.A.E. Automotive Engineering Congress*, January 1966; or *S.A.E. Trans.*, Vol. 75, 664–671 (1967).

32. Lawson, L. J., Borland, R. P., and Puchy, C. G., "Optimal Control System Performance of an AC Electric Vehicular Wheel Drive," S.A.E. Paper No. 660135, *S.A.E. Automotive Engineering Congress*, January 1966 [or *S.A.E. Trans.*, Vol. 75, 672–680 (1967)].

33. Amato, C. J., "An AC Equivalent Circuit for a Cycloconverter," 1966 *IEEE International Conv. Record*, Vol. 14, pt. 8, 24–30

34. Lawson, L. J., and Slabiak, W., "A Thyristor Drive for High Performance Land Vehicles," *Proc. Nat. Elect. Conf.*, Vol. 22, 271–276 (1966).

35. Gyugyi, L., and Pelly, B. R., "Static Frequency Converter with Novel Voltage Control," U.S. Patent No. 3,493,838, Sept. 30, 1966.

36. Reimers, E., and Amato, C. J., "Performance Characteristics of a Controlled Slip Induction Motor Drive," (abstract) IEEE Pub. 34C36, *Conf. Record IGA 1st Annual Meeting*, 499, Oct. 3–6, 1966.

37. Lawson, L. J., "The Practical Cycloconverter," IEEE Pub. 34C36, *Conf. Record IGA 1st Annual Meeting*, 123–128, Oct. 3–6, 1966 (or *IEEE Trans. Ind. Gen. Appl.*, Vol. IGA-4, 141–144, March/April 1968).

38. Bland, R. J., "Factors Affecting the Operation of a Phase-Controlled Cycloconverter," *Proc. Inst. Elect. Eng.*, Vol. 114, No. 12, 1908–16, Dec. 1967.

39. Gyugyi, L., "A Study on the Application of the Force-Commutated Cycloconverter for Variable Speed Control of AC Machines," *M.S. Thesis*, University of Pittsburgh (1967).

40. Fisk, D. A., "VSCF for High Quality Electrical Power and Reliability," *ASME Aviation and Space Division Conference paper*, June 16–19, 1968.

41. Rich, E. A. E., "Concepts of Gearless Ball-Mill Drives," *IEEE Trans. Ind. Gen. Appl.*, Vol. IGA-5, No. 1, 13–17, Jan./Feb. 1969.

42. Jenkins, J. E., "A Modified Cycloconverter for Use with High Frequency Sources," IEE Pub. No. 53, Part 1-Contributions, 313–319, *Conf. on Power Thyristors and their Applications*, London, England, May 6–8, 1969.

43. Bläuenstein, E., "The First Gearless Drive for a Tube Mill," *Brown Boveri Rev.*, Vol. 57, No. 3, 96–105, March 1970.

44. Langer, J., "Static Frequency Changer Supply System for Synchronous Motors Driving Tube Mills," *Brown Boveri Rev.*, Vol. 57, No. 3, 112–119, March 1970.

45. Stemmler, H., "Drive System and Electronic Control Equipment of the Gearless Tube Mill," *Brown Boveri Rev.*, Vol. 57, No. 3, 120–128, March 1970.

46. Tsuchiya, T., "Basic Characteristics of Cycloconverter-Type Commutatorless Motors," *IEEE Trans. Ind. Gen. Appl.*, Vol. IGA-6, No. 4, 349–356, July/August 1970.

47. Würgler, H. U., "The World's First Gearless Mill Drive," *IEEE Trans. Ind. Gen. Appl.*, Vol. IGA-6, No. 5, 524–527, Sept./Oct. 1970.

48. Gyugyi, L., "Generalized Theory of Static Power Frequency Changers," *Ph.D. Thesis*, University of Salford (1970).

49. Long, W. F., and Schnitz, N. L., "Cycloconverter Control of the Doubly Fed Induction Motor," *IEEE Trans. Ind. Gen. Appl.*, Vol. IGA-7, No. 1, 95–100, Jan./Feb. 1971.

50. Gyugyi, L., Rosa, J., and Pelly, B. R., "Novel Integral Firing Angle Control," U.S. Patent No. 3,585,485, June 15, 1971.

51. Brandt, A., "Der Netztaktumrichter," *Assoc. Suisse, Elect.* Vol. 62, No. 15, 714–27, July 1971.

52. Bird, B. M., and Ridge, J., "Amplitude Modulated Frequency Changer," *Proc. Inst. Elect. Eng.*, Vol. 119, No. 8, 1155–61, August 1972.

53. Fallside, F., Jackson, R. D., Miskin, D. J., and Porrelli, C. N., "A Cycloconverter Linear Induction Motor Drive for Air-Cushioned Vehicles," *Conf. on Elect. Var. Speed Drives*, October 1972.

54. Burns, D. O., "Use of Cycloconverters and Variable Speed Alternators as Engine Starters," *Aircr. Eng.*, Vol. 44, No. 10, 8–12, October 1972.

55. Wilson, R. R., "Thyristor Cycloconvertors for Steelworks, Roller Table Drives," *IEE Conf. on Elect. Var. Speed Drives*, October 1972.

56. Gyugyi, L., "Power Frequency Changer with Controllable Input Displacement Factor," U.S. Patent No. 3,707,665, Dec. 26, 1972.

57. Gyugyi, L., "Unity Input Displacement Factor Frequency Changers," U.S. Patent Nos. 3,707,666 and 3,707,667, Dec. 26, 1972.

58. Klerfors, B., "Frequency Convertors for Electric Traction Supplies," *ASEA J.*, Vol. 46, No. 5, 119–122 (1973).

59. Bedford, B. D., "Versatile Cycloinverter Power Converter Circuit," U.S. Patent No. 3,742,336, June 26, 1973.

60. Weiss, H. W., "Adjustable Speed AC Drive Systems for Pump and Compressor Applications," *IEEE Trans. Ind. Appl.*, Vol. IA-10, No. 1, 162–167, Jan./Feb. 1974.

61. Betz, H., "Neu-Ulm System-Tie Frequency Changer, an Installation for Supply to the German Federal Railway," *AEG-Telefunken Prog.*, No. 1, 22–26 (1974).

62. Hill, E. R., and Ivey, C. L., "Cycloconverter Powered Yankee Dryer," *IEEE Pulp and Paper Ind. Tech. Conf.*, Annu. Conf. Rec. (1974).

63. Lafuze, D. L., "VSCF Starter Generator," *IEEE Power Electronics Specialist Conference* (1974).

64. Bird, B. M., and Ford, J. S., "Improvements in Phase-Controlled Circulating Current Cycloconverter Using Communication Principles," *Proc. Inst. Elect. Eng.*, Vol. 121, No. 10, 1146–49, October 1974.

65. Finlayson, P. T., and Washburn, D. C., "Cycloconverter Controlled Synchronous Machine for Load Compensation on AC Power Systems," *IEEE Trans. Ind. Appl.*, Vol. IA-10, No. 6, 806–813, Nov./Dec. 1974.

66. Gyugyi, L., "Static Power Conversion Arrangement and Method," U.S. Patent No. 3,858,105, Dec. 31, 1974.

67. Gyugyi, L., "Electrical Power Generating Arrangement and Method Utilizing an Induction Generator," U.S. Patent No. 3,832,625, Aug. 27, 1975.

68. Stacey, E. J., "An Unrestricted Frequency Changer Employing Force Commutated Thyristors," *IEEE Power Electronics Specialist Conference* (1976).

INDEX